HAESE & HARRIS PUBLICATIONS

Specialists in math

MW00996591

Mathematics

for the international student
Pre-Diploma (MYP 5 Plus)
Presumed Knowledge for SL and HL courses

Sandra Haese

Robert Haese

Michael Haese

John Owen

Edward Kemp

International Baccalaureate

Middle Years Programme (MYP 5 Plus)

MATHEMATICS FOR THE INTERNATIONAL STUDENT
Pre-Diploma (MYP 5 Plus)
Presumed Knowledge for SL and HL courses

Sandra Haese	B.Sc.
Robert Haese	B.Sc.
Michael Haese	B.Sc.(Hons.), Ph.D.
John Owen	B.Sc., Dip.T.
Edward Kemp	B.Sc., M.A.

Haese & Harris Publications
3 Frank Collopy Court, Adelaide Airport, SA 5950, AUSTRALIA
Telephone: +61 8 8355 9444, Fax: +61 8 8355 9471
Email: info@haeseandharris.com.au
Web: www.haeseandharris.com.au

National Library of Australia Card Number & ISBN 1-876543-04-3

© Haese & Harris Publications 2006

Published by Raksar Nominees Pty Ltd
3 Frank Collopy Court, Adelaide Airport, SA 5950, AUSTRALIA

First Edition   2006

Cartoon artwork by John Martin. Artwork by Piotr Poturaj and David Purton
Cover design by Piotr Poturaj
Computer software by David Purton

Typeset in Australia by Susan Haese (Raksar Nominees). Typeset in Times Roman $10\frac{1}{2}/11\frac{1}{2}$

The textbook and its accompanying CD have been developed independently of the International Baccalaureate Organization (IBO). The textbook and CD are in no way connected with, or endorsed by, the IBO.

Acknowledgements: The publishers acknowledge the cooperation of Oxford University Press, Australia, for the reproduction of material originally published in textbooks produced in association with Haese & Harris Publications.

While every attempt has been made to trace and acknowledge copyright, the authors and publishers apologise for any accidental infringement where copyright has proved untraceable. They would be pleased to come to a suitable agreement with the rightful owner.

Disclaimer: All the internet addresses (URL's) given in this book were valid at the time of printing. While the authors and publisher regret any inconvenience that changes of address may cause readers, no responsibility for any such changes can be accepted by either the authors or the publisher.

FOREWORD

Mathematics for the International Student: Pre-Diploma (MYP 5 Plus) is an attempt to cover, in one volume, the Presumed Knowledge required for the IB Diploma courses 'Mathematics SL' and 'Mathematics HL'. It may also be used as a general textbook at about Grade 10 level in schools which require students to complete a rigorous course in preparation for the study of mathematics at a high standard in their final two years.

In terms of the IB Middle Years Programme (MYP), this book does not pretend to be a definitive course. In response to requests from teachers who use 'Mathematics for the International Student' at Diploma level, we have endeavoured to interpret their requirements, as expressed to us, for a book that would prepare students for SL and HL. We have developed the book independently of the International Baccalaureate Organization (IBO) in consultation with experienced teachers of IB Mathematics. The text is not endorsed by the IBO.

It is not our intention that each chapter be worked through in full. Time constraints will not allow for this. Teachers must select exercises carefully, according to the abilities and prior knowledge of their students, to make the most efficient use of time and give as thorough coverage of content as possible.

To avoid producing a book that would be too bulky for students, we have presented certain chapters on the CD as printable pages: *Number*, *Mensuration*, *Logic*, *Networks and trees*, *Bivariate statistics*, *Matrices*, *Linear programming*.

The above were selected because the content could be regarded as either background knowledge that students may have previously covered in earlier years, or extension beyond what might be regarded as an essential prerequisite for Diploma.

This package is language rich and technology rich. We hope the combination of textbook and interactive Student CD will foster the mathematical development of students in a stimulating way. Frequent use of the interactive features on the CD should nurture a much deeper understanding and appreciation of mathematical concepts and the inclusion of our new SELF TUTOR software (see separate note about the CD) is intended as a help for students who have been absent from classes or for those who experience difficulty understanding the material.

The book contains many problems from the basic to the advanced, to cater for a range of student abilities and interests. While some of the exercises are simply designed to build skills, every effort has been made to contextualise problems, so that students can see everyday uses and practical applications of the mathematics they are studying, and appreciate the universality of mathematics. We understand the emphasis that the IB MYP places on the five *Areas of Interaction* and in response there are links on the CD to printable pages which offer ideas for projects and investigations to help busy teachers.

The interactive CD also allows immediate access to our own specially designed geometry packages, graphing packages and more.

In this changing world of mathematics education, we believe that the contextual approach shown in this book, with the associated use of technology, will enhance the students' understanding, knowledge and appreciation of mathematics, and its universal application.

We welcome your feedback.

Email: info@haeseandharris.com.au

Web: www.haeseandharris.com.au   *JTO   RCH   SHH   PMH   EK*

The authors and publishers would like to thank all those teachers who have read the proofs of this book and offered advice and encouragement, in particular Heather Farish and Marjut Mäenpää. Special thanks to Gillian Hendrie, Chris Rebbeck and Sarah Locke who gave a great deal of helpful advice and comment on our attempts to prepare links to the Areas of Interaction. Others who offered to read and comment on the proofs of the textbook and the A of I links include: Carolyn Laslett, Dean Bennett, Dennis Thorpe, Glen Johnson, Glenn Smith, James Norbery, Kathryn Freeburn, Provi Arbe de Zapata, Aliki Papapetros, Dr Andrzej Cichy, Margie Karbassioun, Roger McLoughlin, Todd Sharpe, Brendan Watson, Jeanne-Mari Neefs, Nicola Cardwell, Steve Cormack, Alison Ryan, Mark Willis, Paige Bruner, Rema George. To anyone we may have missed, we offer our apologies.

The publishers wish to make it clear that acknowledging these individuals, does not imply any endorsement of this book by any of them, and all responsibility for the content rests with the authors and publishers.

USING THE INTERACTIVE CD

The interactive CD is ideal for independent study.

Students can revisit concepts taught in class and undertake their own revision and practice. The CD also has the text of the book, allowing students to leave the textbook at school and keep the CD at home.

By clicking on the relevant icon, a range of new interactive features can be accessed:

♦ Self Tutor

♦ Areas of Interaction links to printable pages

♦ Printable Chapters

♦ Interactive Links – to spreadsheets, video clips, graphing and geometry software, graphics calculator instructions, computer demonstrations and simulations

INTERACTIVE LINK

Graphics calculators: instructions for using Texas Instruments and Casio calculators graphics calculators are also given on the CD and can be printed. Click on the relevant icon (TI or C) to access printable instructions.

Examples in the textbook are not always given for both types of calculator. Where that occurs, click on the relevant icon to access the instructions for the other type of calculator.

SELF TUTOR is a new exciting feature of this book.

The ◄) **Self Tutor** icon on each worked example denotes an active link on the CD.

NEW!

Simply 'click' on the ◄) **Self Tutor** (or anywhere in the example box) to access the worked example, with a teacher's voice explaining each step necessary to reach the answer.

Play any line as often as you like. See how the basic processes come alive using movement and colour on the screen.

Ideal for students who have missed lessons or need extra help.

Example 13	◄) **Self Tutor**

Solve for x: $\dfrac{x}{2} = \dfrac{3+x}{5}$

$$\dfrac{x}{2} = \dfrac{3+x}{5} \qquad \text{has LCD} = 10$$

$$\therefore \ \dfrac{x}{2} \times \dfrac{5}{5} = \dfrac{2}{2} \times \left(\dfrac{3+x}{5}\right) \qquad \text{\{to create a common denominator\}}$$

$$\therefore \ 5x = 2(3+x) \qquad \text{\{equating numerators\}}$$

$$\therefore \ 5x = 6 + 2x \qquad \text{\{expanding brackets\}}$$

$$\therefore \ 5x - 2x = 6 + 2x - 2x \qquad \text{\{taking } 2x \text{ from both sides\}}$$

$$\therefore \ 3x = 6$$

$$\therefore \ x = 2 \qquad \text{\{dividing both sides by 3\}}$$

AREAS OF INTERACTION

The International Baccalaureate Middle Years Programme focuses teaching and learning through five Areas of Interaction:

- ♦ Approaches to Learning
- ♦ Community & Service
- ♦ Homo Faber
- ♦ Environment
- ♦ Health & Social Education

The Areas of Interaction are intended as a focus for developing connections between different subject areas in the curriculum and to promote an understanding of the interrelatedness of different branches of knowledge and the coherence of knowledge as a whole.

Click on the heading to access a printable 'pop-up' version of the link.

In an effort to assist busy teachers, we offer the following printable pages of ideas for projects and investigations:

WHAT DETERMINES COIN SIZES?
Area of interaction:
Homo Faber

HOW MUCH OXYGEN IS NEEDED BY A PERSON?
Area of interaction:
Health & Social Education

WHAT IS THE GOLDEN RATIO?
Area of interaction:
Homo Faber

HOW MUCH OXYGEN IS PRODUCED EACH HOUR?
Area of interaction:
Environment

HOW MUCH CAN I SAVE BY NOT SMOKING?
Area of interaction:
Health & Social Education

WHAT ARE YOUR SURVIVAL PROSPECTS?
Area of interaction:
Community & Service

HOW MUCH WATER IS LOST WHEN A TAP IS LEFT DRIPPING?
Area of interaction:
Environment

HOW MANY BRICKS ARE NEEDED TO BUILD A HOUSE?

Area of interaction:
Approaches to Learning

A of I
LINK

 AT WHAT RATE SHOULD A PERSON BREATHE?

Area of interaction:
Health & Social Education

A of I
LINK

 HOW FAR WILL A CAR TRAVEL WHEN BRAKING?

Area of interaction:
Community & Service

A of I
LINK

 ARE MODELS NECESSARY FOR SOLVING SOME PROBLEMS IN MATHEMATICS?

Area of interaction:
Approaches to Learning

A of I
LINK

 WHAT SHAPE CONTAINER SHOULD WE USE?

Area of interaction:
Approaches to Learning

A of I
LINK

 WHAT WILL IT COST TO BRING WATER TO THE GOLDMINES?

Area of interaction:
Environment

A of I
LINK

 HOW CAN WE FIND THE FORMULA FROM QUADRATIC DATA?

Area of interaction:
Approaches to Learning

A of I
LINK

PRINTABLE CHAPTERS

To keep the overall extent of this book within manageable limits for students, we have presented certain chapters on the CD as printable pages, to be accessed by clicking on the icon:

- Number
- Mensuration
- Logic
- Networks and trees
- Bivariate statistics
- Matrices
- Linear programming

These chapters were selected because the content could be regarded as either background knowledge that students may have previously covered in earlier years, or extension beyond what might be regarded as an essential prerequisite for SL and HL.

Review

Click on the icon to access this printable review chapter

PRINTABLE CHAPTER

Number

Mensuration

Chapter 1

Sets and Venn diagrams

Contents:

OPENING PROBLEM

A city has two newspapers, The Sun and The Advertiser.

56% of the people read The Sun and 71% of the people read The Advertiser.

18% read neither of these newspapers.

What percentage of the people read:

- both of the newspapers
- at least one of the newspapers
- The Sun, but not The Advertiser
- exactly one of the two newspapers?

A   NUMBER SETS

We use:

- $\mathbb{N}$ to represent the set of all **natural numbers** $\{0, 1, 2, 3, 4, 5, 6 \ldots\ldots \}$

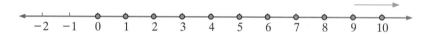

- $\mathbb{Z}$ to represent the set of all **integers** $\{0, \pm 1, \pm 2, \pm 3, \pm 4, \pm 5, \pm 6 \ldots\ldots \}$

- $\mathbb{Z}^{+}$ to represent the set of all **positive integers** $\{1, 2, 3, 4, 5, 6 \ldots\ldots \}$

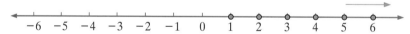

- $\mathbb{Q}$ to represent the set of all **rational numbers**

    Rational numbers have the form $\dfrac{p}{q}$ where p and q are integers, but $q \neq 0$.

    For example: $\frac{15}{4}$, $10 \ (= \frac{20}{2})$, $0.5 \ (= \frac{1}{2})$, $-\frac{3}{8}$ are all rational numbers.

    Note: Surds such as $\sqrt{2}$ and $\sqrt{7}$ are not rational and are called **irrational numbers**.
    π which is $3.14159265\ldots\ldots$ is an irrational number.
    Non-recurring decimal numbers and numbers such as $0.12233344445\ldots\ldots$
    are irrationals.

- $\mathbb{R}$ to represent the set of all **real numbers**

Real numbers are all numbers which can be placed on the number line.

For example, $\frac{1}{8} = 0.125$, $\sqrt{2} = 1.41421356.......$, $\pi = 3.14159265.......$

All real numbers can be written as decimal numbers.

$\frac{2}{0}$ and $\sqrt{-2}$ are not real numbers.

Notation: $\in$ reads   *is an element of*   or   *is a member of*   or   *is in*

$\notin$ reads   *is not an element of*   or   *is not a member of*   or   *is not in*

Examples: $2 \in \mathbb{Z}$ and $\frac{1}{2} \in \mathbb{Q}$,   but $\pi \notin \mathbb{Q}$ and $-2 \notin \mathbb{Z}^+$

EXERCISE 1A

1   True or false?

   a $3 \in \mathbb{Z}^+$ b $6 \in \mathbb{Z}$ c $\frac{3}{4} \in \mathbb{Q}$ d $\sqrt{2} \notin \mathbb{Q}$

   e $-\frac{1}{4} \notin \mathbb{Q}$ f $2\frac{1}{3} \in \mathbb{Z}$ g $0.3684 \in \mathbb{R}$ h $\dfrac{1}{0.1} \in \mathbb{Z}$

2   Which of these are rational?

   a   8   b -8 c $2\frac{1}{3}$ d $-3\frac{1}{4}$

   e $\sqrt{3}$ f $\sqrt{400}$ g 9.176 h $\pi - \pi$

3   List the set of all:

   a   factors of 6   b   multiples of 6   c   factors of 17   d   multiples of 17

   e   prime numbers less than 20   f   composite numbers between 10 and 30

Example 1   ◀)) **Self Tutor**

Show that $0.\overline{36}$, which is $0.36363636.....$, is a rational number.

Let $x = 0.\overline{36} = 0.36363636.....$

$\therefore$ $100x = 36.363636..... = 36 + x$

$\therefore$ $99x = 36$ and so $x = \frac{36}{99} = \frac{4}{11}$

So, $0.\overline{36}$ is actually the rational number $\frac{4}{11}$.

---

4   Show that these numbers are rational: a $0.\overline{7}$ b $0.\overline{41}$ c $0.\overline{324}$

5   a   Why is 0.527 a rational number?

   b $0.\overline{9}$ is a rational number. In fact, $0.\overline{9} \in \mathbb{Z}$. Give evidence to support this statement.

6   Explain why these statements are false:

   a   The sum of two irrationals is irrational.

   b   The product of two irrationals is irrational.

B   INTERVAL NOTATION

Interval or **set notation** allows us to quickly describe sets of numbers using mathematical symbols only.

For example: $\{x \mid -3 < x < 2\}$ or $\{x : -3 < x < 2\}$

reads "the set of all values of real x such that x lies between minus 3 and 2".

Sometimes we want to restrict a set to include only integers or rationals.

For example: $\{x \mid x \in \mathbb{Z}, \ -5 < x < 5\}$

reads "the set of all integers x such that x lies between minus 5 and 5".

Note: $\in$ is used to mean "is in".

EXERCISE 1B

1   Write verbal statements for the meaning of:

   a $\{x \mid x > 4\}$ **b** $\{x \mid x \leqslant 5\}$ **c** $\{y \mid 0 < y < 8\}$
   d $\{x \mid 1 \leqslant x \leqslant 4\}$ **e** $\{t \mid 2 < t < 7\}$ **f** $\{n \mid n \leqslant 3 \ \text{or} \ n > 6\}$

Example 2   ◀ **Self Tutor**

Write in set notation:

a

b

---

   a $\{x \mid x \in \mathbb{N}, \ 1 \leqslant x \leqslant 5\}$ **b** $\{x \mid -3 \leqslant x < 6\}$
   or $\{x \mid x \in \mathbb{Z}, \ 1 \leqslant x \leqslant 5\}$

---

2   Write in set notation:

   a

   b

   c

   d

   e

   f

3   Sketch the following number sets:

   a $\{x \mid x \in \mathbb{N}, \ 4 \leqslant x < 8\}$ **b** $\{x \mid x \in \mathbb{Z}, \ -5 < x \leqslant 4\}$
   c $\{x \mid x \in \mathbb{R}, \ -3 < x \leqslant 5\}$ **d** $\{x \mid x \in \mathbb{Z}, \ x > -5\}$
   e $\{x \mid x \in \mathbb{R}, \ x \leqslant 6\}$ **f** $\{x \mid x \in \mathbb{R}, \ -5 \leqslant x \leqslant 0\}$

VENN DIAGRAMS

The **Universal Set** contains all elements being considered in the problem.

A **Venn diagram** consists of a universal set usually denoted U, represented by a rectangle, and a circle (or circles) within it representing sets being considered.

Example 3	◀)) Self Tutor
Draw a Venn diagram to show the set $S = \{2, 4, 6, 7\}$ within the universal set $U = \{x \mid x \in \mathbb{Z}^+, x \leqslant 10\}$.	$U = \{1, 2, 3, 4, 5, 6, 7, 8, 9, 10\}$ 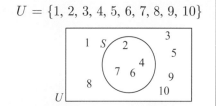

THE COMPLEMENT OF A SET

S', the **complement** of S, consists of all the members of U which are not in S,

i.e., $S' = \{x \mid x \in U, \ x \notin S\}$.

In **Example 3**, $S' = \{1, 3, 5, 8, 9, 10\}$

SUBSETS

Consider two sets A and B.

A is a **subset** of B, written $A \subseteq B$,   if every element of A is also in B.

For example,   for $A = \{2, 3, 5\}$, $B = \{1, 2, 3, 4, 5, 6, 7\}$ and $C = \{3, 5, 8\}$
we see that $A \subseteq B$ as every element of A is also in B,   but
C is not a subset of B as C contains 8 which is not in B.

THE EMPTY SET

An **empty set** has no elements in it and is represented by $\varnothing$ or $\{ \ \}$.

Example 4	◀)) Self Tutor
If $U = \{0, 1, 2, 3, 4, 5, 6, 7\}$ and $E = \{2, 3, 5, 7\}$, list the set E' and illustrate E and E' on a Venn diagram.	
$E' = \{0, 1, 4, 6\}$	

Note: $n(A)$ reads *'the number of elements in set A'*

So, if $A = \{2, 3, 4, 6, 10\}$ then $n(A) = 5$ as A contains 5 elements (or members).

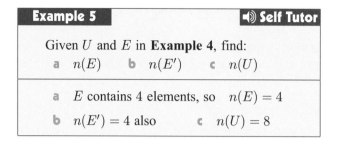

This Venn diagram displays real numbers, rational numbers, integers and natural numbers.

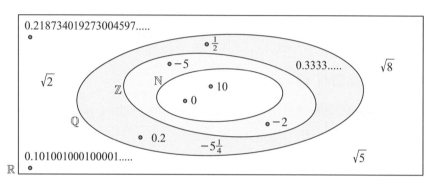

EXERCISE 1C

1   If $U = \{x \mid x \in \mathbb{Z}^+, \ x \leqslant 8\}$ and $A = \{\text{prime numbers} \leqslant 8\}$:
   a   Show set A on a Venn diagram.   b   List the set A'.

2   Suppose $U = \{\text{letters of the English alphabet}\}$ and
              $V = \{\text{letters of the English alphabet which are vowels}\}$.
   a   Show these two sets on a Venn diagram.   b   List the set V'.

3 Suppose the universal set is $U = \mathbb{R}$, the set of all real numbers.

$\mathbb{Q}$, $\mathbb{Z}$, and $\mathbb{N}$ are all subsets of $\mathbb{R}$.

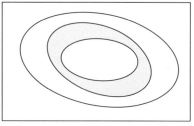

a Copy the given Venn diagram and label the sets U, $\mathbb{Q}$, $\mathbb{Z}$, and $\mathbb{N}$ on it.

b Place these numbers on the Venn diagram:

$\frac{1}{2}$, $\sqrt{2}$, $0.\overline{3}$, -5, $-5\frac{1}{4}$, 0, 10, and

$0.2137005618.....$ which does not terminate or recur.

c True or false?   **i** $\mathbb{N} \subseteq \mathbb{Z}$ **ii** $\mathbb{Z} \subseteq \mathbb{Q}$ **iii** $\mathbb{N} \subseteq \mathbb{Q}$

d Shade the region representing the set of irrationals $\mathbb{Q}'$.

Example 7   🔊 **Self Tutor**

If $U = \{x \mid x \in \mathbb{Z},\ 0 \leqslant x \leqslant 12\}$, $A = \{2, 3, 5, 7, 11\}$
and $B = \{1, 3, 6, 7, 8\}$, show A and B on a Venn diagram.

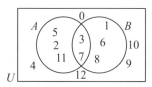

We notice that 3 and 7 are in both A and B so the circles representing A and B must overlap.

We place 3 and 7 in the overlap, then fill in the rest of A, then fill in the rest of B. The remainder go outside the two circles.

---

4 Show A and B on a Venn diagram if:

a $U = \{1, 2, 3, 4, 5, 6\}$, $A = \{1, 2, 3, 4\}$, $B = \{3, 4, 5, 6\}$

b $U = \{4, 5, 6, 7, 8, 9, 10\}$, $A = \{6, 7, 9, 10\}$, $B = \{5, 6, 8, 9\}$

c $U = \{3, 4, 5, 6, 7, 8, 9\}$, $A = \{3, 5, 7, 9\}$, $B = \{4, 6, 8\}$

5 Show the following information on a Venn diagram:

a $U = \{$triangles$\}$, $E = \{$equilateral triangles$\}$, $I = \{$isosceles triangles$\}$

b $U = \{$quadrilaterals$\}$, $P = \{$parallelograms$\}$, $R = \{$rectangles$\}$

D   UNION AND INTERSECTION

THE UNION OF TWO SETS

$A \cup B$ denotes the **union** of sets A and B. This set contains all elements belonging to A **or** B **or both** A and B.

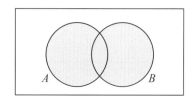

$A \cup B$ is shaded green.

Note: $A \cup B = \{x \mid x \in A \text{ or } x \in B\}$

THE INTERSECTION OF TWO SETS

$A \cap B$ denotes the **intersection** of sets A and B. This is the set of all elements common to both sets.

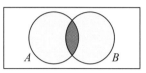

$A \cap B$ is shaded red.

Note: $A \cap B = \{x \mid x \in A \ \text{and} \ x \in B\}$

In the Venn diagram alongside,
$A = \{2, 3, 4, 7\}$ and $B = \{1, 3, 7, 8, 10\}$.

We can see that $A \cap B = \{3, 7\}$

and $A \cup B = \{1, 2, 3, 4, 7, 8, 10\}$

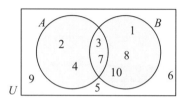

Example 8 ◀)) **Self Tutor**

If $U = \{\text{whole numbers} \leqslant 12\}$, $A = \{\text{primes} \leqslant 12\}$
and $B = \{\text{factors of } 12\}$:

a   List the elements of the sets A and B.
b   Show the sets A, B and U on a Venn diagram.
c   List the elements in   i A' ii $A \cap B$ iii $A \cup B$
d   Find: i $n(A \cap B)$ ii $n(A \cup B)$ iii $n(B')$

---

a $A = \{2, 3, 5, 7, 11\}$ and $B = \{1, 2, 3, 4, 6, 12\}$

b
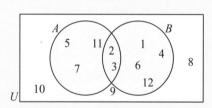

c   i $A' = \{1, 4, 6, 8, 9, 10, 12\}$
    ii $A \cap B = \{2, 3\}$
    iii $A \cup B = \{1, 2, 3, 4, 5, 6, 7, 11, 12\}$

d   i $n(A \cap B) = 2$ ii $n(A \cup B) = 9$
    iii $B' = \{5, 7, 8, 9, 10, 11\}$, so $n(B') = 6$

EXERCISE 1D

1   For

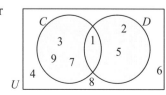

a   List: i set C ii set D iii set U
           iv set $C \cap D$ v set $C \cup D$

b   Find: i $n(C)$ ii $n(D)$ iii $n(U)$
           iv $n(C \cap D)$ v $n(C \cup D)$

2 For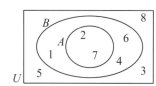

    a List: **i** set A **ii** set B **iii** set U
        iv set $A \cap B$ **v** set $A \cup B$

    b Find: **i** $n(A)$ **ii** $n(B)$ **iii** $n(U)$
        iv $n(A \cap B)$ **v** $n(A \cup B)$

3 Consider $U = \{x \mid x \in \mathbb{Z}^+, \ x \leqslant 12\}$
               $A = \{2, 7, 9, 10, 11\}$ and $B = \{1, 2, 9, 11, 12\}$.

    a Show these sets on a Venn diagram.

    b List the elements of: **i** $A \cap B$ **ii** $A \cup B$ **iii** B'

    c Find: **i** $n(A)$ **ii** $n(B')$ **iii** $n(A \cap B)$ **iv** $n(A \cup B)$

4 If A is the set of all factors of 36 and B is the set of all factors of 63, find:

    a $A \cap B$ **b** $A \cup B$

5 If $X = \{A, B, D, M, N, P, R, T, Z\}$ and $Y = \{B, C, M, T, W, Z\}$, find:

    a $X \cap Y$ **b** $X \cup Y$

6 If $U = \{x \mid x \in \mathbb{Z}^+, \ x \leqslant 30\}$
       $A = \{\text{factors of } 30\}$ and $B = \{\text{prime numbers} \leqslant 30\}$:

    a Find: **i** $n(A)$ **ii** $n(B)$ **iii** $n(A \cap B)$ **iv** $n(A \cup B)$

    b Use **a** to verify that $n(A \cup B) = n(A) + n(B) - n(A \cap B)$

7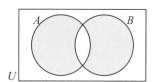

    Use the Venn diagram given to prove that:

    $n(A \cup B) = n(A) + n(B) - n(A \cap B)$.

    Note: $n(A) = a + b$

Example 9   ◀》 **Self Tutor**

On separate Venn diagrams shade the region representing

    a in A or in B but not in both   **b** $A' \cap B$

a

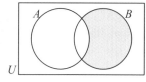

b We look for where the outside of A intersects (overlaps) with B.

---

8 On separate Venn diagrams, like the one given, shade the region representing:

    a not in A **b** in both A and B

    c $A \cap B'$ **d** in either A or B

    e $A \cup B'$ **f** $(A \cup B)'$ 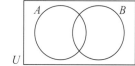

    g $(A \cap B)'$ **h** in exactly one of A or B

9 Describe in words, the shaded region of:

a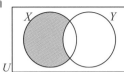
b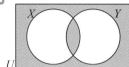
c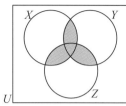

10 Simplify:

a $X \cap Y$ for $X = \{1, 3, 5, 7\}$ and $Y = \{2, 4, 6, 8\}$

b i $A \cup A'$ ii $A \cap A'$ for any set A in universe U.

11 If A and B are two non-disjoint sets, shade the region of a Venn diagram representing:

a A' b $A' \cap B$ c $A \cup B'$ d $A' \cap B'$

12 The diagram alongside is the most general case for three events in the same sample space U.

On separate Venn diagram sketches, shade:

a A b B' c $B \cap C$

d $A \cup C$ e $A \cap B \cap C$ f $(A \cup B) \cap C$?

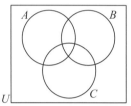

Set identities can be verified using Venn diagrams.

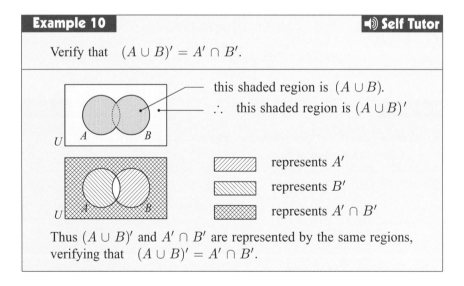

13 Verify that:

a $(A \cap B)' = A' \cup B'$

b $A \cup (B \cap C) = (A \cup B) \cap (A \cup C)$

c $A \cap (B \cup C) = (A \cap B) \cup (A \cap C)$

COMPUTER
DEMO

E PROBLEM SOLVING WITH VENN DIAGRAMS

Example 11   ◀)) **Self Tutor**

If the Venn diagram alongside illustrates the number of people in a sporting club who play tennis (T) and hockey (H), determine the number of people:

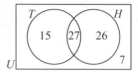

a	in the club	b	who play hockey
c	who play both sports	d	who play neither sport
e	who play at least one sport		

a   Number in the club
$= 15 + 27 + 26 + 7 = 75$

b   Number who play hockey
$= 27 + 26 = 53$

c   Number who play both sports $= 27$

d   Number who play neither sport $= 7$

e   Number who play at least one sport
$= 15 + 27 + 26 = 68$

EXERCISE 1E

1   The Venn diagram alongside illustrates the number of students in a particular class who study French (F) and Spanish (S). Determine the number of students:

   a   in the class
   b   who study both subjects
   c   who study at least one of the subjects
   d   who only study Spanish.

2   In a survey at a resort, people were asked whether they went sailing (S) or fishing (F) during their stay. Use the Venn diagram to determine the number of people:

   a   in the survey
   b   who did both activities
   c   who did neither activity
   d   who did exactly one of the activities.

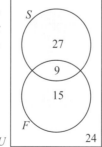

3   In a class of 30 students, 19 study Physics, 17 study Chemistry and 15 study both of these subjects. Display this information on a Venn diagram and hence determine the number of students who study:

   a   both subjects   b   at least one of the subjects
   c   Physics, but not Chemistry   d   exactly one of the subjects
   e   neither subject

4 In a class of 40 students, 19 play tennis, 20 play netball and 8 play neither of these sports. Determine the number of students in the class who:

   a play tennis
   b do not play netball
   c play at least one of the sports
   d play one and only one of the sports
   e play netball, but not tennis

5 In a class of 25 students, 15 play hockey and 16 play basketball. If there are 4 students who play neither sport, determine the number of students who play both hockey and basketball.

6 In a class of 40, 34 like bananas, 22 like pineapples and 2 dislike both fruits. Find the number of students who:

   a like both fruits
   b like at least one fruit

7 In a group of 50 students, 40 study Mathematics, 32 study Physics and each student studies at least one of these subjects. From a Venn diagram find how many students:

   a study both subjects
   b study Mathematics but not Physics

8 In a class of 40 students, 23 have dark hair, 18 have brown eyes, and 26 have dark hair, brown eyes or both. How many students have:

   a dark hair and brown eyes
   b neither dark hair nor brown eyes
   c dark hair but not brown eyes?

9 400 families were surveyed. It was found that 90% had a TV set and 60% had a computer. Every family had at least one of these items. How many of the families had both a TV set and a computer?

10 In a certain town 3 newspapers are published. 20% of the population read A, 16% read B, 14% read C, 8% read A and B, 5% read A and C, 4% read B and C and 2% read all 3 newspapers. What percentage of the population read:

   a none of the papers
   b at least one of the papers
   c exactly one of the papers
   d either A or B
   e A only?

 F   # MORE DIFFICULT PROBLEM SOLVING
(EXTENSION)

EXERCISE 1F

1 In a circle of music lovers, 14 people play the piano or violin, 8 people are piano players, and 5 people play both instruments. Find the number of violin players.

2 Our team scored well in the interschool athletics. Eight of us gained places in running events, 5 gained places in both running and jumping events, and 14 of us collected exactly one place in running or jumping. How many places were gained by our team?

3 64% of students at a school study a language, 79% study mathematics and each student studies at least one of these subjects. What percentage of students study both a language and mathematics?

4   A survey is made of the investments of the members of a club. All of the 133 members own at least one type of share, 96 members owning mining shares, 70 having oil shares and 66 members having industrial shares. Of those who own mining shares, 40 also own oil shares and 45 also have industrial shares, while the number of those who own oil shares and industrial shares is 28. How many members of the club own all three types of shares?

5   At a certain school there are 90 students studying for their matriculation certificate. They are required to study at least one of the subjects: Physics, French and History. Of these students, 50 are studying Physics, 60 are studying French and 55 are studying History. Thirty students are studying both Physics and French, while 10 students are studying both French and History but not Physics. Twenty students are studying all three subjects. Construct and explain a Venn diagram which represents this situation.
Use this diagram to determine:
>   **a**   how many students are studying both Physics and History, but not French
>   **b**   how many students are studying at least two of these three subjects.

6   In a school of 405 pupils, a survey on sporting activities shows that 251 pupils play tennis, 157 play hockey and 111 play softball. There are 45 pupils who play both tennis and hockey, 60 who play hockey and softball and 39 who play tennis and softball. What conclusion may be drawn about the number of those who participate in all three sports?

G   THE ALGEBRA OF SETS (EXTENSION)

For the set of real numbers $\mathbb{R}$, under the operations $+$ and $\times$, you should be aware of the following laws for real numbers a, b and c:

- **commutative** $a + b = b + a$ and $ab = ba$.
- **identity**   Identity elements 0 and 1 exist such that,
  $a + 0 = 0 + a = a$ and $a \times 1 = 1 \times a = a$.
- **associativity** $(a + b) + c = a + (b + c)$ and $(ab)c = a(bc)$
- **distributive** $a(b + c) = ab + ac$

In **Exercise 1D** we used a Venn diagram to verify that: $A \cup (B \cap C) = (A \cup B) \cap (A \cup C)$.

Notice that these results look very much like the *distributive* law for real numbers under $+$ and $\times$, with real numbers replaced by sets, $\times$ replaced by $\cup$ and $+$ replaced by $\cap$.

The following are the **laws for the algebra of sets** under the operations of $\cup$ and $\cap$.

- **commutative** $A \cap B = B \cap A$ and $A \cup B = B \cup A$
- **associativity** $A \cap (B \cap C) = (A \cap B) \cap C$ and $A \cup (B \cup C) = (A \cup B) \cup C$
- **idempotent** $A \cap A = A$ and $A \cup A = A$
- **distributive** $A \cup (B \cap C) = (A \cup B) \cap (A \cup C)$ and
  $A \cap (B \cup C) = (A \cap B) \cup (A \cap C)$
- **DeMorgans** $A \cap \varnothing = \varnothing$, $A \cup U = U$, $(A \cap B)' = A' \cup B'$, $(A \cup B)' = A' \cap B'$
- **Complement** $(A')' = A$

EXERCISE 1G

1 Explain with the aid of a Venn diagram why the *commutative* laws $A \cap B = B \cap A$ and $A \cup B = B \cup A$ are valid.

2 Explain with the aid of a Venn diagram why the *idempotent* laws $A \cap A = A$ and $A \cup A = A$ are valid.

3 Explain with the aid of a Venn diagram why the *associative* laws
$A \cap (B \cap C) = (A \cap B) \cap C$ and $A \cup (B \cup C) = (A \cup B) \cup C$ are valid.

4 Explain with the aid of a Venn diagram why the *complement* law $(A')' = A$ is valid.

5 What is the simplification of   **a** $A \cap A'$ **b** $A \cup A'$?

6 Use the laws for the algebra of sets to show that:

    a $A \cup (B \cup A') = U$ for all B **b** $A \cap (B \cap A') = \varnothing$ for all B

    c $A \cup (B \cap A') = A \cup B$ **d** $(A' \cup B')' = A \cap B$ **e** $(A \cup B) \cap (A' \cap B') = \varnothing$

    f $(A \cup B) \cap (C \cup D) = (A \cap C) \cup (A \cap D) \cup (B \cap C) \cup (B \cap D)$

REVIEW SET 1A

1 **a** Explain why 1.3 is a rational number.

    b True or false: $\sqrt{4000} \in \mathbb{Q}$?

    c List the set of all prime numbers between 20 and 40.

    d Write a verbal statement for the meaning of $\{t : -1 \leqslant t < 3\}$.

    e Write in set notation:

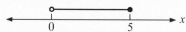

    f Sketch the number set $\{x \mid x \in \mathbb{N}, \ -2 \leqslant x \leqslant 3\}$.

2 If $U = \{x \mid x \in \mathbb{Z}^+, \ x \leqslant 12\}$ and $A = \{$multiples of $3 \leqslant 12\}$:

    a Show A on a Venn diagram.

    b List the set A'.

    c Find $n(A')$.

    d True or false: If $C = \{1, 2, 4\}$, then $C \subseteq A$?

3 True or false: **a** $\mathbb{N} \subseteq \mathbb{Z}^+$ **b** $\mathbb{Q} \subseteq \mathbb{Z}$?

4 For

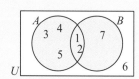

    a List **i** set A **ii** set B **iii** set U
               iv set $A \cup B$ **v** set $A \cap B$

    b Find **i** $n(A)$ **ii** $n(B)$
               iii $n(A \cup B)$

5 Consider $U = \{x \mid x \in \mathbb{Z}^+, \ x \leqslant 10\}$, $P = \{2, 3, 5, 7\}$ and $Q = \{2, 4, 6, 8\}$.

    a Show these sets on a Venn diagram.

    b List the elements of: **i** $P \cap Q$ **ii** $P \cup Q$ **iii** Q'

    c Find: **i** $n(P')$ **ii** $n(P \cap Q)$ **iii** $n(P \cup Q)$

    d True or false: $P \cap Q \subseteq P$?

6 Describe in words the shaded region of:

a

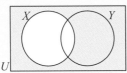

b

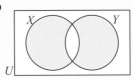

c

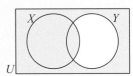

REVIEW SET 1B

1 **a** True or false: $-2 \in \mathbb{Z}^+$?

b True or false: $\frac{1}{\sqrt{7}} \in \mathbb{Q}$?

c Show that $0.\overline{41}$ is a rational number.

d Write in set notation:

e Sketch the number set $\{x \mid x \in \mathbb{R},\ x \leqslant 3 \ \text{or} \ x > 7\}$

2 Illustrate these numbers on a Venn diagram like the one shown alongside:

$-1,\ \sqrt{2},\ 2,\ 3.1,\ \pi,\ 4.\overline{2}$

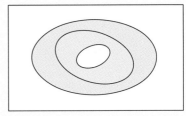

3 Show this information on a Venn diagram.

a $U = \{10, 11, 12, 13, 14, 15\}$, $A = \{10, 12, 14\}$, $B = \{11, 12, 13\}$

b $U = \{\text{quadrilaterals}\}$, $S = \{\text{squares}\}$, $R = \{\text{rectangles}\}$

4 If A is the set of all factors of 24 and B is the set of all factors of 18, find:

a $A \cap B$ **b** $A \cup B$

5 On separate Venn diagrams, like the one shown, shade the region representing:

a B' **b** in A and in B **c** $(A \cup B)'$

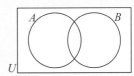

6

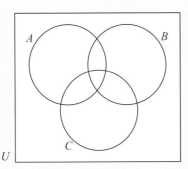

Using separate Venn diagrams like the one shown, shade regions to verify that $(A \cap B) \cup C = (A \cup C) \cap (B \cup C)$.

CHALLENGE SET 1

1 Store A reduces its prices by 10% and then one week later increases its prices by $x\%$ so that its prices are now the same as they were originally. Find x.

2 The diagram alongside shows overhead plan views of tennis balls in piles.
  a How many balls in pile 4?
  b How many balls in pile 8?

pile 1   pile 2   pile 3

3 When Janice numbers the pages of her algebra book she uses 264 digits. How many pages are there in Janice's algebra book?

4

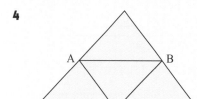

A, B and C are the midpoints of the three sides of a triangle.

Is it always possible to bend along AB, BC and CA to form a tetrahedron? Explain.

5 A ship is sailing at 15 km/h directly towards a lighthouse. Kerryn walks at 6 km/h from the front of the ship (the bow) to the rear (the stern). At what speed is Kerryn moving relative to an observer in the lighthouse?

6 Two numbers differ by 2 and their reciprocals differ by $\frac{1}{24}$. Find their product.

$$\left(\textbf{Hint:} \quad \frac{1}{a} - \frac{1}{b} = ?\right)$$

7 Prove that "if the product of 3 consecutive integers is increased by the middle integer, then the result will always be a perfect cube," e.g., $3 \times 4 \times 5 + 4 = 64 = 4^3$.

8 If 2^{1000} is divided by 5, what will the remainder be?
(**Hint:** Consider dividing $2^1, 2^2, 2^3, 2^4, 2^5$, etc., by 5.)

Below are icons which you can click on to produce 15 other **Challenge sets**.

CHALLENGE SET 1   CHALLENGE SET 2   CHALLENGE SET 3   CHALLENGE SET 4   CHALLENGE SET 5   CHALLENGE SET 6   CHALLENGE SET 7   CHALLENGE SET 8

CHALLENGE SET 9   CHALLENGE SET 10   CHALLENGE SET 11   CHALLENGE SET 12   CHALLENGE SET 13   CHALLENGE SET 14   CHALLENGE SET 15   CHALLENGE SET 16

Chapter 2

Pythagoras' Theorem

Right angles (90° angles) are used in the construction of buildings and in the division of areas of land into rectangular regions.

The ancient **Egyptians** used a rope with 12 equally spaced knots to form a triangle with sides in the ratio 3 : 4 : 5. This triangle has a right angle between the sides of length 3 and 4 units, and is, in fact, the simplest right angled triangle with sides of integer length.

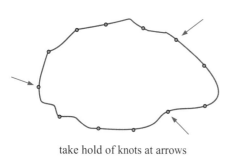

take hold of knots at arrows

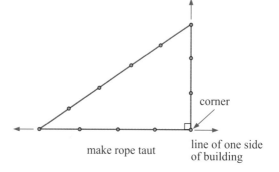

corner

make rope taut

line of one side of building

OPENING PROBLEM

Karrie is playing golf in the US Open but hits a wayward tee shot on the opening hole. Her caddy paces out some distances and finds that Karrie has hit the ball 250 m, but is 70 m from the line of sight from the tee to the hole. A marker which is 150 m from the pin is further up the fairway as shown:

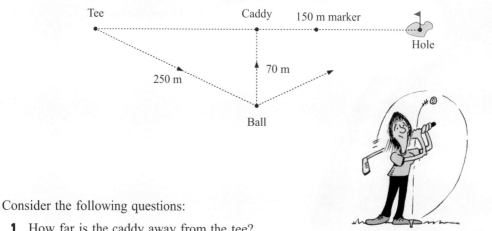

Consider the following questions:

1 How far is the caddy away from the tee?

2 From where the caddy stands on the fairway, what distance is left to the 150 m marker if he knows the hole is 430 m long?

3 How far does Karrie need to hit her ball with her second shot to reach the hole?

INTRODUCTION

A **right angled triangle** is a triangle which has a right angle as one of its angles.

The side **opposite** the **right angle** is called the **hypotenuse** and is the **longest** side of the triangle.

The other two sides are called the **legs** of the triangle.

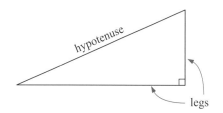

Around 500 BC, the Greek mathematician **Pythagoras** formulated a rule which connects the lengths of the sides of all right angled triangles. It is thought that he discovered the rule while studying tessellations of tiles on bathroom floors. Such patterns, like the one illustrated, were common on the walls and floors of bathrooms in ancient **Greece**.

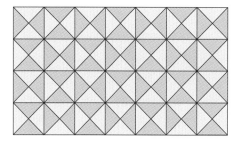

A   PYTHAGORAS' THEOREM

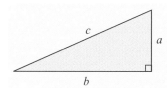

In a right angled triangle, with hypotenuse c and legs a and b,

$$c^2 = a^2 + b^2.$$

In geometric form, the **Theorem of Pythagoras** is:

In any right angled triangle, the area of the square on the hypotenuse is equal to the sum of the areas of the squares on the other two sides.

GEOMETRY PACKAGE

Can you see how Pythagoras may have discovered the rule by looking at the tile pattern above?

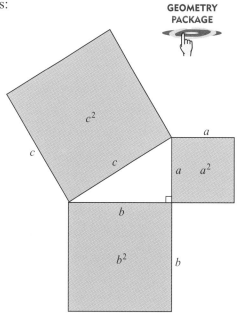

Over 400 different proofs of the Pythagorean Theorem exist. Here is one of them:

Proof:

On a square we draw 4 identical (congruent) right angled triangles, as illustrated. A smaller square in the centre is formed.

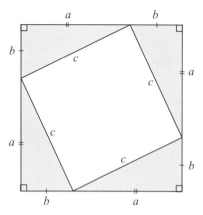

Suppose the legs are of length a and b and the hypotenuse has length c.

Since total area of large square
$= 4 \times$ area of one triangle $+$ area of smaller square,

$$(a+b)^2 = 4(\tfrac{1}{2}ab) + c^2$$
$$\therefore \quad a^2 + 2ab + b^2 = 2ab + c^2$$
$$\therefore \quad a^2 + b^2 = c^2$$

Note: When using Pythagoras' Theorem we often see **surds**, which are square root numbers like $\sqrt{7}$.

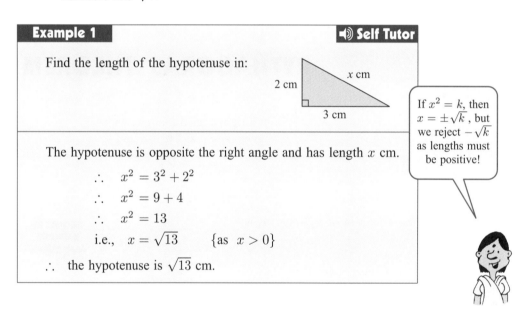

| Example 1 | ◀) Self Tutor |

Find the length of the hypotenuse in:

2 cm

3 cm

x cm

If $x^2 = k$, then $x = \pm\sqrt{k}$, but we reject $-\sqrt{k}$ as lengths must be positive!

The hypotenuse is opposite the right angle and has length x cm.

$$\therefore \quad x^2 = 3^2 + 2^2$$
$$\therefore \quad x^2 = 9 + 4$$
$$\therefore \quad x^2 = 13$$
$$\text{i.e.,} \quad x = \sqrt{13} \qquad \{\text{as } x > 0\}$$
$$\therefore \quad \text{the hypotenuse is } \sqrt{13} \text{ cm.}$$

EXERCISE 2A

1   Find the length of the hypotenuse in the following triangles, leaving your answer in surd (square root) form if appropriate:

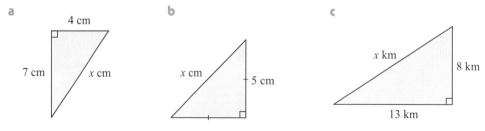

a

4 cm

7 cm

x cm

b

x cm

5 cm

c

x km

8 km

13 km

Example 2   ◀⦚ **Self Tutor**

Find the length of the third side of:

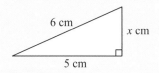

The hypotenuse has length 6 cm.

$\therefore \quad x^2 + 5^2 = 6^2 \quad$ {Pythagoras}

$\therefore \quad x^2 + 25 = 36$

$\therefore \quad x^2 = 11$

$\therefore \quad x = \sqrt{11} \quad$ {as $x > 0$}

$\therefore \quad$ third side is $\sqrt{11}$ cm long.

2 Find the length of the third side of the following right angled triangles.
Where appropriate leave your answer in surd (square root) form.

a
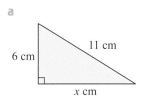

b
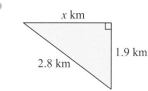

c
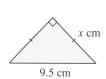

Example 3   ◀⦚ **Self Tutor**

Find x in the following:

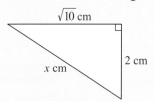

The hypotenuse has length x cm.

$\therefore \quad x^2 = 2^2 + (\sqrt{10})^2 \quad$ {Pythagoras}

$\therefore \quad x^2 = 4 + 10$

$\therefore \quad x^2 = 14$

$\therefore \quad x = \pm\sqrt{14}$

But $x > 0$, $\therefore$ $x = \sqrt{14}$.

3 Find x in the following:

a
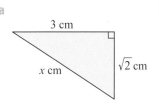

b
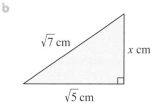

c
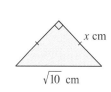

Example 4   ◀⦚ **Self Tutor**

Solve for x:

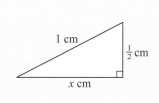

$x^2 + \left(\frac{1}{2}\right)^2 = 1^2 \quad$ {Pythagoras}

$\therefore \quad x^2 + \frac{1}{4} = 1$

$\therefore \quad x^2 = \frac{3}{4}$

$\therefore \quad x = \pm\sqrt{\frac{3}{4}}$

$\therefore \quad x = \sqrt{\frac{3}{4}} \quad$ {as $x > 0$}

4 Solve for x:

a

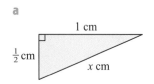

b

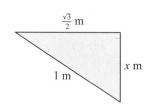

c

Example 5	🔊 Self Tutor

Find the value of x:

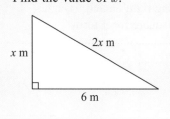

$$(2x)^2 = x^2 + 6^2 \quad \{\text{Pythagoras}\}$$
$$\therefore \quad 4x^2 = x^2 + 36$$
$$\therefore \quad 3x^2 = 36$$
$$\therefore \quad x^2 = 12$$
$$\therefore \quad x = \pm\sqrt{12}$$
$$\text{But} \quad x > 0, \quad \therefore \quad x = \sqrt{12}.$$

---

5 Find the value of x:

a

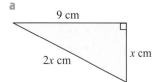

b

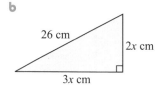

c

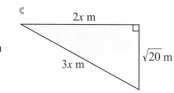

Example 6	🔊 Self Tutor

Find the value of any unknowns:

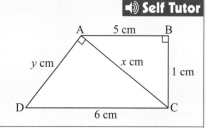

In triangle ABC, the hypotenuse is x cm.
$$\therefore \quad x^2 = 5^2 + 1^2 \qquad \{\text{Pythagoras}\}$$
$$\therefore \quad x^2 = 26$$
$$\therefore \quad x = \pm\sqrt{26}$$
$$\therefore \quad x = \sqrt{26} \qquad \{x > 0\}$$

In $\triangle$ACD, the hypotenuse is 6 cm.
$$\therefore \quad y^2 + (\sqrt{26})^2 = 6^2 \qquad \{\text{Pythagoras}\}$$
$$\therefore \quad y^2 + 26 = 36$$
$$\therefore \quad y^2 = 10$$
$$\therefore \quad y = \pm\sqrt{10}$$
$$\therefore \quad y = \sqrt{10} \qquad \{y > 0\}$$

6 Find the value of any unknowns:

a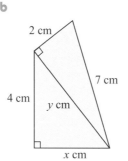

b

c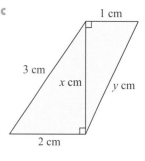

7 Find x:

a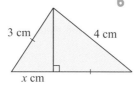

b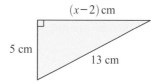

8 Find the length of AC in:

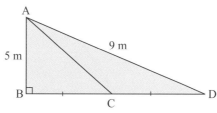

9 Find the distance AB, in the following figures.
(**Hint:** It is necessary to draw an additional line or two on the figure in each case.)

a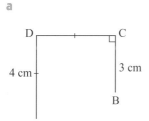

b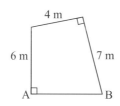

c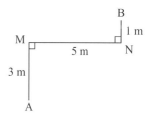

B THE CONVERSE OF PYTHAGORAS' THEOREM

If we have a triangle whose three sides have known lengths, we can use the **converse** of **Pythagoras' Theorem** to test whether (or not) it is right angled.

THE CONVERSE OF PYTHAGORAS' THEOREM

GEOMETRY PACKAGE

If a triangle has sides of length a, b and c units and $a^2 + b^2 = c^2$, then the triangle is right angled.

Example 7   ◀)) **Self Tutor**

Is the triangle with sides 6 cm, 8 cm and 5 cm right angled?

The two shorter sides have lengths 5 cm and 6 cm, and $5^2 + 6^2$
$= 25 + 36$
$= 61$

But $8^2 = 64$

∴ $5^2 + 6^2 \neq 8^2$ and hence the triangle is not right angled.

EXERCISE 2B

1   The following figures are not drawn accurately. Which of the triangles are right angled?

a
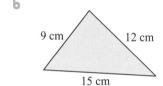

b

c
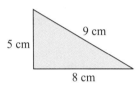

d
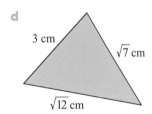

e
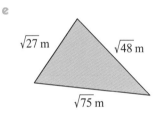

f
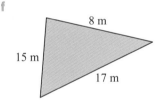

2   If any of the following triangles (not drawn accurately) is right angled, find the right angle:

a
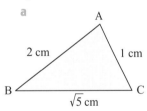

b
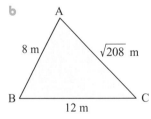

c
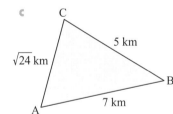

PYTHAGOREAN TRIPLES

The simplest right angled triangle with sides of **integer** length is the **3-4-5 triangle**.
The numbers 3, 4, and 5 satisfy the rule $3^2 + 4^2 = 5^2$.

The set of integers $\{a,\ b,\ c\}$ is a **Pythagorean triple** if it obeys the rule $a^2 + b^2 = c^2$.

Other examples are: $\{5,\ 12,\ 13\}$, $\{7,\ 24,\ 25\}$, $\{8,\ 15,\ 17\}$.

Example 8	◀») **Self Tutor**

Show that $\{5, 12, 13\}$ is a Pythagorean triple.

We find the square of the **largest** number first.

$$13^2 = 169$$
$$\text{and} \quad 5^2 + 12^2 = 25 + 144 = 169$$
$$\therefore \quad 5^2 + 12^2 = 13^2$$

i.e., $\{5, 12, 13\}$ is a Pythagorean triple.

3 Determine if the following are Pythagorean triples:

   a $\{8, 15, 17\}$ **b** $\{6, 8, 10\}$ **c** $\{5, 6, 7\}$

   d $\{14, 48, 50\}$ **e** $\{1, 2, 3\}$ **f** $\{20, 48, 52\}$

Example 9	◀») **Self Tutor**

Find k if $\{9, k, 15\}$ is a Pythagorean triple.

$$\text{Let} \quad 9^2 + k^2 = 15^2 \qquad \{\text{Pythagoras}\}$$
$$\therefore \quad 81 + k^2 = 225$$
$$\therefore \quad k^2 = 144$$
$$\therefore \quad k = \pm\sqrt{144}$$
$$\therefore \quad k = 12 \qquad \{k > 0\}$$

4 Find k if the following are Pythagorean triples:

   a $\{8, 15, k\}$ **b** $\{k, 24, 26\}$ **c** $\{14, k, 50\}$

   d $\{15, 20, k\}$ **e** $\{k, 45, 51\}$ **f** $\{11, k, 61\}$

5 For what values of n does $\{n, n+1, n+2\}$ form a Pythagorean triple?

6 Show that $\{n, n+1, n+3\}$ cannot form a Pythagorean triple.

INVESTIGATION 1   **PYTHAGOREAN TRIPLES SPREADSHEET**

Well known Pythagorean triples are $\{3, 4, 5\}$, $\{5, 12, 13\}$,
$\{7, 24, 25\}$ and $\{8, 15, 17\}$.

Formulae can be used to generate Pythagorean triples.

An example is $2n + 1$, $2n^2 + 2n$, $2n^2 + 2n + 1$ where n is a positive integer.

A **spreadsheet** will quickly generate sets of Pythagorean triples using such formulae.

What to do:

1 Open a new spreadsheet and enter the following:

	A	B	C	D
1	n	a	b	c
2	1	=2*A2+1	=2*A2^2+2*A2	=C2+1
3	=A2+1	↓	↓	↓
4	↓			↓
5	↓		fill down	↓

2 Highlight the formulae in B2, C2 and D2 and **fill down** to Row 3. You should now have generated two sets of triples:

	A	B	C	D
1	n	a	b	c
2	1	3	4	5
3	2	5	12	13
4				
5				

3 Highlight the formulae in Row 3 and **fill down** to Row 11 to generate 10 sets of triples.

4 Check that each set of numbers is actually a triple by adding two more columns to your spreadsheet.

In E1 enter the heading '$a\hat{}2+b\hat{}2$' and in F1 enter the heading '$c\hat{}2$'.

In E2 enter the formula =B2^2+C2^2 and in F2 enter the formula =D2^2.

	A	B	C	D	E	F
1	n	a	b	c	$a\hat{}2+b\hat{}2$	$c\hat{}2$
2	1	3	4	5	=B2^2+C2^2	=D2^2
3	2	5	12	13		
4	3	7	24	25		
5						

5 Highlight the formulae in E2 and F2 and **fill down** to Row 11. Is each set of numbers a Pythagorean triple? [**Hint:** Does $a^2 + b^2 = c^2$?]

6 Your task is to **prove** that the formulae $\{2n+1, \quad 2n^2+2n, \quad 2n^2+2n+1\}$ will produce sets of Pythagorean triples for positive integer values of n.

We let $a = 2n+1$, $b = 2n^2+2n$ and $c = 2n^2+2n+1$.

Simplify $c^2 - b^2 = (2n^2+2n+1)^2 - (2n^2+2n)^2$ using *the difference of two squares* factorisation, and hence show that it equals $(2n+1)^2 = a^2$.

C   PROBLEM SOLVING USING PYTHAGORAS' THEOREM

Right angled triangles occur frequently in **problem solving** and often the presence of right angled triangles indicates that **Pythagoras' Theorem** is likely to be used.

SPECIAL GEOMETRICAL FIGURES

All of these figures contain right angled triangles where Pythagoras' Theorem applies:

rectangle

In a **rectangle**, a right angle exists between adjacent sides.

Construct a **diagonal** to form a right angled triangle.

square

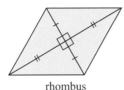

rhombus

In a **square** and a **rhombus**, the *diagonals bisect each other at right angles.*

isosceles triangle

equilateral triangle

In an **isosceles triangle** and an **equilateral triangle**, the *altitude bisects the base at right angles.*

Things to remember

- Draw a neat, clear diagram of the situation.
- Mark on known lengths and right angles.
- Use a symbol, such as x, to represent the unknown length.
- Write down Pythagoras' Theorem for the given information.
- Solve the equation.
- Write your answer in sentence form (where necessary).

Example 10   ◆⏾ **Self Tutor**

A rectangular gate is 3 m wide and has a 3.5 m diagonal. How high is the gate?

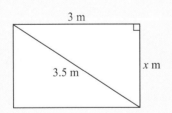

Let x m be the height of the gate.

$$\text{Now} \quad (3.5)^2 = x^2 + 3^2 \qquad \{\text{Pythagoras}\}$$
$$\therefore \quad 12.25 = x^2 + 9$$
$$\therefore \quad 3.25 = x^2$$
$$\therefore \quad x = \sqrt{3.25} \qquad \{\text{as } x > 0\}$$
$$\therefore \quad x \doteqdot 1.80$$

Thus the gate is approximately 1.80 m high.

EXERCISE 2C.1

1 A rectangle has sides of length 8 cm and 3 cm. Find the length of its diagonals.

2 The longer side of a rectangle is three times the length of the shorter side. If the length of the diagonal is 10 cm, find the dimensions of the rectangle.

3 A rectangle with diagonals of length 20 cm has sides in the ratio 2 : 1. Find the
   a perimeter   **b** area of the rectangle.

Example 11   ◄◗ **Self Tutor**

A rhombus has diagonals of length 6 cm and 8 cm.
Find the length of its sides.

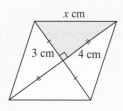

The diagonals of a rhombus *bisect at right angles.*
Let a side be x cm.

$\therefore \quad x^2 = 3^2 + 4^2 \qquad$ {Pythagoras}

$\therefore \quad x^2 = 9 + 16$

$\therefore \quad x^2 = 25$

$\therefore \quad x = \pm\sqrt{25}$

$\therefore \quad x = 5 \qquad\qquad \{x > 0\}$

i.e., the sides are 5 cm in length.

4   A rhombus has sides of length 6 cm. One of its diagonals is 10 cm long. Find the length of the other diagonal.

5   A square has diagonals of length 10 cm. Find the length of its sides.

6   A rhombus has diagonals of length 8 cm and 10 cm. Find its perimeter.

Example 12   ◄◗ **Self Tutor**

A man travels due east by bicycle at 16 kmph. His son travels due south on his bicycle at 20 kmph. How far apart are they after 4 hours, if they both leave point A at the same time?

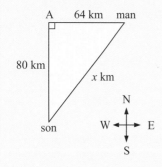

After 4 hours the man has travelled $4 \times 16 = 64$ km and his son has travelled $4 \times 20 = 80$ km.

Thus $x^2 = 64^2 + 80^2$ {Pythagoras}

i.e., $x^2 = 4096 + 6400$

$\therefore \quad x^2 = 10\,496$

$\therefore \quad x = \sqrt{10\,496}$ {as $x > 0$}

$\therefore \quad x \doteqdot 102$

$\therefore$ they are 102 km apart after 4 hours.

7   A yacht sails 5 km due west and then 8 km due south. How far is it from its starting point?

8   Town A is 50 km south of town B and town C is 120 km east of town B. Is it quicker to travel directly from A to C by car at 90 kmph or from A to C via B in a train travelling at 120 kmph?

9 Two runners set off from town A at the same time. If one runs due east to town B and the other runs due south to town C at twice the speed, they arrive at B and C respectively two hours later. If B and C are 50 km apart, find the speed at which each runner travelled.

Example 13   ◆) **Self Tutor**

An equilateral triangle has sides of length 6 cm. Find its area.

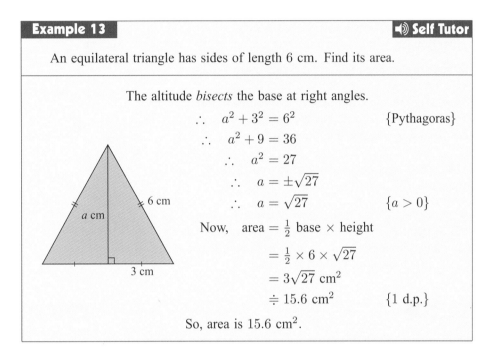

The altitude *bisects* the base at right angles.

$$\therefore \quad a^2 + 3^2 = 6^2 \qquad \text{\{Pythagoras\}}$$
$$\therefore \quad a^2 + 9 = 36$$
$$\therefore \quad a^2 = 27$$
$$\therefore \quad a = \pm\sqrt{27}$$
$$\therefore \quad a = \sqrt{27} \qquad \text{\{}a > 0\text{\}}$$

Now, area $= \frac{1}{2}$ base $\times$ height

$$= \frac{1}{2} \times 6 \times \sqrt{27}$$
$$= 3\sqrt{27} \text{ cm}^2$$
$$\doteqdot 15.6 \text{ cm}^2 \qquad \text{\{1 d.p.\}}$$

So, area is 15.6 cm².

---

10 Find any unknowns in the following:

a
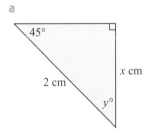

b
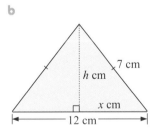

c
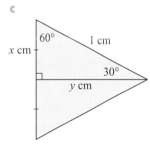

11 An equilateral triangle has sides of length 12 cm. Find the length of one of its altitudes.

12 An isosceles triangle has equal sides of length 8 cm and a base of length 6 cm. Find the area of the triangle.

13 When an extension ladder rests against a wall it reaches 4 m up the wall. The ladder is extended a further 0.8 m without moving the foot of the ladder and it now rests against the wall 1 m further up. How long is the extended ladder?

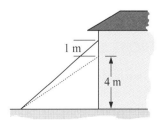

14 An equilateral triangle has area $16\sqrt{3}$ cm^2. Find the length of its sides.

15 Revisit the **Opening Problem** on page **30** and answer the questions posed.

TRUE BEARINGS

When using **true bearings** we measure the direction of travel by comparing it with the **true north direction**. Measurements are always taken in the **clockwise** direction.

Imagine you are standing at point A, facing north. You turn **clockwise** through an angle until you face B. The **bearing of B from A** is the angle through which you have turned. That is, the bearing of B from A is the measure of the angle between AB and the 'north' line through A.

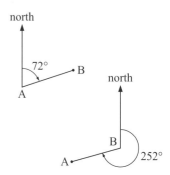

In the diagram at right, the bearing of B from A is 72° from true north. We write this as 72^oT or 072°.

If we want to find the true **bearing of A from B**, we place ourselves at point B and face north and then measure the clockwise angle through which we have to turn so that we face A. The true bearing of A from B is 252°.

Example 14   ◀)) **Self Tutor**

A helicopter travels from base station S on a true bearing of 074° for 112 km to outpost A. It then travels 134 km on a true bearing of 164° to outpost B. How far is outpost B from base station S?

> In bearings problems, notice the use of the properties of parallel lines for finding angles.

Let SB be x km.

From the diagram alongside, in triangle SAB
$\angle SAB = 90^o$.

$$x^2 = 112^2 + 134^2 \qquad \{\text{Pythagoras}\}$$
$$\therefore \quad x^2 = 12\,544 + 17\,956$$
$$\therefore \quad x^2 = 30\,500$$
$$\therefore \quad x = \sqrt{30\,500} \qquad \{\text{as } x > 0\}$$
$$\therefore \quad x \doteqdot 175$$

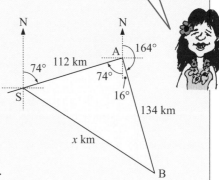

i.e., outpost B is 175 km from base station S.

EXERCISE 2C.2

1 Two bushwalkers set off from base camp at the same time. If one walks on a true bearing of 049° at an average speed of 5 kmph and the other walks on a true bearing of 319° at an average speed of 4 kmph, find their distance apart after 3 hours.

2 James is about to tackle an orienteering course. He has been given these instructions:

  • the course is triangular and starts and finishes at S
  • the first checkpoint A is in a direction 056° from S
  • the second checkpoint B is in a direction 146° from A
  • the distance from A to B is twice the distance from S to A
  • the distance from B to S is 2.6 km.

Find the length of the orienteering course.

3 A fighter plane and a helicopter set off from airbase A at the same time. If the helicopter travels on a bearing of 152° and the fighter plane travels on a bearing of 242° at three times the speed, they arrive at bases B and C respectively 2 hours later. If B and C are 1200 km apart, find the average speed of the helicopter.

 # CIRCLE PROBLEMS

There are certain properties of circles where right angles occur and so Pythagoras' Theorem can be used. These properties are examined in more detail in **Chapter 16**.

A CHORD OF A CIRCLE

The line drawn from the centre of a circle at right angles to a chord bisects the chord.

This follows from the **isosceles triangle theorem**. The construction of radii from the centre of the circle to the endpoints of the chord produces two right angled triangles.

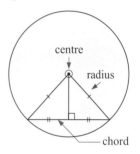

Example 15   ◀) **Self Tutor**

A circle has a chord of length 10 cm, and the radius of the circle is 8 cm.
Find the shortest distance from the centre of the circle to the chord.

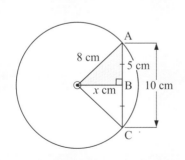

The shortest distance is the 'perpendicular distance'.
Since the line drawn from the centre of a circle, perpendicular to a chord, bisects the chord, then
$$AB = BC = 5 \text{ cm.}$$
In ΔAOB, $5^2 + x^2 = 8^2$ {Pythagoras}
$$\therefore \quad x^2 = 64 - 25 = 39$$
$$\therefore \quad x = \sqrt{39} \qquad \{\text{as } x > 0\}$$
$$\therefore \quad x \doteqdot 6.2 \qquad \{\text{to 1 dec. pl.}\}$$

Thus the shortest distance is 6.2 cm.

EXERCISE 2D.1

1 A chord of a circle has length 3 cm and the circle has radius 4 cm. Find the shortest distance from the centre of the circle to the chord.

2 A chord of length 6 cm is 3 cm from the centre of a circle. Find the length of the circle's radius.

3 A chord is 5 cm from the centre of a circle of radius 8 cm. Find the length of the chord.

TANGENT-RADIUS PROPERTY

A tangent to a circle and a radius at the point of contact meet at right angles.

Notice that we can now form a right angled triangle.

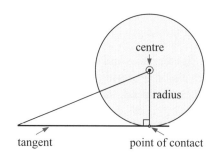

Example 16   🔊 **Self Tutor**

A tangent of length 10 cm is drawn to a circle with radius 7 cm. How far is the centre of the circle from the end point of the tangent?

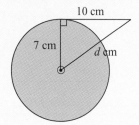

Let the distance be d cm.

$$\therefore \quad d^2 = 7^2 + 10^2 \qquad \{\text{Pythagoras}\}$$
$$\therefore \quad d^2 = 49 + 100$$
$$\therefore \quad d^2 = 149$$
$$\therefore \quad d = \sqrt{149} \qquad \{\text{as } d > 0\}$$
$$\therefore \quad d \doteqdot 12.2 \qquad \{\text{to 1 dec. place}\}$$

i.e., the centre is 12.2 cm from the end point of the tangent.

EXERCISE 2D.2

1 A circle has radius 3 cm. A tangent is drawn to the circle from point P which is 9 cm from O, the circle's centre. How long is the tangent?

2 Find the radius of a circle if a tangent of length 12 cm has its end point 16 cm from the circle's centre.

3 If the Earth has a radius of 6400 km and you are in a rocket 40 km directly above the Earth's surface, determine the distance to the horizon.

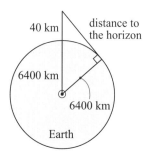

4 A circular table of diameter 2 m is placed in one corner of a room so that its edges touch two adjacent walls. Find the shortest distance from the corner of the room to the edge of the table.

Example 17   ◀) **Self Tutor**

Two circles have a common tangent with points of contact at A and B. The radii are 4 cm and 2 cm respectively. Find the distance between the centres, given that AB is 7 cm.

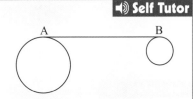

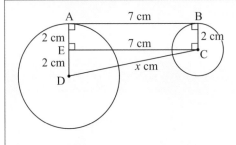

For centres C and D, we draw BC, AD, CD and CE∥AB. ∴   ABCE is a rectangle

and consequently CE = 7 cm   {CE = AB} and   DE = 4 − 2 = 2 cm.

Now $x^2 = 2^2 + 7^2$ {Pythagoras in △DEC}

∴ $x^2 = 4 + 49$

∴ $x^2 = 53$

∴ $x = \sqrt{53}$ {as $x > 0$}

∴ $x \doteqdot 7.3$ {1 dec. pl.}

∴   the distance between the centres is 7.3 cm.

---

5 A and B are the centres of two circles with radii 4 m and 3 m respectively. The illustrated common tangent has length 10 m. Find the distance between the centres.

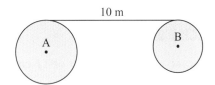

6 The illustration shows two circles of radii 4 cm and 2 cm respectively. The distance between the two circles' centres is 8 cm. Find the length of the common tangent, AB.

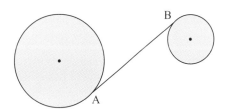

7 In the given figure   AB = 1 cm   and AC = 3 cm.   Find the radius of the circle.

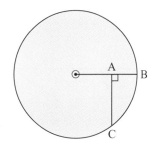

E   THREE-DIMENSIONAL PROBLEMS

Pythagoras' Theorem is often used when finding lengths in **three-dimensional solids**.

Example 18	◀)) **Self Tutor**

A 50 m rope is attached inside an empty cylindrical wheat silo of diameter 12 m as shown. How high is the wheat silo?

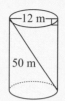

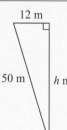

Let the height be h m. $\therefore$ $h^2 + 12^2 = 50^2$ {Pythagoras}

$\therefore$ $h^2 + 144 = 2500$

$\therefore$ $h^2 = 2356$

$\therefore$ $h = \sqrt{2356}$ {as $h > 0$}

$\therefore$ $h \doteqdot 48.5$ {to 1 dec. place}

i.e.,   the wheat silo is 48.5 m high.

EXERCISE 2E

1   A cone has a slant height of 17 cm and a base radius of 8 cm. How high is the cone?

2   Find the length of the longest nail that could be put entirely within a cylindrical can of radius 3 cm and height 8 cm.

3   A 20 cm nail just fits inside a cylindrical can. Three identical spherical balls need to fit entirely within the can. What is the maximum radius of each ball?

In three-dimensional problem solving questions we often need the theorem of Pythagoras *twice*. We look for right angled triangles which have two sides of known length.

Example 19	◀)) **Self Tutor**

A room is 6 m by 4 m at floor level and the floor to ceiling height is 3 m. Find the distance from a floor corner point to the opposite corner point on the ceiling.

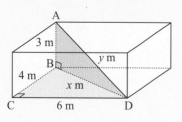

The required distance is AD. We join BD.

In $\triangle$BCD, $x^2 = 4^2 + 6^2$ {Pythagoras}

In $\triangle$ABD, $y^2 = x^2 + 3^2$ {Pythagoras}

$\therefore$ $y^2 = 4^2 + 6^2 + 3^2$

$\therefore$ $y^2 = 61$

$\therefore$ $y = \pm\sqrt{61}$

But $y > 0$ $\therefore$ the required distance is $\sqrt{61} \doteqdot 7.81$ m.

4 A cube has sides of length 3 cm. Find the length of a diagonal of the cube.

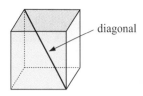

diagonal

5 A room is 6 m by 4 m and has a height of 3 m. Find the distance from a corner point on the floor to the opposite corner of the ceiling.

6 A rectangular box is 2 cm by 3 cm by 2 cm (internally). Find the length of the longest toothpick that can be placed within the box.

7 Determine the length of the longest piece of timber which could be stored in a rectangular shed 6 m by 5 m by 2 m high.

Example 20 ◀ **Self Tutor**

A pyramid of height 40 m has a square base with edges 50 m. Determine the length of the slant edges.

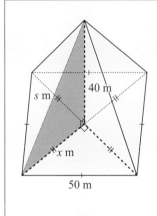

Let a slant edge have length s m.

Let half a diagonal have length x m.

Using
$$x^2 + x^2 = 50^2 \quad \{\text{Pythagoras}\}$$
$$\therefore \quad 2x^2 = 2500$$
$$\therefore \quad x^2 = 1250$$

Using
$$s^2 = x^2 + 40^2 \quad \{\text{Pythagoras}\}$$
$$\therefore \quad s^2 = 1250 + 1600$$
$$\therefore \quad s^2 = 2850$$
$$\therefore \quad s = \sqrt{2850} \quad \{\text{as } s > 0\}$$
$$\therefore \quad s \doteq 53.4 \quad \{\text{to 1 dec. place}\}$$

i.e., each slant edge is 53.4 m long.

---

8 ABCDE is a square-based pyramid. E, the apex of the pyramid is vertically above M, the point of intersection of AC and BD.

If an Egyptian Pharoah wished to build a square-based pyramid with all edges 100 m, how high (to the nearest metre) would the pyramid reach above the desert sands?

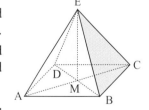

9 A symmetrical square-based pyramid has height 10 cm and slant edges of 15 cm. Find the dimensions of its square base.

10 A cube has sides of length 2 m. B is at the centre of one face, and A is an opposite vertex. Find the direct distance from A to B.

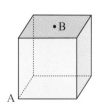

F   MORE DIFFICULT PROBLEMS (EXTENSION)

EXERCISE 2F

1 A highway runs in an East-West direction joining towns C and B 25 km apart. Town A lies directly north from C, at a distance of 15 km. A straight road is built from A to the highway and meets the highway at D which is equidistant from A and B. Find the position of D on the highway.

2 An aircraft hangar is semi-cylindrical, with diameter 40 m and length 50 m. A helicopter places an inelastic rope across the top of the hangar and one end is pinned to a corner, at A. The rope is then pulled tight and pinned at the opposite corner, B. Determine the length of the rope.

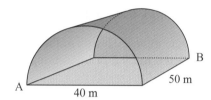

3 President Garfield's proof of the theorem of Pythagoras (published in 1876) is the only contribution to mathematics ever made by a president of the United States. Alongside is the figure he used.

Write out the proof.

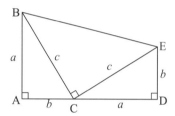

4 A rectangular piece of paper, 10 cm by 24 cm, is folded so that a pair of diagonally opposite corners coincide. Find the length of the crease.

5

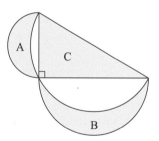

Show that, Area A + Area B = Area C.

6 An extension ladder rests against a vertical wall and reaches 4.5 m up the wall from the horizontal ground. When the ladder is extended a further 0.9 m it reaches a further 1 m up the wall without its feet being moved from their original position. Find the original length of the ladder.

7 You are given a rectangle in which a point has been located which is 3 cm, 4 cm and 5 cm from three of the vertices. How far is the point from the fourth vertex?

REVIEW SET 2A

1 Find the lengths of the unknown sides in the following triangles:

a 2 cm
5 cm
x cm

b 4 cm
x cm
7 cm

c 9 cm
$2x$ cm
x cm

2 Is the following triangle right angled?
Give evidence.

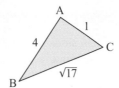

A
1
4
C
$\sqrt{17}$
B

3 Show that $\{5, 11, 13\}$ is not a Pythagorean triple.

4 A rectangle has diagonal 15 cm and one side 8 cm. Find the perimeter of the rectangle.

5 A chord of a circle is 14 cm in length and is 8 cm from the centre of the circle. Find the radius of the circle.

6 A circle has a chord of length 10 cm. The shortest distance from the circle's centre to the chord is 5 cm. Find the radius of the circle.

7 A boat leaves X and travels due east for 10 km. It then sails 10 km south to Y. Find the distance and bearing of X from Y.

8 What is the length of the longest toothpick which can be placed inside a rectangular box that is 3 cm × 5 cm × 8 cm?

9 Two rally car drivers set off from town C at the same time. A travels in a direction 63^oT at 120 kmph and B travels in a direction 333^oT at 135 kmph. How far apart are they after one hour?

REVIEW SET 2B

1 Find the value of x in the following:

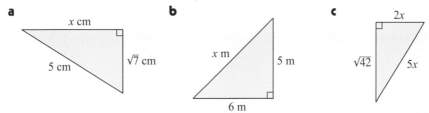

a x cm
5 cm
$\sqrt{7}$ cm

b x m
5 m
6 m

c $2x$
$\sqrt{42}$
$5x$

2 Show that the following triangle is right angled and state which vertex is the right angle:

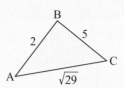

3 If the diameter of a circle is 20 cm, find the shortest distance from a chord of length 16 cm to the centre of the circle.

4 A rectangular gate is twice as wide as it is high. If a diagonal strut is 3.2 m long, find the height of the gate to the nearest millimetre.

5 If a softball diamond has sides of length 30 m, determine the distance a fielder must throw the ball from second base to reach home base.

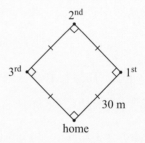

6 Town B is 27 km in a direction 134^oT from town A, and town C is 21 km in a direction 224^oT from town B. Find the distance between A and C.

7 If a 15 m ladder reaches twice as far up a vertical wall as the base is out from the wall, determine the distance up the wall to the top of the ladder.

8 Can an 11 m long piece of timber be placed in a rectangular shed of dimensions 8 m by 7 m by 3 m? Give evidence.

9 Two circles have a common tangent with points of contact X and Y.

The radii of the circles are 4 cm and 5 cm respectively.

The distance between the centres is 10 cm.

Find the length of the common tangent XY.

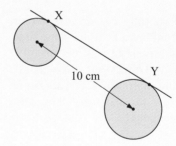

Chapter **3**

Surds

Contents:

INTRODUCTION

In **Chapter 2** we used Pythagoras' Theorem.

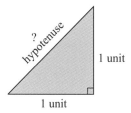

Finding the length of the longest side **(hypotenuse)** of a right angled triangle with legs one unit may have been Pythagoras' initial problem.

We know today that this length is $\sqrt{2}$ units, where $\sqrt{2} \doteqdot 1.41421....$ and that this decimal expansion neither terminates, nor does it recur.

SQUARE ROOTS

$\sqrt{a}$ is the **positive** number which obeys the rule $\sqrt{a} \times \sqrt{a} = a$.

For example, $\sqrt{2} \times \sqrt{2} = 2$, $\sqrt{3} \times \sqrt{3} = 3$, $\sqrt{4} \times \sqrt{4} = 4$, ... etc.

Note:
- $\sqrt{}$ reads: *the square root of.*

- The symbol $\sqrt{}$ is called **the square root sign** or **radical sign**.

- $\sqrt{a}$ has meaning for $a \geqslant 0$ only.

OPENING PROBLEM

Since $\sqrt{2} \times \sqrt{2} = 2 = \sqrt{4}$, we might suspect that $\sqrt{a} \times \sqrt{b} = \sqrt{ab}$ for all whole numbers a and b.

One way of checking that this is a possible rule is to use a calculator with various substitutions for a and b.

Are these possible laws or rules for operating with surds?

- $\sqrt{a} \times \sqrt{b} = \sqrt{ab}$ for all $a \geqslant 0$ and $b \geqslant 0$.

- $\sqrt{\dfrac{a}{b}} = \dfrac{\sqrt{a}}{\sqrt{b}}$ for all $a \geqslant 0$ and $b > 0$.

- $\sqrt{a+b} = \sqrt{a} + \sqrt{b}$ for all $a \geqslant 0$ and $b \geqslant 0$.

- $\sqrt{a-b} = \sqrt{a} - \sqrt{b}$ for all $a \geqslant 0$ and $b \geqslant 0$.

$\sqrt{2}$ IS IRRATIONAL AND IS A SURD

$\sqrt{2}$ is said to be an **irrational number**, because it cannot be written as a ratio or fraction of integers. More formally:

An **irrational number** is a number which cannot be written in the form $\frac{p}{q}$, where p and q are integers with $q \neq 0$.

$\sqrt{2}$ is also called a "**surd**" because its exact value can only be written with a radical sign.

Other examples of surds are $\sqrt{3}$, $\sqrt{7}$, $\sqrt[3]{29}$ etc.

A   OPERATIONS WITH SURDS

Example 1 · Self Tutor

Simplify: a $(\sqrt{5})^2$

b $\left(\dfrac{1}{\sqrt{5}}\right)^2$

a $(\sqrt{5})^2$
$= \sqrt{5} \times \sqrt{5}$
$= 5$

b $\left(\dfrac{1}{\sqrt{5}}\right)^2$
$= \dfrac{1}{\sqrt{5}} \times \dfrac{1}{\sqrt{5}}$
$= \tfrac{1}{5}$

EXERCISE 3A.1

1 Simplify:

a $(\sqrt{7})^2$ b $(\sqrt{13})^2$ c $(\sqrt{15})^2$ d $(\sqrt{24})^2$

e $\left(\dfrac{1}{\sqrt{3}}\right)^2$ f $\left(\dfrac{1}{\sqrt{11}}\right)^2$ g $\left(\dfrac{1}{\sqrt{17}}\right)^2$ h $\left(\dfrac{1}{\sqrt{23}}\right)^2$

Example 2 · Self Tutor

Simplify:

a $(2\sqrt{5})^3$ b $-2\sqrt{5} \times 3\sqrt{5}$

a $(2\sqrt{5})^3$
$= 2\sqrt{5} \times 2\sqrt{5} \times 2\sqrt{5}$
$= 2 \times 2 \times 2 \times \sqrt{5} \times \sqrt{5} \times \sqrt{5}$
$= 8 \times 5 \times \sqrt{5}$
$= 40\sqrt{5}$

b $-2\sqrt{5} \times 3\sqrt{5}$
$= -2 \times 3 \times \sqrt{5} \times \sqrt{5}$
$= -6 \times 5$
$= -30$

2 Simplify:

a $3\sqrt{2} \times 4\sqrt{2}$ b $-2\sqrt{3} \times 5\sqrt{3}$ c $3\sqrt{5} \times (-2\sqrt{5})$

d $-2\sqrt{2} \times (-3\sqrt{2})$ e $(3\sqrt{2})^2$ f $(3\sqrt{2})^3$

g $(2\sqrt{3})^2$ h $(2\sqrt{3})^3$ i $(2\sqrt{2})^4$

ADDING AND SUBTRACTING SURDS

'Like surds' can be added and subtracted to simplify.

Consider $2\sqrt{3} + 4\sqrt{3}$. This has the same form as $2x + 4x$.

If we interpret this as 2 'lots' of $\sqrt{3}$ plus 4 'lots' of $\sqrt{3}$, we have 6 'lots' of $\sqrt{3}$,

i.e., $2\sqrt{3} + 4\sqrt{3} = 6\sqrt{3}$ (compare with $2x + 4x = 6x$).

Example 3   ◄》 **Self Tutor**

Simplify:

a $3\sqrt{2} + 4\sqrt{2}$

b $5\sqrt{3} - 6\sqrt{3}$

a $3\sqrt{2} + 4\sqrt{2}$
   $= 7\sqrt{2}$

b $5\sqrt{3} - 6\sqrt{3}$
    $= -1\sqrt{3}$
    $= -\sqrt{3}$

{Compare: $3x + 4x = 7x$}   {Compare: $5x - 6x = -x$}

EXERCISE 3A.2

1 Simplify:

a $\sqrt{2} + \sqrt{2}$

b $\sqrt{2} - \sqrt{2}$

c $3\sqrt{2} - 2\sqrt{2}$

d $2\sqrt{3} - \sqrt{3}$

e $5\sqrt{7} + 2\sqrt{7}$

f $3\sqrt{5} - 6\sqrt{5}$

g $3\sqrt{2} + 4\sqrt{2} - \sqrt{2}$

h $6\sqrt{2} - 9\sqrt{2}$

i $\sqrt{5} + 7\sqrt{5}$

j $3\sqrt{2} - 5\sqrt{2} - \sqrt{2}$

k $3\sqrt{3} - \sqrt{3} + 2\sqrt{3}$

l $3\sqrt{5} + 7\sqrt{5} - 10$

2 Simplify:

a $3\sqrt{2} + 2\sqrt{3} - \sqrt{2} + 5\sqrt{3}$

b $7\sqrt{2} - 4\sqrt{3} - 2\sqrt{2} + 3\sqrt{3}$

c $-6\sqrt{2} - 2\sqrt{3} - \sqrt{2} + 6\sqrt{3}$

d $2\sqrt{5} + 4\sqrt{2} + 9\sqrt{5} - 9\sqrt{2}$

e $3\sqrt{2} - 5\sqrt{7} - \sqrt{2} - 5\sqrt{7}$

f $3\sqrt{2} + 4\sqrt{11} + 6 - \sqrt{2} - \sqrt{11} - 3$

g $6\sqrt{6} - 2\sqrt{2} - \sqrt{2} - 5\sqrt{6} + 4$

h $5\sqrt{3} - 6\sqrt{7} - 5 + 4\sqrt{3} + \sqrt{7} - 8$

RULES OF SURDS

Notice that $\sqrt{4 \times 9} = \sqrt{36} = 6$ and $\sqrt{4} \times \sqrt{9} = 2 \times 3 = 6$

which suggests that $\sqrt{4} \times \sqrt{9} = \sqrt{4 \times 9}$.

Also, $\sqrt{\dfrac{36}{4}} = \sqrt{9} = 3$ and $\dfrac{\sqrt{36}}{\sqrt{4}} = \dfrac{6}{2} = 3$

which suggests that $\dfrac{\sqrt{36}}{\sqrt{4}} = \sqrt{\dfrac{36}{4}}$.

Examples like the ones above lead to the following rules:

- $\sqrt{a} \times \sqrt{b} = \sqrt{a \times b}$ for $a \geqslant 0, \ b \geqslant 0$

- $\dfrac{\sqrt{a}}{\sqrt{b}} = \sqrt{\dfrac{a}{b}}$ for $a \geqslant 0, \ b > 0$

Example 4
◄)) Self Tutor

Write in simplest form:

a $\sqrt{3} \times \sqrt{2}$

b $2\sqrt{5} \times 3\sqrt{2}$

a $\sqrt{3} \times \sqrt{2}$
$= \sqrt{3 \times 2}$
$= \sqrt{6}$

b $2\sqrt{5} \times 3\sqrt{2}$
$= 2 \times 3 \times \sqrt{5} \times \sqrt{2}$
$= 6 \times \sqrt{5 \times 2}$
$= 6\sqrt{10}$

EXERCISE 3A.3

1   Simplify:

a $\sqrt{2} \times \sqrt{5}$

b $\sqrt{3} \times \sqrt{7}$

c $\sqrt{3} \times \sqrt{11}$

d $\sqrt{7} \times \sqrt{7}$

e $\sqrt{3} \times 2\sqrt{3}$

f $2\sqrt{2} \times \sqrt{5}$

g $3\sqrt{3} \times 2\sqrt{2}$

h $2\sqrt{3} \times 3\sqrt{5}$

i $\sqrt{2} \times \sqrt{3} \times \sqrt{5}$

j $\sqrt{3} \times \sqrt{2} \times 2\sqrt{2}$

k $-3\sqrt{2} \times (\sqrt{2})^3$

l $(3\sqrt{2})^3 \times (\sqrt{3})^3$

Example 5
◄)) Self Tutor

Simplify:

a $\dfrac{\sqrt{32}}{\sqrt{2}}$

b $\dfrac{\sqrt{12}}{2\sqrt{3}}$

a $\dfrac{\sqrt{32}}{\sqrt{2}}$

$= \sqrt{\dfrac{32}{2}}$

$= \sqrt{16}$
$= 4$

b $\dfrac{\sqrt{12}}{2\sqrt{3}}$

$= \tfrac{1}{2}\sqrt{\dfrac{12}{3}}$ $\left\{\text{using } \dfrac{\sqrt{a}}{\sqrt{b}} = \sqrt{\dfrac{a}{b}}\right\}$

$= \tfrac{1}{2}\sqrt{4}$
$= \tfrac{1}{2} \times 2$
$= 1$

2   Simplify:

a $\dfrac{\sqrt{8}}{\sqrt{2}}$

b $\dfrac{\sqrt{2}}{\sqrt{8}}$

c $\dfrac{\sqrt{18}}{\sqrt{2}}$

d $\dfrac{\sqrt{2}}{\sqrt{18}}$

e $\dfrac{\sqrt{20}}{\sqrt{5}}$

f $\dfrac{\sqrt{5}}{\sqrt{20}}$

g $\dfrac{\sqrt{27}}{\sqrt{3}}$

h $\dfrac{\sqrt{18}}{\sqrt{3}}$

i $\dfrac{\sqrt{3}}{\sqrt{30}}$

j $\dfrac{\sqrt{50}}{\sqrt{2}}$

k $\dfrac{2\sqrt{6}}{\sqrt{24}}$

l $\dfrac{5\sqrt{75}}{\sqrt{3}}$

Example 6   ◀) **Self Tutor**

Write $\sqrt{32}$ in
the form $k\sqrt{2}$.

$\sqrt{32}$
$= \sqrt{16 \times 2}$
$= \sqrt{16} \times \sqrt{2}$ $\{$using $\sqrt{ab} = \sqrt{a} \times \sqrt{b}\}$
$= 4\sqrt{2}$

3 Write the following in the form $k\sqrt{2}$:

a $\sqrt{8}$ b $\sqrt{18}$ c $\sqrt{50}$ d $\sqrt{98}$

e $\sqrt{200}$ f $\sqrt{288}$ g $\sqrt{20\,000}$ h $\sqrt{\frac{1}{2}}$

4 Write the following in the form $k\sqrt{3}$:

a $\sqrt{12}$ b $\sqrt{27}$ c $\sqrt{75}$ d $\sqrt{\frac{1}{3}}$

5 Write the following in the form $k\sqrt{5}$:

a $\sqrt{20}$ b $\sqrt{45}$ c $\sqrt{125}$ d $\sqrt{\frac{1}{5}}$

Example 7   ◀) **Self Tutor**

Write $\sqrt{28}$ in simplest surd form.

Look for the
largest perfect
square factor.

$\sqrt{28}$
$= \sqrt{4 \times 7}$ $\{4$ is the largest perfect square factor of $28\}$
$= \sqrt{4} \times \sqrt{7}$
$= 2\sqrt{7}$

Note: A surd is in **simplest form** when the number under the radical sign
             is the smallest integer possible.

6 Write the following in simplest surd form:

a $\sqrt{24}$ b $\sqrt{50}$ c $\sqrt{54}$ d $\sqrt{40}$

e $\sqrt{56}$ f $\sqrt{63}$ g $\sqrt{52}$ h $\sqrt{44}$

i $\sqrt{60}$ j $\sqrt{90}$ k $\sqrt{96}$ l $\sqrt{68}$

m $\sqrt{175}$ n $\sqrt{162}$ o $\sqrt{128}$ p $\sqrt{700}$

7 a Find:

i $\sqrt{16} + \sqrt{9}$ ii $\sqrt{16 + 9}$ iii $\sqrt{25} - \sqrt{9}$ iv $\sqrt{25 - 9}$

b i Does $\sqrt{16 + 9} = \sqrt{16} + \sqrt{9}$?   ii Does $\sqrt{25 - 9} = \sqrt{25} - \sqrt{9}$?

c Copy and complete: In general $\sqrt{a + b} \neq$ .... and $\sqrt{a - b} \neq$ ......

HISTORICAL NOTE

 The name **surd** and the symbol used to represent surds $\sqrt{}$ (the **radical** sign) both had a rather absurd past. Many centuries after Pythagoras, when the Golden Age of the Greeks was past, the writings of the Greeks were preserved, translated and extended by Arab mathematicians.

The Arabs thought of a square number as growing out of its roots. The roots had to be extracted. The Latin word for "root" is **radix** from which we get the word **radical** (and radish!). The root symbol is called the radical sign. The printed symbol for radix was first **R**, then **r**, which was copied by hand as $\sqrt{}$. This developed into the radical sign used today.

The word **surd** actually came about because of an error of translation by the Arab mathematician Al-Khwarizmi in the 9th century AD. The Greek word **a-logos** technically means "irrational" but also means "deaf". So, the Greek **a-logos** was interpreted as "deaf" which in Latin is **surdus**. Hence to this day, **irrational numbers** like $\sqrt{2}$ are called **surds**.

B | MULTIPLICATION OF SURDS

The rules for expanding brackets involving surds are identical to those for ordinary algebra.

Reminder: $\quad a(b + c) = ab + ac \quad$ This is known as the **distributive law**.

Example 8 | ◀)) Self Tutor

Simplify:　a　$\sqrt{2}(\sqrt{2} + \sqrt{3})$ 　　b　$\sqrt{3}(6 - 2\sqrt{3})$

a　$\sqrt{2}(\sqrt{2} + \sqrt{3})$
$= \sqrt{2} \times \sqrt{2} + \sqrt{2} \times \sqrt{3}$
$= 2 + \sqrt{6}$

b　$\sqrt{3}(6 - 2\sqrt{3})$
$= (\sqrt{3})(6 + -2\sqrt{3})$
$= (\sqrt{3})(6) + (\sqrt{3})(-2\sqrt{3})$
$= 6\sqrt{3} + -6$
$= 6\sqrt{3} - 6$

EXERCISE 3B

1 Expand and simplify:

a　$\sqrt{2}(\sqrt{5} + \sqrt{2})$ 　　　　b　$\sqrt{2}(3 - \sqrt{2})$ 　　　　c　$\sqrt{3}(\sqrt{3} + 1)$

d　$\sqrt{3}(1 - \sqrt{3})$ 　　　　　　e　$\sqrt{7}(7 - \sqrt{7})$ 　　　　f　$\sqrt{5}(2 - \sqrt{5})$

g　$\sqrt{11}(2\sqrt{11} - 1)$ 　　　h　$\sqrt{6}(1 - 2\sqrt{6})$ 　　　i　$\sqrt{3}(\sqrt{3} + \sqrt{2} - 1)$

j　$2\sqrt{3}(\sqrt{3} - \sqrt{5})$ 　　　k　$2\sqrt{5}(3 - \sqrt{5})$ 　　　l　$3\sqrt{5}(2\sqrt{5} + \sqrt{2})$

Example 9   ◀)) Self Tutor

Expand and simplify:

a $-\sqrt{2}(\sqrt{2}+3)$

b $-\sqrt{3}(7-2\sqrt{3})$

a $-\sqrt{2}(\sqrt{2}+3)$
$= -\sqrt{2}\times\sqrt{2}\ +\ -\sqrt{2}\times 3$
$= -2-3\sqrt{2}$

b $-\sqrt{3}(7-2\sqrt{3})$
$= (-\sqrt{3})(7-2\sqrt{3})$
$= (-\sqrt{3})(7)\ +\ (-\sqrt{3})(-2\sqrt{3})$
$= -7\sqrt{3}+6$

2 Expand and simplify:

a $-\sqrt{2}(3-\sqrt{2})$

b $-\sqrt{2}(\sqrt{2}+\sqrt{3})$

c $-\sqrt{2}(4-\sqrt{2})$

d $-\sqrt{3}(1+\sqrt{3})$

e $-\sqrt{3}(\sqrt{3}+2)$

f $-\sqrt{5}(2+\sqrt{5})$

g $-(\sqrt{2}+3)$

h $-\sqrt{5}(\sqrt{5}-4)$

i $-(3-\sqrt{7})$

j $-\sqrt{11}(2-\sqrt{11})$

k $-(\sqrt{3}-\sqrt{7})$

l $-2\sqrt{2}(1-\sqrt{2})$

m $-3\sqrt{3}(5-\sqrt{3})$

n $-7\sqrt{2}(\sqrt{2}+\sqrt{6})$

o $(-\sqrt{2})^3(3-\sqrt{2})$

Example 10   ◀)) Self Tutor

Expand and simplify: $(3-\sqrt{2})(4+2\sqrt{2})$

$(3-\sqrt{2})(4+2\sqrt{2})$
$= (3-\sqrt{2})(4)\ +\ (3-\sqrt{2})(2\sqrt{2})$
$= 12\ -\ 4\sqrt{2}\ +\ 6\sqrt{2}\ -\ 4$
$= 8+2\sqrt{2}$

Reminder: You could use, $(a+b)(c+d)\ =\ ac\ +\ ad\ +\ bc\ +\ bd$

Firsts   Outers   Inners   Lasts

3 Expand and simplify:

a $(1+\sqrt{2})(2+\sqrt{2})$

b $(2+\sqrt{3})(2+\sqrt{3})$

c $(\sqrt{3}+2)(\sqrt{3}-1)$

d $(4-\sqrt{2})(3+\sqrt{2})$

e $(1+\sqrt{3})(1-\sqrt{3})$

f $(5+\sqrt{7})(2-\sqrt{7})$

g $(\sqrt{5}+2)(\sqrt{5}-3)$

h $(\sqrt{7}-\sqrt{3})(\sqrt{7}+\sqrt{3})$

i $(2\sqrt{2}+\sqrt{3})(2\sqrt{2}-\sqrt{3})$

j $(4-\sqrt{2})(3-\sqrt{2})$

Reminder: The perfect square expansion rules $(a+b)^2 = a^2 + 2ab + b^2$
$(a-b)^2 = a^2 - 2ab + b^2$

Example 11

Expand and simplify:

a $(\sqrt{3}+2)^2$

b $(\sqrt{3}-\sqrt{7})^2$

a $(\sqrt{3}+2)^2$
$= (\sqrt{3})^2 + 2\times\sqrt{3}\times 2 + 2^2$
$= 3 + 4\sqrt{3} + 4$
$= 7 + 4\sqrt{3}$

b $(\sqrt{3}-\sqrt{7})^2$
$= (\sqrt{3})^2 - 2\times\sqrt{3}\times\sqrt{7} + (\sqrt{7})^2$
$= 3 - 2\sqrt{21} + 7$
$= 10 - 2\sqrt{21}$

4 Expand and simplify:

a $(1+\sqrt{2})^2$ b $(2-\sqrt{3})^2$ c $(\sqrt{3}+2)^2$

d $(1+\sqrt{5})^2$ e $(\sqrt{2}-\sqrt{3})^2$ f $(5-\sqrt{2})^2$

g $(\sqrt{2}+\sqrt{7})^2$ h $(4-\sqrt{6})^2$ i $(\sqrt{6}-\sqrt{2})^2$

j $(\sqrt{5}+2\sqrt{2})^2$ k $(\sqrt{5}-2\sqrt{2})^2$ l $(6+\sqrt{8})^2$

m $(5\sqrt{2}-1)^2$ n $(3-2\sqrt{2})^2$ o $(1+3\sqrt{2})^2$

Reminder: $(a+b)(a-b)=a^2-b^2$ is the **difference of two squares** rule.

Example 12

Expand and simplify:

a $(3+\sqrt{2})(3-\sqrt{2})$

b $(2\sqrt{3}-5)(2\sqrt{3}+5)$

a $(3+\sqrt{2})(3-\sqrt{2})$
$= 3^2 - (\sqrt{2})^2$
$= 9 - 2$
$= 7$

b $(2\sqrt{3}-5)(2\sqrt{3}+5)$
$= (2\sqrt{3})^2 - 5^2$
$= (4\times 3) - 25$
$= 12 - 25$
$= -13$

Did you notice that these answers are **integers**?

5 Expand and simplify:

a $(4+\sqrt{3})(4-\sqrt{3})$ b $(5-\sqrt{2})(5+\sqrt{2})$ c $(\sqrt{5}-2)(\sqrt{5}+2)$

d $(\sqrt{7}+4)(\sqrt{7}-4)$ e $(3\sqrt{2}+2)(3\sqrt{2}-2)$ f $(2\sqrt{5}-1)(2\sqrt{5}+1)$

g $(5-3\sqrt{3})(5+3\sqrt{3})$ h $(2-4\sqrt{2})(2+4\sqrt{2})$ i $(1+5\sqrt{7})(1-5\sqrt{7})$

C   DIVISION BY SURDS (EXTENSION)

When an expression involves division by a surd, we can write the expression with an **integer denominator** (one that does **not** contain surds).

To do this we use the rule $\sqrt{a} \times \sqrt{a} = a$.

For example: $\dfrac{6}{\sqrt{3}}$ can be written as $\dfrac{6}{\sqrt{3}} \times \dfrac{\sqrt{3}}{\sqrt{3}}$ where we are really multiplying the

original fraction by 1 (in the form $\dfrac{\sqrt{3}}{\sqrt{3}}$).

$\dfrac{6}{\sqrt{3}} \times \dfrac{\sqrt{3}}{\sqrt{3}}$ then simplifies to $\dfrac{6\sqrt{3}}{3}$ or $2\sqrt{3}$.

Example 13	◀ Self Tutor

Express with integer denominator:

a $\dfrac{7}{\sqrt{3}}$ b $\dfrac{10}{\sqrt{5}}$ c $\dfrac{10}{2\sqrt{2}}$

a $\dfrac{7}{\sqrt{3}}$

$= \dfrac{7}{\sqrt{3}} \times \dfrac{\sqrt{3}}{\sqrt{3}}$

$= \dfrac{7\sqrt{3}}{3}$

b $\dfrac{10}{\sqrt{5}}$

$= \dfrac{10}{\sqrt{5}} \times \dfrac{\sqrt{5}}{\sqrt{5}}$

$= \dfrac{10}{5}\sqrt{5}$

$= 2\sqrt{5}$

c $\dfrac{10}{2\sqrt{2}}$

$= \dfrac{10}{2\sqrt{2}} \times \dfrac{\sqrt{2}}{\sqrt{2}}$

$= \dfrac{10\sqrt{2}}{4}$

$= \dfrac{5\sqrt{2}}{2}$

EXERCISE 3C

1 Express with integer denominator:

a $\dfrac{1}{\sqrt{2}}$ b $\dfrac{2}{\sqrt{2}}$ c $\dfrac{4}{\sqrt{2}}$ d $\dfrac{10}{\sqrt{2}}$ e $\dfrac{\sqrt{7}}{\sqrt{2}}$

f $\dfrac{1}{\sqrt{3}}$ g $\dfrac{3}{\sqrt{3}}$ h $\dfrac{4}{\sqrt{3}}$ i $\dfrac{18}{\sqrt{3}}$ j $\dfrac{\sqrt{11}}{\sqrt{3}}$

k $\dfrac{1}{\sqrt{5}}$ l $\dfrac{3}{\sqrt{5}}$ m $\dfrac{\sqrt{3}}{\sqrt{5}}$ n $\dfrac{15}{\sqrt{5}}$ o $\dfrac{125}{\sqrt{5}}$

p $\dfrac{\sqrt{10}}{\sqrt{2}}$ q $\dfrac{1}{2\sqrt{3}}$ r $\dfrac{2\sqrt{2}}{\sqrt{3}}$ s $\dfrac{15}{2\sqrt{5}}$ t $\dfrac{1}{(\sqrt{2})^3}$

Example 14   ◀) **Self Tutor**

Express $\dfrac{1}{3+\sqrt{2}}$ with integer denominator.

> We are really multiplying by one, which does not change the value of the original expression.

$$\dfrac{1}{3+\sqrt{2}} = \left(\dfrac{1}{3+\sqrt{2}}\right)\left(\dfrac{3-\sqrt{2}}{3-\sqrt{2}}\right)$$

$$= \dfrac{3-\sqrt{2}}{3^2-(\sqrt{2})^2} \qquad \{\text{using} \quad (a+b)(a-b)=a^2-b^2\}$$

$$= \dfrac{3-\sqrt{2}}{7}$$

2 Express with integer denominator:

a $\dfrac{1}{3-\sqrt{5}}$ b $\dfrac{1}{2+\sqrt{3}}$ c $\dfrac{1}{4-\sqrt{11}}$ d $\dfrac{\sqrt{2}}{5+\sqrt{2}}$

e $\dfrac{\sqrt{3}}{3+\sqrt{3}}$ f $\dfrac{5}{2-3\sqrt{2}}$ g $\dfrac{-\sqrt{5}}{3+2\sqrt{5}}$ h $\dfrac{3-\sqrt{7}}{2+\sqrt{7}}$

INVESTIGATION   **CONTINUED SQUARE ROOTS**

$$X = \sqrt{2+\sqrt{2+\sqrt{2+\sqrt{2+\sqrt{2+......}}}}}$$

is an example of a **continued square root**.

Some continued square roots have actual values which are integers.

What to do:

1 Use your calculator to show that

$$\sqrt{2} \doteqdot 1.41421$$

$$\sqrt{2+\sqrt{2}} \doteqdot 1.84776 \quad \text{and}$$

$$\sqrt{2+\sqrt{2+\sqrt{2}}} \doteqdot 1.96157.$$

2 Find the values, correct to 6 decimal places for

a $\sqrt{2+\sqrt{2+\sqrt{2+\sqrt{2}}}}$ b $\sqrt{2+\sqrt{2+\sqrt{2+\sqrt{2+\sqrt{2}}}}}$

3 Continue the process and hence predict the actual value of X.

4 The actual value of X can be determined algebraically. Can you find X algebraically? (**Hint:** Find X^2 in terms of X.)

5 If you work the algebraic solution backwards you can find a continued square root whose actual value is 3. Show how to do this.

REVIEW SET 3A

1 **a** Simplify $(3\sqrt{2})^2$

   b Simplify $-2\sqrt{3} \times 5\sqrt{3}$

   c Simplify $3\sqrt{2} - \sqrt{8}$

   d Write $\sqrt{48}$ in the form $a\sqrt{b}$ where a is as large as possible and b is an integer.

2 Expand and simplify:

   a $2\sqrt{3}(4 - \sqrt{3})$ **b** $(3 - \sqrt{7})^2$ **c** $(2 - \sqrt{3})(2 + \sqrt{3})$

   d $(3 + 2\sqrt{5})(2 - \sqrt{5})$ **e** $(4 - \sqrt{2})(3 + 2\sqrt{2})$

3 Express with integer denominator:

   a $\dfrac{8}{\sqrt{2}}$ **b** $\dfrac{15}{\sqrt{3}}$ **c** $\dfrac{\sqrt{3}}{\sqrt{2}}$ **d** $\dfrac{5}{6 - \sqrt{3}}$

4 Write $\sqrt{\frac{1}{7}}$ in the form $k\sqrt{7}$.

REVIEW SET 3B

1 Simplify:

   a $2\sqrt{3} \times 3\sqrt{5}$ **b** $(2\sqrt{5})^2$ **c** $5\sqrt{2} - 7\sqrt{2}$

   d $-\sqrt{2}(2 - \sqrt{2})$ **e** $(\sqrt{3})^4$ **f** $\sqrt{3} \times \sqrt{5} \times \sqrt{15}$

2 Write $\sqrt{75}$ in the form $a\sqrt{b}$ where a is the largest possible integer and b is also an integer.

3 Expand and simplify:

   a $(5 - \sqrt{3})(5 + \sqrt{3})$ **b** $-(2 - \sqrt{5})^2$ **c** $2\sqrt{3}(\sqrt{3} - 1) - 2\sqrt{3}$

   d $(2\sqrt{2} - 5)(1 - \sqrt{2})$

4 Express with integer denominator:

   a $\dfrac{14}{\sqrt{2}}$ **b** $\dfrac{\sqrt{2}}{\sqrt{3}}$ **c** $\dfrac{\sqrt{2}}{3 + \sqrt{2}}$ **d** $\dfrac{-5}{4 - \sqrt{3}}$

Chapter 4

Algebra (notation and equations)

Contents:

Algebra is a very powerful tool which is used to make problem solving easier. Algebra involves using **pronumerals** (letters) to represent **unknown** values, or values which can **vary** depending on the situation.

Many worded problems can be converted to algebraic symbols to make algebraic **equations**. We learn how to **solve** equations in order to find **solutions** to the problems.

Algebra can also be used to construct **formulae**, which are equations that connect two or more **variables**. Many people use formulae as part of their jobs, so an understanding of how to **substitute** into and **rearrange** formulae is essential. Builders, nurses, pharmacists, engineers, financial planners and computer programmers all use formulae which rely on algebra.

OPENING PROBLEM

Holly bought XBC shares for $2.50 each and NLG shares for $4.00 each.

Consider the following:

- What did Holly pay, in total, for 500 XBC shares and 600 NGL shares?
- What did Holly pay in total for x XBC shares and $(x + 100)$ NGL shares?
- Bob knows that Holly paid, in total, $5925 for her XBC and NGL shares. He also knows that she bought 100 more NGL shares than XBC shares. How can Bob use algebra to find how many of each share type Holly bought?

A   ALGEBRAIC NOTATION

The ability to convert worded sentences and problems into algebraic symbols, and to understand algebraic notation, is essential in the problem solving process.

Notice that:
- $x^2 + 3x$ is an algebraic **expression**, whereas
- $x^2 + 3x = 8$ is an **equation**, and
- $x^2 + 3x > 28$ is an **inequality** (sometimes called an **inequation**).

Recall that when we simplify **repeated sums**, we use **product** notation:

i.e., $x + x$ and $x + x + x$
         $= 2$ 'lots' of x $= 3$ 'lots' of x
         $= 2 \times x$ $= 3 \times x$
         $= 2x$ $= 3x$

Also, when we simplify **repeated products**, we use **index** notation:

i.e., $x \times x = x^2$ and $x \times x \times x = x^3$

Example 1   ◀)) **Self Tutor**

Write, in words, the meaning of:

a $x - 5$ b $a + b$ c $3x^2 + 7$

---

a $x - 5$ is   "5 less than x".

b $a + b$ is   "the sum of a and b",   or   "b more than a".

c $3x^2 + 7$ is   "7 more than three times the square of x".

EXERCISE 4A

1   Write, in words, the meaning of:

a $2a$ b pq c $\sqrt{m}$ d a^2

e $a - 3$ f $b + c$ g $2x + c$ h $(2a)^2$

i $2a^2$ j $a - c^2$ k $a + b^2$ l $(a + b)^2$

Example 2   ◀)) **Self Tutor**

Write the following as algebraic expressions:

a   the sum of p and the square of q b   the square of the sum of p and q

c b less than double a

---

a $p + q^2$ b $(p + q)^2$ c $2a - b$

---

2   Write the following as algebraic expressions:

a   the sum of a and c b   the sum of p, q and r

c   the product of a and b d   the sum of r and the square of s

e   the square of the sum of r and s f   the sum of the squares of r and s

g   the sum of twice a and b h   the difference between p and q, if $p > q$

i a less than the square of b j   half the sum of a and b

k   the sum of a and a quarter of b l   the square root of the sum of m and n

m   the sum of x and its reciprocal   n   a quarter of the sum of a and b

o   the square root of the sum of the squares of x and y

Example 3   ◀)) **Self Tutor**

Write, in sentence form, the meaning of:

a $D = ct$ b $A = \dfrac{b + c}{2}$

---

a D is equal to the product of c and t.

b A is equal to a half of the sum of b and c,
    or, A is the average of b and c.

3 Write, in sentence form, the meaning of:

   a $L = a + b$
   b $K = \dfrac{a + b}{2}$
   c $M = 3d$

   d $N = bc$
   e $T = bc^2$
   f $F = ma$

   g $K = \sqrt{\dfrac{n}{t}}$
   h $c = \sqrt{a^2 + b^2}$
   i $A = \dfrac{a + b + c}{3}$

Example 4   ◄)) **Self Tutor**

Write 'S is the sum of a and the product of g and t' as an equation.

The product of g and t is $\;gt$.

The sum of a and gt is $\;a + gt$, $\;\;\therefore\;$ the equation is $\;S = a + gt$.

---

4 Write the following as algebraic equations:

   a S is the sum of p and r

   b D is the difference between a and b where $b > a$

   c A is the average of k and l

   d M is the sum of a and its reciprocal

   e K is the sum of t and the square of s

   f N is the product of g and h

   g y is the sum of x and the square of x

   h P is the square root of the sum of d and e

The **difference** between two numbers is the larger one minus the smaller one.

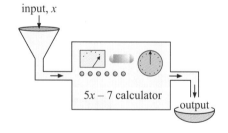

B   ALGEBRAIC SUBSTITUTION

Consider the number crunching machine alongside:

input, x

If we place any number x, into the machine, it calculates $\;5x - 7$, i.e., $\;x$ is multiplied by 5 and then 7 is subtracted.

$5x - 7$ calculator

output

For example: if $\;x = 2,$

$$\begin{aligned}&5x - 7\\ &= 5 \times 2 \;-\; 7\\ &= 10 - 7\\ &= 3\end{aligned}$$

and   if $\;x = -2,$

$$\begin{aligned}&5x - 7\\ &= 5 \times -2 \;-\; 7\\ &= -10 - 7\\ &= -17\end{aligned}$$

To **evaluate** an algebraic expression, we substitute numerical values for the unknown, then calculate the result.

Example 5 ◀)) **Self Tutor**

If $p = 4$, $q = -2$ and $r = 3$, find the value of:

a $3q - 2r$ **b** $2pq - r$ **c** $\dfrac{p - 2q + 2r}{p + r}$

a $3q - 2r$
$= 3 \times -2 \; - \; 2 \times 3$
$= -6 \; - \; 6$
$= -12$

b $2pq - r$
$= 2 \times 4 \times -2 \; - \; 3$
$= -16 \; - \; 3$
$= -19$

c $\dfrac{p - 2q + 2r}{p + r}$

$= \dfrac{4 \; - \; 2 \times -2 \; + \; 2 \times 3}{4 + 3}$

$= \dfrac{4 + 4 + 6}{4 + 3}$

$= \dfrac{14}{7}$

$= 2$

EXERCISE 4B

1 If $p = 5$, $q = 3$ and $r = -4$ find the value of:

a $5p$ **b** $4q$ **c** $3pq$ **d** pqr

e $3p - 2q$ **f** $5r - 4q$ **g** $4q - 2r$ **h** $2pr + 5q$

2 If $w = 3$, $x = 1$ and $y = -2$, evaluate:

a $\dfrac{y}{w}$ **b** $\dfrac{y + w}{x}$ **c** $\dfrac{3x - y}{w}$ **d** $\dfrac{5w - 2x}{y - x}$

e $\dfrac{y - x + w}{2(y - w)}$ **f** $\dfrac{xy + w}{y - x}$ **g** $\dfrac{x - wy}{y + w - 2x}$ **h** $\dfrac{y}{x} - w$

Example 6 ◀)) **Self Tutor**

If $a = 3$, $b = -2$ and $c = -1$, evaluate:
a b^2 **b** $ab - c^3$

a b^2
$= (-2)^2$
$= -2 \times -2$
$= 4$

b $ab - c^3$
$= 3 \times -2 \; - \; (-1)^3$
$= -6 \; - \; -1$
$= -6 + 1$
$= -5$

Notice the use of brackets!

3 If $a = -3$, $b = -4$ and $c = -1$, evaluate:

a c^2 **b** b^3 **c** $a^2 + b^2$ **d** $(a + b)^2$

e $b^3 + c^3$ **f** $(b + c)^3$ **g** $(2a)^2$ **h** $2a^2$

Example 7   ◀》 **Self Tutor**

If $p = 4$, $q = -3$ and $r = 2$, evaluate:

a $\sqrt{p - q + r}$ b $\sqrt{p + q^2}$

a $\sqrt{p - q + r}$

$= \sqrt{4 - -3 + 2}$

$= \sqrt{4 + 3 + 2}$

$= \sqrt{9}$

$= 3$

b $\sqrt{p + q^2}$

$= \sqrt{4 + (-3)^2}$

$= \sqrt{4 + 9}$

$= \sqrt{13}$

$\doteqdot 3.61$

4   If $p = 4$, $q = -1$ and $r = 2$, evaluate:

a $\sqrt{p} + q$ b $\sqrt{p + q}$ c $\sqrt{r - q}$ d $\sqrt{p - pq}$

e $\sqrt{pr - q}$ f $\sqrt{p^2 + q^2}$ g $\sqrt{p + r + 2q}$ h $\sqrt{2q - 5r}$

INVESTIGATION   SOLVING EQUATIONS

Linear equations like $5x - 3 = 12$ can be solved using a table of values on a **graphics calculator**.

We try to find the value of x which makes the expression $5x - 3$ equal to 12 upon *substitution*. This is the **solution** to the equation.

What to do:

1   Enter the **function** $Y_1 = 5X - 3$ into your calculator.

2   Set up a **table** that calculates the value of $y = 5x - 3$ for x values from -5 to 5.

X	Y1	
-1	-8	
0	-3	
1	2	
2	7	
3	12	
4	17	
5	22	

X=3

3   View the table and scroll down until you find the value of x that makes Y_1 equal to 12.

As we can see, the solution is $x = 3$.

4   Use your calculator and the method given above to solve the following equations:

a $7x + 1 = -20$ b $8 - 3x = -4$

c $\dfrac{x}{4} + 2 = 1$ d $\frac{1}{3}(2x - 1) = 3$

5   The solutions to the following equations are *not integers*, so change your table to investigate x values from -5 to 5 in intervals of 0.5:

a $2x - 3 = -6$ b $6 - 4x = 8$ c $x - 5 = -3.5$

6   Use a calculator to solve the following equations:

a $3x + 2 = 41$ b $5 - 4x = 70$ c $\dfrac{2x}{3} + 5 = 2\frac{2}{3}$

LINEAR EQUATIONS

Linear equations are equations which can be written in the form $ax + b = 0$, where x is the **unknown (variable)** and a, b are **constants**.

SOLVING EQUATIONS

The following steps should be followed when solving linear equations:

Step 1: Decide how the expression containing the unknown has been '**built up**'.

Step 2: **Isolate** the unknown by performing **inverse** operations on **both sides** of the equation to 'undo' the 'build up' in reverse order.

Step 3: Check your solution by substitution.

The inverse of $+$ is $-$ and $\times$ is $\div$

Example 8 | ◀) Self Tutor

Solve for x: **a** $4x - 1 = 7$ **b** $5 - 3x = 6$

a
$$4x - 1 = 7$$
$$\therefore \quad 4x - 1 + 1 = 7 + 1 \quad \{\text{adding 1 to both sides}\}$$
$$\therefore \quad 4x = 8$$
$$\therefore \quad \frac{4x}{4} = \frac{8}{4} \quad \{\text{divide both sides by 4}\}$$
$$\therefore \quad x = 2$$
Check: $4 \times 2 - 1 = 8 - 1 = 7$ ✓

b
$$5 - 3x = 6$$
$$\therefore \quad 5 - 3x - 5 = 6 - 5 \quad \{\text{subtracting 5 from both sides}\}$$
$$\therefore \quad -3x = 1$$
$$\therefore \quad \frac{-3x}{-3} = \frac{1}{-3} \quad \{\text{dividing both sides by } -3\}$$
$$\therefore \quad x = -\tfrac{1}{3}$$
Check: $5 - 3 \times -\tfrac{1}{3} = 5 + 1 = 6$ ✓

EXERCISE 4C

1 Solve for x:

a $x + 9 = 4$ **b** $5x = 45$ **c** $-24 = -6x$ **d** $3 - x = 12$

e $2x + 5 = 17$ **f** $3x - 2 = -14$ **g** $3 - 4x = -17$ **h** $8 = 9 - 2x$

Example 9   ◀))) **Self Tutor**

Solve for x: **a** $\dfrac{x}{5} - 3 = -1$ **b** $\dfrac{1}{5}(x - 3) = -1$

a $\dfrac{x}{5} - 3 = -1$

$\therefore$ $\dfrac{x}{5} - 3 + 3 = -1 + 3$ {adding 3 to both sides}

$\therefore$ $\dfrac{x}{5} = 2$

$\therefore$ $\dfrac{x}{5} \times 5 = 2 \times 5$ {multiplying both sides by 5}

$\therefore$ $x = 10$ Check: $\dfrac{10}{5} - 3 = 2 - 3 = -1$ ✓

b $\dfrac{1}{5}(x - 3) = -1$

$\therefore$ $\dfrac{1}{5}(x - 3) \times 5 = -1 \times 5$ {multiplying both sides by 5}

$\therefore$ $x - 3 = -5$

$\therefore$ $x - 3 + 3 = -5 + 3$ {adding 3 to both sides}

$\therefore$ $x = -2$

Check: $\dfrac{1}{5}(-2 - 3) = \dfrac{1}{5} \times -5 = -1$ ✓

2 Solve for x:

a $\dfrac{x}{4} = 12$ **b** $\dfrac{1}{2}x = 6$ **c** $5 = \dfrac{x}{-2}$ **d** $\dfrac{x}{3} + 4 = -2$

e $\dfrac{x + 3}{5} = -2$ **f** $\dfrac{1}{3}(x + 2) = 3$ **g** $\dfrac{2x - 1}{3} = 7$ **h** $\dfrac{1}{2}(5 - x) = -2$

If the unknown appears more than once, **expand** any brackets, **collect like terms**, and then **solve** the equation.

Example 10   ◀))) **Self Tutor**

Solve for x: $3(2x - 5) - 2(x - 1) = 3$

$3(2x - 5) - 2(x - 1) = 3$

$\therefore$ $6x - 15 - 2x + 2 = 3$ {expanding brackets}

$\therefore$ $4x - 13 = 3$ {collecting like terms}

$\therefore$ $4x - 13 + 13 = 3 + 13$ {adding 13 to both sides}

$\therefore$ $4x = 16$

$\therefore$ $x = 4$ {dividing both sides by 4}

Check: $3(2 \times 4 - 5) - 2(4 - 1) = 3 \times 3 - 2 \times 3 = 3$ ✓

3 Solve for x:

    a $2(x+8)+5(x-1)=60$ **b** $2(x-3)+3(x+2)=-5$

    c $3(x+3)-2(x+1)=0$ **d** $4(2x-3)+2(x+2)=32$

    e $3(4x+1)-2(3x-4)=-7$ **f** $5(x+2)-2(3-2x)=-14$

If the unknown appears on **both sides** of the equation, we

-   **expand** any brackets and **collect like terms**
-   move the **unknown to one side** of the equation and the remaining terms to the other side
-   **simplify** and **solve** the equation.

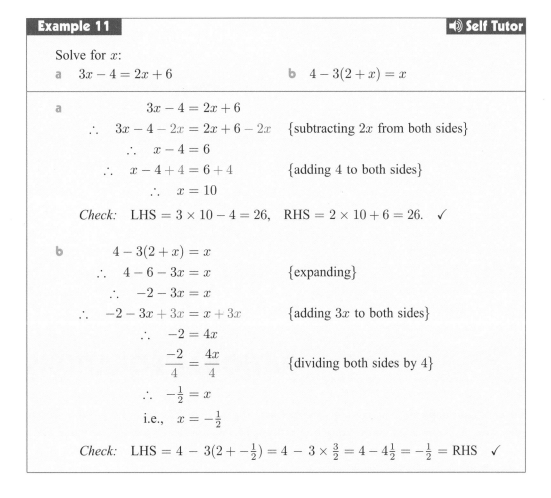

Example 11   **◄)) Self Tutor**

Solve for x:

    a $3x-4=2x+6$ **b** $4-3(2+x)=x$

a
$$3x-4=2x+6$$
$$\therefore\ 3x-4-2x=2x+6-2x \quad \{\text{subtracting } 2x \text{ from both sides}\}$$
$$\therefore\ x-4=6$$
$$\therefore\ x-4+4=6+4 \quad \{\text{adding 4 to both sides}\}$$
$$\therefore\ x=10$$

Check: LHS $=3\times10-4=26$, RHS $=2\times10+6=26$. ✓

b
$$4-3(2+x)=x$$
$$\therefore\ 4-6-3x=x \quad \{\text{expanding}\}$$
$$\therefore\ -2-3x=x$$
$$\therefore\ -2-3x+3x=x+3x \quad \{\text{adding } 3x \text{ to both sides}\}$$
$$\therefore\ -2=4x$$
$$\frac{-2}{4}=\frac{4x}{4} \quad \{\text{dividing both sides by 4}\}$$
$$\therefore\ -\tfrac{1}{2}=x$$
$$\text{i.e.,}\quad x=-\tfrac{1}{2}$$

Check: LHS $=4-3(2+-\tfrac{1}{2})=4-3\times\tfrac{3}{2}=4-4\tfrac{1}{2}=-\tfrac{1}{2}=$ RHS ✓

4 Solve for x:

    a $2x-3=3x+6$ **b** $3x-4=5-x$

    c $4-5x=3x-8$ **d** $-x=2x+4$

    e $12-7x=3x+7$ **f** $5x-9=1-3x$

    g $4-x-2(2-x)=6+x$ **h** $5-3(1-x)=2-3x$

    i $5-2x-(2x+1)=-6$ **j** $3(4x+2)-x=-7+x$

Sometimes when more complicated equations are expanded a linear equation results.

Example 12
◀ Self Tutor

Solve for x: $(x-3)^2 = (4+x)(2+x)$

$$(x-3)^2 = (4+x)(2+x)$$
$$\therefore \quad x^2 - 6x + 9 = 8 + 4x + 2x + x^2 \qquad \text{\{expanding each side\}}$$
$$\therefore \quad x^2 - 6x + 9 - x^2 = 8 + 4x + 2x + x^2 - x^2 \qquad \text{\{subtracting } x^2 \text{ from both sides\}}$$
$$\therefore \quad -6x + 9 = 8 + 6x$$
$$\therefore \quad -6x + 9 + 6x = 8 + 6x + 6x \qquad \text{\{adding } 6x \text{ to both sides\}}$$
$$\therefore \quad 9 = 12x + 8$$
$$\therefore \quad 9 - 8 = 12x + 8 - 8 \qquad \text{\{subtracting 8 from both sides\}}$$
$$\therefore \quad 1 = 12x$$
$$\therefore \quad \frac{1}{12} = \frac{12x}{12} \qquad \text{\{dividing both sides by 12\}}$$
$$\therefore \quad x = \tfrac{1}{12}$$

5 Solve for x:

   a $x(x+5) = (x-2)(x-3)$ **b** $x(2x+1) - 2(x-3) = 2x(x+1)$

   c $(x+1)(x-2) = (4-x)^2$ **d** $x^2 - 3 = (2+x)(1+x)$

   e $(x-2)(2x-1) = 2x(x+3)$ **f** $(x+4)^2 = (x+1)(x-3)$

6 Solve for x:

   a $2(3x+1) - 3 = 6x - 1$ **b** $3(4x+1) = 6(2x+1)$

   c Comment on your solutions to **a** and **b**.

D   RATIONAL EQUATIONS

Rational equations are equations involving fractions. We simplify them by writing all fractions with the same **least common denominator (LCD)**, and then equating the numerators.

Consider the following rational equations:

$$\frac{x}{2} = \frac{x}{3} \qquad \text{LCD is } 2 \times 3 \quad \text{i.e., } \quad 6$$

$$\frac{5}{2x} = \frac{3x}{5} \qquad \text{LCD is } 2x \times 5 \quad \text{i.e., } \quad 10x$$

$$\frac{x-7}{3} = \frac{x}{2x-1} \qquad \text{LCD is } 3 \times (2x-1) \quad \text{i.e., } \quad 3(2x-1)$$

Example 13 ◄» Self Tutor

Solve for x: $\dfrac{x}{2} = \dfrac{3+x}{5}$

$\dfrac{x}{2} = \dfrac{3+x}{5}$ has LCD $= 10$

$\therefore \ \dfrac{x}{2} \times \dfrac{5}{5} = \dfrac{2}{2} \times \left(\dfrac{3+x}{5}\right)$ {to create a common denominator}

$\therefore \quad 5x = 2(3+x)$ {equating numerators}

$\therefore \quad 5x = 6 + 2x$ {expanding brackets}

$\therefore \ 5x - 2x = 6 + 2x - 2x$ {taking $2x$ from both sides}

$\therefore \quad 3x = 6$

$\therefore \quad x = 2$ {dividing both sides by 3}

Notice the insertion of brackets here.

EXERCISE 4D

1 Solve for x:

a $\dfrac{x}{2} = \dfrac{4}{7}$

b $\dfrac{5}{8} = \dfrac{x}{6}$

c $\dfrac{x}{2} = \dfrac{x-2}{3}$

d $\dfrac{x+1}{3} = \dfrac{2x-1}{4}$

e $\dfrac{2x}{3} = \dfrac{5-x}{2}$

f $\dfrac{3x+2}{5} = \dfrac{2x-1}{2}$

g $\dfrac{2x-1}{3} = \dfrac{4-x}{6}$

h $\dfrac{4x+7}{7} = \dfrac{5-x}{2}$

i $\dfrac{3x+1}{6} = \dfrac{4x-1}{-2}$

Example 14 ◄» Self Tutor

Solve for x: $\dfrac{4}{x} = \dfrac{3}{4}$

$\dfrac{4}{x} = \dfrac{3}{4}$ has LCD $= 4x$

$\therefore \ \dfrac{4}{x} \times \dfrac{4}{4} = \dfrac{3}{4} \times \dfrac{x}{x}$ {to create a common denominator}

$\therefore \quad 16 = 3x$ {equating numerators}

$\therefore \quad x = \dfrac{16}{3}$ {dividing both sides by 3}

2 Solve for x:

a $\dfrac{5}{x} = \dfrac{2}{3}$

b $\dfrac{6}{x} = \dfrac{3}{5}$

c $\dfrac{4}{3} = \dfrac{5}{x}$

d $\dfrac{3}{2x} = \dfrac{7}{6}$

e $\dfrac{3}{2x} = \dfrac{7}{3}$

f $\dfrac{7}{3x} = -\dfrac{1}{6}$

g $\dfrac{5}{4x} = -\dfrac{1}{12}$

h $\dfrac{4}{7x} = \dfrac{3}{2x}$

Example 15   ◄») **Self Tutor**

Solve for x: $\dfrac{2x+1}{3-x} = \dfrac{3}{4}$

$$\dfrac{2x+1}{3-x} = \dfrac{3}{4} \qquad \text{has LCD} = 4(3-x)$$

$\therefore \quad \dfrac{4}{4} \times \left(\dfrac{2x+1}{3-x}\right) = \dfrac{3}{4} \times \left(\dfrac{3-x}{3-x}\right)$ {to create a common denominator}

Notice the use of brackets here.

$\therefore \quad 4(2x+1) = 3(3-x)$ {equating numerators}

$\therefore \quad 8x+4 = 9-3x$ {expanding the brackets}

$\therefore \quad 8x+4+3x = 9-3x+3x$ {adding $3x$ to both sides}

$\therefore \quad 11x+4 = 9$

$\therefore \quad 11x+4-4 = 9-4$ {subtracting 4 from both sides}

$\therefore \quad 11x = 5$

$\therefore \quad x = \frac{5}{11}$ {dividing both sides by 11}

3 Solve for x:

a $\dfrac{2x+3}{x+1} = \dfrac{5}{3}$

b $\dfrac{x+1}{1-2x} = \dfrac{2}{5}$

c $\dfrac{2x-1}{4-3x} = -\dfrac{3}{4}$

d $\dfrac{x+3}{2x-1} = \dfrac{1}{3}$

e $\dfrac{4x+3}{2x-1} = 3$

f $\dfrac{3x-2}{x+4} = -3$

g $\dfrac{6x-1}{3-2x} = 5$

h $\dfrac{5x+1}{x+4} = 4$

i $2 + \dfrac{2x+5}{x-1} = -3$

Example 16   ◄») **Self Tutor**

Solve for x: $\dfrac{x}{3} - \dfrac{1-2x}{6} = -4$

$$\dfrac{x}{3} - \dfrac{1-2x}{6} = -4 \qquad \text{has LCD of 6}$$

$\therefore \quad \dfrac{x}{3} \times \dfrac{2}{2} - \left(\dfrac{1-2x}{6}\right) = -4 \times \dfrac{6}{6}$ {to create a common denominator}

$\therefore \quad 2x - (1-2x) = -24$ {equating numerators}

$\therefore \quad 2x-1+2x = -24$ {expanding}

$\therefore \quad 4x-1 = -24$

$\therefore \quad 4x-1+1 = -24+1$ {adding 1 to both sides}

$\therefore \quad 4x = -23$

$\therefore \quad x = -\frac{23}{4}$ {dividing both sides by 4}

4 Solve for x:

a $\dfrac{x}{2} - \dfrac{x}{6} = 4$

b $\dfrac{x}{4} - 3 = \dfrac{2x}{3}$

c $\dfrac{x}{8} + \dfrac{x+2}{2} = -1$

d $\dfrac{x+2}{3} + \dfrac{x-3}{4} = 1$

e $\dfrac{2x-1}{3} - \dfrac{5x-6}{6} = -2$

f $\dfrac{x}{4} = 4 - \dfrac{x+2}{3}$

g $\dfrac{2x-7}{3} - 1 = \dfrac{x-4}{6}$

h $\dfrac{x+1}{3} - \dfrac{x}{6} = \dfrac{2x-3}{2}$

i $\dfrac{x}{5} - \dfrac{2x-5}{3} = \dfrac{3}{4}$

j $\dfrac{x+1}{3} + \dfrac{x-2}{6} = \dfrac{x+4}{12}$

k $\dfrac{x-6}{5} - \dfrac{2x-1}{10} = \dfrac{x-1}{2}$

l $\dfrac{2x+1}{4} - \dfrac{1-4x}{2} = \dfrac{3x+7}{6}$

E   LINEAR INEQUATIONS

The speed limit (s km/h) when passing roadworks is often 25 km/h.

This can be written as a **linear inequation**,

i.e., $s \leqslant 25$ (reads 's is less than or equal to 25').

We can also represent the allowable speeds on a **number line**,

i.e.,

The number line shows that any speed of 25 km/h or less (24, 23, 18, $7\frac{1}{2}$ etc), is an acceptable speed. We say these are **solutions** of the inequation.

RULES FOR HANDLING INEQUATIONS

Notice that $5 > 3$ and $3 < 5$,   and
similarly $-3 < 2$ and $2 > -3$

This suggests that if we **interchange** the LHS and RHS of an inequation, then we must **reverse** the inequation sign.

Note: $>$ is the reverse of $<$; $\geqslant$ is the reverse of $\leqslant$.

Recall also that:

- If we *add* or *subtract* the same number to both sides the inequation sign is *maintained*,   for example, if $5 > 3$,   then $5 + 2 > 3 + 2$.
- If we *multiply* or *divide* both sides by a *positive number* the inequation sign is *maintained*,   for example, if $5 > 3$,   then $5 \times 2 > 3 \times 2$.
- If we *multiply* or *divide* both sides by a *negative number* the inequation sign is *reversed*,   for example, if $5 > 3$,   then $5 \times -1 < 3 \times -1$.

Consequently, we can say that the method of solution of linear inequalities is identical to that of linear equations with the exceptions that:

- **interchanging** the sides **reverses** the inequation sign
- **multiplying** or **dividing** both sides by a **negative** number, **reverses** the inequation sign.

GRAPHING SOLUTIONS

Suppose our solution to an inequation is $x \geqslant 4$, so *every* number which is 4 or greater than 4 is a possible value for x. We could represent this on a number line by

The filled-in circle indicates that 4 **is** included.

The arrowhead indicates that all numbers on the number line in this direction are included.

Likewise if our solution is $x < 5$ our representation would be

The hollow circle indicates that 5 **is not** included.

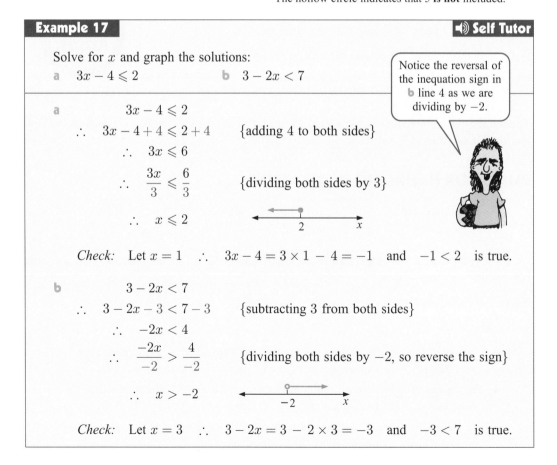

Example 17

Solve for x and graph the solutions:

a $3x - 4 \leqslant 2$

b $3 - 2x < 7$

Notice the reversal of the inequation sign in b line 4 as we are dividing by −2.

a
$$3x - 4 \leqslant 2$$
$$\therefore \quad 3x - 4 + 4 \leqslant 2 + 4 \quad \text{\{adding 4 to both sides\}}$$
$$\therefore \quad 3x \leqslant 6$$
$$\therefore \quad \frac{3x}{3} \leqslant \frac{6}{3} \quad \text{\{dividing both sides by 3\}}$$
$$\therefore \quad x \leqslant 2$$

Check: Let $x = 1$ $\therefore$ $3x - 4 = 3 \times 1 - 4 = -1$ and $-1 < 2$ is true.

b
$$3 - 2x < 7$$
$$\therefore \quad 3 - 2x - 3 < 7 - 3 \quad \text{\{subtracting 3 from both sides\}}$$
$$\therefore \quad -2x < 4$$
$$\therefore \quad \frac{-2x}{-2} > \frac{4}{-2} \quad \text{\{dividing both sides by −2, so reverse the sign\}}$$
$$\therefore \quad x > -2$$

Check: Let $x = 3$ $\therefore$ $3 - 2x = 3 - 2 \times 3 = -3$ and $-3 < 7$ is true.

EXERCISE 4E

1 Solve for x and graph the solutions:

     a $3x + 2 < 0$ **b** $5x - 7 > 2$ **c** $2 - 3x \geqslant 1$

     d $5 - 2x \leqslant 11$ **e** $2(3x - 1) < 4$ **f** $5(1 - 3x) \geqslant 8$

Example 18   ◄)) **Self Tutor**

Solve for x and graph the solutions: $-5 < 9 - 2x$

$$-5 < 9 - 2x$$
$$\therefore \quad -5 + 2x < 9 - 2x + 2x \qquad \text{\{adding } 2x \text{ to both sides\}}$$
$$\therefore \quad 2x - 5 < 9$$
$$\therefore \quad 2x - 5 + 5 < 9 + 5 \qquad \text{\{adding 5 to both sides\}}$$
$$\therefore \quad 2x < 14$$
$$\therefore \quad \frac{2x}{2} < \frac{14}{2} \qquad \text{\{dividing both sides by 2\}}$$

i.e., $x < 7$

Check: if $x = 5$, say $-5 < 9 - 2 \times 5$,   i.e., $-5 < -1$ is true.

---

2 Solve for x and graph the solutions:

     a $7 \geqslant 2x - 1$ **b** $-13 < 3x + 2$ **c** $20 > -5x$

     d $-3 \geqslant 4 - 3x$ **e** $3 < 5 - 2x$ **f** $2 \leqslant 5(1 - x)$

Example 19   ◄)) **Self Tutor**

Solve for x and graph the solutions: $3 - 5x \geqslant 2x + 7$

$$3 - 5x \geqslant 2x + 7$$
$$\therefore \quad 3 - 5x - 2x \geqslant 2x + 7 - 2x \qquad \text{\{subtract } 2x \text{ from both sides\}}$$
$$\therefore \quad 3 - 7x \geqslant 7$$
$$\therefore \quad 3 - 7x - 3 \geqslant 7 - 3 \qquad \text{\{subtract 3 from both sides\}}$$
$$\therefore \quad -7x \geqslant 4$$
$$\therefore \quad \frac{-7x}{-7} \leqslant \frac{4}{-7} \qquad \text{\{divide both sides by } -7; \\ \text{reverse the sign\}}$$

$$\therefore \quad x \leqslant -\tfrac{4}{7}$$

Check: if $x = -1$, say, $3 - 5 \times -1 \geqslant 2 \times -1 + 7$,   i.e., $8 \geqslant 5$ is true.

3 Solve for x and graph the solutions:

  a $3x + 2 > x - 5$

  c $5 - 2x \geqslant x + 4$

  e $3x - 2 > 2(x - 1) + 5x$

  b $2x - 3 < 5x - 7$

  d $7 - 3x \leqslant 5 - x$

  f $1 - (x - 3) \geqslant 2(x + 5) - 1$

4 Solve for x:

  a $3x + 1 > 3(x + 2)$ **b** $5x + 2 < 5(x + 1)$ **c** $2x - 4 \geqslant 2(x - 2)$

  d Comment on your solutions to **a**, **b** and **c**.

F   PROBLEM SOLVING

Many problems can be translated into **algebraic equations**. When problems are solved using algebra, we follow these steps:

Step 1: Decide the unknown quantity and allocate a pronumeral.

Step 2: Decide which operations are involved.

Step 3: Translate the problem into an equation and check your translation is correct.

Step 4: Solve the equation by isolating the pronumeral.

Step 5: Check that your solution does satisfy the original problem.

Step 6: Write your answer in sentence form. Remember, there is usually no pronumeral in the original problem.

Example 20   ◀) Self Tutor

When a number is trebled and subtracted from 7 the result is -11. Find the number.

Let x be the number.

$\therefore$ $3x$ is the number trebled.

$\therefore$ $7 - 3x$ is this number subtracted from 7.

  So, $7 - 3x = -11$

$\therefore$ $7 - 3x - 7 = -11 - 7$ {subtracting 7 from both sides}

  $\therefore$ $-3x = -18$

    $\therefore$ $x = 6$ {dividing both sides by -3}

So, the number is 6.

Check: $7 - 3 \times 6 = 7 - 18 = -11$ ✓

EXERCISE 4F

1 When three times a certain number is subtracted from 15, the result is -6. Find the number.

2 Five times a certain number, minus 5, is equal to 7 more than three times the number. What is the number?

3 Three times the result of subtracting a certain number from 7 gives the same answer as adding eleven to the number. Find the number.

4 I think of a number. If I divide the sum of 6 and the number by 3, the result is 4 more than one quarter of the number. Find the number.

5 The sum of two numbers is 15. When one of these numbers is added to three times the other, the result is 27. What are the numbers?

Example 21   ◀) **Self Tutor**

What number must be added to both the numerator and the denominator of the fraction $\frac{1}{3}$ to get the fraction $\frac{7}{8}$?

Let x be the number.

$$\therefore \quad \frac{1+x}{3+x} = \frac{7}{8} \qquad\qquad \text{where the LCD is } 8(3+x)$$

$$\therefore \quad \frac{8}{8} \times \left(\frac{1+x}{3+x}\right) = \frac{7}{8} \times \left(\frac{3+x}{3+x}\right) \qquad \{\text{to get a common denominator}\}$$

$$\therefore \quad 8(1+x) = 7(3+x) \qquad \{\text{equating numerators}\}$$

$$\therefore \quad 8 + 8x = 21 + 7x \qquad \{\text{expanding brackets}\}$$

$$\therefore \quad 8 + 8x - 7x = 21 + 7x - 7x \qquad \{\text{subtracting } 7x \text{ from both sides}\}$$

$$\therefore \quad 8 + x = 21$$

$$\therefore \quad x = 13 \qquad\qquad \text{So, 13 is added to both.}$$

---

6 What number must be added to both the numerator and the denominator of the fraction $\frac{2}{5}$ to get the fraction $\frac{7}{8}$?

7 What number must be subtracted from both the numerator and the denominator of the fraction $\frac{3}{4}$ to get the fraction $\frac{1}{3}$?

Example 22   ◀) **Self Tutor**

Sarah's age is one third her father's age and in 13 years time her age will be a half of her father's age. How old is Sarah now?

Let Sarah's present age be x years.

$\therefore$ father's present age is $3x$ years.

Table of ages:

	Now	13 *years time*
Sarah	x	$x+13$
Father	$3x$	$3x+13$

So, $3x + 13 = 2(x + 13)$

$\therefore \quad 3x + 13 = 2x + 26$

$\therefore \quad 3x - 2x = 26 - 13$

$\therefore \quad x = 13$

$\therefore$ Sarah's present age is 13.

8 Eli is now one-quarter of his father's age and in 5 years time his age will be one-third the age of his father. How old is Eli now?

9 When Maria was born her mother was 24 years old. At present Maria's age is 20% of her mother's age. How old is Maria now?

10 Five years ago Jacob was one-sixth the age of his brother. In three years time his age doubled will match his brother's age. How old is Jacob now?

G MONEY AND INVESTMENT PROBLEMS

Problems involving money are frequently made easier to understand by constructing a table and placing the given information into it.

Example 23   ◄)) **Self Tutor**

Brittney has only 2-cent and 5-cent stamps with a total value of $1.78 and there are two more 5-cent stamps than there are 2-cent stamps. How many 2-cent stamps are there?

If there are x 2-cent stamps then there are $(x + 2)$ 5-cent stamps

Type	Number	Value
2-cent	x	$2x$ cents
5-cent	$x + 2$	$5(x + 2)$ cents

$$\begin{aligned}
\therefore \quad 2x + 5(x + 2) &= 178 \quad \text{\{equating values in cents\}} \\
\therefore \quad 2x + 5x + 10 &= 178 \\
\therefore \quad 7x + 10 &= 178 \\
\therefore \quad 7x &= 168 \\
\therefore \quad x &= 24 \qquad \text{So, there are 24, 2-cent stamps.}
\end{aligned}$$

EXERCISE 4G

1 Michaela has 5-cent and 10-cent stamps with a total value of $5.75. If she has 5 more 10-cent stamps than 5-cent stamps, how many of each stamp does she have?

2 The school tuck-shop has milk in 600 mL and 1 litre cartons. If there are 54 cartons and 40 L of milk in total, how many 600 mL cartons are there?

3 Aaron has a collection of American coins. He has three times as many 10 cent coins as 25 cent coins, and he has some 5 cent coins as well. If he has 88 coins with total value $11.40, how many of each type does he have?

4 Tickets at a football match cost $8, $15 or $20 each. The number of $15 tickets sold was double the number of $8 tickets sold. 6000 more $20 tickets were sold than $15 tickets. If the total gate receipts were $783 000, how many of each type of ticket was sold?

5 Kelly blends coffee. She mixes brand A costing $6 per kilogram with brand B costing $8 per kilogram. How many kilograms of each brand does she have to mix to make 50 kg of coffee costing her $7.20 per kg?

6  Su Li has 13 kg of almonds costing $5 per kg. How many kg of cashews costing $12 per kg should be added to get a mixture of the two nut types which would cost $7.45 per kg?

Example 24   ◀) **Self Tutor**

I invest in oil shares which earn me 12% yearly, and in coal mining shares which pay 10% yearly. If I invest $3000 more in oil shares than in coal mining shares and my total yearly earnings amount to $910, how much did I invest in each type of share?

Let the amount I invest in coal mining shares be x. Draw up a table:

Type of Shares	Amount invested ($)	Interest	Earnings ($)
Coal	x	10%	10% of x
Oil	$(x + 3000)$	12%	12% of $(x + 3000)$
		Total	910

From the table we can write the equation from the information about earnings:

10% of $x + 12\%$ of $(x + 3000) = 910$

$\therefore \quad 0.1x + 0.12(x + 3000) = 910$

$\therefore \quad 0.1x + 0.12x + 360 = 910$

$\therefore \quad 0.22x + 360 = 910$

$\therefore \quad 0.22x = 550$

$\therefore \quad x = \dfrac{550}{0.22}$

$\therefore \quad x = 2500$

$\therefore$ I invested $2500 in coal shares and $5500 in oil shares.

---

7 Qantas shares pay a yearly return of 9% and Telstra shares pay 11%. John invests $1500 more on Telstra shares than on Qantas shares and his total yearly earnings from the two investments is $1475. How much did he invest in Qantas shares?

8 I invested twice as much money in technology shares as I invested in mining shares. Technology shares earn me 10% yearly and mining shares earn me 9% yearly. My yearly income from these shares is $1450. Find how much I invested in each type of share.

9 Wei has three types of shares; A, B and C. A shares pay 8%, B shares pay 6% and C shares pay 11% dividends. Wei has twice as much invested in B shares as A shares and has $50 000 invested altogether. The yearly return from the share dividends is $4850. How much is invested in each type of share?

10 Mrs Jones invests $4000 at 10% annual return and $6000 at 12% annual return. How much should she invest at 15% return so that her total annual return is 13% of the total amount she has invested?

H   MOTION PROBLEMS (EXTENSION)

Motion problems are problems concerned with speed, distance travelled and time taken.

Recall that speed is measured in kilometres per hour,   i.e., $\dfrac{\text{kilometres}}{\text{hours}}$.

So, $\text{speed} = \dfrac{\text{distance}}{\text{time}}$, $\text{distance} = \text{speed} \times \text{time}$ and $\text{time} = \dfrac{\text{distance}}{\text{speed}}$.

Example 25   ◀) Self Tutor

A car travels for 2 hours at a certain speed and then 3 hours more at a speed 10 km/h faster than this. If the entire distance travelled is 455 km, find the car's speed in the first two hours of travel.

Let the speed in the first 2 hours be s km/h. Draw up a table.

	Speed (km/h)	Time (h)	Distance (km)
First section	s	2	$2s$
Second section	$(s+10)$	3	$3(s+10)$
		Total	455

Using
distance
= speed × time

$$\text{So,}\quad 2s + 3(s+10) = 455$$
$$\therefore\quad 2s + 3s + 30 = 455$$
$$\therefore\quad 5s = 425 \quad\text{and so}\quad s = 85$$

$\therefore$ the car's speed in the first two hours was 85 km/h.

EXERCISE 4H

1 Joe can run twice as fast as Pete. They start at the same point and run in opposite directions for 40 minutes and the distance between them is then 16 km. How fast does Joe run?

2 A car leaves a country town at 60 km per hour and 2 hours later a second car leaves the town and catches the first car in 5 hours. Find the speed of the second car.

3 A boy cycles from his house to a friend's house at 20 km/h and home again at 25 km/h. If his round trip takes $\frac{9}{10}$ of an hour, how far is it to his friend's house?

4 A motor cyclist makes a trip of 500 km. If he had increased his speed by 10 km/h, he could have covered 600 km in the same time. What was his original speed?

5 Normally I drive to work at 60 km/h. If I drive at 72 km/h I cut 8 minutes off my time for the trip. What distance do I travel?

6 My motor boat normally travels at 24 km/h in still water. One day I travelled 36 km against a constant current in a river and it took me the same time to travel 48 km with the current. How fast was the current?

OPENING PROBLEM

Revisit the **Opening Problem** on page **64**.   Answer the questions posed.

REVIEW SET 4A

1 Write in algebraic form:

   a "3 more than the square of x"   **b** "the square of the sum of 3 and x"

2 Write, in words, the meaning of:

   a $\sqrt{a}+3$ **b** $\sqrt{a+3}$

3 If $p=1$, $q=-2$ and $r=-3$, find the value of $\dfrac{4q-p}{r}$.

4 Solve for x:

   a $5-2x=3x+4$ **b** $\dfrac{x-1}{2}-\dfrac{2-3x}{7}=\dfrac{1}{3}$

5 Solve the following and graph the solutions: $5-2x\geqslant 3(x+6)$

6 If a number is increased by 5 and then trebled, the result is six more than two thirds of the number. Find the number.

7 A drinks stall sells small, medium and large cups of fruit drink for $1.50, $2 and $2.50 respectively. In one morning three times as many medium cups were sold as small cups, and the number of large cups sold was 140 less than the number of medium cups. If the total of the drink sales was $1360, how many of each size cup was sold?

8 Ray drives between towns A and B at an average speed of 75 km/h. Mahmoud drives the same distance at 80 km/h and takes 10 minutes less. What is the distance between A and B?

REVIEW SET 4B

1 Write, in words, the meaning of:

    a $\dfrac{a+b}{2}$ **b** $a + \dfrac{b}{2}$

2 Write in algebraic form:

    a "the sum of a and the square root of b"

    b "the square root of the sum of a and b"

3 If $a = -1$, $b = 4$ and $c = -6$, find the value of $\dfrac{2b + 3c}{2a}$.

4 Solve the following inequation and graph the solution set: $5x + 2(3 - x) < 8 - x$

5 Solve for x:

    a $2(x - 3) + 4 = 5$ **b** $\dfrac{2x + 3}{3} - \dfrac{3x + 1}{4} = 2$

6 What number must be added to the numerator and denominator of $\frac{3}{4}$ in order to finish with $\frac{1}{3}$?

7 X shares pay 8% dividend and Y shares pay 9%. Reiko has invested \$2000 more on X shares than she has on Y shares. Her total earnings for the year for the two investments is \$2710. How much does she invest in X shares?

8 Carlos cycles for 2 hours at a fast speed, then cycles for 3 more hours at a speed 10 km/h slower than this. If the entire distance travelled is 90 km, find Carlos' speed in the first two hours of travel.

Chapter 5

Coordinate geometry

Contents:

THE NUMBER PLANE

The position of any point in the **number plane** can be specified in terms of an **ordered pair** of numbers (x, y), where:

x is the **horizontal step** from a fixed point O, and
y is the **vertical step** from O.

Once an **origin** O, has been given, two perpendicular axes are drawn.

The **x-axis** is horizontal and the **y-axis** is vertical.

The **number plane** is also known as either:

• the **2-dimensional plane**, or
• the **Cartesian plane**, (named after **René Descartes**).

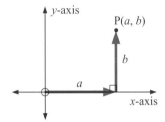

Note: In the diagram, the point P is at (a, b), where a and b are referred to as **the coordinates** of the point.
a is called the **x-coordinate** and
b is called the **y-coordinate**.

Examples: The coordinates of the given points are

A(4, 2)
B(0, 2)
C(−3, 1)
D(−1, 0)
E(1, −2).

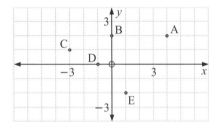

HISTORICAL NOTE

History now shows that the two Frenchmen René Descartes and Pierre de Fermat seem to have arrived at the idea of **analytical geometry** at about the same time. Descartes' work "*La Geometrie*", however, was published first (in 1637) and Fermat's "*Introduction to Loci*" was not published until after his death.

Today, they are considered the co-founders of this important branch of mathematics, which links algebra and geometry.

Their initial approaches were quite different. In contrast, Descartes

Pierre de Fermat

began with a line or curve and then found the equation which described it. Fermat, to a large extent, started with an equation and investigated the shape of the curve it described. This interaction between algebra and geometry shows the power of **analytical geometry** as a branch of mathematics.

René Descartes

Analytical geometry and its use of coordinates, provided the mathematical tools which enabled Isaac Newton to later develop another important branch of mathematics called calculus.

Newton humbly stated: *"If I have seen further than Descartes, it is because I have stood on the shoulders of giants."*

OPENING PROBLEM

Dave and Jen live in two towns which are 100 km apart. They decide to rendezvous somewhere between the towns. Jen leaves Boolaroo and rides her bike at a constant speed of 24 km/h. Dave leaves one hour later from Allandale and he rides at a constant speed of 30 km/h.

Things to think about:

- Can you write an equation for the distance travelled by each rider in terms of the time variable t hours?

- Can you graph each equation?

- Would each graph be linear?

- What would be the interpretation of the vertical axis intercept in each case?

- If the graphs are linear, what would be your interpretation of their gradients?

- What can be found from the point of intersection of the graphs?

- Can you use the graphs to find how far apart Dave and Jen will be 30 minutes after Dave has left Allandale?

A   DISTANCE BETWEEN TWO POINTS

Consider the points A(1, 3) and B(4, 1). We can join the points by a straight line segment of length d units. Suppose we draw a right angled triangle with hypotenuse AB and with sides parallel to the axes.

It is clear that $d^2 = 3^2 + 2^2$ {Pythagoras' Thm}

$$\therefore \quad d^2 = 13$$

$$\therefore \quad d = \sqrt{13} \qquad \{\text{as } d > 0\}$$

$\therefore$ the distance from A to B is $\sqrt{13}$ units.

EXERCISE 5A.1

1   If necessary, use the theorem of Pythagoras to find the distance between:

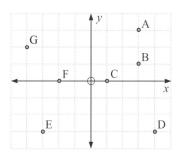

    a   A and B   **b**   A and D

    c   C and A   **d**   F and C

    e   G and F   **f**   C and G

    g   E and C   **h**   E and D

2 By plotting points and using Pythagoras' Theorem, find the distance between:

    a   A(3, 5) and B(2, 6)   **b**   P(2, 4) and Q(-3, 2)   **c**   R(0, 6) and S(3, 0)

THE DISTANCE FORMULA

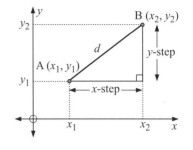

To avoid drawing a diagram each time we wish to find a distance, a **distance formula** can be developed.

In going from A to B, the x-step $= x_2 - x_1$, and

$$y\text{-step} = y_2 - y_1.$$

Now, using Pythagoras' Theorem,

$$(AB)^2 = (x\text{-step})^2 + (y\text{-step})^2$$

$$\therefore \quad AB = \sqrt{(x\text{-step})^2 + (y\text{-step})^2}$$

$$\therefore \quad d = \sqrt{(x_2 - x_1)^2 + (y_2 - y_1)^2}.$$

If $A(x_1, y_1)$ and $B(x_2, y_2)$ are two points in a plane, then the distance d, between these points is given by

$$AB = \sqrt{(x_2 - x_1)^2 + (y_2 - y_1)^2}$$

$$\text{or} \quad d = \sqrt{(x\text{-step})^2 + (y\text{-step})^2}$$

Example 1　　　　　　　　　　　　　　🔊 **Self Tutor**

Find the distance between A(-2, 1) and B(3, 4).

$$
\begin{array}{ll}
\text{A}(-2, 1) \quad \text{B}(3, 4) & AB = \sqrt{(3 - -2)^2 + (4 - 1)^2} \\
\quad \uparrow \ \uparrow \qquad \uparrow \ \uparrow & \quad = \sqrt{5^2 + 3^2} \\
\quad x_1 \ y_1 \quad\ x_2 \ y_2 & \quad = \sqrt{25 + 9} \\
& \quad = \sqrt{34} \text{ units}
\end{array}
$$

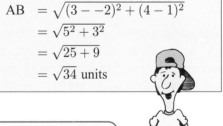

This distance formula saves us having to graph the points each time we want to find a distance.

EXERCISE 5A.2

1 Find the distance between the following pairs of points:

    a   A(3, 1) and B(5, 3)   **b**   C(-1, 2) and D(6, 2)

    c   O(0, 0) and P(-2, 4)   **d**   E(8, 0) and F(2, 0)

    e   G(0, -2) and H(0, 5)   **f**   I(2, 0) and J(0, -1)

    g   R(1, 2) and S(-2, 3)   **h**   W(5, -2) and Z(-1, -5)

Example 2
🔊 **Self Tutor**

Use the distance formula to determine if the triangle ABC, where A is $(-2, 0)$, B is $(2, 1)$ and C is $(1, -3)$, is equilateral, isosceles or scalene.

A$(-2, 0)$

B$(2, 1)$

C$(1, -3)$

$AB = \sqrt{(2 - -2)^2 + (1 - 0)^2}$

$\therefore \; AB = \sqrt{4^2 + 1^2}$

$= \sqrt{17}$ units

$AC = \sqrt{(1 - -2)^2 + (-3 - 0)^2}$

$\therefore \; AC = \sqrt{3^2 + (-3)^2}$

$= \sqrt{18}$ units

$BC = \sqrt{(1 - 2)^2 + (-3 - 1)^2}$

$\therefore \; BC = \sqrt{(-1)^2 + (-4)^2}$

$= \sqrt{17}$ units

As $AB = BC$, triangle ABC is isosceles.

2 Use the distance formula to classify triangle ABC, as either equilateral, isosceles or scalene:

   a A$(3, -1)$, B$(1, 8)$, C$(-6, 1)$ **b** A$(1, 0)$, B$(3, 1)$, C$(4, 5)$

   c A$(-1, 0)$, B$(2, -2)$, C$(4, 1)$ **d** A$(\sqrt{2}, 0)$, B$(-\sqrt{2}, 0)$, C$(0, -\sqrt{5})$

   e A$(\sqrt{3}, 1)$, B$(-\sqrt{3}, 1)$, C$(0, -2)$ **f** A(a, b), B$(-a, b)$, C$(0, 2)$

Example 3
🔊 **Self Tutor**

Use the distance formula to show that triangle ABC is right angled if A is $(1, 2)$, B is $(2, 5)$ and C is $(4, 1)$.

$AB = \sqrt{(2 - 1)^2 + (5 - 2)^2}$

$\therefore \; AB = \sqrt{1^2 + 3^2}$

$= \sqrt{10}$ units

$AC = \sqrt{(4 - 1)^2 + (1 - 2)^2}$

$\therefore \; AC = \sqrt{3^2 + (-1)^2}$

$= \sqrt{10}$ units

$BC = \sqrt{(4 - 2)^2 + (1 - 5)^2}$

$\therefore \; BC = \sqrt{2^2 + (-4)^2}$

$= \sqrt{20}$ units

Now $AB^2 + AC^2 = 10 + 10 = 20$

and $BC^2 = 20$

$\therefore$ triangle ABC is right angled at A.

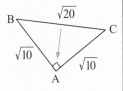

The right angle is opposite the longest side.

3 Use the distance formula to show that the following triangles are right angled and in each case state the right angle:

   a A$(-2, -1)$, B$(3, -1)$, C$(3, 3)$ **b** A$(-1, 2)$, B$(4, 2)$, C$(4, -5)$

   c A$(1, -2)$, B$(3, 0)$, C$(-3, 2)$ **d** A$(3, -4)$, B$(-2, -5)$, C$(2, 1)$

Example 4   ◄) **Self Tutor**

Find b given that   A(3, −2)   and   B(b, 1)   are $\sqrt{13}$ units apart.

From A to B x-step $= b - 3$

y-step $= 1 - -2 = 3$

$\therefore \quad \sqrt{(b-3)^2 + 3^2} = \sqrt{13}$

$\therefore \quad (b-3)^2 + 9 = 13$

$\therefore \quad (b-3)^2 = 4$

$\therefore \quad b - 3 = \pm 2$

$\therefore \quad b = 3 \pm 2$

i.e., $b = 5$ or 1.

> Notice that there are two possible solutions in this example. Draw a diagram to see why this is so.

4   Find a given that:

   a   P(2, 3)   and   Q(a, −1)   are 4 units apart

   b   P(−1, 1)   and   Q(a, −2)   are 5 units apart

   c   X(a, a)   is $\sqrt{8}$ units from the origin

   d   A(0, a)   is equidistant from   P(3, −3)   and   Q(−2, 2)

B   MIDPOINTS

THE MIDPOINT FORMULA

If point M is halfway between points A and B then M is the **midpoint** of AB.

Consider the points   A(1, 2)   and   B(5, 4).

It is clear from the diagram at right that the midpoint M, of AB is (3, 3).

We notice that: $\dfrac{1+5}{2} = 3$ and $\dfrac{2+4}{2} = 3$.

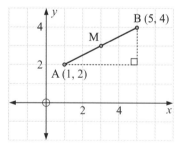

So,   the x-coordinate of M is the *average* of the x-coordinates of A and B,

and   the y-coordinate of M is the *average* of the y-coordinates of A and B.

In general,

> if A(x_1, y_1) and B(x_2, y_2) are two points then the **midpoint** M of AB has coordinates
>
> $$\left(\frac{x_1 + x_2}{2}, \frac{y_1 + y_2}{2} \right)$$

EXERCISE 5B

1

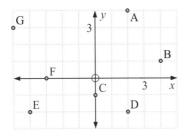

Use this diagram only to find the coordinates of the midpoint of the line segment:

a	GA	**b**	ED
c	AC	**d**	AD
e	CD	**f**	GF
g	EG	**h**	GD

Example 5   ◀)) **Self Tutor**

Find the coordinates of the midpoint of AB for   A$(-1, 3)$ and   B$(4, 7)$.

x-coordinate of midpoint

$= \dfrac{-1+4}{2}$

$= \dfrac{3}{2}$

$= 1\tfrac{1}{2}$

y-coordinate of midpoint

$= \dfrac{3+7}{2}$

$= 5$

$\therefore$ the midpoint of AB is $(1\tfrac{1}{2}, 5)$

---

2   Find the coordinates of the midpoint of the line segment joining the pairs of points:

a	$(8, 1)$ and $(2, 5)$	**b**	$(2, -3)$ and $(0, 1)$
c	$(3, 0)$ and $(0, 6)$	**d**	$(-1, 4)$ and $(1, 4)$
e	$(5, -3)$ and $(-1, 0)$	**f**	$(-2, 4)$ and $(4, -2)$
g	$(5, 9)$ and $(-3, -4)$	**h**	$(3, -2)$ and $(1, -5)$

Example 6   ◀)) **Self Tutor**

M is the midpoint of AB. Find the coordinates of B if A is $(1, 3)$ and M is $(4, -2)$.

A $(1, 3)$

M $(4, -2)$

B (a, b)

Let B be (a, b)

$\therefore$ $\dfrac{a+1}{2} = 4$ and $\dfrac{b+3}{2} = -2$

$\therefore$ $a + 1 = 8$ and $b + 3 = -4$

$\therefore$ $a = 7$ and $b = -7$

i.e.,   B is $(7, -7)$

---

3   M is the midpoint of AB. Find the coordinates of B for:

a	A$(6, 4)$ and M$(3, -1)$	**b**	A$(-5, 0)$ and M$(0, -1)$
c	A$(3, -2)$ and M$(1\tfrac{1}{2}, 2)$	**d**	A$(-1, -2)$ and M$(-\tfrac{1}{2}, 2\tfrac{1}{2})$
e	A$(7, -3)$ and M$(0, 0)$	**f**	A$(3, -1)$ and M$(0, -\tfrac{1}{2})$

| **Example 7** | ◀)) **Self Tutor** |

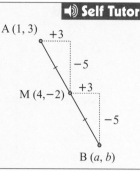

Find the coordinates of B if M is the midpoint of AB
and A is (1, 3) and M is (4, −2) using *equal steps*.

x-step: 1 $\xrightarrow{+3}$ 4 $\xrightarrow{+3}$ 7

y-step: 3 $\xrightarrow{-5}$ − 2 $\xrightarrow{-5}$ − 7

∴ B is (7, −7).

4 Check your answers to questions **3a** and **3b** using the equal steps method given in
Example 7.

5 If T is the midpoint of PQ, find the coordinates of P for:

   a   T(−3, 4) and Q(3, −2)   **b**   T(2, 0) and Q(−2, −3)

6 AB is the diameter of a circle, centre C. If A is (3, −2) and B is (−1, −4), find the
coordinates of C.

7 PQ is a diameter of a circle, centre $(3, -\frac{1}{2})$. Find the coordinates of P given that Q is
(−1, 2).

8 The diagonals of parallelogram PQRS bisect each
other at X. Find the coordinates of S.

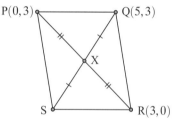

9 Triangle ABC has   A(−1, 3),   B(1, −1),   and   C(5, 2)   as vertices. Find the length
of the line segment from A to the midpoint of BC.

C   GRADIENT (OR SLOPE)

When looking at line segments drawn on a set of axes, it is clear that different line segments
are inclined to the horizontal at different angles,   i.e.,   some appear to be steeper than others.

> The **gradient** or **slope** of a line is a measure of its steepness.

If we choose any two distinct (different) points on the line, a **horizontal step** and a **vertical
step** may be determined.

Case 1:   *Case 2:*

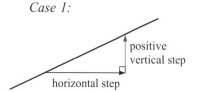

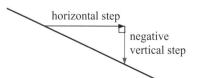

The **gradient** of a line may be determined by the fraction $\dfrac{\textbf{vertical step}}{\textbf{horizontal step}}$, i.e., $\dfrac{\textbf{y-step}}{\textbf{x-step}}$.

Notes:
- In *Case 1*, both steps are positive and so the gradient is positive.
- In *Case 2*, the steps are opposite in sign and so the gradient is negative.

Lines like  are forward sloping and have **positive gradients**,

whereas lines like 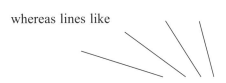 are backwards sloping and have **negative gradients**.

Have you ever wondered why gradient is measured by y-step divided by x-step rather than x-step divided by y-step?

Perhaps it is because horizontal lines have no gradient and zero (0) should represent this. Also as lines become steeper we would want their numerical gradients to increase.

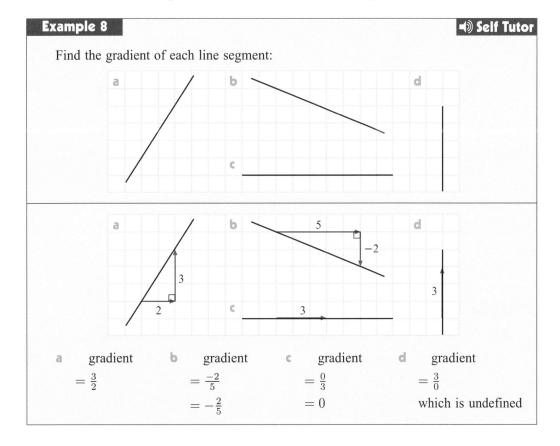

Example 8   ◀) **Self Tutor**

Find the gradient of each line segment:

| a | gradient $= \frac{3}{2}$ | b | gradient $= \frac{-2}{5}$ $= -\frac{2}{5}$ | c | gradient $= \frac{0}{3}$ $= 0$ | d | gradient $= \frac{3}{0}$ which is undefined |

Note:

- The gradient of a **horizontal** line is **0**, since the vertical step (i.e., the numerator) is 0.
- The gradient of a **vertical** line is **undefined**, since the horizontal step (i.e., the denominator) is 0.

EXERCISE 5C.1

1 Find the gradient of each line segment:

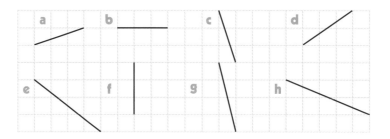

2 On grid paper draw a line segment with gradient:

    a $\frac{3}{4}$ **b** $-\frac{1}{2}$ **c**   2   **d** -3 **e**   0   **f** $-\frac{2}{5}$

THE GRADIENT FORMULA

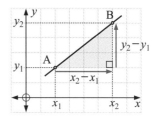

If A is $(x_1,\ y_1)$ and B is $(x_2,\ y_2)$ then

the **gradient** of AB is $\dfrac{y_2 - y_1}{x_2 - x_1}$

Example 9 ◀) **Self Tutor**

Find the gradient of the line through $(3,\ -2)$ and $(6,\ 4)$.

$(3,\ -2)\quad (6,\ 4)$
$\uparrow\quad\uparrow\qquad\uparrow\ \uparrow$
$x_1\ \ y_1\quad\ x_2\ y_2$

$$\begin{aligned}
\text{gradient} &= \frac{y_2 - y_1}{x_2 - x_1}\\[2mm]
&= \frac{4 - -2}{6 - 3}\\[2mm]
&= \frac{6}{3}\\[2mm]
&= 2
\end{aligned}$$

EXERCISE 5C.2

1 Find the gradient of the line segment joining the following pairs of points:

    a $(2, 3)$ and $(7, 4)$ **b** $(5, 7)$ and $(1, 6)$

    c $(1, -2)$ and $(3, 6)$ **d** $(5, 5)$ and $(-1, 5)$

    e $(3, -1)$ and $(3, -4)$ **f** $(5, -1)$ and $(-2, -3)$

    g $(-5, 2)$ and $(2, 0)$ **h** $(0, -1)$ and $(-2, -3)$

Example 10   ◀)) **Self Tutor**

Through (2, 4) draw a line with gradient $-\frac{2}{3}$.

Plot the point (2, 4)

$$\text{gradient} = \frac{y\text{-step}}{x\text{-step}} = \frac{-2}{3}$$

∴   let y-step $= -2$, x-step $= 3$.

Use these steps to find another
point and draw the line through
these points.

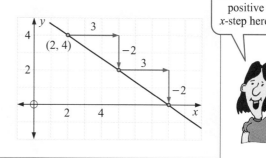

It is a good
idea to use a
positive
x-step here.

---

2 On the same set of axes draw lines through (1, 2) with gradients of $\frac{3}{4}$, $\frac{1}{2}$, 1, 2 and 3.

3 On the same set of axes draw lines through $(-2, -1)$ with gradients of 0, $-\frac{1}{2}$, -1 and -3.

PARALLEL LINES

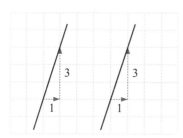

Notice that the given lines are parallel and both
of them have a gradient or slope of 3.

In fact:

- if two lines are **parallel**, then they have
  equal gradient,
- if two lines have **equal gradient**, then
  they are **parallel**.

PERPENDICULAR LINES

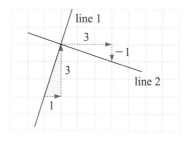

Notice that *line 1* and *line 2* are perpendicular.

Line 1 has gradient $\frac{3}{1} = 3$

Line 2 has gradient $\frac{-1}{3} = -\frac{1}{3}$

We see that the gradients are *negative reciprocals*
of each other and their product is $3 \times -\frac{1}{3} = -1$.

For lines which are not horizontal or vertical:

- if the lines are **perpendicular** their gradients are **negative reciprocals**
- if the gradients are **negative reciprocals** the lines are **perpendicular**.

Proof:

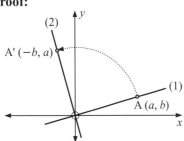

Suppose the two perpendicular lines are translated so that they intersect at the origin O. If A(a, b) lies on one line, under an anti-clockwise rotation about O of $90°$ it finishes on the other line and its coordinates are A' ($-b$, a).

The gradient of line (1) is $\dfrac{b - 0}{a - 0} = \dfrac{b}{a}$.

The gradient of line (2) is $\dfrac{a - 0}{-b - 0} = -\dfrac{a}{b}$.

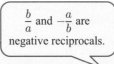

$\dfrac{b}{a}$ and $-\dfrac{a}{b}$ are negative reciprocals.

Example 11	◄)) **Self Tutor**

If a line has gradient $\frac{2}{3}$, find the gradient of:

a   all lines parallel to the given line

b   all lines perpendicular to the given line.

a   Since the original line has gradient $\frac{2}{3}$, the gradient of all parallel lines is also $\frac{2}{3}$.

b   The gradient of all perpendicular lines is $-\frac{3}{2}$.   {the negative reciprocal}

EXERCISE 5C.3

1   Find the gradient of all lines perpendicular to a line with a gradient of:

a $\frac{1}{2}$ b $\frac{2}{5}$ c   3   d   7

e $-\frac{2}{5}$ f $-2\frac{1}{3}$ g -5 h -1

2   The slopes of two given lines are listed below. Which of the line pairs are perpendicular?

a $\frac{1}{3}$, 3   b   5, -5 c $\frac{3}{7}$, $-2\frac{1}{3}$ d   4, $-\frac{1}{4}$

e   6, $-\frac{5}{6}$ f $\frac{2}{3}$, $-\frac{3}{2}$ g $\frac{p}{q}$, $\frac{q}{p}$ h $\frac{a}{b}$, $-\frac{b}{a}$

Example 12	◄)) **Self Tutor**

Find a given that the line joining A(2, 3) to B(a, -1) is parallel to a line with gradient -2.

gradient of AB $= -2$ {parallel lines have equal gradient}

$\therefore \dfrac{-1 - 3}{a - 2} = -2$ {gradient formula}

$\therefore \dfrac{-4}{a - 2} = \dfrac{-2}{1}$

$\therefore \dfrac{-4}{a - 2} = \dfrac{-2}{1}\left(\dfrac{a - 2}{a - 2}\right)$ {achieving a common denominator}

$$\therefore \quad -4 = -2(a-2) \qquad \{\text{equating numerators}\}$$
$$\therefore \quad -4 = -2a + 4$$
$$\therefore \quad 2a = 8$$
$$\therefore \quad a = 4$$

3 Find a given that the line joining:

    a A$(1, 3)$ to   B$(3, a)$ is parallel to a line with gradient 3

    b P$(a, -3)$ to   Q$(4, -2)$ is parallel to a line with gradient $\frac{1}{3}$

    c M$(3, a)$ to   N$(a, 5)$ is parallel to a line with gradient $-\frac{2}{5}$.

Example 13   ◀) **Self Tutor**

Find t given that the line joining D$(-1, -3)$ to C$(1, t)$ is perpendicular to a line with gradient 2.

gradient of DC $= -\frac{1}{2}$ $\{\text{perpendicular to line of gradient 2}\}$

$$\therefore \quad \frac{t - -3}{1 - -1} = -\frac{1}{2} \qquad \{\text{gradient formula}\}$$

$$\therefore \quad \frac{t+3}{2} = \frac{-1}{2} \qquad \{\text{simplifying}\}$$

$$\therefore \quad t + 3 = -1 \qquad \{\text{equating numerators}\}$$

$$\therefore \quad t = -4$$

---

4 Find t given that the line joining:

    a A$(2, -3)$ to   B$(-2, t)$ is perpendicular to a line with slope $1\frac{1}{4}$

    b C$(t, -2)$ to   D$(1, 4)$ is perpendicular to a line with slope $\frac{2}{3}$

    c P$(t, -2)$ to   Q$(5, t)$ is perpendicular to a line with slope $-\frac{1}{4}$.

5 Given the points   A$(1, 4)$,   B$(-1, 0)$,   C$(6, 3)$ and   D$(t, -1)$,   find t if:

a AB is parallel to CD	**b** AC is parallel to DB
c AB is perpendicular to CD	**d** AD is perpendicular to BC

COLLINEAR POINTS

> Three or more points are **collinear** if they lie on the same straight line.

If three points A, B and C are collinear, the gradient of AB is equal to the gradient of BC (and the gradient of AC).

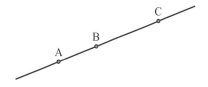

| Example 14 | ◀) Self Tutor |

Show that the following points are collinear: A(1, −1),   B(6, 9),   C(3, 3)

gradient of AB $= \dfrac{9 - -1}{6 - 1}$ gradient of BC $= \dfrac{3 - 9}{3 - 6}$

$= \dfrac{10}{5}$ $= \dfrac{-6}{-3}$

$= 2$ $= 2$

∴   AB is parallel to BC and as point B is common to both line segments, then A, B and C are *collinear*.

6   Determine whether or not the following sets of three points are collinear:

  a   A(1, 2), B(4, 6) and C(−4, −4)   **b**   P(−6, −6), Q(−1, 0) and R(4, 6)

  c   R(5, 2), S(−6, 5) and T(0, −4)   **d**   A(0, −2), B(−1, −5) and C(3, 7)

7   Find c given that:

  a   A(−4, −2),   B(0, 2)   and   C(c, 5)   are collinear

  b   P(3, −2),   Q(4, c)   and   R(−1, 10)   are collinear.

D   USING GRADIENTS

In the previous exercise we considered the gradients of straight lines or gradients between points. In real life gradients occur in many situations and can be interpreted in a variety of ways.

For example, the sign alongside would indicate to motor vehicle drivers that there is an uphill climb ahead.

Consider the situation in the graph alongside where a motor vehicle travels at a constant speed for a distance of 600 km in 8 hours.

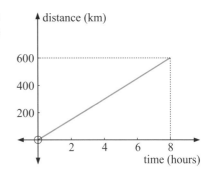

Clearly, the gradient of the line $= \dfrac{\text{vertical step}}{\text{horizontal step}}$

$= \dfrac{600}{8}$

$= 75$

However,   speed $= \dfrac{\text{distance}}{\text{time}} = \dfrac{600 \text{ km}}{8 \text{ hours}} = 75$ km/h.

In a graph of distance against time the *gradient* can be interpreted as the *speed*.

In the following exercise we will consider a number of problems related to speed and similar relationships.

EXERCISE 5D

1

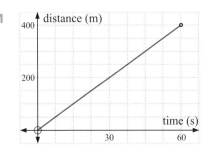

The graph alongside indicates the distance run by a sprinter in a number of seconds.

   a   Find the gradient of the line.

   b   Interpret the gradient found in **a**.

   c   Is the speed of the runner constant or variable? What evidence do you have for your answer?

2 The graph alongside indicates the distances travelled by a truck driver. Determine:

   a   the average speed for the whole trip

   b   the average speed from

       i O to A   **ii** B to C

   c   the time interval over which the average speed is greatest.

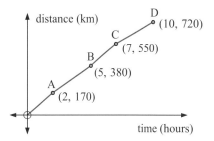

3

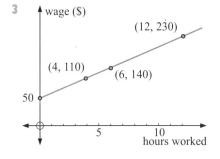

The graph alongside indicates the wages paid to sales assistants.

   a   What does the intercept on the vertical axis mean?

   b   Find the gradient of the line. What does this gradient mean?

   c   Determine the wages for working:

       i 6 hours   **ii** 18 hours.

   d   If no payment was made for not working but the same payment was made for 8 hours work, what would be the new rate of pay?

4 The graphs alongside indicate the fuel consumption and distance travelled at speeds of 60 kmph (graph A) and 90 kmph (graph B).

   a   Find the slope of each line.

   b   What do these slopes mean?

   c   If fuel costs $1.24 per litre, how much more would it cost to travel 1000 km at 90 kmph compared with 60 kmph?

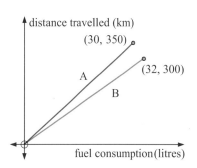

5 The graph alongside indicates the courier charge for distance travelled.

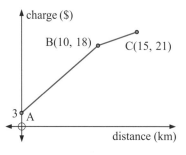

  a What does the value at A indicate?

  b Find the gradients of the line segments AB and BC. What do these gradients indicate?

  c If a straight line segment was drawn from A to C, find its gradient. What would this gradient mean?

E   USING COORDINATE GEOMETRY

Coordinate geometry is a powerful tool which can be used:

- to **check** the truth of a geometrical fact
- to **prove** a geometrical fact by using general cases.

Tools of the trade

We can find
- **distances** using the **distance formula**
- **midpoints** using the **midpoint formula**
- **gradients** using the **gradient formula**.

Remember that
- equal gradients indicate that the lines are parallel
- product of gradients $= -1$ indicates that the lines are perpendicular.

Example 15   🔊 **Self Tutor**

P(3, −1), Q(1, 7) and R(−1, 5) are the vertices of triangle PQR.
M is the midpoint of PQ and N is the midpoint of PR.

  a Find the coordinates of M and N.   **b** Find the gradients of MN and QR.

  c What can be deduced from **b**?   **d** Find distances MN and QR.

  e What can be deduced from **d**?

Sketch of situation:

a M is $\left(\dfrac{3+1}{2}, \dfrac{-1+7}{2}\right)$ i.e., (2, 3)

    N is $\left(\dfrac{3+-1}{2}, \dfrac{-1+5}{2}\right)$ i.e., (1, 2)

b   gradient of MN   gradient of QR

           $= \dfrac{2-3}{1-2}$ $= \dfrac{5-7}{-1-1}$

           $= 1$ $= 1$

> **c** Equal gradients implies that MN ∥ QR.
>
> **d** $\text{MN} = \sqrt{(1-2)^2 + (2-3)^2}$ $\text{QR} = \sqrt{(-1-1)^2 + (5-7)^2}$
> $\phantom{\text{MN}} = \sqrt{1+1}$ $\phantom{\text{QR}} = \sqrt{4+4}$
> $\phantom{\text{MN}} = \sqrt{2}$ units $\phantom{\text{QR}} = \sqrt{8}$
> $\phantom{\text{QR} = } = 2\sqrt{2}$ units
>
> **e** From **d**, QR is twice as long as MN.

EXERCISE 5E

1 Given P(1, 5), Q(5, 7), R(3, 1):
  a Show that triangle PQR is isosceles.
  b Find the midpoint M of QR.
  c Use gradients to verify that PM is perpendicular to QR.
  d Draw a sketch to illustrate what you have found in **a**, **b** and **c**.

2 Given A(6, 8), B(14, 6), C(−1, −3) and D(−9, −1):
  a Use gradients to show that:
    i AB is parallel to DC   **ii** BC is parallel to AD.
  b What kind of figure is ABCD?
  c Check that AB = DC and BC = AD using the distance formula.
  d Find the midpoints of diagonals: **i** AC **ii** BD.
  e What property of parallelograms has been checked in **d**?

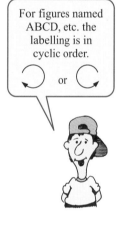

For figures named ABCD, etc. the labelling is in cyclic order.

3 Given A(−1, 1), B(1, 5) and C(5, 1), where M is the midpoint of AB and N is the midpoint of BC:
  a show that MN is parallel to AC, using gradients
  b show that MN is half the length of AC.

4 Given A(1, 3), B(6, 3), C(3, −1) and D(−2, −1):
  a show that ABCD is a rhombus, using the distance formula
  b find the midpoints of AC and BD
  c show that AC and BD are perpendicular, using gradients.

5 An inaccurate sketch of quadrilateral ABCD is given. P, Q, R and S are the midpoints of AB, BC, CD and DA respectively.
  a Find the coordinates of:
    i P **ii** Q **iii** R **iv** S
  b Find the gradient of:
    i PQ **ii** QR **iii** RS **iv** SP
  c What can be deduced about quadrilateral PQRS from **b**?

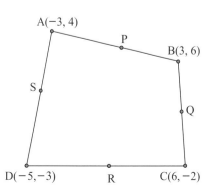

6 S(s, 8) lies on a semi-circle as shown.

  a Find s.

  b Using this value of s, find the slope of: **i** PS   **ii** SQ.

  c Use **b** to show that angle PSQ is a right angle.

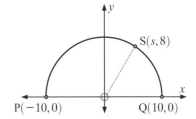

F   VERTICAL AND HORIZONTAL LINES

Every point on the vertical line illustrated has an x-coordinate of 3.

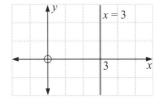

Thus $x = 3$ is the equation of this line.

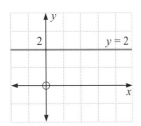

Every point on the horizontal line illustrated has a y-coordinate of 2.

Thus $y = 2$ is the equation of this line.

In general:

> All **vertical lines** have equations of the form $x = a$, (a is a constant).
>
> All **horizontal lines** have equations of the form $y = c$, (c is a constant).

Example 16	◀ Self Tutor

For A(-1, 3) and B(-1, 7), find:

  a the gradient of line AB   **b** the equation of line AB.

  a The gradient of AB is $\dfrac{7 - 3}{-1 - -1} = \dfrac{4}{0}$ which is undefined.

  b An undefined gradient indicates a vertical line and since the x-coordinates of both A and B are -1, the equation of the line AB is $x = -1$.

EXERCISE 5F

1 Find **i** the gradient **ii** the equation of the line through:

  a (3, 2) and (5, 2)   **b** (5, -3) and (5, 0)

  c (3, -2) and (-5, -2)   **d** (-4, 1) and (-4, -1)

  e (5, -3) and (5, 3)   **f** (-3, -4) and (4, -4)

2 Determine the slope of the line with equation:

  a $y = 3$ **b** $x = -4$ **c** $x = 5$ **d** $y = 0$

  e $x + 2 = 0$ **f** $y + 5 = 0$ **g** $x = 0$ **h** $y = \frac{1}{2}$

3 Sketch the graph of the line with equation:

  a $x = 1$ **b** $y = 4$ **c** $x = -2$ **d** $y = 0$

 INVESTIGATION 1   **GRAPHS OF THE FORM** $y = mx + c$

  The use of a graphics calculator or suitable graphing package is recommended for this investigation.

GRAPHING PACKAGE

What to do:

1 On the same set of axes graph the family of lines of the form $y = mx$:

  a where $m = 1, 2, 4, \frac{1}{2}, \frac{1}{10}$ **b** where $m = -1, -2, -4, -\frac{1}{2}, -\frac{1}{10}$

2 What are the gradients of the lines in question **1**?

3 What is your interpretation of m in the equation $y = mx$?

4 On the same set of axes, graph the family of lines of the form $y = 2x + c$ where $c = 0, 2, 4, -1, -3$.

5 What is your interpretation of c for the equation $y = 2x + c$?

G   EQUATIONS OF STRAIGHT LINES

The **equation of a line** is an equation which connects the x and y values for every point on the line.

In the above investigation we established that:

  $y = mx + c$ is the equation of a line with gradient m and y-intercept c.

For example:

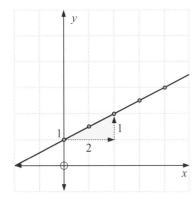

The illustrated line has

gradient $= \dfrac{y\text{-step}}{x\text{-step}} = \frac{1}{2}$

and the y-intercept is 1

$\therefore$ its equation is $y = \frac{1}{2}x + 1$.

Consider the equation $y = 2x - 3$.

We could set up a table of values which satisfy this equation:

x	-1	0	1	2	3	4
y	-5	-3	-1	1	3	5

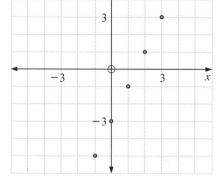

The graph alongside shows only discrete points for integer values of x.

However, x can take any value. Click on the demonstration to see the complete line being generated using non-integer values of x, e.g., $\frac{1}{2}, \frac{1}{4}, \frac{1}{8}$.

Experiment with other linear equations of your choosing.

DEMO

Every point on the line has coordinates which satisfy the equation.

For example, if $x = -0.316$ in $y = 2x - 3$ there is a corresponding value of y which could be found by substitution.

FINDING THE EQUATION OF A LINE

Consider the illustrated line which has gradient $\frac{1}{2}$ and passes through the point (2, 3).

Suppose (x, y) is any point on the line.

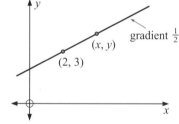

The gradient between (2, 3) and (x, y) is $\dfrac{y - 3}{x - 2}$.

Equating gradients gives us $\dfrac{y - 3}{x - 2} = \dfrac{1}{2}$ {gradient formula}

Consider two rearrangements of this equation of the line.

$$\frac{y - 3}{x - 2} = \frac{1}{2}$$

$$\therefore \quad y - 3 = \tfrac{1}{2}(x - 2) \qquad \text{\{multiplying both sides by } (x - 2)\}$$

$$\therefore \quad y - 3 = \tfrac{1}{2}x - 1 \qquad \text{\{expanding the bracket\}}$$

$$\therefore \quad y = \tfrac{1}{2}x + 2 \qquad \text{\{adding 3 to both sides\}}$$

and this is in the form $y = mx + c$ called the **gradient-intercept** form.

or $\dfrac{y - 3}{x - 2} = \dfrac{1}{2}$

$$\therefore \quad \frac{2}{2}\left(\frac{y - 3}{x - 2}\right) = \frac{1}{2}\left(\frac{x - 2}{x - 2}\right) \qquad \text{\{as LCD is } 2(x - 2)\}$$

$$\therefore \quad 2(y - 3) = 1(x - 2) \qquad \text{\{equating numerators\}}$$

$\therefore \quad 2y - 6 = x - 2 \quad$ {expanding brackets}

$\therefore \quad x - 2y = -4 \qquad$ {rearranging}

and this is in the form $\quad Ax + By = C \quad$ called the **general** form.

$$(A = 1, \quad B = -2, \quad C = -4)$$

So, to find the equation of a line we need to:

- know (or be able to find) the **gradient** and
- the coordinates of any **point** on the line.

Summary:

If a straight line has gradient m and passes through (a, b) then it has equation $\dfrac{y - b}{x - a} = m$

which can be rearranged into $\qquad y = mx + c \qquad$ {**gradient-intercept** form}

$or \quad Ax + By = C \quad$ {**general** form}

Example 17   ◀) **Self Tutor**

Find, in *gradient-intercept form*, the equation of the line through $(-1, 3)$ with a gradient of 5.

The equation of the line is $\qquad \dfrac{y - 3}{x - -1} = 5$

i.e., $\dfrac{y - 3}{x + 1} = 5$

To find the equation of a line we need to know its gradient and a point on it.

$\therefore \quad y - 3 = 5(x + 1)$

$\therefore \quad y - 3 = 5x + 5$

$\therefore \quad y = 5x + 8$

EXERCISE 5G

1 Find, in *gradient-intercept form*, the equation of the line through:

a $(2, -5)$ having a gradient of 5

b $(-1, -2)$ having a gradient of -2

c $(7, -3)$ having a gradient of -4

d $(3, 4)$ having a gradient of $\frac{1}{2}$

e $(-2, 3)$ having a gradient of $-\frac{1}{3}$

f $(5, -1)$ having a gradient of 0

Example 18   ◀)) **Self Tutor**

Find, in *general form*, the equation of the line with gradient $\frac{3}{4}$ and passing through $(5, -2)$.

The equation of the line is

$$\frac{y - -2}{x - 5} = \frac{3}{4}$$

i.e., $\dfrac{y + 2}{x - 5} = \dfrac{3}{4}$

$\therefore\quad 4(y + 2) = 3(x - 5)$

$\therefore\quad 4y + 8 = 3x - 15$

$\therefore\quad 3x - 4y = 23$

2 Find, in *general form*, the equation of the line through:

   a $(2, 5)$ having gradient $\frac{3}{4}$

   b $(-1, 4)$ having gradient $\frac{2}{5}$

   c $(5, 0)$ having gradient $-\frac{1}{2}$

   d $(6, -2)$ having gradient $-\frac{3}{4}$

   e $(-3, -1)$ having gradient 5

   f $(5, -3)$ having gradient -3

Example 19   ◀)) **Self Tutor**

Find the equation of the line which passes through the points A$(-1, 5)$ and B$(2, 3)$.

The gradient of the line is $\dfrac{3 - 5}{2 - -1} = \dfrac{-2}{3}$

$\therefore$ using point A the equation is $\dfrac{y - 5}{x - -1} = -\dfrac{2}{3}$ $\left\{\text{or}\quad \dfrac{y - 3}{x - 2} = \dfrac{-2}{3}\right.$

$\therefore\quad \dfrac{y - 5}{x + 1} = -\dfrac{2}{3}$ using point B$\}$

$\therefore\quad 3(y - 5) = -2(x + 1)$

$\therefore\quad 3y - 15 = -2x - 2$

$\therefore\quad 2x + 3y = 13$

> Check that you get the same final answer using point B instead of A.

3 Find the equation of the line which passes through the points:

   a A$(1, 5)$ and B$(4, 8)$

   b A$(0, 4)$ and B$(-1, 5)$

   c A$(-3, -2)$ and B$(4, -2)$

   d C$(-3, 1)$ and D$(6, 0)$

   e P$(2, -1)$ and Q$(-1, -2)$

   f R$(-2, -3)$ and S$(-4, -1)$

4 Find the equation of the line:

   a which has gradient $\frac{1}{2}$, and cuts the y-axis at 3

   b which is parallel to a line with slope 2, and passes through the point $(-1, 4)$

   c which cuts the x-axis at 5, and the y-axis at -2

d which cuts the x axis at -1, and passes through $(-3, 4)$

e which is perpendicular to a line with gradient $\frac{3}{4}$, and cuts the x-axis at 5

f which is perpendicular to a line with gradient -2, and passes through $(-2, 3)$.

FINDING THE GRADIENT FROM THE EQUATION OF THE LINE

From equations of lines such as $y = \frac{1}{3}x + \frac{2}{3}$ and $y = 5 - 2x$, we can easily find the gradient by looking at the coefficient of x. But how do we find the gradients of equations of lines in the general form? One method is to rearrange them.

Example 20   ◀)) **Self Tutor**

Find the gradient of the line $2x + 5y = 17$.

$$2x + 5y = 17$$
$$\therefore \quad 5y = 17 - 2x \qquad \{\text{subtracting } 2x \text{ from both sides}\}$$
$$\therefore \quad y = \frac{17}{5} - \frac{2x}{5} \qquad \{\text{dividing both sides by 5}\}$$
$$\therefore \quad y = -\tfrac{2}{5}x + \tfrac{17}{5} \quad \text{and so, the gradient is } -\tfrac{2}{5}.$$

---

5 Find the gradient of the line with equation:

a $y = 3x + 5$

b $y = 1 - 2x$

c $y = 0$

d $x = 2$

e $y = \dfrac{2x - 5}{3}$

f $3x + y = 4$

g $2x - 7y = 3$

h $2x + 7y = 4$

i $3x - 4y = 1$

j $3x + 4y = 7$

k $Ax - By = C$

l $Ax + By = C$

EQUATIONS FROM GRAPHS

Provided that a graph contains sufficient information we can determine its equation. Remember that we must have at least one point and we must be able to determine its gradient.

Example 21   ◀)) **Self Tutor**

Find the equation (in gradient-intercept form) of the line with graph:

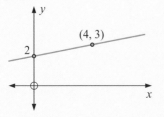

Two points on the line are $(0, 2)$ and $(4, 3)$

$$\therefore \quad \text{gradient } m = \frac{3 - 2}{4 - 0} = \tfrac{1}{4}$$

and the y-intercept, $c = 2$

$$\therefore \quad \text{the equation is } y = \tfrac{1}{4}x + 2.$$

(gradient-intercept form)

Example 22   ◀) **Self Tutor**

Find the equation (in general form) of the line with graph:

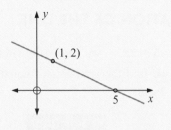

Two points on the line are $(1, 2)$ and $(5, 0)$

$\therefore$ gradient $m = \dfrac{0 - 2}{5 - 1} = \dfrac{-2}{4} = \dfrac{-1}{2}$

As we do not know the y-intercept we use

equation is $\dfrac{y - 2}{x - 1} = \dfrac{-1}{2}$

$\therefore \quad 2(y - 2) = -1(x - 1)$

$\therefore \quad 2y - 4 = -x + 1$

$\therefore \quad x + 2y = 5$ (general form)

6 Find the equation of the line with:

a gradient 3 and y-intercept 5

b gradient 2 and y-intercept -5

c gradient -3 and y-intercept -2

d gradient $-\frac{1}{2}$ and y-intercept -1

e gradient 0 and y-intercept 4

f undefined gradient, through $(-1, -4)$

7 Find the equations of the illustrated lines:

a
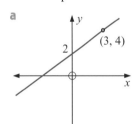

b
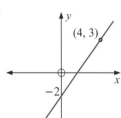

c
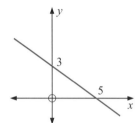

d
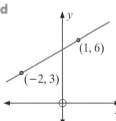

e
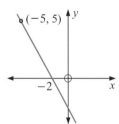

f
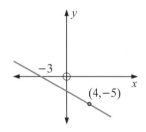

Example 23   ◀) **Self Tutor**

Find the equation connecting the variables in:

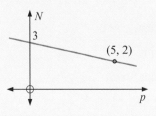

$(0, 3)$ and $(5, 2)$ lie on the straight line

$\therefore$ gradient $m = \dfrac{2 - 3}{5 - 0} = -\frac{1}{5}$

and as the Y-intercept is $c = 3$,

the equation is of the form $Y = mX + c$

where $Y \equiv N$, $X \equiv p$ ($\equiv$ means 'is equivalent to')

$\therefore$ is $N = -\frac{1}{5}p + 3$.

8 Find the equation connecting the variables given:

a
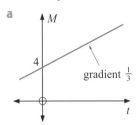

b
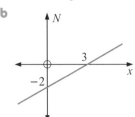

c
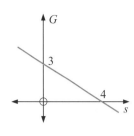

d
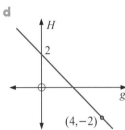

e
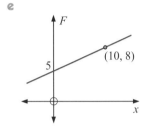

f
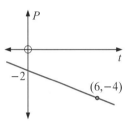

H   GRAPHING LINES

GRAPHING FROM THE GRADIENT-INTERCEPT FORM

Lines with equations given in the gradient-intercept form are easily graphed by finding two points on the graph, one of which is the y-intercept.

The other can be found by substitution or using the gradient.

Example 24   ◀) **Self Tutor**

Graph the line with equation $y = \frac{1}{3}x + 2$.

Method 1:

The y-intercept is 2

when $x = 3$, $y = 1 + 2 = 3$

$\therefore$ $(0, 2)$ and $(3, 3)$ lie on the line.

Method 2:

The y-intercept is 2

and the gradient $= \frac{1}{3}$ $\quad\leftarrow y$-step
$\quad\quad\quad\quad\quad\quad\quad\quad\leftarrow x$-step

So we start at $(0, 2)$ and move to another point by moving across 3, then up 1.

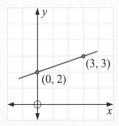

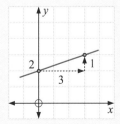

EXERCISE 5H

1   Draw the graph of the line with equation:

   a $y = \frac{1}{2}x + 1$

   b $y = 3x + 4$

   c $y = -x - 1$

   d $y = -3x - 3$

   e $y = -\frac{1}{2}x$

   f $y = -2x + 2$

   g $y = \frac{3}{2}x$

   h $y = \frac{2}{3}x - 1$

   i $y = -\frac{3}{4}x + 4$

2   a   The line with equation $y = 4x - 3$ is reflected in the x-axis. Graph the line and draw its image. Find the equation of the reflected line.

   b   The line with equation $y = \frac{1}{2}x + 3$ is reflected in the y-axis. Graph the line and draw its image. Find the equation of the reflected line.

GRAPHING FROM THE GENERAL FORM

The easiest method used to graph lines in the general form $Ax + By = C$ is to use axis intercepts.

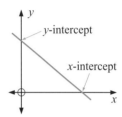

The x-intercept is found by letting $y = 0$.
The y-intercept is found by letting $x = 0$.

Example 25	◄)) Self Tutor

Graph the line with equation $2x - 3y = 12$ using axis intercepts.

For $2x - 3y = 12$,

when $x = 0$, $-3y = 12$
                      $\therefore \quad y = -4$

when $y = 0$, $2x = 12$
                      $\therefore \quad x = 6$

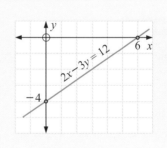

3   Use axis intercepts to draw sketch graphs of:

   a $x + 2y = 4$

   b $3x - y = 9$

   c $2x + 3y = 6$

   d $4x + 3y = 18$

   e $x + y = 4$

   f $x - y = -2$

   g $2x - y = -6$

   h $9x + 2y = 9$

   i $3x + 4y = -12$

4   a   i   Graph the line with equation $3x + 2y = 1$ and show that $(-1, 2)$ lies on it.

      ii   If the line with equation $3x + 2y = 1$ is rotated clockwise about the point $(-1, 2)$ through an angle of $90°$, find the equation of the rotated line.

   b   Graph the line with equation $3x - 5y = 15$. If the line is rotated anticlockwise about the origin through an angle of $180°$, find the equation of this new line.

POINTS ON LINES

A point lies on a line if its coordinates satisfy the equation of the line.

For example,   (2, 3) lies on the line $3x + 4y = 18$ as $3 \times 2 + 4 \times 3 = 6 + 12 = 18$ ✓

whereas   (4, 1) does not lie on the line as $3 \times 4 + 4 \times 1 = 12 + 4 = 16.$

EXERCISE 5I

1 **a** Does (3, 4) lie on the line with equation $5x + 2y = 23$?

   b Does (−1, 4) lie on the line with equation $3x - 2y = 11$?

   c Does $(5, -\frac{1}{2})$ lie on the line with equation $3x + 8y = 11$?

2 Find k if:

   a (2, 5) lies on the line with equation $3x - 2y = k$

   b (−1, 3) lies on the line with equation $5x + 2y = k.$

3 Find a given that:

   a $(a, 3)$ lies on the line with equation $y = 2x - 11$

   b $(a, -5)$ lies on the line with equation $y = 4 - x$

   c $(4, a)$ lies on the line with equation $y = \frac{1}{2}x + 3$

   d $(-2, a)$ lies on the line with equation $y = 1 - 3x.$

4 Find b if:

   a $(2, b)$ lies on the line with equation $x + 2y = -4$

   b $(-1, b)$ lies on the line with equation $3x - 4y = 6$

   c $(b, 4)$ lies on the line with equation $5x + 2y = 1$

   d $(b, -3)$ lies on the line with equation $4x - y = 8.$

J WHERE LINES MEET

Consider plotting the graphs of two straight lines to find the point of **intersection**.

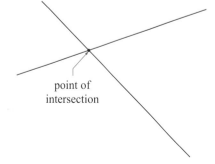

point of intersection

Recall that a straight line is easily graphed by finding the:

- x-intercept   (let $y = 0$)
- y-intercept   (let $x = 0$).

Example 26   ◀)) **Self Tutor**

Use graphical methods to find where the lines $x + y = 6$ and $2x - y = 6$ meet.

For $x + y = 6$

when $x = 0$, $y = 6$
when $y = 0$, $x = 6$

x	0	6
y	6	0

For $2x - y = 6$

when $x = 0$, $-y = 6$, $\therefore$ $y = -6$
when $y = 0$, $2x = 6$, $\therefore$ $x = 3$

x	0	3
y	-6	0

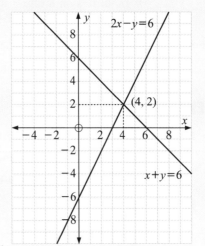

The graphs meet at (4, 2).

Check: $4 + 2 = 6$ ✓ and $2 \times 4 - 2 = 6$ ✓

Observe that there are three possible situations which may occur. These are:

Case 1:

The lines meet in a
single **point of
intersection**.

Case 2:

The lines are **parallel**
and **never meet**.
There is no point of
intersection.

Case 3:

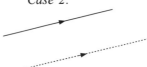

The lines are **coincident**
(the same line).
There are infinitely many
points of intersection.

EXERCISE 5J

1 Use graphical methods to find the point of intersection of:

   a $y = x + 3$
       $y = 1 - x$

   b $x + y = 6$
       $y = 2x$

   c $4x + 3y = 15$
       $x - 2y = 1$

   d $3x + y = -3$
       $2x - 3y = -13$

   e $3x + y = 6$
       $3x - 2y = -12$

   f $x - 3y = -9$
       $2x - 3y = -8$

   g $2x - y = 3$
       $x + 2y = 4$

   h $y = 2x - 3$
       $2x - y = 2$

   i $y = -x - 3$
       $2x + 2y = -6$

2 How many points of intersection do the following pairs of lines have?
   Explain, but **do not** graph them.

   a $2x + y = 6$
       $2x + y = 8$

   b $3x + y = 2$
       $6x + 2y = 4$

   c $4x - y = 5$
       $4x - y = k$ (k takes all values)

INVESTIGATION 2 FINDING WHERE LINES MEET USING TECHNOLOGY

Graphing packages and **graphics calculators** can be used to plot straight line graphs and hence find points of intersection of the straight lines. This can be useful if the solutions are not integer values, although an algebraic method can also be used.

Most graphing packages and graphics calculators require the equation to be entered in the form $y = mx + c$. Consequently, if an equation is given in **general form**, it must be rearranged into **gradient-intercept form**.

For example, to find the point of intersection of $4x + 3y = 10$ and $x - 2y = -3$:

Step 1: If you are using a **graphics calculator**, you will need to **rearrange** each equation into the form $y = mx + c$, i.e.,

$$4x + 3y = 10 \qquad\qquad \text{and} \quad x - 2y = -3$$
$$\therefore \quad 3y = -4x + 10 \qquad\qquad \therefore \quad -2y = -x - 3$$
$$\therefore \quad y = -\tfrac{4}{3}x + \tfrac{10}{3} \qquad\qquad \therefore \quad y = \frac{x}{2} + \frac{3}{2}$$

Enter the functions $Y_1 = -4X/3 + 10/3$ and $Y_2 = X/2 + 3/2$.

If you are using the **graphing package**, click on the icon to open the package and enter the two equations in any form.

GRAPHING PACKAGE

Step 2: Draw the **graphs** of the functions on the same set of axes. (You may have to change the viewing **window** if using a graphics calculator.)

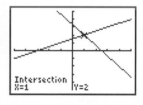

Step 3: Use the built in functions to calculate the point of **intersection**.

Thus, the point of intersection is (1, 2).

What to do:

1 Use technology to find the point of intersection of:

  a $y = x + 4$
  $5x - 3y = 0$

  b $x + 2y = 8$
  $y = 7 - 2x$

  c $x - y = 5$
  $2x + 3y = 4$

  d $2x + y = 7$
  $3x - 2y = 1$

  e $y = 3x - 1$
  $3x - y = 6$

  f $y = -\dfrac{2x}{3} + 2$
  $2x + 3y = 6$

2 Comment on the use of technology to find the point(s) of intersection in **1 e** and **1 f**.

REVIEW SET 5A

1   **a**   Find the equation of the vertical line through $(-1, 5)$.

    b   Find the distance between the points S$(7, -2)$ and T$(-1, 1)$.

    c   Given P$(-3, 2)$ and Q$(3, -1)$, find the midpoint of PQ.

    d   Find the gradient of the line perpendicular to a line with gradient $-\frac{1}{2}$.

    e   Find the y-intercept for the line $4x - 3y = -9$.

    f   Determine the gradient of the line with equation $4x + 5y = 11$.

    g   Find the axis intercepts and gradient of the line with equation $2x + 3y = 6$.

2   If X$(-2, 3)$ and Y$(a, -1)$ are 6 units apart, find the value of a.

3   Determine the equation of the illustrated line:

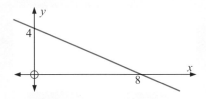

4   Find the equation of the line through $(1, -2)$ and $(3, 4)$.

5   Show that   A$(1, -2)$,   B$(4, 4)$ and   C$(5, 6)$ are collinear.

6   Find b given that   A$(-6, 2)$, B$(b, 0)$ and C$(3, -4)$ are collinear.

7   Draw the graph of $y = -3x + 5$ using the gradient and y-intercept.

8   Two lines with gradients k and $5 - k$ are parallel. Find k.

9   Draw the graph of the line with equation $2x - 5y = 10$ by finding the axis intercepts.

10   Use graphical methods to find the point of intersection of $y = 2x + 1$ and $x + 3y = 10$.

11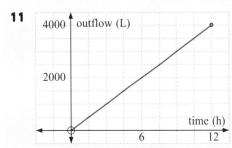

The graph alongside indicates the number of litres of water run from a tank over a period of time.

    a   Find the gradient of the line.

    b   Interpret the gradient found in **a**.

    c   Is the rate of outflow of water constant or variable? What evidence do you have for your answer?

12   Given A$(-3, 1)$, B$(1, 4)$ and C$(4, 0)$:

    a   Show that triangle ABC is isosceles.

    b   Find the midpoint X of AC.

    c   Use gradients to verify that BX is perpendicular to AC.

REVIEW SET 5B

1 **a** Find the midpoint of the line segment joining A(−2, 3) to B(−4, 3).

    b Find the distance from C(−3, −2) to D(0, 5).

    c Find the equation of the x-axis.

    d Find the gradient of all lines perpendicular to a line with slope $\frac{2}{3}$.

    e Write down the gradient and y-intercept of the line with equation $y = 5 - 2x$.

2 Determine the equation of the illustrated line:

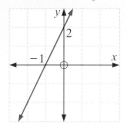

3 K(−3, 2) and L(3, m) are 9 units apart. Find m.

4 A(−1, 2), B(3, a) and C(−3, 7) are collinear. Find a.

5 Find the equations of the following lines:

    a with gradient −2 and y-intercept 5

    b passing through (−1, 3) and (2, 1)

    c parallel to a line with gradient $\frac{3}{2}$ and passing through (5, 0).

6 If (k, 5) lies on the line with equation $3x - y = -8$,   find k.

7 Draw the graph of the line $y = 7 - x$ using the gradient and the y-intercept.

8 Find the equation connecting the variables given:

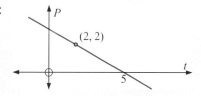

9 Use graphical methods to find the point of intersection of $y = x - 5$ and $4x + y = 10$.

10 The graphs alongside indicate the fuel consumption and distance travelled at speeds of 50 kmph (graph A) and 80 kmph (graph B).

    a Find the gradient of each line.

    b What do these gradients mean?

    c If fuel costs $1.17 per litre, how much more would it cost to travel 1000 km at 80 km/h compared with 50 km/h?

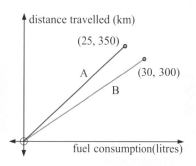

11 Given A(-3, 2), B(2, 3), C(4, -1) and D(-1, -2) are the vertices of quadrilateral ABCD:

  a Find the gradient of AB and DC.

  b Find the gradient of AD and BC.

  c What do you deduce from your answers to **a** and **b**?

  d Find the midpoints of the diagonals of the quadrilateral. What property of parallelograms does this check?

Chapter **6**

Algebraic expansion and simplification

Contents:

The study of **algebra** is an important part of the problem solving process. Many real life problems can be converted to algebraic equations which contain expressions that need to be **expanded** and **simplified**.

Factorisation is the reverse process of expansion and is commonly used to solve equations which are **quadratic** in nature.

In this chapter, we will revise the skills needed to commence solving such problems. In the chapter on **factorisation** we will learn further skills required to complete the solutions.

OPENING PROBLEM

Charlie, a chicken farmer, wants to build a rectangular 'free-range' chicken pen with area 150 m^2 against an existing brick fence.

He has 35 m of fencing available to construct the three sides. Can you help Charlie with the following questions?

- If we let the width of the pen be x m, can you find the length of the pen, given that 35 m of fencing is available?
- Can you find an expression for the area of the pen in terms of x?
- Can you form an equation involving x if the area of the pen is 150 m^2?
- Can you solve the equation for x?
- Can you find the dimensions of the chicken pen?

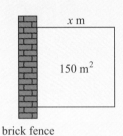

brick fence

A   PRODUCTS AND EXPANSIONS

A **product** of two (or more) *factors* is the result obtained when *multiplying* them together.

Consider the *factors* $-3x$ and $2x^2$. Their product $-3x \times 2x^2$ can be simplified by following the steps below:

Step 1:   Find the product of the **signs**.

Step 2:   Find the product of the **numerals** (numbers).

Step 3:   Find the product of the **pronumerals** (letters).

> In $-3x$, the sign is $-$, the numeral is 3, and the pronumeral is x.

So,
$$-3x \times 2x^2 = -6x^3$$

$- \times + = -$ $\quad$ $x \times x^2 = x^3$

$3 \times 2 = 6$

Example 1   ◀) **Self Tutor**

Simplify the following products:

a $-3 \times 4x$ b $2x \times -x^2$ c $-4x \times -2x^2$

a $-3 \times 4x$
   $= -12x$

b $2x \times -x^2$
   $= -2x^3$

c $-4x \times -2x^2$
   $= 8x^3$

EXERCISE 6A

1 Simplify the following:

a $4 \times 3x$ b $3x \times 6$ c $-3 \times 6x$ d $4 \times -3x$

e $2x \times 3x$ f $3x \times x$ g $-4x \times x$ h $-5x \times 6$

i $-4x \times -2x$ j $-6x \times x^2$ k $-2x^2 \times -7x$ l $3n \times -4n$

m $(-b)^2$ n $(-2b)^2$ o $3a^2 \times 4a^2$ p $a^2 \times -12a$

Other simplifications of two factors are possible using the **expansion** (or **distributive**) rules:

$$a(b + c) = ab + ac \qquad \text{and} \qquad a(b - c) = ab - ac$$

Geometric Demonstration:

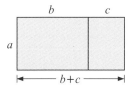

The overall area is $a(b + c)$,

and could also be found by adding the areas of the two small rectangles, i.e., $ab + ac$.

Hence, $a(b + c) = ab + ac$. {equating areas}

Example 2   ◀) **Self Tutor**

Expand the following:

a $3(4x + 1)$ b $2x(5 - 2x)$ c $-2x(x - 3)$

a $3(4x + 1)$
   $= 3 \times 4x + 3 \times 1$
   $= 12x + 3$

b $2x(5 - 2x)$
   $= 2x \times 5 - 2x \times 2x$
   $= 10x - 4x^2$

c $-2x(x - 3)$
   $= -2x \times x - -2x \times 3$
   $= -2x^2 + 6x$

2 Expand and simplify:

a $2(x + 3)$ b $3(1 - 2x)$ c $-(x + 5)$ d $-(2 - 3x)$

e $-5(x + 2)$ f $-2(3x - 2)$ g $x(2x + 1)$ h $3x(x - 2)$

i $b(a + c)$ j $-x(x - y)$ k $t(2t - 1)$ l $2x(x^2 - 3x - 7)$

Example 3   ◀》 **Self Tutor**

Expand and simplify:

   a $2(3x - 1) + 3(5 - x)$ b $x(2x - 1) - 2x(5 - x)$

a $2(3x - 1) + 3(5 - x)$	b $x(2x - 1) - 2x(5 - x)$
$= 6x - 2 + 15 - 3x$	$= 2x^2 - x - 10x + 2x^2$
$= 3x + 13$	$= 4x^2 - 11x$

Notice that the minus sign in front of $2x$ in **b** affects both terms inside the following bracket.

3 Expand and simplify:

   a $2(x - 1) + 3(4 + x)$ b $3a + (2a - 3b)$ c $3a - (2a - 3b)$

   d $2(y + 2) + 5(3 - y)$ e $3(y - 2) - 2(4y + 2)$ f $5x - 2(3 - 4x)$

   g $3(b - a) + 2(a + b)$ h $x(x + 2) + 3(x - 1)$ i $x(x + 2) - 3(x - 2)$

   j $2x^2 + x(x - 5)$ k $-2x^2 - x(x - 4)$ l $x(x + z) - z(x + z)$

   m $-2(x - 3) - (2 - x)$ n $4(5x - 1) - (6x + 11)$ o $3x(x - 7) - 4x(6 - x)$

B   THE PRODUCT $(a + b)(c + d)$

Consider the **factors** $(a + b)$ and $(c + d)$.

The product $(a + b)(c + d)$ can be found using the distributive law several times.

$$(a + b)(c + d) = a(c + d) + b(c + d)$$
$$= ac + ad + bc + bd$$

i.e., $\boldsymbol{(a + b)(c + d) = ac + ad + bc + bd}$

Remember, this is sometimes called the **FOIL** rule.

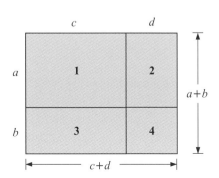

Notice that the final result contains four terms:

  ac is the product of the **F**irst terms of each bracket.

  ad is the product of the **O**uter terms of each bracket.

  bc is the product of the **I**nner terms of each bracket.

  bd is the product of the **L**ast terms of each bracket.

EXERCISE 6B

1 Consider the figure alongside:

   Give an expression for the area of:

   a   rectangle 1   b   rectangle 2

   c   rectangle 3   d   rectangle 4

   e   the overall rectangle.

   What can you conclude?

Example 4   ◄》 Self Tutor

Expand and simplify: $(x + 3)(x + 2)$

$(x + 3)(x + 2)$

$= x \times x + x \times 2 + 3 \times x + 3 \times 2$

$= x^2 + 2x + 3x + 6$

$= x^2 + 5x + 6$

Example 5   ◄》 Self Tutor

Expand and simplify: $(2x + 1)(3x - 2)$

$(2x + 1)(3x - 2)$

$= 2x \times 3x - 2x \times 2 + 1 \times 3x - 1 \times 2$

$= 6x^2 - 4x + 3x - 2$

$= 6x^2 - x - 2$

In practice we do not include the second line of these worked examples.

2 Use the rule $(a + b)(c + d) = ac + ad + bc + bd$ to expand and simplify:

a $(x + 2)(x + 6)$

b $(x + 7)(x - 3)$

c $(x - 2)(x + 8)$

d $(x + 3)(x - 3)$

e $(x - 9)(x + 4)$

f $(3x + 1)(2x + 1)$

g $(2 - 3x)(5x + 1)$

h $(3 - x)(3x + 2)$

i $(2x - 3)(1 + 3x)$

j $(4 - x)(6 + x)$

k $(9 - x)(3x + 4)$

l $(4x + 5)(4x + 5)$

Example 6   ◄》 Self Tutor

Expand and simplify:

a $(x + 3)(x - 3)$

b $(3x - 5)(3x + 5)$

a $(x + 3)(x - 3)$

$= x^2 - 3x + 3x - 9$

$= x^2 - 9$

b $(3x - 5)(3x + 5)$

$= 9x^2 + 15x - 15x - 25$

$= 9x^2 - 25$

What do you notice about the two middle terms?

3 Expand and simplify:

a $(x + 5)(x - 5)$

b $(a - 8)(a + 8)$

c $(3 + x)(3 - x)$

d $(3x + 1)(3x - 1)$

e $(7a + 4)(7a - 4)$

f $(5 + 2a)(5 - 2a)$

Example 7   ◀)) **Self Tutor**

Expand and simplify:

a $(3x+1)^2$ b $(2x-3)^2$

a	$(3x+1)^2$	b	$(2x-3)^2$
	$=(3x+1)(3x+1)$		$=(2x-3)(2x-3)$
	$=9x^2+3x+3x+1$		$=4x^2-6x-6x+9$
	$=9x^2+6x+1$		$=4x^2-12x+9$

What do you notice about the two middle terms?

4   Expand and simplify:

a $(x+4)^2$ b $(x-3)^2$ c $(2x-3)^2$

d $(1-2x)^2$ e $(2-5x)^2$ f $(3x-y)^2$

g $(2x-y)^2$ h $(ab-c)^2$ i $(3x-4y)^2$

C   DIFFERENCE OF TWO SQUARES

a^2 and b^2 are perfect squares and so a^2-b^2 is called the **difference of two squares**.

Notice that $(a+b)(a-b) = a^2 \underbrace{-ab+ab} -b^2 = a^2-b^2$

the middle
two terms
add to zero

Geometric Demonstration:

Consider the figure drawn alongside:

The shaded area
= area of large square − area of small square
= a^2-b^2

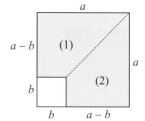

Cutting along the dotted line, and flipping (2) over, we form a rectangle.

Notice that the rectangle's area is $(a+b)(a-b)$.

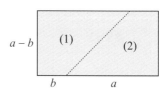

Thus, $(a+b)(a-b) = a^2-b^2$

DEMO

Example 8   🔊 **Self Tutor**

Expand and simplify:

  a $(x+5)(x-5)$ b $(3-y)(3+y)$

  a $(x+5)(x-5)$
      $= x^2 - 5^2$
      $= x^2 - 25$

  b $(3-y)(3+y)$
      $= 3^2 - y^2$
      $= 9 - y^2$

EXERCISE 6C

1 Expand and simplify using the rule $(a+b)(a-b) = a^2 - b^2$:

  a $(x+3)(x-3)$ b $(x-9)(x+9)$ c $(3+x)(3-x)$

  d $(5-x)(5+x)$ e $(x+7)(x-7)$ f $(2-x)(2+x)$

  g $(x+10)(x-10)$ h $(c+12)(c-12)$ i $(d-13)(d+13)$

  j $(x+a)(x-a)$ k $(6+d)(6-d)$ l $(11+e)(11-e)$

Example 9   🔊 **Self Tutor**

Expand and simplify:

  a $(2x-3)(2x+3)$ b $(5-3y)(5+3y)$

  a $(2x-3)(2x+3)$
      $= (2x)^2 - 3^2$
      $= 4x^2 - 9$

  b $(5-3y)(5+3y)$
      $= 5^2 - (3y)^2$
      $= 25 - 9y^2$

2 Expand and simplify using the rule $(a+b)(a-b) = a^2 - b^2$:

  a $(3x-1)(3x+1)$ b $(2x+3)(2x-3)$ c $(4y-5)(4y+5)$

  d $(7y+5)(7y-5)$ e $(5x+3)(5x-3)$ f $(3-7x)(3+7x)$

  g $(4-y)(4+y)$ h $(6+5a)(6-5a)$ i $(7+6a)(7-6a)$

Example 10   🔊 **Self Tutor**

Expand and simplify: $(3x+4y)(3x-4y)$

      $(3x+4y)(3x-4y)$
      $= (3x)^2 - (4y)^2$
      $= 9x^2 - 16y^2$

Your answers should be a **difference** of **two squares**!

3 Expand and simplify using the rule $(a+b)(a-b) = a^2 - b^2$:

   a $(3a+b)(3a-b)$ **b** $(a-3b)(a+3b)$ **c** $(6x+y)(6x-y)$

   d $(8x+5y)(8x-5y)$ **e** $(7x+3y)(7x-3y)$ **f** $(9x-2y)(9x+2y)$

INVESTIGATION 1   THE PRODUCT OF 3 CONSECUTIVE INTEGERS

Con was trying to multiply $19 \times 20 \times 21$ without a calculator. Aimee told him to 'cube the middle integer and then subtract the middle integer' to get the answer.

What to do:

1 Find $19 \times 20 \times 21$ using a calculator.

2 Find $20^3 - 20$ using a calculator. Does Aimee's rule seem to work?

3 Check that Aimee's rule works for the following products:

   a $4 \times 5 \times 6$ **b** $9 \times 10 \times 11$ **c** $49 \times 50 \times 51$

4 Try to prove Aimee's rule using algebra. By letting the middle integer be x, the other integers must be $(x-1)$ and $(x+1)$.

   Find the product $(x-1) \times x \times (x+1)$ by expanding and simplifying. Have you proved Aimee's rule?

   (**Hint:** Rearrange as $x \times (x-1) \times (x+1)$ and use the difference between two squares expansion.)

D   PERFECT SQUARES EXPANSION

$(a+b)^2$ and $(a-b)^2$ are called **perfect squares**.

Notice that:

$$\begin{aligned}(a+b)^2 \\ = (a+b)(a+b) \\ = a^2 \underbrace{+ ab + ab} + b^2 \quad \{\text{using 'FOIL'}\} \\ \text{the middle} \\ \text{two terms} \\ \text{are identical} \\ = a^2 + 2ab + b^2\end{aligned}$$

Also,

$$\begin{aligned}(a-b)^2 \\ = (a-b)(a-b) \\ = a^2 \underbrace{- ab - ab} + b^2 \\ \text{the middle} \\ \text{two terms} \\ \text{are identical} \\ = a^2 - 2ab + b^2\end{aligned}$$

Thus, we can state the perfect square expansion rules:

$$(a+b)^2 = a^2 + 2ab + b^2$$
$$(a-b)^2 = a^2 - 2ab + b^2$$

The following is a useful way of remembering the perfect square expansion rules:

   Step 1:   Square the *first term*.

   Step 2:   Add or subtract twice the product of the *first* and *last terms*.

   Step 3:   Add on the square of the *last term*.

EXERCISE 6D

1 Consider the figure alongside:

Give an expression for the area of:

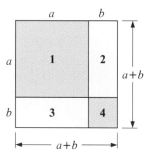

    a square 1
    b rectangle 2

    c rectangle 3
    d square 4

    e the overall square.

What can you conclude?

Example 11   ◄) **Self Tutor**

Expand and simplify:
    a $(x+3)^2$
    b $(x-5)^2$

    a $(x+3)^2$
         $= x^2 + 2 \times x \times 3 + 3^2$
         $= x^2 + 6x + 9$

    b $(x-5)^2$
         $= x^2 - 2 \times x \times 5 + 5^2$
         $= x^2 - 10x + 25$

---

2 Use the rule $(a+b)^2 = a^2 + 2ab + b^2$ to expand and simplify:

    a $(x+3)^2$
    b $(x+7)^2$
    c $(x+8)^2$

    d $(a+1)^2$
    e $(5+c)^2$
    f $(10+x)^2$

3 Use the rule $(a-b)^2 = a^2 - 2ab + b^2$ to expand and simplify:

    a $(x-9)^2$
    b $(x-5)^2$
    c $(y-11)^2$

    d $(a-8)^2$
    e $(6-x)^2$
    f $(5-y)^2$

Example 12   ◄) **Self Tutor**

Expand and simplify using perfect square expansion rules:
    a $(5x+1)^2$
    b $(4-3x)^2$

    a $(5x+1)^2$
         $= (5x)^2 + 2 \times 5x \times 1 + 1^2$
         $= 25x^2 + 10x + 1$

    b $(4-3x)^2$
         $= 4^2 - 2 \times 4 \times 3x + (3x)^2$
         $= 16 - 24x + 9x^2$

---

4 Expand and simplify using perfect square expansion rules:

    a $(2x+5)^2$
    b $(3a-4)^2$
    c $(2y+1)^2$

    d $(3x-5)^2$
    e $(4y-5)^2$
    f $(7+5a)^2$

    g $(1+6x)^2$
    h $(8-3y)^2$
    i $(5+4a)^2$

Example 13   ◀⑴ **Self Tutor**

Expand and simplify: a $(2x^2 + 3)^2$ b $5 - (x + 2)^2$

a $(2x^2 + 3)^2$
  $= (2x^2)^2 + 2 \times 2x^2 \times 3 + 3^2$
  $= 4x^4 + 12x^2 + 9$

b $5 - (x + 2)^2$
  $= 5 - [x^2 + 4x + 4]$
  $= 5 - x^2 - 4x - 4$
  $= 1 - x^2 - 4x$

Notice the use of square brackets in the second line. These remind us we are subtracting **the whole** of the perfect square.

5   Expand and simplify:

a $(x^2 + 3)^2$ b $(y^2 - 4)^2$ c $(2a^2 + 3)^2$
d $(1 - 5x^2)^2$ e $(x^2 + a^2)^2$ f $(x^2 - y^2)^2$

6   Expand and simplify:

a $2x + 3 - (x + 4)^2$ b $4x - 3 + (x - 1)^2$
c $(x + 5)(x - 5) + (x + 4)^2$ d $(x + 3)(x - 3) - (x + 6)^2$
e $(1 - 3x)^2 - (x - 2)(x + 3)$ f $(2 - 3x)^2 + (x + 3)(x - 4)$
g $(x + 4)(2x - 3) - (x + 2)^2$ h $(3x + 4)(x - 1) - (1 - x)^2$
i $(2 - x)^2 + (x + 1)^2$ j $(3 - x)^2 - (x + 3)^2$

E   FURTHER EXPANSION (EXTENSION)

Consider the expansion of $(a + b)(c + d + e)$.

Now $(a + b)(c + d + e)$ Compare: $\square(c + d + e)$
  $= (a + b)c + (a + b)d + (a + b)e$ $= \square c + \square d + \square e$
  $= ac + bc + ad + bd + ae + be$

Notice that there are 6 terms in this expansion and that each term within the first bracket is multiplied by each term in the second,

i.e.,   2 terms in first bracket $\times$ 3 terms in second bracket $\longrightarrow$ 6 terms in expansion.

Example 14   ◀⑴ **Self Tutor**

Expand and simplify: $(2x + 3)(x^2 + 4x + 5)$

$(2x + 3)(x^2 + 4x + 5)$

$= 2x^3 + 8x^2 + 10x$ {all terms of 2nd bracket $\times 2x$}
  $+ 3x^2 + 12x + 15$ {all terms of 2nd bracket $\times 3$}
$= 2x^3 + 11x^2 + 22x + 15$ {collecting like terms}

EXERCISE 6E

1 Expand and simplify:

When expanding, each term of the first bracket is multiplied by each term of the second bracket.

    a $(x+2)(x^2+x+4)$ **b** $(x+3)(x^2+2x-3)$

    c $(x+3)(x^2+2x+1)$ **d** $(x+1)(2x^2-x-5)$

    e $(2x+3)(x^2+2x+1)$ **f** $(2x-5)(x^2-2x-3)$

    g $(x+5)(3x^2-x+4)$ **h** $(4x-1)(2x^2-3x+1)$

Example 15   ◀) **Self Tutor**

Expand and simplify: $(x+2)^3$

$(x+2)^3 = (x+2)^2 \times (x+2)$

$ = (x^2+4x+4)(x+2)$

$ = x^3+4x^2+4x$ {all terms in 1st bracket $\times\ x$}

$ +2x^2+8x+8$ {all terms in 1st bracket $\times\ 2$}

$ = x^3+6x^2+12x+8$ {collecting like terms}

---

2 Expand and simplify:

    a $(x+1)^3$ **b** $(x+4)^3$ **c** $(x-2)^3$

    d $(x-5)^3$ **e** $(2x+1)^3$ **f** $(3x-2)^3$

Example 16   ◀) **Self Tutor**

Expand and simplify:

  a $x(x+1)(x+2)$ **b** $(x+1)(x-2)(x+2)$

  a $x(x+1)(x+2)$

     $= (x^2+x)(x+2)$ {all terms in first bracket $\times\ x$}

     $= x^3+2x^2+x^2+2x$ {expand remaining factors}

     $= x^3+3x^2+2x$ {collect like terms}

  b $(x+1)(x-2)(x+2)$

     $= (x^2-2x+x-2)(x+2)$ {expand first two factors}

     $= (x^2-x-2)(x+2)$ {collect like terms}

     $= x^3+2x^2-x^2-2x-2x-4$ {expand remaining factors}

     $= x^3+x^2-4x-4$ {collect like terms}

---

3 Expand and simplify:

    a $x(x+2)(x+4)$ **b** $x(x-3)(x+2)$ **c** $x(x-4)(x-5)$

    d $2x(x+2)(x+5)$ **e** $3x(x-2)(3-x)$ **f** $-x(2+x)(6-x)$

    g $-3x(3x-1)(x+4)$ **h** $x(1-5x)(2x+3)$ **i** $(x-2)(x+2)(x-3)$

4 Expand and simplify:

   a $(x+4)(x+3)(x+2)$ **b** $(x-3)(x-2)(x+4)$

   c $(x-3)(x-2)(x-5)$ **d** $(2x-3)(x+3)(x-1)$

   e $(3x+5)(x+1)(x+2)$ **f** $(4x+1)(3x-1)(x+1)$

   g $(2-x)(3x+1)(x-7)$ **h** $(x-2)(4-x)(3x+2)$

5 State how many terms would be in the expansion of the following:

   a $(a+b)(c+d)$ **b** $(a+b+c)(d+e)$

   c $(a+b)(c+d+e)$ **d** $(a+b+c)(d+e+f)$

   e $(a+b+c+d)(e+f)$ **f** $(a+b+c+d)(e+f+g)$

   g $(a+b)(c+d)(e+f)$ **h** $(a+b+c)(d+e)(f+g)$

INVESTIGATION 2   THE EXPANSION OF $(a+b)^3$

The purpose of this investigation is to discover the binomial expansion for $(a+b)^3$.

What to do:

1 Find a large potato and cut it to obtain a 4 cm by 4 cm by 4 cm cube.

2 Now, by making 3 cuts parallel to the cube's surfaces, divide the cube as shown in the given figure into 8 rectangular prisms.

3 Find how many prisms are:

   a 3 by 3 by 3   **b** 3 by 3 by 1

   c 3 by 1 by 1   **d** 1 by 1 by 1

4 Now instead of using $4\text{ cm} = 3\text{ cm} + 1\text{ cm}$, suppose the original cube has dimensions $(a+b)$ cm, and make cuts so each edge is divided into a cm and b cm. How many prisms are:

   a a by a by a **b** a by a by b

   c a by b by b **d** b by b by b?

5 Why is the volume of the cube in **4** in terms of a and b given by $(a+b)^3$?

By adding the volumes of the 8 rectangular prisms, find an expression for the total volume, and hence write down the expansion formula for $(a+b)^3$.

F   THE BINOMIAL EXPANSION (EXTENSION)

Consider $(a + b)^n$. We note that:

- $a + b$ is called a **binomial** as it contains two terms
- any expression of the form $(a + b)^n$ is called a **power of a binomial**.

Consider $(a + b)^3$.

$$\begin{aligned} \text{Now}\quad (a + b)^3 &= (a + b)^2(a + b) \\ &= (a^2 + 2ab + b^2)(a + b) \\ &= a^3 + 2a^2b + ab^2 + a^2b + 2ab^2 + b^3 \end{aligned}$$

$$\text{So,}\quad (a + b)^3 = a^3 + 3a^2b + 3ab^2 + b^3$$

We say the **binomial expansion** of $(a + b)^3$ is $a^3 + 3a^2b + 3ab^2 + b^3$.

The binomial expansion of $(a + b)^3$ can be used to expand other cubes.

For example:

to expand $(2x + 3)^3$ we substitute $a = (2x)$ and $b = 3$,

so, $(2x + 3)^3$
$$= (2x)^3 \;+\; 3 \times (2x)^2 \times 3 \;+\; 3 \times (2x) \times 3^2 \;+\; 3^3$$

To expand $(3x - 4)^3$ we substitute $a = (3x)$ and $b = (-4)$,

so, $(3x - 4)^3$
$$= (3x)^3 \;+\; 3 \times (3x)^2 \times (-4) \;+\; 3 \times (3x) \times (-4)^2 \;+\; (-4)^3$$

> Notice the use of brackets in these expansions.

Example 17   🔊 **Self Tutor**

Expand and simplify using the rule $(a + b)^3 = a^3 + 3a^2b + 3ab^2 + b^3$:

a $(x + 2)^3$ **b** $(x - 5)^3$

---

a $(x + 2)^3 = x^3 \;+\; 3 \times x^2 \times 2 \;+\; 3 \times x \times 2^2 \;+\; 2^3$
$$= x^3 + 6x^2 + 12x + 8$$
{replacing a by x and b by 2 in $(a + b)^3 = a^3 + 3a^2b + 3ab^2 + b^3$}

b $(x - 5)^3 = x^3 \;+\; 3 \times x^2 \times (-5) \;+\; 3 \times x \times (-5)^2 \;+\; (-5)^3$
$$= x^3 - 15x^2 + 75x - 125$$

{replacing a by x and b by (-5)}

EXERCISE 6F

1 Use the binomial expansion for $(a+b)^3$ to expand and simplify:

   a $(x+1)^3$ **b** $(x+3)^3$ **c** $(x+4)^3$ **d** $(x+y)^3$

   e $(x-1)^3$ **f** $(x-5)^3$ **g** $(x-4)^3$ **h** $(x-y)^3$

   i $(2+y)^3$ **j** $(2x+1)^3$ **k** $(3x+1)^3$ **l** $(2y+3x)^3$

   m $(2-y)^3$ **n** $(2x-1)^3$ **o** $(3x-1)^3$ **p** $(2y-3x)^3$

2 Copy and complete the argument

$$(a+b)^4 = (a+b)(a+b)^3$$
$$= (a+b)(a^3 + 3a^2b + 3ab^2 + b^3)$$
$$\vdots \quad \text{etc.}$$

3 Use the binomial expansion $(a+b)^4 = a^4 + 4a^3b + 6a^2b^2 + 4ab^3 + b^4$ to expand and simplify:

   a $(x+y)^4$ **b** $(x+1)^4$ **c** $(x+2)^4$ **d** $(x+3)^4$

   e $(x-y)^4$ **f** $(x-1)^4$ **g** $(x-2)^4$ **h** $(2x-1)^4$

4 Consider:

$$(a+b)^1 = a+b$$
$$(a+b)^2 = a^2 + 2ab + b^2$$
$$(a+b)^3 = a^3 + 3a^2b + 3ab^2 + b^3$$
$$(a+b)^4 = a^4 + 4a^3b + 6a^2b^2 + 4ab^3 + b^4$$

The expressions on the right hand side of each identity contain coefficients

```
            1      1
        1      2      1
     1      3      3      1
  1      4      6      4      1
```

and this triangle of numbers is called **Pascal's triangle**.

   a Predict the next two rows of Pascal's triangle and explain how you found them.

   b Hence, write down the binomial expansion for:

     i $(a+b)^5$ **ii** $(a-b)^5$ **iii** $(a+b)^6$ **iv** $(a-b)^6$

ACTIVITY   3 DIGIT REVERSALS

Consider any 3-digit number. Reverse its digits to form a second number.

Your task is to examine the **difference** between these numbers. Remember the difference between numbers is always the larger number less the smaller number. See if the differences for several sets of 3-digit numbers have anything in common.

What to do:

1 Consider   **a** $\begin{array}{r} 932 \\ -239 \\ \hline \\ \hline \end{array}$ **b** $\begin{array}{r} 463 \\ -364 \\ \hline \\ \hline \end{array}$ **c** $\begin{array}{r} 741 \\ -147 \\ \hline \\ \hline \end{array}$

2 Write each **answer** from **question 1** as a product of prime factors.

3 Copy and complete: *When the difference between any 3-digit number and the number obtained by reversing its digits is found, this number is divisible by ......*

4 Give five more examples of your own choosing, including ones where digits are repeated.

5 Use algebra to prove that your statement in **3** above is correct.
   [**Hint:** Any 3-digit number with digit form '*abc*' has the value $100a + 10b + c$.]

REVIEW SET 6A

1 Expand and simplify:
   a $4x \times -8$　　　　**b** $5x \times 2x^2$　　　　**c** $-4x \times -6x$

2 Expand and simplify:
   a $-3(x+6)$　　　**b** $2x(x^2-4)$　　　**c** $2(x-5)+3(2-x)$
   d $3(1-2x)-(x-4)$

3 Expand and simplify:
   a $(3x+2)(x-2)$　　**b** $(2x-1)^2$　　**c** $(4x+1)(4x-1)$
   d $(5-x)^2$　　　　**e** $(3x-7)(2x-5)$　　**f** $x(x+2)(x-2)$

4 Expand and simplify:
   a $5+2x-(x+3)^2$　　　　　**b** $(x+2)^3$
   c $(3x-2)(x^2+2x+7)$　　　　**d** $(x-1)(x-2)(x-3)$

5 **a** Write down the first three rows of Pascal's Triangle.
   b Use the 3rd row of Pascal's Triangle, or otherwise, to write down the binomial expansion for:
      i $(a+b)^3$　　　　　　**ii** $(2x+5)^3$

REVIEW SET 6B

1 Expand and simplify:
   a $3x \times -2x^2$　　**b** $2x^2 \times -3x$　　**c** $-5x \times -8x$

2 Expand and simplify:
   a $-7(2x-5)$　　**b** $2(x-3)+3(2-x)$　　**c** $-x(3-4x)-2x(x+1)$

3 Expand and simplify:
   a $(2x+5)(x-3)$　　**b** $(3x-2)^2$　　**c** $(2x+3)(2x-3)$
   d $(5x-1)(x-2)$　　**e** $(2x-3)^2$　　**f** $(1-5x)(1+5x)$

4 Expand and simplify:

    a $(2x+1)^2 - (x-2)(3-x)$ **b** $(x^2 - 4x + 3)(2x - 1)$

    c $(x+3)^3$ **d** $(x+1)(x-2)(x+5)$

5 Use the binomial expansion $(a+b)^4 = a^4 + 4a^3b + 6a^2b^2 + 4ab^3 + b^4$ to expand and simplify:

    a $(2x+1)^4$ **b** $(x-3)^4$

Chapter 7

Transformation geometry

Contents:

In **transformation geometry** figures are changed (or transformed) in size, shape, orientation or position according to certain rules.

The original figure is called the **object** and the new figure is called the **image**.

One transformation of interest is known as the *rubber stretching transformation*. Imagine drawing a figure on a piece of rubber, such as a balloon, on a flat surface and then stretching the rubber to distort the shape. We could create almost any other shape we would wish.

For example,

We can see how a circle can be transformed into a square.

The following example illustrates how a salmon can be transformed into a schnapper. {Ref: On Growth and Form. *D'Arcy W Thompson*}

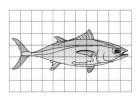   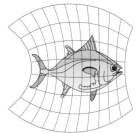

The transformations that we will consider in this chapter are:
- **Translations**, sometimes referred to as sliding transformations.
- **Rotations**, where we turn objects about a point.
- **Reflections**, or mirror images.
- **Enlargements** and **reductions**, where objects are transformed into larger (or smaller) objects of the same shape.

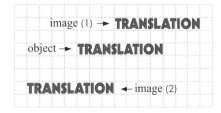   

The word TRANSLATION has been slid 3 units to the right and 2 units upwards to (1). It has been slid 4 units to the left and 3 units down to (2).

Place a mirror along dotted line A and (1) is the reflection in A. What do you notice? Place a mirror along dotted line B and (2) is the reflection in B. Describe what you see.

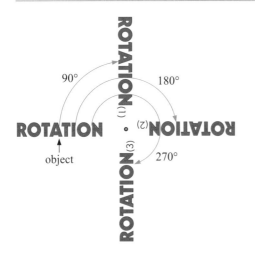

ENLARGEMENT (1)

object → **ENLARGEMENT**

ENLARGEMENT(2)

The word ROTATION has been rotated about • clockwise through 90° to (1), through 180° to (2) and through 270° to (3).

The word ENLARGEMENT has been enlarged (made bigger) at (1) and reduced (made smaller) at (2).

Here are some more examples of translations, reflections, rotations and enlargements:

a **translation** (or **slide**)   a **reflection**

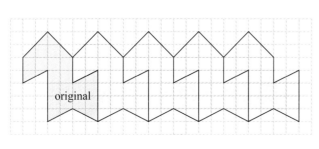

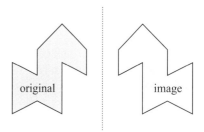

slide 4 units to the right each time to the new position   mirror line

a **rotation** about O   an **enlargement**

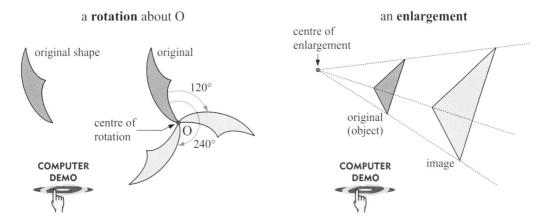

An important application of enlargements is the work on **similar figures** which leads on to the study of a very important branch of mathematics called **trigonometry**.

OPENING PROBLEM

 Dean wishes to accurately find the height of a tree in his back yard. Local Council regulations prohibit the growth of back yard trees beyond 20 m. They argue that in storm conditions, falling branches and uprooted large trees are dangerous to houses and lives.

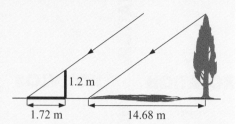

As Dean cannot climb the tree he decides to use shadows to help solve the problem. On a windless sunny day he stands a 1.2 m stick vertically on the ground. The length of the stick's shadow is 1.72 m and at the same time the tree's shadow measures 14.68 m.

Can you:

- produce an accurate scale drawing of the situation
- use the scale drawing to find the tree's height and the angle of elevation of the sun (the angle that the sun's rays make with the horizontal ground)
- recognise the transformation occurring in this problem
- use ratios to find the height of the tree?

A   TRANSLATIONS

A **translation** is a transformation in which every point of a figure moves a fixed distance in a given direction.

All points move under a translation.

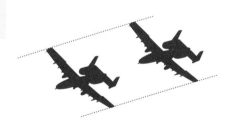

Consider this translation:

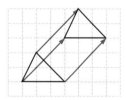

We could specify (give details) of the transformation in one of the following ways:

- $3\sqrt{2}$ units in a North East direction {using Pythagoras}

- $\begin{bmatrix} 3 \\ 3 \end{bmatrix}$ using a **translation vector**

  where the first number (or top number) indicates the x-step and the second one the y-step for each point

- using a directed line segment which clearly shows the direction and distance.

EXERCISE 7A

1   The object A has been translated to give an image B in each diagram. Give the translation in each case.

a
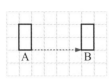

b

c

d
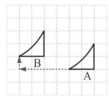

e

f

2   The figure A has been translated to B, then B has been translated to C.

   a   Give the translation vector from A to B.

   b   Give the translation vector from B to C.

   c   What translation vector would move A to C?

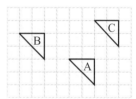

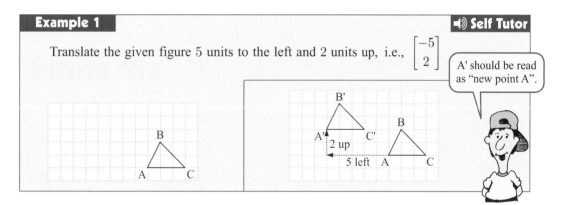

Example 1   ◀》 **Self Tutor**

Translate the given figure 5 units to the left and 2 units up, i.e., $\begin{bmatrix} -5 \\ 2 \end{bmatrix}$

A' should be read as "new point A".

3   Copy the figures given onto grid paper and translate in the direction and distance indicated:

a
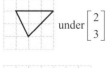 under $\begin{bmatrix} 2 \\ 3 \end{bmatrix}$

b
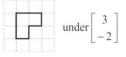 under $\begin{bmatrix} 3 \\ -2 \end{bmatrix}$

c
 under $\begin{bmatrix} -1 \\ 3 \end{bmatrix}$

d
 under

e
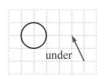 under

f
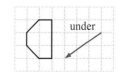 under

4 Which of the following represent translations?

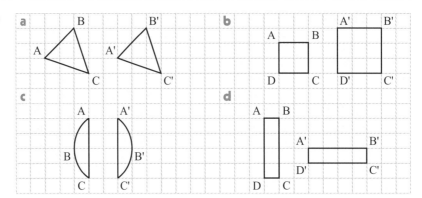

5 **a** Write down the coordinates of A, B, C and D.

   b Each point is translated 5 units to the right and 2 units up. What are the coordinates of the image points A′, B′, C′ and D′?

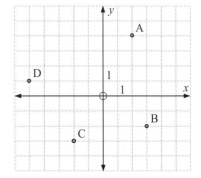

6 Draw triangle ABC where A is $(-1, 3)$, B is $(4, 1)$ and C is $(0, -2)$.

   a Translate the figure through translation vector $\begin{bmatrix} 4 \\ -2 \end{bmatrix}$.

   b State the coordinates of the image vertices A′, B′ and C′.

   c Find the slope of AA′, BB′ and CC′.

   d Through what distance has every point moved?

B   ROTATIONS

When a wheel, such as that on a motorcycle, moves about its axle, we say that the wheel *rotates*.

The centre point on the axle is called the **centre of the rotation**.

The angle through which the wheel turns is called the **angle of rotation**.

Other examples of rotation are:

- the movement of the hands of a clock
- opening and closing a door.

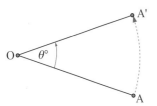

Rotations are transformations in which one point (called O) is fixed and all other points are rotated through the same angle $\theta°$, about O.

O is called the **centre of the rotation** and θ is known as **the angle of rotation**.

Notice that $OA = OA'$ and AA′ is an arc of a circle, centre O.

To completely describe a rotation we need to know:

- the **centre** of the rotation
- the **direction** of the rotation (clockwise or anticlockwise)
- the **angle** of the rotation.

ACTIVITY   ROTATIONS USING PLASTIC SHEET OR ROTAGRAMS

Rotations of figures can be nicely demonstrated on an overhead projector. Suppose we wish to rotate a figure such as a triangle about a point O.

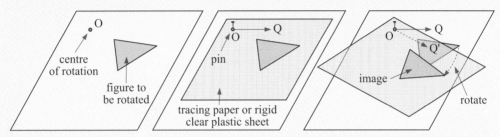

VIDEO CLIP

Steps:

- On an overhead transparency draw the figure to be rotated and indicate the centre of rotation O. Draw a ray OQ from the centre of rotation.
- Place another transparency or piece of tracing paper over the figure to be rotated and join the sheets together with a split pin at the centre of the rotation.
- Trace the object figure and the ray onto the top sheet.
- Rotate the top sheet in the desired direction through the desired angle.
  (This is the angle formed between the ray OQ and its image.)
- Use pins to mark the positions of special points of the image through the top sheet onto the bottom sheet. Draw the image on the bottom sheet.

What to do:

1 Using the method described, draw these diagrams on plastic sheet and rotate them *clockwise* through the angle given. Make sure that the centre of rotation O, is also on the sheet.

    a Rotate 90° about O.   **b** Rotate 45° about O.   **c** Rotate 60° about O.

2 **a** Name any points on your sheet that do not move during a rotation.

    b What can you say about the size and shape of the image formed under a rotation?

    c Comment on your results in **1c**.

Example 2   🔊 **Self Tutor**

Rotate the given figures, about O, through the angle indicated:

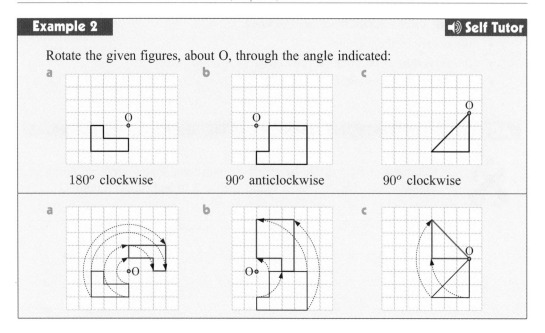

a   b   c

180° clockwise   90° anticlockwise   90° clockwise

EXERCISE 7B

1 Rotate the figures through the angle given about O:

a   b   c

180°   180°   90° anticlockwise

d   e   f

90° clockwise   90° clockwise   90° anticlockwise

2 Which of the following alphabet letterings either remain the same letter or become a different letter under a rotation of some kind?

A B C D E F G H I J K L M
N O P Q R S T U V W X Y Z

(**Note:** A full 360° rotation is not allowed.)

3 Which of the following transformations represent rotations?

a

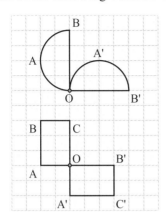

b

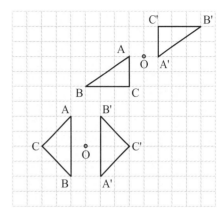

c

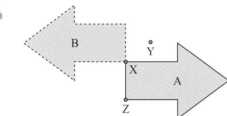

d

4

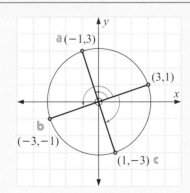

Figure B is the image of A after a rotation.

a Through how many degrees has A been rotated?

b Which point (X, Y or Z) was the centre of rotation?

5 A figure is rotated 75° clockwise about a point O. Describe a rotation which will return the figure to its original position.

Example 3 ◀) **Self Tutor**

Find the coordinates of the image of (3, 1) under a rotation about O through:
a 90° anticlockwise   **b** 180° **c** 90° clockwise

a (3, 1) becomes (−1, 3)

b (3, 1) becomes (−3, −1)

c (3, 1) becomes (1, −3)

---

6 Find the coordinates of the images of these points under a 90° anticlockwise rotation about O:

   a (4, 1)   **b** (5, −2)   **c** (0, −5)   **d** (−1, −5)   **e** (−3, 4)

7 Find the coordinates of the images of these points under a 180° rotation about O:

   a (−3, 5)   **b** (3, 0)   **c** (1, 4)   **d** (−3, −2)   **e** (4, −2)

8 Find the coordinates of the images of the following points under a 90° clockwise rotation about O:

    a $(0, -2)$ **b** $(4, 2)$ **c** $(-1, -5)$ **d** $(4, -2)$ **e** $(-3, 2)$

9 O is the midpoint of AC of triangle ABC and AB $\neq$ BC. Redraw the figure and rotate it through 180° about O.

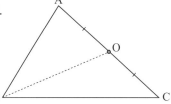

    a   Name the resulting figure which is made up of the original and its image.

    b   Use the resulting figure to list its geometrical properties. Give reasons.

10

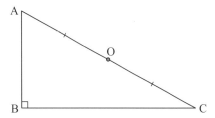

Repeat question **9** for the figure alongside.

REFLECTIONS

We encounter reflections every day as we look in a mirror, peer into a pond of water or glance at the traffic behind us in a car.

INVESTIGATION 1   **REFLECTIONS**

You will need: A mirror, paper, pencil, ruler.

What to do:

    1   Make two copies of the figures shown below:

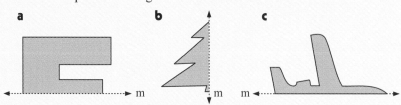

    2   Put the mirror along the line marked m (the mirror line) on one copy. What do you notice in the mirror?

    3   Draw the reflection as accurately as you can on the second copy.

    4   Cut out the second copy with its reflection and fold it along the mirror line.

    5   You should find that the two parts of the figure can be folded exactly onto one another along the mirror line.

INVESTIGATION 2   PROPERTIES OF REFLECTION

The diagram shows a triangle and its reflection in a mirror line.

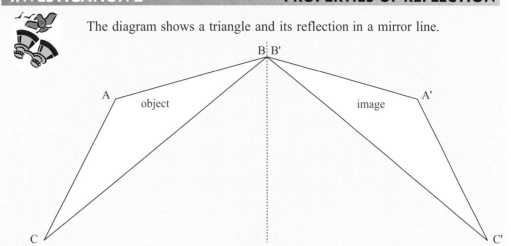

What to do:

1 Copy the diagram.

2 Join point A to its image point A′ on the reflection, and join C to C′.

   a Measure the distance from A to the mirror line and the distance from A′ to the mirror line. What do you notice?

   b Measure the angles that the line AA′ makes with the mirror line.

   c Repeat **a** and **b** using the point C and its image point C′.

   d Measure the lengths of sides of triangle ABC and the lengths of sides of triangle A′B′C′. What do you notice?

   e Measure the angles of triangle ABC and the angles of triangle A′B′C′. What do you notice?

   f What do you notice about the image of a point that is on the mirror line?

From the above investigation, you should have found that:

- The image is as far behind the mirror line as the object is in front of it.
- The line joining an image point to its object point is at right angles to the mirror line.
- All lengths and angles are the same size in the image as they were in the object.
- Points on the mirror line do not move.

We say that the mirror line is the **perpendicular bisector** of every object and image point.

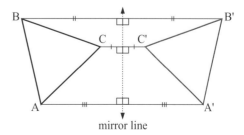

We can use these facts to help us draw reflections. It is easy to work on grid paper because we can count squares and see right angles.

Example 4   ◄ッ **Self Tutor**

Reflect the following figures in the given mirror line:

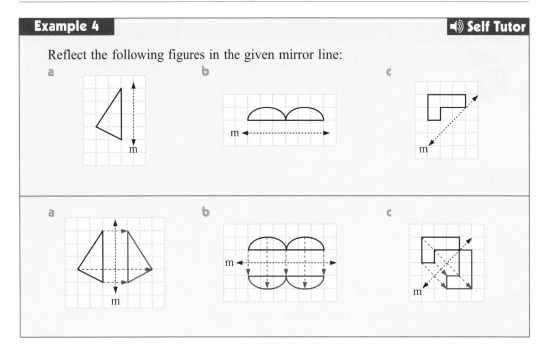

EXERCISE 7C

1   Copy the following figures onto grid paper and reflect in the given mirror line:

a

b
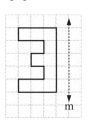

c

d

e

f
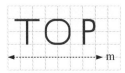

2   Which of the following transformations represent reflections?

a

b

c

d

3 **a** Copy the word and
reflect in the line given:

i no

ii think

b Print your name and reflect it in a similar way. This is called mirror writing. Hold it up to a mirror and you should be able to read it properly.

c 'TOOT' is one example of a word which is the same in mirror writing. Can you think of some more? Check in a mirror.

4 **a** By plotting points on grid paper, complete the table alongside showing the images of the given points under a reflection in the x-axis.

	P	P'
i	(5, 2)	
ii	(−3, 4)	
iii	(−2, −5)	
iv	(3, −7)	
v	(4, 0)	
vi	(0, 3)	

b Use your table from **a** to complete the following statement:

Under a reflection in the x-axis, (a, b) maps onto (...., ...).

5 **a** Copy the table from question **4** and this time reflect the original points in the y-axis.

b Use your table to complete the following statement:

Under a reflection in the y-axis, (a, b) maps onto (...., ...).

6 The line $y = x$ can be used as a mirror line.

a Copy the table from question **4** and this time reflect the given points in the line $y = x$.

b Copy and complete: For a reflection in the line $y = x$,   point (a, b) becomes (....., ...).

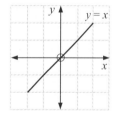

7 A roadway must go from A to the pipeline and then to B by the shortest route.

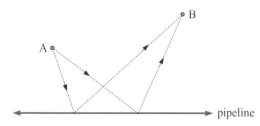

pipeline

Alec Smart's solution is as follows:

Step 1: Reflect B in the pipeline (mirror line) to obtain B'.

Step 2: Join AB', and let AB' meet the pipeline at X.

Step 3: Then join BX.

Step 4: AX + XB provides us with the shortest route.

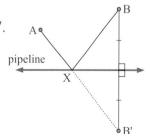

a What can be said about triangle BXB'? Why?

b Can you explain why Alec's solution is correct?
(**Hint:**   Let Y be any point on the pipeline other than X. Join AY and YB'.)

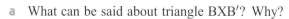

AXIS OF SYMMETRY (LINE SYMMETRY)

A figure has an **axis of symmetry** if it can be reflected in that line so that each half of the figure is reflected onto the other half of the figure.

For example, an isosceles triangle has one axis of symmetry. The line drawn from its apex to the midpoint of its base is the axis of symmetry.

A square has 4 axes of symmetry.

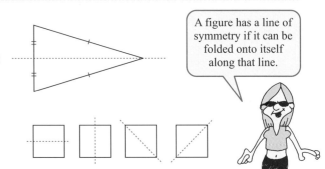

A figure has a line of symmetry if it can be folded onto itself along that line.

Example 5   ◀) **Self Tutor**

For the following figures draw all lines of symmetry if they exist:

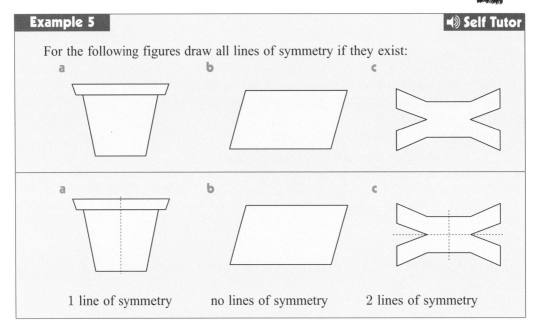

1 line of symmetry   no lines of symmetry   2 lines of symmetry

---

8   Copy the following figures and if possible draw the lines of symmetry:

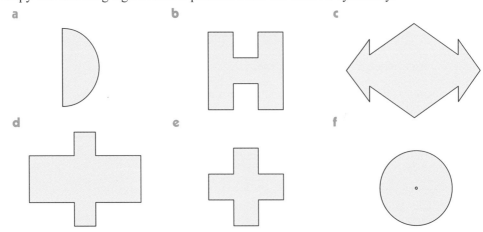

9 Draw the following figures and mark in all the axes of symmetry, if any. Cutting and folding may help. Record the number of axes of symmetry for each.

    a   a square   **b**   an equilateral triangle   **c**   a parallelogram

    d   a rectangle   **e**   a rhombus   **f**   a regular pentagon

    g   a circle   **h**   a kite   **i**   an isosceles triangle

D   ENLARGEMENTS AND REDUCTIONS

We are all familiar with enlargements in the form of photographs, zoom tools in computer software, or looking through a microscope. Plans and maps are examples of reductions.

The size of the image has been reduced but the proportions are the same as the original. Most photocopiers can make images either smaller or larger than the original.

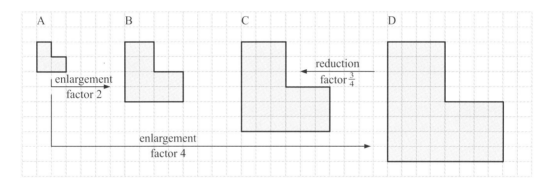

Look carefully at the diagrams above, with the smallest shape A as our starting shape. Shape B has each length twice the size it was in shape A. We say shape B is an **enlargement** of shape A with a **scale factor** of 2.

Shape C has each length three times the size it was in shape A. Shape C is an enlargement of shape A with a scale factor of 3. Similarly shape D is an enlargement of shape A with a scale factor of 4.

> A scale factor of 2 **does not** mean that the shape formed is 2 times larger than the original. In fact, it is 2 × 2, or 4 times larger. Count the squares inside to prove it for shapes A and B.

COMPUTER DEMO

You might also notice that shape D is an enlargement of shape B with a scale factor of 2.

Now, suppose that shape D is our starting shape.

Shape B is a **reduction** of shape D with scale factor $\frac{1}{2}$. Similarly shape A is a reduction of shape D with scale factor $\frac{1}{4}$.

Shape C is a reduction of shape D with scale factor $\frac{3}{4}$ (for every 3 unit length in C there is a 4 unit length in D).

Notice that the scale factor is **greater** than 1 for an enlargement but **less** than 1 for a reduction.

EXERCISE 7D

1 In the following diagrams, A has been enlarged to A′. Find the scale factor.

a

b

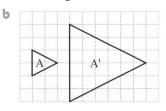

c

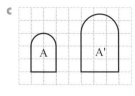

2 In the following diagrams, B′ is a reduction of B. Find the scale factor.

a

b

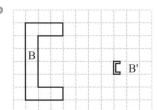

c

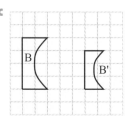

DISCUSSION   **CENTRE OF ENLARGEMENT**

Look carefully at the diagrams below. In each case triangle PQR has been enlarged to triangle P′Q′R′ with a scale factor of 3.

A

B

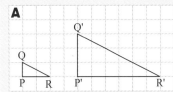

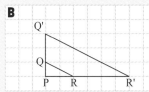

C

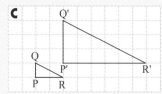

1 What is the difference between these enlargements?

2 What does 'enlargement with scale factor 3' tell you?

3 What additional instructions would you need to be able to draw an enlargement of the right size in the right position?

A

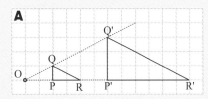

C

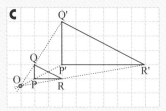

Consider again the diagrams A and C from above. If we draw lines through each original point and the corresponding point on the enlargement, the lines always meet at a point which we label O.

Notice on each diagram that length OP′ = 3 times length OP, length OQ′ = 3 times length OQ and length OR′ = 3 times length OR. This is because our enlargement had a scale factor of 3.

The point O is called the **centre of enlargement**. In diagram B, the centre of enlargement is the point P.

Example 6   ◀)) **Self Tutor**

Find the image of the following figures for the centre of enlargement O and the scale factor given:

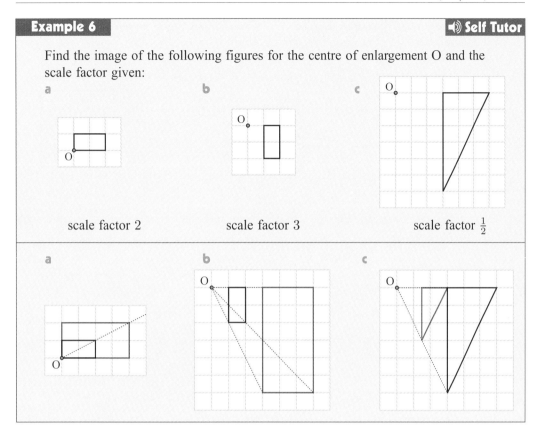

a   b   c

scale factor 2   scale factor 3   scale factor $\frac{1}{2}$

a   b   c

Sometimes the centre of enlargement can lie within the original figure.

Example 7   ◀)) **Self Tutor**

Find the image of the following figures for the centre of enlargement O and the scale factor given:

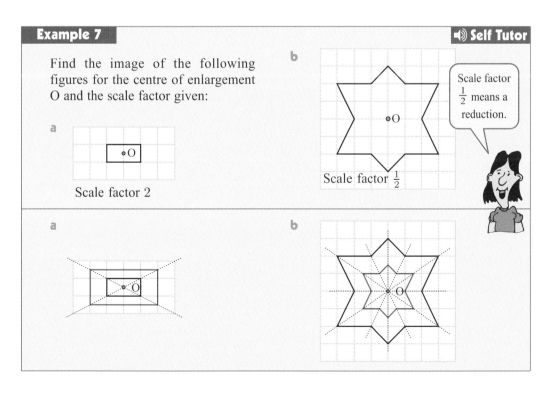

a

Scale factor 2

b

Scale factor $\frac{1}{2}$

Scale factor $\frac{1}{2}$ means a reduction.

a   b

3 Copy the following diagrams. Locate the centre of enlargement for each of the following by drawing lines on your diagrams if necessary:

a
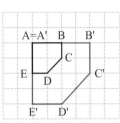

b
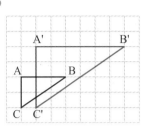

c
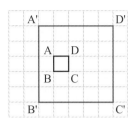

4 Copy the given figures and enlarge with the given scale factor and centre of enlargement:

a   Scale factor 2

b   Scale factor 3

c   Scale factor $\frac{1}{2}$

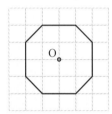

d   Scale factor 2

e   Scale factor $\frac{1}{3}$

f   Scale factor 3

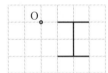

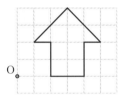

5 Copy the given figures and enlarge with the given scale factor and centre of enlargement:

a   Scale factor 2

b   Scale factor $\frac{1}{2}$

c   Scale factor 3

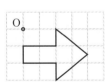

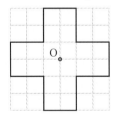

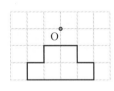

6 For the examples in question **5**, copy and complete the table alongside where the area is in square units:

Part	Area of object	Area of image	Scale factor, k
a			
b			
c			

In each case find the value of the fraction $\dfrac{\text{area of image}}{\text{area of object}}$ and k^2.

State in equation form how the area of the image is connected to the area of the object.

7   Jason made a $\frac{1}{100}$ scale model of a yacht and the mainsail of his scale model had an area of 56 cm². What was the actual sail area, in m², of the full sized yacht?

8   A 10 cm by 8 cm photograph is to be enlarged so that the longer side will be 25 cm.
  a   What is the value of k, the enlargement factor?
  b   Find the length of the enlarged shorter side.
  c   The cost of printing depends on its area. If the smaller photograph costs $3.00 to print, find the cost of printing the larger photograph.

9   A gardener wishes to double the area of his 5 m by 8 m rectangular garden bed. However, he likes its shape and consequently wants the new garden bed to be an enlargement of the old one. What dimensions must he make the new garden bed?

E   TESSELLATIONS

Maurits Escher, who died in 1972 aged 74, created many clever and fascinating patterns, called tessellations. The pattern above is like one of his better known examples. Here are some tessellations made from polygons:

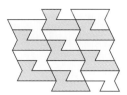      

Each of the three tile patterns is made by using tiles of the same size and shape. A pattern made like this is called a tessellation.

For a tessellation the shapes must fit together with no gaps.

BRICK PAVING

A simple tessellation is the brick or tiling pattern using rectangles.

The two tessellations on the previous page are both obtained by translations only. Can you think why brick walls are usually constructed using the first pattern rather than the second?

Two more tessellations of rectangles are shown below. These involve translations and rotations, and are common patterns for pavers.

Herringbone

Basketweave

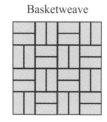

For these particular patterns to work, the length of each rectangle needs to be twice the width.

It is clear that rectangles tessellate in a variety of ways.

The only **regular** polygons to tessellate are equilateral triangles, squares and regular hexagons,

i.e.,   •   **equilateral triangles**   •   **squares**   •   **hexagons**

   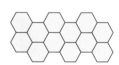

Example 8   ◄)) **Self Tutor**

Draw tessellations of the following shapes:

a   b

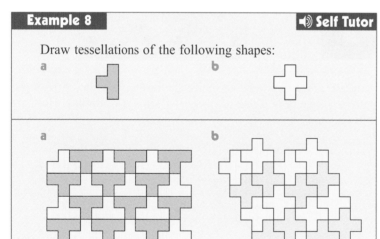

EXERCISE 7E

1   Draw tessellations using the following shapes:

a   b   c

2 Would the following shapes tessellate?

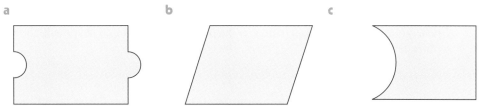

We can use the three regular polygons (and any other shapes which we know tessellate, e.g., rectangles, parallelograms) as a starting point to create more interesting patterns and designs. We can **alter** these basic shapes using translations, rotations and reflections in certain ways.

Translations can be used on parts of a regular shape to produce another more complex tessellating shape.

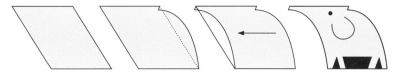

Start with a parallelogram; alter the side; translate to the other side; add the final detail.

Note that tessellations are created by changing one side and then **translating** that change to the **opposite**, **parallel** side. This method can be used to create tessellating shapes from parallelograms (including rhombus, square, rectangle) and regular hexagons. More complicated tessellating shapes can be produced by changing more than one side and translating these changes to their respective parallel sides.

3 Side(s) of the following rectangles have been altered as shown. Redraw and translate the change(s) to the opposite side(s) to create a tessellating shape.

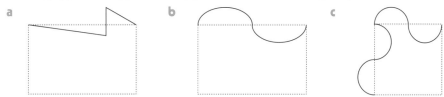

4 A popular paver produced by a leading paver manufacturer is shown below.

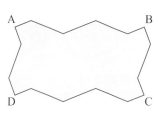

- **a** Trace this design into your book.
- **b** Show how it has been created by altering the sides of rectangle ABCD.
- **c** Draw several to show that they tessellate.
- **d** Apart from their visual appeal, what advantage do these pavers have over rectangular ones?

    e   The manufacturer has decided that it is time to market different pavers and has hired you as a designer. Your job is to design two new pavers, both based on a rectangle.

5 Create your own artistic tessellation by beginning with a simple shape which tessellates by translating.

ACTIVITY   **MAKE YOUR OWN 'ESCHER' TESSELLATION**

To make the 'bird' tessellation at the start of this section follow these steps:

Step 1: Begin with an equilateral triangle.   *Step 2:* Change side AB as shown.

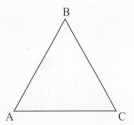   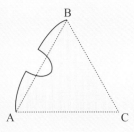

Step 3: Rotate 60° about vertex A to side AC.   *Step 4:* Change side BC as shown.

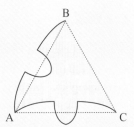   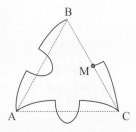

Step 5: Rotate change 180° about midpoint M.   *Step 6:* Final detail added.

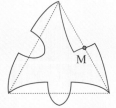   

What to do:

- Photocopy your 'bird' many times and carefully cut each one out with scissors.
- Show how six of these shapes tessellate by rotating about point A.
- Continue the tessellation to cover a wider area to poster size.
- Repeat the exercise using two different shapes shown in this section on a figure of your own design.

REVIEW SET 7A

1 Copy the figure alongside and on separate diagrams carry out the following transformations:

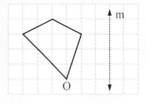

   a translation under $\begin{bmatrix} 3 \\ -2 \end{bmatrix}$

   b rotation about O, $90°$ clockwise

   c reflection in the mirror line m

   d enlargement with scale factor 2 and centre of enlargement O.

2 Figure A has been translated to give an image B.

   Give the translation.

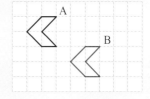

3 Draw triangle ABC where A is $(3, 3)$, B is $(-3, -2)$ and C is $(3, -2)$.

   a Translate the figure under translation vector $\begin{bmatrix} 3 \\ 2 \end{bmatrix}$.

   b State the coordinates of the image vertices A′, B′, C′.

4 By plotting points on grid paper, complete the table alongside showing the images of the given points under a reflection in the x-axis.

	P	P'
a	$(1, 4)$	
b	$(-2, 3)$	
c	$(-3, -1)$	
d	$(4, 2)$	

5 Copy the following figures and draw in all axes of symmetry (if any):

   a   **b**   **c**

6 **a** 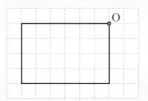 Reduce with scale factor $\frac{1}{2}$ and centre O.

   b Copy the given diagram. Locate the centre of enlargement by drawing lines on your diagram if necessary.

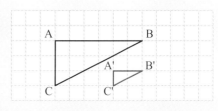

REVIEW SET 7B

1 Copy the figure alongside and on separate diagrams carry out the following transformations:

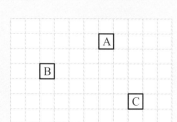

   a translation under $\begin{bmatrix} -3 \\ 4 \end{bmatrix}$

   b rotation about O, $180°$ clockwise

   c reflection in the mirror line m

   d enlargement with scale factor 2 and centre of enlargement O.

2 Figure A has been translated to B, then B has been translated to C.

   a Give the translation vector from A to B.

   b Give the translation vector from B to C.

   c What translation vector would move A to C?

3 Find the coordinates of the images of these points under a $90°$ anticlockwise rotation about O:

   a $(0, 2)$ **b** $(-5, 0)$ **c** $(1, -3)$ **d** $(-2, -4)$ **e** $(-3, 2)$

4 By plotting points on grid paper, complete the table alongside showing the images of the given points under a reflection in the y-axis.

	P	P'
a	$(1, 5)$	
b	$(-2, 4)$	
c	$(-4, -3)$	
d	$(3, 2)$	

5 Draw a rectangle and draw in all lines of symmetry.

6 A figure is enlarged with a scale factor of 2. What happens to the area of the figure?

7 Which of the following shapes will tessellate? Draw a diagram to illustrate your answer.

   a   **b**   **c**

Chapter 8

Factorisation

Contents:

When an expression is written as a **product** of its **factors**, we say it has been **factorised**.

For example $3x + 15 = 3 \times (x + 5)$ where the factors are 3 and $(x + 5)$.

Notice that $3(x + 5) = 3x + 15$ using the **distributive law** and so **factorisation** is really the **reverse** process to **expansion**.

Factorisation is an important process used when attempting to solve **quadratic equations** such as $x^2 + 3x - 40 = 0$.

OPENING PROBLEM

During a golf tournament, Karrie needs to hit her tee shot on a par 4 hole over a lake as shown.

Her caddy tells her that she must hit the ball 205 m to clear the lake and she knows the pin is 240 m 'as the crow flies' from the tee.

Karrie hits her shot and watches it sail directly towards the pin over the lake. However the ball hits a power line and falls into the water. Karrie is entitled to play another ball from the tee without being penalised any strokes and does so. But this time her shot is nowhere near as good.

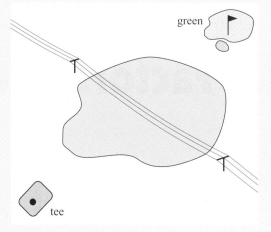

Officials view a video tape of the first shot and are able to obtain these measurements:

Horizontal distance (x m) from the tee	25	50	75	100	125
Height (h m) of the ball above the ground	17.5	30	37.5	40	37.5

A relationship is found connecting the *horizontal distance* the ball travels and the *height* of the golf ball above the ground. The relationship is $h = 0.8x - 0.004x^2$.

Consider the following questions:

1 Can the officials use this relationship to determine where Karrie's ball would have landed?

2 Would her ball have cleared the lake if it did not hit the power line?

A   COMMON FACTORS

Numbers can be expressed as products of **factors**. A **prime number** has only two different factors, the number itself and 1. Some prime numbers are 2, 3, 5, 7, 11, ...

1 is not a prime number.

Factors that are prime numbers are called **prime factors**. Prime factors of any number can be found by repeated division.

For example:

$$2 \mid \underline{24}$$
$$2 \mid \underline{12} \qquad \therefore \quad 24 = 2 \times 2 \times 2 \times 3$$
$$2 \mid \underline{6}$$
$$3 \mid \underline{3}$$
$$ 1$$

$$2 \mid \underline{42}$$
$$3 \mid \underline{21} \qquad \therefore \quad 42 = 2 \times 3 \times 7$$
$$7 \mid \underline{7}$$
$$ 1$$

COMMON FACTORS AND HCF

Notice that 2 and 3 are factors of both 24 and 42. They are called **common factors**. Obviously, (2×3) or 6 would be a common factor as well.

> **Common factors** are numbers that are factors of two or more numbers.
>
> The **highest common factor (HCF)** is the largest factor that is common to two or more numbers.

To find the highest common factor of a group of numbers it is often best to express the numbers as products of prime factors. Then the common prime factors can be found and multiplied to give the HCF.

Example 1	◀ Self Tutor

Find the highest common factor of 36 and 81.

$$2 \mid \underline{36}$$
$$2 \mid \underline{18} \qquad \therefore \quad 36 = 2 \times 2 \times 3 \times 3$$
$$3 \mid \underline{9}$$
$$3 \mid \underline{3}$$
$$ 1$$

$$3 \mid \underline{81}$$
$$3 \mid \underline{27} \qquad \therefore \quad 81 = 3 \times 3 \times 3 \times 3$$
$$3 \mid \underline{9}$$
$$3 \mid \underline{3}$$
$$ 1$$

$$\therefore \quad \text{HCF} = 3 \times 3 = 9$$

EXERCISE 8A

1   Find the highest common factor of:

    a   81 and 63   **b**   25 and 40   **c**   24 and 36

    d   90 and 120   **e**   49 and 112   **f**   72 and 108

Algebraic products are made up of factors just as numbers have factors. It is also possible to find the **highest common factor** of a group of algebraic products.

2   Find the missing factor:

    a $2 \times \square = 4a$ **b** $3 \times \square = 6b$ **c** $4 \times \square = 8xy$

    d $2x \times \square = 6x^2$ **e** $\square \times 2x = 2x^2$ **f** $\square \times 3x = -6x^2$

    g $-a \times \square = ab$ **h** $\square \times a^2 = 2a^3$ **i** $4x \times \square = -8x^2y$

Example 2

Find the highest common factor of:

a $8a$ and $12b$

b $4x^2$ and $6xy$

> Write each term as a product of its **factors**!

a $8a = 2 \times 2 \times 2 \times a$
     $12b = 2 \times 2 \times 3 \times b$
     $\therefore \ \text{HCF} = 2 \times 2$
     $= 4$

b $4x^2 = 2 \times 2 \times x \times x$
     $6xy = 2 \times 3 \times x \times y$
     $\therefore \ \text{HCF} = 2 \times x$
     $= 2x$

3   Find the highest common factor of the following:

a $2a$ and 4

b $2c$ and $5c$

c $8r$ and 25

d $10k$ and $7k$

e $4a$ and $12a$

f $3n$ and $9n$

g $15x$ and $10x$

h $16y$ and $24y$

i $45d$ and $81d$

4   Find the HCF of the following:

a $17st$ and $13ts$

b abc and $2abc$

c $36cd$ and $12c$

d a^2 and a

e $5r$ and r^3

f $2q$ and qr

g $3d$ and $6d^2$

h dp^2 and pd

i $4r$ and $8r^2$

j $3pq$ and $6pq^2$

k $2a^2b$ and $4ab$

l $6xy$ and $12x^2y^2$

m $15f$, $20fg$ and $25g$

n $12wxz$, $12wz$, $24wxyz$

o $18p^2qr$, $24pqr^2$

ACTIVITY   ALGEBRAIC COMMON FACTOR MAZE

To find your way through this maze, follow the instructions below. After you have completed the maze you may like to construct your own maze for a friend to follow.

Instructions:

1   You are permitted to move horizontally or vertically but **not** diagonally.

2   Start at the starting term, 12. A move to the next cell is only possible if that cell has a factor (other than 1) in common with the one you are presently on.

$6m$	$2a$	3	$9c^2$	$3c$	c^2	8	$2p^2$	
$4m$	mn	$6n$	$5c$	25	$5m$	12	$4p$	
$8y$	xy	2	$6a$	$5a$	mn	$6n^2$	7	
$7y$	21	$3z$	$5x$	$3y$	y^2	$3p$	p	EXIT
ab	$7a$	yz	xy	$15x$	xy	p^2	7	
17	pq	$3q$	q^2	63	$7b$	b^2	6	
START 12	5	10	$10b$	12	y^2	$9b$	$3b$	
$6a$	a^2	$5a$	$3a$	$4x$	xy	$2x$	x^2	

3   Try to get to the exit following the rules above.

Example 3	◀ **Self Tutor**

Find the HCF of $3(x+3)$ and $(x+3)(x+1)$.

$$3(x+3) = 3 \times (x+3) \qquad\qquad (x+3)(x+1) = (x+3) \times (x+1)$$

$$\therefore \ \ \text{HCF} = (x+3)$$

5 Find the HCF of:

    a $2(x+2)$ and $(x+3)(x+2)$ **b** $2(x+5)^2$ and $4(x+1)(x+5)$

    c $3x(x+1)$ and $x^2(x+2)$ **d** $6(x+1)^2$ and $3(x+1)(x+4)$

    e $2(x+3)^2$ and $4(x+3)(x-5)$ **f** $4x(x-2)$ and $6x(x-2)^2$

B   FACTORISING WITH COMMON FACTORS

Factorisation is the process of writing an expression as a **product** of its **factors**.
Factorisation is the reverse process of expansion.

In **expansions** we have to *remove brackets*, whereas in **factorisation** we have to *insert brackets*.

Notice that $3(x+2)$ is the *product of two factors*, 3 and $x+2$.

The brackets are essential as: $3(x+2)$ multiplies 3 by the whole of $x+2$,   whereas in
$3x+2$ only the x is multiplied by 3.

is **expansion**

$$3(x+2) = 3x + 6$$

is **factorisation**

To factorise an algebraic expression involving a number of terms we look for the HCF of
the terms and write it down in front of a set of brackets. We then find the contents of the
brackets.

For example, $5x^2$ and $10xy$ have HCF of $5x$.

$$\text{So,} \quad 5x^2 + 10xy = 5x \times x \ + \ 5x \times 2y$$
$$= 5x(x+2y)$$

FACTORISE FULLY

Notice that $4a+12 = 2(2a+6)$ is not fully factorised as $(2a+6)$ still has a common
factor of 2 which could be removed. Although 2 is a common factor it is not the HCF. The
HCF is 4 and so

$$4a+12 = 4(a+3) \quad \text{is fully factorised.}$$

Note: All factorisations can be checked by expansion.

Example 4 ◄)) **Self Tutor**

Fully factorise: **a** $3a + 6$ **b** $ab - 2bc$

a $3a + 6$	**b** $ab - 2bc$
$= 3 \times a + 3 \times 2$	$= a \times b - 2 \times b \times c$
$= 3(a + 2)$ {HCF is 3}	$= b(a - 2c)$ {HCF is b}

With practice the middle line is not necessary.

EXERCISE 8B

1 Copy and complete:

a $3x + 6 = 3(x + ...)$ **b** $4a - 12 = 4(a - ...)$

c $20 - 5p = 5(... - p)$ **d** $16x + 12 = 4(... + 3)$

e $3x^2 - 9x = 3x(x - ...)$ **f** $2m + 8m^2 = 2m(... + 4m)$

2 Copy and complete:

a $4x + 12 = 4(... + ...)$ **b** $9 + 3d = 3(... + ...)$

c $3c - 3 = 3(... - ...)$ **d** $cd + de = d(... ...)$

e $6a + 8ab = ...(3 + 4b)$ **f** $4x - 2x^2 = ...(2 - x)$

g $4ab - 4a = ...(b - 1)$ **h** $4ab - 6bc = ...(2a - 3c)$

3 Fully factorise:

a $5a + 5b$	**b** $2x - 4$	**c** $7d + 14$	**d** $21 - 14x$
e $6x - 12$	**f** $12 + 3x$	**g** $ac + bc$	**h** $12y - 6a$
i $2a + ab$	**j** $bc - 3cd$	**k** $2x - xy$	**l** $xy + y$
m $a + ab$	**n** $ab - bc$	**o** $2an + ab$	**p** $ab - a$

Remember to check your factorisations by expanding back out!

Example 5 ◄)) **Self Tutor**

Fully factorise: **a** $8x^2 + 12x$ **b** $3y^2 - 6xy$

a $8x^2 + 12x$	**b** $3y^2 - 6xy$
$= 2 \times 4 \times x \times x + 3 \times 4 \times x$	$= 3 \times y \times y - 2 \times 3 \times x \times y$
$= 4x(2x + 3)$ {HCF is $4x$}	$= 3y(y - 2x)$ {HCF is $3y$}

4 Fully factorise:

a $x^2 + 5x$	**b** $7x - 2x^2$	**c** $3x^2 + 6x$
d $9x - 3x^2$	**e** $4x^2 + 12x$	**f** $x^3 + 2x^2$
g $x^2y + xy^2$	**h** $2x^3 - 4x^2$	**i** $2x^3 - 8xy$
j $a^3 + a^2 + a$	**k** $3a^2 + 6a + 9$	**l** $3a^3 - 6a^2 + 9a$

Example 6   ◀️ **Self Tutor**

Fully factorise: $-2a + 6ab$

$-2a + 6ab$
$= 6ab - 2a$ {Rewrite with $6ab$ first. Why?}
$= 2 \times 3 \times a \times b \ - \ 2 \times a$
$= 2a(3b - 1)$ {as $2a$ is the HCF}

5 Fully factorise:

a $-2a + 2b$	**b** $-3 + 6b$	**c** $-4a + 8b$
d $-3c + cd$	**e** $-a + ab$	**f** $-7x^2 + 14x$
g $-6x + 12x^2$	**h** $-4b^2 + 2ab$	**i** $-a + a^2$

Example 7   ◀️ **Self Tutor**

Fully factorise: $-2x^2 - 4x$

$-2x^2 - 4x$
$= -2 \times x \times x + -2 \times 2 \times x$
$= -2x(x + 2)$ {as HCF is $-2x$}

6 Fully factorise:

a $-3a - 3b$	**b** $-4 - 8x$	**c** $-3y - 6b$
d $-5c - cd$	**e** $-x - xy$	**f** $-5x^2 - 10x$
g $-4y - 12y^2$	**h** $-6a^2 - 3ab$	**i** $-8x^2 - 24x$

Example 8   ◀️ **Self Tutor**

Fully factorise:
  a $2(x + 3) + x(x + 3)$ **b** $x(x + 4) - (x + 4)$

a $2(x + 3) + x(x + 3)$ has HCF of $(x + 3)$
$= (x + 3)(2 + x)$

b $x(x + 4) - (x + 4)$
$= x(x + 4) - 1(x + 4)$ has HCF of $(x + 4)$
$= (x + 4)(x - 1)$

7 Fully factorise:

a $4(x + 7) + x(x + 7)$	**b** $5(x - 3) + a(x - 3)$
c $3(x + 2) - x(x + 2)$	**d** $x(x + 7) + (x + 7)$

e $a(b+3) - (b+3)$ f $a(b+c) + d(b+c)$

g $a(m+n) - b(m+n)$ h $x(x+2) - x - 2$

Notice the use of square brackets in the second line.

Example 9   ◄)) Self Tutor

Fully factorise $(x-1)(x+2) + 3(x-1)$

$(x-1)(x+2) + 3(x-1)$
$= (x-1)[(x+2) + 3]$ has HCF of $(x-1)$
$= (x-1)(x+5)$

8   Fully factorise:

a $(x+3)(x+5) + 2(x+3)$ b $5(x+7) + (x+7)(x+2)$

c $(x+6)(x-4) - 7(x+6)$ d $(x-2)^2 - 3(x-2)$

e $(x+2)^2 + (x+2)(x+1)$ f $3(a+b) - (a+b)(a-1)$

g $3(a+2)^2 - 6(a+2)$ h $(x+4)^2 - 2(x+4)(x-1)$

i $x(x+1) - 2(x+1)(x-5)$ j $2(x+3) - 4(x+3)^2$

C   DIFFERENCE OF TWO SQUARES FACTORISATION

On expanding, $(a+b)(a-b) = a^2 - ab + ab - b^2$ {using FOIL}
$= a^2 - b^2$

So, $$a^2 - b^2 = (a+b)(a-b)$$

Note: The two terms a^2 and b^2 are subtracted, so we call this "**the difference of two squares**".

Example 10   ◄)) Self Tutor

Fully factorise:

a $x^2 - 4$ b $1 - 25y^2$

a $x^2 - 4$ b $1 - 25y^2$
$= x^2 - 2^2$ $= 1^2 - (5y)^2$
$= (x+2)(x-2)$ $= (1+5y)(1-5y)$

Write each term as a square.

EXERCISE 8C

1   Fully factorise:

a $c^2 - d^2$ b $m^2 - n^2$ c $n^2 - m^2$ d $m^2 - x^2$

e $x^2 - 16$ f $x^2 - 81$ g $a^2 - 9$ h $4x^2 - 1$

i $4x^2 - 9$ j $9y^2 - 25$ k $64 - x^2$ l $16 - 9a^2$

Example 11   ◀》 **Self Tutor**

Fully factorise:

a $2x^2 - 18$ b $x^3 - xy^2$

a $2x^2 - 18$ b $x^3 - xy^2$
  $= 2(x^2 - 9)$ $= x(x^2 - y^2)$
  $= 2(x+3)(x-3)$ $= x(x+y)(x-y)$

When factorising,
always look for
common factors first.

2   Fully factorise:

    a $3x^2 - 12$ b $8x^2 - 72$ c $2a^2 - 50$ d $4x^2 - 25$

    e $9b^2 - 900$ f $3b^2 - 48$ g $\pi R^2 - \pi r^2$ h $10 - 10x^2$

    i $p^3 - 4p$ j $x^3 - x$ k $x^4 - x^2$ l $x^3y - xy^3$

Example 12   ◀》 **Self Tutor**

Fully factorise:

a $4a^2 - 9b^2$ b $x^2y^2 - 16$

a $4a^2 - 9b^2$ b $x^2y^2 - 16$
  $= (2a)^2 - (3b)^2$ $= (xy)^2 - 4^2$
  $= (2a+3b)(2a-3b)$ $= (xy+4)(xy-4)$

3   Fully factorise:

    a $49a^2 - b^2$ b $y^2 - 36x^2$ c $9x^2 - 25y^2$ d $9a^2 - 16b^2$

    e $a^2 - 81b^2$ f $a^2b^2 - 4$ g $36x^2 - p^2q^2$ h $16a^2 - 25b^2c^2$

Notice the use of
the square brackets.

EXTENSION

Example 13   ◀》 **Self Tutor**

Fully factorise:

a $(x+2)^2 - 9$ b $25 - (x-2)^2$

a $(x+2)^2 - 9$ b $25 - (x-2)^2$
  $= (x+2)^2 - 3^2$ $= 5^2 - (x-2)^2$
  $= [(x+2)+3][(x+2)-3]$ $= [5+(x-2)][5-(x-2)]$
  $= [x+2+3][x+2-3]$ $= [5+x-2][5-x+2]$
  $= (x+5)(x-1)$ $= (x+3)(7-x)$

4 Fully factorise:

a $(x+3)^2 - 4$ **b** $(x-2)^2 - 25$ **c** $16 - (x+1)^2$

d $36 - (x-3)^2$ **e** $(x+4)^2 - 1$ **f** $1 - (x-4)^2$

g $4(x+1)^2 - 9$ **h** $81 - 16(x+1)^2$ **i** $(x+2)^2 - 9(x-1)^2$

j $4(x-5)^2 - (x-1)^2$ **k** $9x^2 - (x+2)^2$ **l** $4(x+1)^2 - (2-x)^2$

D   PERFECT SQUARES FACTORISATION

Recall that

$$(a+b)^2$$
$$= (a+b)(a+b)$$
$$= a^2 + ab + ab + b^2$$
$$= a^2 + 2ab + b^2$$

and

$$(a-b)^2$$
$$= (a-b)(a-b)$$
$$= a^2 - ab - ab + b^2$$
$$= a^2 - 2ab + b^2$$

Expressions such as $a^2 + 2ab + b^2$ and $a^2 - 2ab + b^2$ are called **perfect squares** because they factorise into two identical factors (a factor squared),

i.e., $$a^2 + 2ab + b^2 = (a+b)^2$$

and $$a^2 - 2ab + b^2 = (a-b)^2.$$

For example, $x^2 + 6x + 9$ and $x^2 - 6x + 9$ are perfect squares because they factorise into two identical factors.

$$x^2 + 6x + 9 = (x+3)^2 \quad \text{and} \quad x^2 - 6x + 9 = (x-3)^2$$

You can check this for yourself by expanding $(x+3)^2$ and $(x-3)^2$.

IDENTIFYING PERFECT SQUARES

Notice that $(a+b)^2 = a^2 + 2ab + b^2$ and $(a-b)^2 = a^2 - 2ab + b^2$.

         └─ squares ─┘   └─ squares ─┘

So, when we expand a perfect square $(a \pm b)^2$ we get **two squares** and a **middle term** of $\pm 2ab$.

For example, $x^2 + 10x + 25$ and $x^2 - 10x + 25$

$$= x^2 + 2 \times 5 \times x + 5^2 \qquad = x^2 - 2 \times 5 \times x + 5^2$$
$$= (x+5)^2 \qquad\qquad\qquad = (x-5)^2$$

How can we detect that $x^2 + 6x + 9$ is a perfect square whereas $x^2 + 6x + 8$ is not?

$x^2 + 6x + 9$ contains two squares x^2 and 3^2 and a middle term $2 \times 3 \times x$.

$x^2 + 6x + 8$ does not satisfy these conditions.

Example 14	◀⑴ **Self Tutor**

Find all perfect squares of the form:

a $x^2 + \square + 25$ **b** $4x^2 + \square + 9$

a For $x^2 + \square + 25$,

i.e., $x^2 + \square + 5^2$ $a = x$, $b = 5$ {compare with $(a+b)^2 = a^2 + 2ab + b^2$}

$\therefore$ $2ab = 2 \times x \times 5 = 10x$ and so $-2ab = -10x$

$\therefore$ perfect squares are $x^2 + 10x + 25$ and $x^2 - 10x + 25$.

b For $4x^2 + \square + 9$,

i.e., $(2x)^2 + \square + 3^2$ $a = 2x$, $b = 3$ {compare with $(a+b)^2 = a^2 + 2ab + b^2$}

$\therefore$ $2ab = 2 \times 2x \times 3 = 12x$ and so $-2ab = -12x$

$\therefore$ perfect squares are $4x^2 + 12x + 9$ and $4x^2 - 12x + 9$.

EXERCISE 8D

1 Find all perfect squares of the form:

a $x^2 + \square + 1$	**b** $x^2 + \square + 4$	**c** $x^2 + \square + 16$
d $4x^2 + \square + 1$	**e** $9x^2 + \square + 4$	**f** $16x^2 + \square + 81$
g $4x^2 + \square + c^2$	**h** $x^2 + \square + 4d^2$	**i** $a^2c^2 + \square + 4$

Example 15	◀)) Self Tutor

Factorise:

a $x^2 + 20x + 100$ **b** $x^2 - 8x + 16$

a $x^2 + 20x + 100$

$= x^2 + 2 \times x \times 10 + 10^2$

$= (x + 10)^2$

b $x^2 - 8x + 16$

$= x^2 - 2 \times x \times 4 + 4^2$

$= (x - 4)^2$

2 Factorise:

a $x^2 + 2x + 1$	**b** $x^2 - 4x + 4$	**c** $x^2 - 6x + 9$
d $x^2 + 10x + 25$	**e** $x^2 - 16x + 64$	**f** $x^2 + 20x + 100$
g $x^2 - 12x + 36$	**h** $x^2 + 14x + 49$	**i** $x^2 - 18x + 81$

Example 16	◀)) Self Tutor

Factorise:

a $16x^2 + 24x + 9$ **b** $4x^2 - 20x + 25$

a $16x^2 + 24x + 9$

$= (4x)^2 + 2 \times 4x \times 3 + 3^2$

$= (4x + 3)^2$

b $4x^2 - 20x + 25$

$= (2x)^2 - 2 \times 2x \times 5 + 5^2$

$= (2x - 5)^2$

3 Factorise:

a $4x^2 + 4x + 1$	**b** $16x^2 - 40x + 25$	**c** $4x^2 + 28x + 49$
d $4x^2 - 12x + 9$	**e** $9x^2 + 6x + 1$	**f** $9x^2 - 30x + 25$

Example 17   ◀ϡ **Self Tutor**

Fully factorise:

a $3x^2 - 18x + 27$ b $-2x^2 + 8x - 8$

a $3x^2 - 18x + 27$
= $3(x^2 - 6x + 9)$
= $3(x^2 - 2 \times x \times 3 + 3^2)$
= $3(x - 3)^2$

b $-2x^2 + 8x - 8$
= $-2(x^2 - 4x + 4)$
= $-2[x^2 - 2 \times x \times 2 + 2^2]$
= $-2(x - 2)^2$

4   Fully factorise (removing a common factor wherever possible):

a $2x^2 + 4x + 2$ b $2x^2 - 12x + 18$ c $3x^2 + 30x + 75$

d $-x^2 + 6x - 9$ e $-x^2 - 8x - 16$ f $-x^2 + 16x - 64$

g $-2x^2 + 40x - 200$ h $-4b^2 + 28b - 49$ i $ax^2 - 10ax + 25a$

E   FACTORISING EXPRESSIONS WITH FOUR TERMS

Some four-termed expressions do not have an overall common factor, but can be factorised by pairing the four terms.

For example, $\underbrace{ab + ac} + \underbrace{bd + cd}$

= $a(b + c) + d(b + c)$ {factorising each pair separately}

= $(b + c)(a + d)$ {removing common factor $(b + c)$}

Note: •   Many 4-termed expressions cannot be factorised using the above technique.
           •   Sometimes it is necessary to reorder the terms before using the above method.

Example 18   ◀ϡ **Self Tutor**

Factorise:

a $3ab + d + 3ad + b$ b $x^2 + 2x + 5x + 10$

a $3ab + d + 3ad + b$
= $\underbrace{3ab + b} + \underbrace{3ad + d}$ {reorder}
= $b(3a + 1) + d(3a + 1)$
= $(3a + 1)(b + d)$

b $\underbrace{x^2 + 2x} + \underbrace{5x + 10}$
= $x(x + 2) + 5(x + 2)$
= $(x + 2)(x + 5)$

EXERCISE 8E

1   Factorise:

a $2a + 2 + ab + b$ b $4d + ac + ad + 4c$ c $ab + 6 + 2b + 3a$

d $mn + 3p + np + 3m$ e $x^2 + 3x + 7x + 21$ f $x^2 + 5x + 4x + 20$

g $2x^2 + x + 6x + 3$ h $3x^2 + 2x + 12x + 8$ i $20x^2 + 12x + 5x + 3$

Example 19   ◀) **Self Tutor**

Factorise:

a $x^2 + 3x - 4x - 12$ b $x^2 + 3x - x - 3$

a $\underbrace{x^2 + 3x}\ \underbrace{- 4x - 12}$

$= x(x+3)\ -\ 4(x+3)$

$= (x+3)(x-4)$

b $\underbrace{x^2 + 3x}\underbrace{- x - 3}$

$= x(x+3)\ -\ (x+3)$

$= x(x+3)\ -\ 1(x+3)$

$= (x+3)(x-1)$

2 Factorise:

a $x^2 - 4x + 5x - 20$ b $x^2 - 7x + 2x - 14$ c $x^2 - 3x - 2x + 6$

d $x^2 - 5x - 3x + 15$ e $x^2 + 7x - 8x - 56$ f $2x^2 + x - 6x - 3$

g $3x^2 + 2x - 12x - 8$ h $4x^2 - 3x - 8x + 6$ i $9x^2 + 2x - 9x - 2$

F   FACTORISING QUADRATIC TRINOMIALS

A **quadratic trinomial** is an algebraic expression of the form $ax^2 + bx + c$ where x is a variable and a, b, c are constants where $a \neq 0$.

Consider the expansion of the product $(x+2)(x+5)$:

$(x+2)(x+5)$

$= x^2 + 5x + 2x + 2 \times 5$ {using FOIL}

$= x^2 + [5+2]x + [2 \times 5]$

$= x^2 + [\textbf{sum of 2 and 5}]x + [\textbf{product of 2 and 5}]$

$= x^2 + 7x + 10$

This shows that, if we want to factorise a quadratic trinomial such as $x^2 + 7x + 10$ into $(x + ...)(x + ...)$ we must find two numbers (to go into the vacant places) which have a *sum* of 7 and a *product* of 10.

In the general case, $x^2\ +\ \ (\boldsymbol{\alpha + \beta})\boldsymbol{x}\ \ +\ \ \ \boldsymbol{\alpha\beta}\ \ \ = (x+\alpha)(x+\beta)$

the coefficient   the constant term
of x is the **sum**   is the **product** of
of α and β α and β

EXERCISE 8F

1 Find two numbers which have:

a   product 12 and sum 7   b   product 15 and sum 8

c   product 16 and sum 10   d   product 18 and sum 11

e   product −21 and sum 4   f   product −21 and sum −4

g   product −12 and sum −4   h   product −30 and sum 13

Example 20   ◀)) Self Tutor

Factorise: $x^2 + 11x + 24$

We need to find two numbers which have sum $= 11$, product $= 24$.
Pairs of factors of 24:

Factor product	1×24	2×12	3×8	4×6
Factor sum	25	14	11	10

↑
this one

The numbers we want are 3 and 8.

So, $x^2 + 11x + 24$
$$= (x+3)(x+8)$$

Most of the time we can find these two numbers mentally.

Note: Only the last two lines of this example need to be shown in your working.

2 Factorise:

a $x^2 + 4x + 3$ b $x^2 + 11x + 24$ c $x^2 + 10x + 21$

d $x^2 + 15x + 54$ e $x^2 + 9x + 20$ f $x^2 + 8x + 15$

g $x^2 + 10x + 24$ h $x^2 + 9x + 14$ i $x^2 + 6x + 8$

Example 21   ◀)) Self Tutor

Factorise: $x^2 - 7x + 12$

sum $= -7$ and   product $= 12$

∴   numbers are -3 and -4

So, $x^2 - 7x + 12$
$$= (x-3)(x-4)$$

As the sum is negative but the product is positive, both numbers must be negative.

3 Factorise:

a $x^2 - 3x + 2$ b $x^2 - 4x + 3$ c $x^2 - 5x + 6$

d $x^2 - 14x + 33$ e $x^2 - 16x + 39$ f $x^2 - 19x + 48$

g $x^2 - 11x + 28$ h $x^2 - 14x + 24$ i $x^2 - 20x + 36$

Example 22   🔊 **Self Tutor**

Factorise: **a** $x^2 - 2x - 15$ **b** $x^2 + x - 6$

a   sum $= -2$ and product $= -15$

∴   numbers are -5 and $+3$

So, $x^2 - 2x - 15$
$= (x - 5)(x + 3)$

b   sum $= 1$ and   product $= -6$

∴   numbers are $+3$ and -2

So, $x^2 + x - 6$
$= (x + 3)(x - 2)$

As the product is negative, the numbers are opposite in sign.

4 Factorise:

a $x^2 - 7x - 8$ **b** $x^2 + 4x - 21$ **c** $x^2 - x - 2$

d $x^2 - 2x - 8$ **e** $x^2 + 5x - 24$ **f** $x^2 - 3x - 10$

g $x^2 + 3x - 54$ **h** $x^2 + x - 72$ **i** $x^2 - 4x - 21$

j $x^2 - x - 6$ **k** $x^2 - 7x - 60$ **l** $x^2 + 7x - 60$

Example 23   🔊 **Self Tutor**

Fully factorise by first removing a common factor: $3x^2 + 6x - 72$

$3x^2 + 6x - 72$ {first look for a **common factor**}
$= 3(x^2 + 2x - 24)$ {sum $= 2$,   product $= -24$ i.e., 6 and -4}
$= 3(x + 6)(x - 4)$

5 Fully factorise by first removing a common factor:

a $2x^2 + 10x + 8$ **b** $3x^2 - 21x + 18$ **c** $2x^2 + 14x + 24$

d $2x^2 - 44x + 240$ **e** $4x^2 - 8x - 12$ **f** $3x^2 - 42x + 99$

g $2x^2 - 2x - 180$ **h** $3x^2 - 6x - 24$ **i** $2x^2 + 18x + 40$

j $x^3 - 7x^2 - 8x$ **k** $x^3 - 3x^2 - 28x$ **l** $x^4 + 2x^3 + x^2$

Example 24　　　　　　　　　　　　　　　　　　　　◄⬤ **Self Tutor**

Fully factorise by first removing a common factor: $77 + 4x - x^2$

$$77 + 4x - x^2$$
$$= -x^2 + 4x + 77 \qquad \text{\{rewrite in descending powers of } x\text{\}}$$
$$= -1(x^2 - 4x - 77) \qquad \text{\{remove } -1 \text{ as a common factor\}}$$
$$= -(x - 11)(x + 7) \qquad \text{\{sum } = -4, \text{ product } = -77 \text{ i.e., } -11 \text{ and } 7\text{\}}$$

6　Fully factorise:

 a $-x^2 - 3x + 54$ **b** $-x^2 - 7x - 10$ **c** $-x^2 - 10x - 21$

 d $4x - x^2 - 3$ **e** $-4 + 4x - x^2$ **f** $3 - x^2 - 2x$

 g $-2x^2 + 4x + 126$ **h** $20x - 2x^2 - 50$ **i** $-x^3 + x^2 + 2x$

G　　MISCELLANEOUS FACTORISATION

The following flowchart may prove useful:

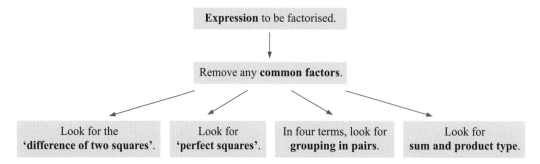

EXERCISE 8G.1

1　Fully factorise:

 a $3x^2 + 2x$ **b** $x^2 - 81$ **c** $2p^2 + 8$

 d $3b^2 - 75$ **e** $2x^2 - 32$ **f** $n^4 - 4n^2$

 g $x^2 - 8x - 9$ **h** $d^2 + 6d - 7$ **i** $x^2 + 8x - 9$

 j $4t + 8t^2$ **k** $3x^2 - 108$ **l** $2g^2 - 12g - 110$

 m $4a^2 - 9d^2$ **n** $5a^2 - 5a - 10$ **o** $2c^2 - 8c + 6$

 p $x^4 - x^2$ **q** $d^4 + 2d^3 - 3d^2$ **r** $x^3 + 4x^2 + 4x$

2　Find the pattern in the following expressions and factorise:

 a $x^2 - 6x + 9$ **b** $x^2 - 121$ **c** $x^2 - 2x + 1$

 d $y^2 + 10y + 25$ **e** $x^2 + 22x + 121$ **f** $x^2 - 2xy + y^2$

 g $1 - x^2$ **h** $25y^2 - 1$ **i** $49y^2 - 36z^2$

 j $4d^2 + 28d + 49$ **k** $4ab^2 - ac^2$ **l** $2\pi R^2 - 2\pi r^2$

3 Fully factorise:

a $ab + ac - 2a$	**b** $a^2b^2 - 2ab$	**c** $18x - 2x^3$
d $x^2 + 14x + 49$	**e** $4a^3 - 4ab^2$	**f** $x^3y - 4xy$
g $4x^4 - 4x^2$	**h** $(x-2)y - (x-2)z$	**i** $(x+1)a + (x+1)b$
j $(x-y)a + (x-y)$	**k** $x(x+2) + 3(x+2)$	**l** $x^3 + x^2 + x + 1$

4 Factorise completely:

a $7x - 35y$	**b** $2g^2 - 8$	**c** $-5x^2 - 10x$
d $m^2 + 3mp$	**e** $a^2 + 8a + 15$	**f** $m^2 - 6m + 9$
g $5x^2 + 5xy - 5x^2y$	**h** $xy + 2x + 2y + 4$	**i** $y^2 + 5y - 9y - 45$
j $2x^2 + 10x + x + 5$	**k** $3y^2 - 147$	**l** $3p^2 - 3q^2$
m $4c^2 - 1$	**n** $3x^2 + 3x - 36$	**o** $2bx - 6b + 10x - 30$

5 Fully factorise:

a $12 - 11x - x^2$	**b** $-2x^2 - 6 + 8x$	**c** $14 - x^2 - 5x$
d $4x^2 - 2x^3 - 2x$	**e** $(a+b)^2 - 9$	**f** $(x+2)^2 - 4$

INVESTIGATION   FACTORISATION BY SPLITTING THE MIDDLE TERM

Consider $(2x + 3)(4x + 5)$

$= 8x^2 + 10x + 12x + 15$ {using FOIL}

$= 8x^2 + 22x + 15$

In reverse, $8x^2 + 22x + 15$

$= \underline{8x^2 + 10x} + \underline{12x + 15}$

$= 2x(4x + 5) + 3(4x + 5)$

$= (4x + 5)(2x + 3)$

So, we can factorise, $8x^2 + 22x + 15$ into $(2x + 3)(4x + 5)$ if we can split the $22x$ into a suitable sum, in this case $+ 10x + 12x$.

To do the splitting, we look at the expansion in greater detail.

Now $(2x + 3)(4x + 5) = 2 \times 4 \times x^2 + [2 \times 5 + 3 \times 4]x + 3 \times 5$.

Notice that the four numbers: 2, 3, 4 and 5, are present in the *middle term*, and the *first* and *last* terms combined.

As 2×5 and 3×4 are factors of $2 \times 3 \times 4 \times 5 = 120$ this gives us the method for performing the splitting.

Step 1: Multiply the coefficient of x and the constant term.   In our case, $8 \times 15 = 120$.

Step 2: Look for the factors of this number which add to make the coefficient of the middle term.   What factors of 120 when added give us 22? These are: 10 and 12.

Step 3: These numbers are the coefficients of the split terms.   So, the split is $10x + 12x$

Consider another example, $6x^2 + 17x + 12$.

The *product* of the *coefficient of x^2* and the *constant term* is $6 \times 12 = 72$.

We now try to find the factors of 72 with *sum* of 17.   These numbers are: 8 and 9.

So, $6x^2 + 17x + 12$

$= \underbrace{6x^2 + 8x} + \underbrace{9x + 12}$ {$17x$ has been split into $8x$ and $9x$}

$= 2x(3x + 4) + 3(3x + 4)$

$= (3x + 4)(2x + 3)$

or $6x^2 + 17x + 12$

$= \underbrace{6x^2 + 9x} + \underbrace{8x + 12}$

$= 3x(2x + 3) + 4(2x + 3)$

$= (2x + 3)(3x + 4)$

Note: When splitting the middle term it does not matter the order in which you list the two new terms.

What to do:

1 For the following quadratics, copy and complete the table below:

	quadratic	product	sum	'split'
e.g.	$10x^2 + 29x + 21$	210	29	$14x + 15x$
a	$2x^2 + 11x + 12$			
b	$3x^2 + 14x + 8$			
c	$4x^2 + 16x + 15$			
d	$6x^2 - 5x - 6$			
e	$4x^2 - 13x + 3$			
f	$6x^2 - 17x + 5$			

2   Use your tabled results above to factorise each of the quadratics **a** to **f**.

EXERCISE 8G.2

1 Fully factorise:

   a $2x^2 + 5x + 3$ **b** $2x^2 + 7x + 5$ **c** $7x^2 + 9x + 2$

   d $3x^2 + 7x + 4$ **e** $3x^2 + 13x + 4$ **f** $3x^2 + 8x + 4$

   g $8x^2 + 14x + 3$ **h** $21x^2 + 17x + 2$ **i** $6x^2 + 5x + 1$

   j $6x^2 + 19x + 3$ **k** $10x^2 + 17x + 3$ **l** $14x^2 + 37x + 5$

2 Fully factorise:

   a $2x^2 - 9x - 5$ **b** $3x^2 + 5x - 2$ **c** $3x^2 - 5x - 2$

   d $2x^2 + 3x - 2$ **e** $2x^2 + 3x - 5$ **f** $5x^2 - 14x - 3$

   g $5x^2 - 8x + 3$ **h** $11x^2 - 9x - 2$ **i** $3x^2 - 7x - 6$

   j $2x^2 - 3x - 9$ **k** $3x^2 - 17x + 10$ **l** $5x^2 - 13x - 6$

   m $3x^2 + 10x - 8$ **n** $2x^2 + 17x - 9$ **o** $2x^2 + 9x - 18$

   p $2x^2 + 11x - 21$ **q** $15x^2 + x - 2$ **r** $21x^2 - 62x - 3$

3 Fully factorise:

a	$15x^2 + 19x + 6$	b	$15x^2 + x - 6$	c	$15x^2 - x - 6$
d	$30x^2 - 38x + 12$	e	$18x^2 - 12x + 2$	f	$48x^2 + 72x + 27$
g	$16x^2 + 12x + 2$	h	$16x^2 + 4x - 2$	i	$40x^2 - 5x - 5$
j	$32x^2 - 24x + 4$	k	$25x^2 + 25x + 6$	l	$25x^2 - 25x + 6$
m	$25x^2 - 10x - 8$	n	$25x^2 - 149x - 6$	o	$36x^2 + 24x - 5$
p	$36x^2 + 11x - 5$	q	$36x^2 + 9x - 10$	r	$36x^2 + 52x - 3$

REVIEW SET 8A

1 Find the HCF of:

    a $3a^2b$ and $6ab$ b $3(x + 1)$ and $6(x + 1)^2$

2 Fully factorise:

    a $x^2 - 3x$ b $3mn + 6n^2$

3 Fully factorise:

    a $d(t + 2) - 4(t + 2)$ b $3x + 7 + 6bx + 14b$

4 Fully factorise:

    a $9 - 16x^2$ b $x^2 - 12x + 36$

5 Fully factorise: $5x - 5 + xy - y$

6 Fully factorise:

a	$x^2 + 10x + 21$	b	$x^2 + 4x - 21$	c	$x^2 - 4x - 21$
d	$6 - 5x + x^2$	e	$4x^2 - 8x - 12$	f	$-x^2 - 13x - 36$

7 Fully factorise:

a	$8x^2 + 22x + 15$	b	$12x^2 - 20x + 3$	c	$12x^2 - 7x - 10$

REVIEW SET 8B

1 Find the HCF of:

    a $6y^2$ and $8y$ b $4(x - 2)$ and $2(x - 2)(x + 3)$

2 Fully factorise:

    a $2x^2 + 6x$ b $-2xy - 4x$

3 Fully factorise:

    a $p(a + 2) - q(a + 2)$ b $xy + 2x + y + 2$

4 Fully factorise:

    a $2x^2 - 50$ b $4x^2 + 20x + 25$

5 Fully factorise: $2xy - z - 2xz + y$

6 Fully factorise:

    a $x^2 + 12x + 35$ **b** $x^2 + 2x - 35$ **c** $x^2 - 12x + 35$

    d $2x^2 - 4x - 70$ **e** $30 - 11x + x^2$ **f** $-x^2 + 12x - 20$

7 Fully factorise:

    a $12x^2 + 5x - 2$ **b** $12x^2 + x - 6$ **c** $24x^2 + 28x - 12$

Chapter 9

Congruence and similarity

Contents:

CONGRUENCE AND SIMILARITY

We are similar.

We are congruent.

Two figures are **congruent** if they are identical in every respect, apart from position.

Two figures are **similar** if one figure is an enlargement of the other.

OPENING PROBLEM

If a group of people were each asked to draw triangle ABC in which $\angle ABC = 40^o$, $\angle BCA = 65^o$ and $\angle CAB = 75^o$, would every person draw an identical triangle? In other words, if each triangle was cut out with a pair of scissors, would they match perfectly when placed on top of each other?

The question arises: "What information is sufficient to draw a **unique** triangle?"

You should find that: • given the lengths of its three sides is sufficient
                         • given the size of its three angles is not sufficient.

A   CONGRUENCE OF FIGURES

In mathematics we use the term **congruent** to describe things which are the same shape and size. The closest we get to congruence in human life is with identical twins.

EXERCISE 9A

1   Which of the following figures are congruent?

2   Which of the following geometric figures are congruent?

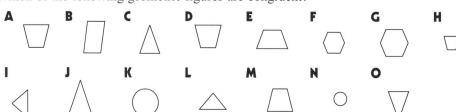

3 Here are some pairs of congruent geometric figures.

    i Identify the side in the second figure corresponding to the side AB in the first figure.

    ii Identify the angle in the second figure corresponding to ∠ABC in the first figure.

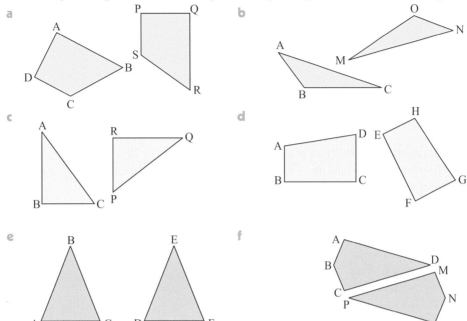

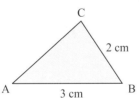

B   CONSTRUCTING AND DRAWING TRIANGLES

If several people are asked to accurately draw triangle ABC in which AB = 3 cm and BC = 2 cm, many different shaped triangles would probably be drawn.

Here are three such triangles:

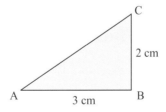
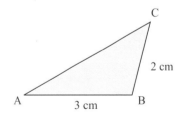

The information given is insufficient (not sufficient) to draw a triangle of one particular shape.

However, if we are asked to accurately draw triangle ABC in which AB = 3 cm, BC = 2 cm and AC = 4 cm one and only one triangular shape can be drawn.

The easiest way of drawing this triangle is to use a ruler and compass construction.

Everyone using this construction would draw **the same** (identical) figure.

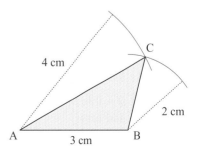

EXERCISE 9B

1   Construct the following triangles:

    a   with sides of length 2 cm, 3 cm and 3 cm

    b   with sides of length 2 cm, 3 cm and 4 cm

    c   with sides of length 2 cm, 3 cm and 5 cm

    d   with sides of length 2 cm, 3 cm and 7 cm.

2   Copy and complete:

"The sum of the lengths of any two sides of a triangle must be .... the length of the third side".

3   Draw a triangle ABC with all sides greater than 6 cm in length and the angles at A, B and C are 60°, 50° and 70° respectively. Place a ruler and set square as shown in the figure and slide the set square on the ruler to the left keeping the ruler firmly in place.

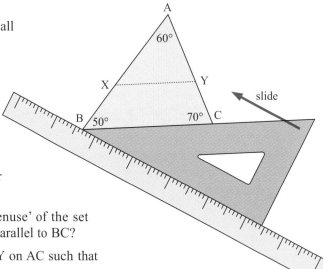

    a   Why does the 'hypotenuse' of the set square produce lines parallel to BC?

    b   Locate X on AB and Y on AC such that XY = 4 cm.
You should now have a triangle which has angles of 60°, 50° and 70° and the side opposite the 60° angle is 4 cm long.

INVESTIGATION   CONSTRUCTING AND DRAWING TRIANGLES

You will need: a ruler, a sharp pencil, a protractor and a compass

What to do:

A   Given two sides and the angle between them (the included angle)

1   Accurately draw triangle ABC in which AB = 5 cm, BC = 4 cm and ∠ABC = 50° by following these steps:

    a   Draw AB first.

    b   At B, use your protractor to draw ∠ABC to be 50°.

    c   From B measure 4 cm to locate C.   Join AC.

COMPUTER DEMO

2   Is it possible to draw this triangle just as accurately, in some other way, without using trial and error?

B   Given one angle is a right angle, the hypotenuse and one other side

1   Accurately draw triangle PQR in which $\angle PQR = 90°$, the hypotenuse PR is 4 cm and RQ is 2 cm by following these steps:

    a   Draw RQ first.

    b   At Q, use your protractor to draw a right angle.

    c   With your compass set at 4 cm, and with its point at R, draw an arc to intersect the perpendicular at P.   Join RP.

2   Is it possible to draw this triangle just as accurately, in some other way, without using trial and error?

C   Given two sides and a non-included angle

1   Accurately draw triangle XYZ in which XY = 6 cm, $\angle YXZ = 45°$ and YZ = 5 cm by following these steps:

    a   Draw XY first.

    b   At X, use your protractor to draw an angle at X of $45°$.

    c   With compass set at 5 cm, and with its point at Y, draw a circle.

    d   Locate Z on your figure.   At this stage you may be thinking you have done something wrong.

2   Show on your figure that there are *two* triangles which can be drawn which satisfy the original conditions.

D   Given two angles and a side

When given two angles, we are really given all three since the angles of a triangle sum to $180°$.   We saw earlier that this is not sufficient to draw a unique triangle.   However, one given side will then fix the triangle's shape.

1   Draw triangle CDE where $\angle CDE = 80°$, $\angle DEC = 40°$ and

    a   DE = 5 cm   **b**   CE = 5 cm   **c**   CD = 5 cm.

2   In each case is one and only one triangle formed?

C   CONGRUENT TRIANGLES

Two triangles are **congruent** if they are identical in every respect except for position.

> This means that if one triangle was cut out with scissors and placed on the top of the other, they would match each other perfectly.

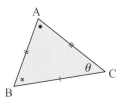 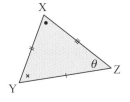

The above triangles are congruent.

We write $\triangle ABC \cong \triangle XYZ$,   where $\cong$ reads   *"is congruent to"*.

Note: When writing the congruence statement above, we label the vertices that are in corresponding positions in the same order,   i.e., we write $\triangle ABC \cong \triangle XYZ$ **not** $\triangle YXZ$ **or** $\triangle ZYX$, etc.

We have already seen how triangles being equiangular (having all three angles equal) is *not* a test for congruence.

For example, these triangles are equiangular but clearly triangle **B** is much larger than triangle **A**.

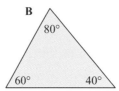

If we are given two sides and a non-included angle, more than one triangle can be drawn.

For example, triangles **C** and **D** have two equal sides and a non-included angle equal, and they are *not* the same triangle.

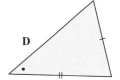

In the **Investigation** on *Constructing and drawing triangles* we have seen that one and only one triangle can be drawn if we are given:

- two sides and the angle between them (the included angle)
- one angle is a right angle, the hypotenuse and one other side
- two angles and a side.

There are, however, four acceptable tests for the **congruence** of two triangles.

TESTS FOR TRIANGLE CONGRUENCE

Two triangles are congruent if one of the following is true:

- All corresponding sides are equal in length. (**SSS**)

- Two sides and the **included** angle are equal. (**SAS**)

- Two angles and a pair of **corresponding sides** are equal. (**AAcorS**)

- For right angled triangles, the hypotenuses and one pair of sides are equal (**RHS**).

The information we are given will help us decide which test to use to prove two triangles are congruent. The diagrams in the following exercise are sketches only and **are not** drawn to scale. However, the information on them is **correct**.

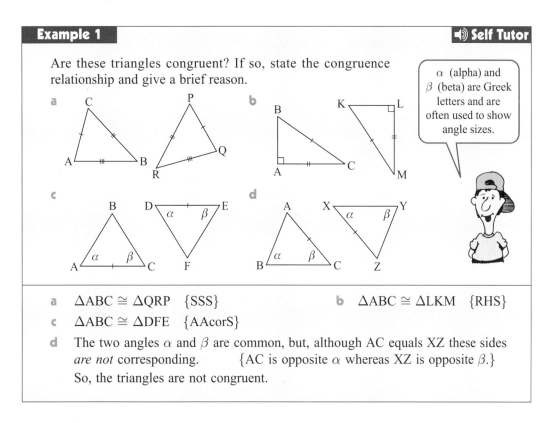

a   Are these triangles congruent? If so, state the congruence relationship and give a brief reason.

α (alpha) and β (beta) are Greek letters and are often used to show angle sizes.

a $\triangle ABC \cong \triangle QRP$ {SSS}

b $\triangle ABC \cong \triangle LKM$ {RHS}

c $\triangle ABC \cong \triangle DFE$ {AAcorS}

d   The two angles α and β are common, but, although AC equals XZ these sides *are not* corresponding.   {AC is opposite α whereas XZ is opposite β.}
So, the triangles are not congruent.

EXERCISE 9C

1   In each set of three triangles, two are congruent. The diagrams are *not* drawn to scale. State which pair is congruent, together with a reason (SSS, SAS, AAcorS or RHS).

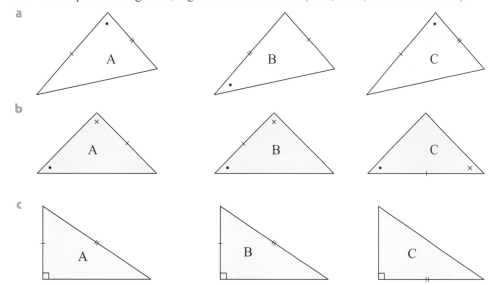

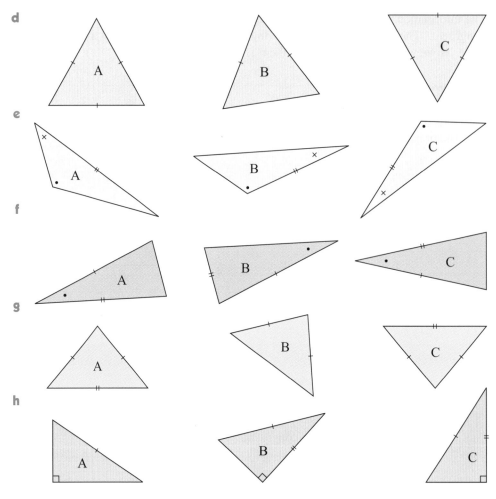

2 Are the following pairs of triangles congruent? If so, state the congruence relationship and give a brief reason.

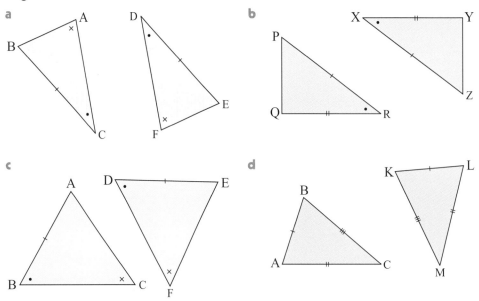

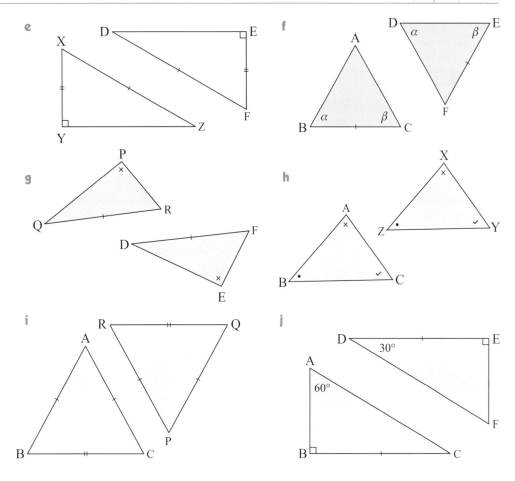

USING CONGRUENCE

Consider the figure opposite:

Are the two triangles congruent?

If so, what can we deduce about the length DE?

What else can we deduce about DE?

We could give this answer:

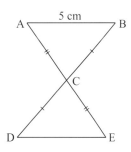

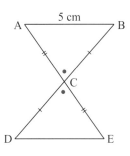

In Δ's ABC and EDC
- BC = DC   {given}
- AC = EC   {given}
- ∠ACB = ∠DCE   {vertically opposite}

∴   ΔABC ≅ ΔEDC   {SAS}

Consequently,   (1)   DE = BA = 5 cm

(2)   ∠BAC = ∠DEC
and so AB ∥ DE
{equal alternate angles}

So, we see from this example that congruence arguments give us a powerful tool for proving that certain geometrical observations are true.

Example 2   ◄» **Self Tutor**

Explain why △ABC and △DBC are congruent:

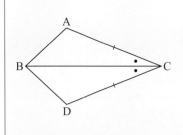

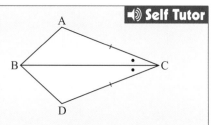

In △'s ABC and DBC:
- AC = DC
- ∠ACB = ∠DCB, and
- BC is common to both.

The triangles are ∴ congruent (SAS).

Example 3   ◄» **Self Tutor**

For the given figure are there congruent triangles?
If so, what can be deduced?

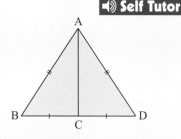

In △'s ABC, ADC
- AB = AD   {given}
- BC = DC   {given}
- AC is a common side.

△'s ABC, ADC are congruent {SSS}

Consequently,
- ∠BAC = ∠DAC
- ∠ABC = ∠ADC
- ∠ACB = ∠ACD,   and so   AC ⊥ BD.
  {as these angles are equal and add to 180°}

3

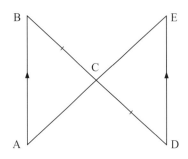

a Explain why triangles ABC and EDC are congruent.

b If AC = 5 cm and ∠BAC = 37°, find:
  i   the length of CE
  ii the size of ∠DEC.

Example 4

🔊 **Self Tutor**

Triangle ABC is isosceles with AC = BC. BC and AC are produced to E and D respectively so that CE = CD.

Prove that AE = BD.

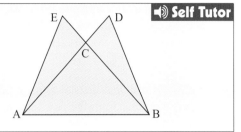

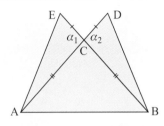

In triangles ACE and BCD:
- AC = BC   {given}
- $\alpha_1 = \alpha_2$ {vertically opposite}
- CE = CD   {given}

∴ the triangles are congruent (SAS) and in particular AE = BD.

4 PQRS is a kite and QS is added to the figure.

   a Show that the triangles are congruent.

   b What other facts can then be deduced about the figure?

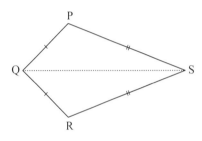

5

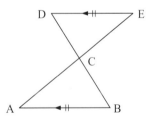

In the given figure DE is parallel to AB and DE = AB.

   a Show that the triangles are congruent.

   b What other facts can then be deduced about the figure?

6 C is the centre of the circle.

   a Show that the figure contains congruent triangles.

   b What other facts can then be deduced about the figure?

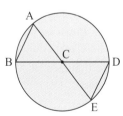

7

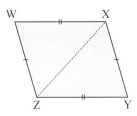

WXYZ is a quadrilateral with opposite sides equal. XZ is added to the figure.

   a Show that the two created triangles are congruent.

   b Now deduce that WXYZ is a parallelogram.

8 Point P is equidistant from both AB and AC. Use congruence to show that P lies on the bisector of ∠BAC.

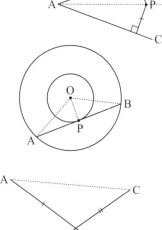

Note: To find the distance from P to either line we draw a perpendicular from the point to the line. So the figure becomes:

9 Two concentric circles are drawn. At P on the inner circle a tangent is drawn and it meets the other circle at A and B.

Use triangle congruence to prove that P is the midpoint of AB.

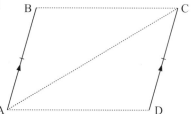

10 **a** Prove that triangles AMC and BMD are congruent.

b Deduce that AC and DB are parallel and equal in length.

c What can be deduced about the quadrilateral ACBD?

11 You are given that AB and DC are parallel and equal in length.

a Join BC, AC and AD and show that Δ's ABC and CDA are congruent.

b Now show that ABCD is a parallelogram.

c Copy and complete: *If a pair of opposite sides of a quadrilateral are parallel and equal in length then the quadrilateral is ......"*

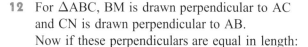

12 For ΔABC, BM is drawn perpendicular to AC and CN is drawn perpendicular to AB. Now if these perpendiculars are equal in length:

a prove that Δ's BCM and CBN are congruent

b prove that ΔABC is isosceles.

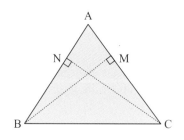

13 For ΔPQR, M is the midpoint of QR. MX is drawn perpendicular to PQ. MY is drawn perpendicular to PR. Now if the perpendiculars are equal in length:

a prove that ΔMQX is congruent to ΔMRY

b prove that ΔPQR is isosceles.

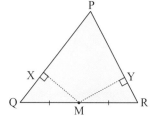

ISOSCELES TRIANGLES

An **isosceles triangle** is a triangle in which two sides are equal in length.

The angles opposite the two equal sides are called the **base angles**.

The vertex where the two equal sides meet is called the **apex**.

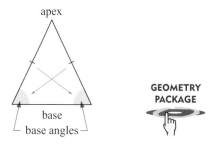

GEOMETRY
PACKAGE

The Isosceles Triangle Theorem

In an isosceles triangle:

- base angles are equal
- the line joining the apex to the midpoint of the base bisects the vertical angle and meets the base at right angles.

We actually proved this special result in **Example 3**. You should look back at the working given.

CONVERSES

With many theorems there are converses which we often use in problem solving.

Converse 1:   If a triangle has two equal angles then it is isosceles.

Converse 2:   The angle bisector of the apex of an isosceles triangle bisects the base at right angles.

Converse 3:   The perpendicular bisector of the base of an isosceles triangle passes through its apex.

- To prove *Converse 1*, Sam tries to use Figure 1 and triangle congruence.

  Will he be successful?

  Why/why not? Could Sam be successful using Figure 2?

- Can you prove *Converse 2* using triangle congruence?

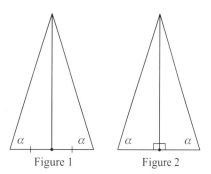

Figure 1   Figure 2

DISCUSSION

What does the word *converse* mean?

Can you find any other converses to the isosceles triangle theorem?

D   SIMILARITY

Two figures are **similar** if one is an enlargement of the other (regardless of orientation).

DISCUSSION

- Discuss whether the following pairs of figures are similar:

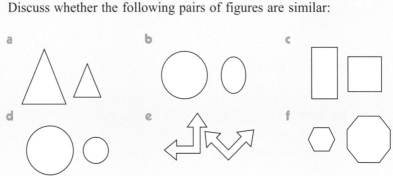

- Are congruent figures similar? Give reasons for your answer.

Consider the enlargement given below where the enlargement factor is 1.5.

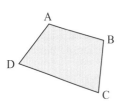

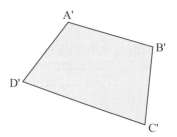

Notice that $k = 1.5 = \dfrac{A'B'}{AB} = \dfrac{B'C'}{BC} = \dfrac{C'D'}{CD} = \dfrac{D'A'}{DA} = \dfrac{B'D'}{BD} = ...$ etc.

We say that corresponding lengths are *in proportion* (the same ratio).

Since angle sizes do not change under enlargements we conclude that:

If two figures are **similar** then

- the figures are equiangular and
- the corresponding sides are in proportion.

Note: If two angles of one triangle are equal in size to two angles of the other triangle then the remaining angles of each triangle are equal.

SIMILAR TRIANGLES

If two triangles are equiangular then they are **similar**.

Similar triangles have corresponding sides in the same ratio.

To test if two triangles are similar, we need to show that:

- at least two pairs of angles are equal in size   *or*
- their sides are in proportion.

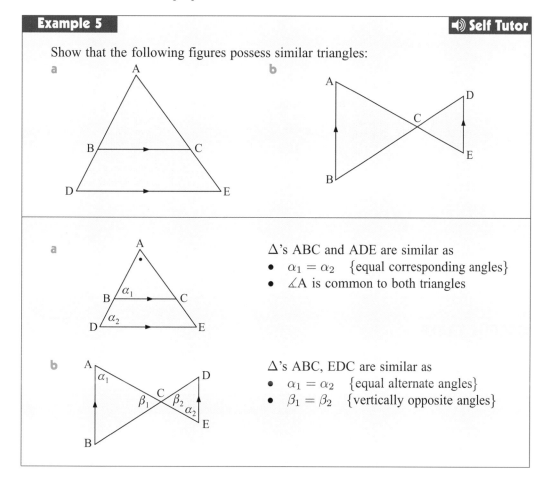

Example 5   ◆)) **Self Tutor**

Show that the following figures possess similar triangles:

a

b

a

Δ's ABC and ADE are similar as
- $\alpha_1 = \alpha_2$ {equal corresponding angles}
- $\angle$A is common to both triangles

b

Δ's ABC, EDC are similar as
- $\alpha_1 = \alpha_2$ {equal alternate angles}
- $\beta_1 = \beta_2$ {vertically opposite angles}

EXERCISE 9D

1   Show that the following figures possess similar triangles:

a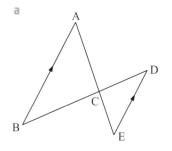

b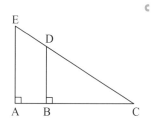

c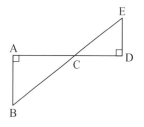

Example 6

◀) **Self Tutor**

In the following, establish that a pair of triangles is similar and find x:

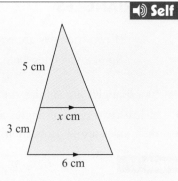

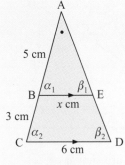

Δ's ABE and ACD are similar as
$\alpha_1 = \alpha_2$ and $\beta_1 = \beta_2$ {corresponding angles}

So, as corresponding sides are in the same ratio, we have

$$\therefore \quad \frac{AB}{AC} = \frac{BE}{CD}$$

$$\therefore \quad \frac{5}{5+3} = \frac{x}{6}$$

$$\therefore \quad \frac{x}{6} = \frac{5}{8}$$

$$\therefore \quad x = \tfrac{5}{8} \times 6$$

i.e., $x = 3.75$

Note that we label the vertices of the figure so that we can refer to them.

USEFUL TABLE

A useful way of creating the equation is to set up a table of side lengths opposite equal angles.

In **Example 6** this would be

	●	α	β
ΔABE	x	-	5
ΔACD	6	-	8

$$\therefore \quad \frac{x}{6} = \frac{5}{8}$$

2   In the following, establish that a pair of triangles is similar and find x:

a

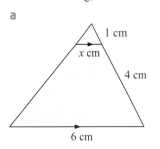

b

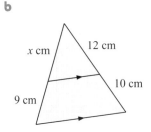

c

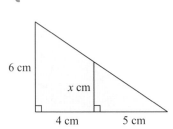

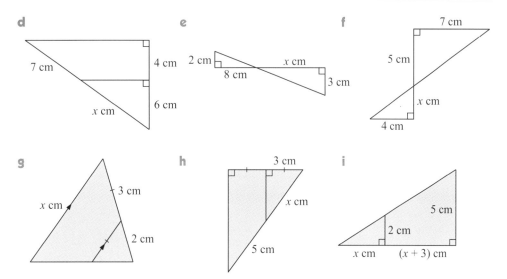

3 A path up to the car-park from the beach has a constant slope of 2 in 7. This means that for every 7 m horizontally the path rises 2 m. The car-park is 60 m horizontally from the beach end of the path. How high in the sand-dunes is the car-park?

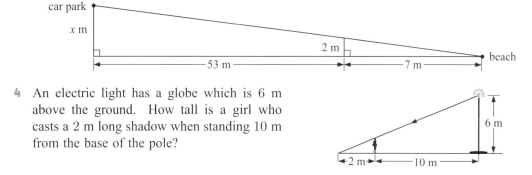

4 An electric light has a globe which is 6 m above the ground. How tall is a girl who casts a 2 m long shadow when standing 10 m from the base of the pole?

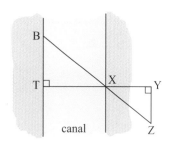

5 A picket fence surrounding a church is 150 cm high. At a certain time of the day it was noticed that the shadow of the fence was 250 cm long and the shadow of the church's steeple was 18 m long. How high is the steeple?

6 On a bright sunny day the shadow cast by a flagpole is 12 m long. At the same time the shadow cast by a 30 cm long ruler is 45 cm long. Find the height of the flag pole.

7 It is known that a boulder B, is 50 paces from the tree T, on the bank of a canal. From a point X, directly opposite T, Harry the hiker walks 10 paces directly away from the bank to point Y. He turns right and walks to point Z which is in line with B and X.

    a Explain why triangles TXB and YXZ are similar.

    b If Y and Z are 20 paces apart, calculate the width of the canal in paces.

8 A 3.5 m ladder leans on a 2.4 m fence. One end is on the ground and the other end touches a vertical wall 2.9 m from the ground.

How far is the bottom of the ladder from the fence?

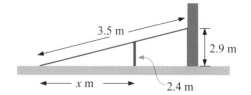

9 Two surveyors estimate the height of a nearby hill. One stands 5 m away from the other on horizontal ground holding a 3 m stick vertically. The other surveyor finds a "line of sight" to the top of the hill, and observes this line passes the vertical stick at 2.4 m. The distance from the stick to the top of the hill is 1500 m (as measured by laser equipment).

How high, correct to the nearest metre, is their estimate of the height of the hill?

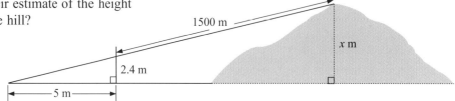

REVIEW SET 9A

1 Which of the following figures are congruent?

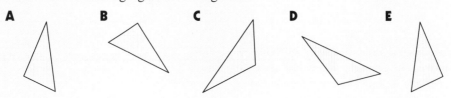

2 Using a ruler and compass, construct a triangle with sides of length 3 cm, 5 cm and 6 cm.

3 In each set of three triangles, two are congruent. The diagrams are not drawn to scale. State which pair is congruent, together with a reason (SSS, SAS, AAcorS or RHS).

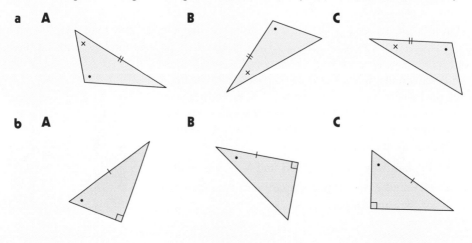

4 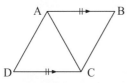 ABCD is a quadrilateral where AB ∥ DC.

    a Show that triangles ABC and ADC are congruent.

    b Now deduce that ABCD is a parallelogram.

5 Show that the following figures possess similar triangles.

  a 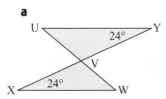   **b** 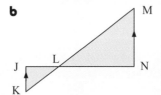   **c**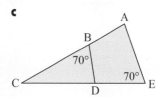

6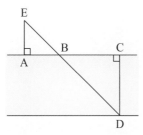

A, B and C are pegs on the bank of a canal which has parallel straight sides. C and D are directly opposite each other. AB = 30 m and BC = 140 m.

When I walk from A directly away from the bank, I reach a point E, 25 m from A, where E, B and D line up. How wide is the canal?

REVIEW SET 9B

1 In this pair of congruent figures:

    a Identify the side in the second figure corresponding to the side AB in the first figure.

    b Identify the angle in the second figure corresponding to ∠ABC in the first figure.

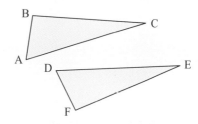

2 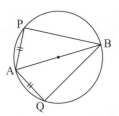 AB is the diameter of the circle.

    a Show that the figure contains congruent triangles.

    b What other facts can then be deduced about the figure?

3 Using a compass and ruler, construct a triangle with sides of length 12 cm, 5 cm and 13 cm.

    What do you notice about this triangle?

4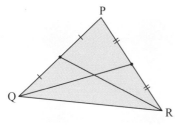

For triangle PQR, X is the midpoint of PQ and Y is the midpoint of PR. If XR and QY are equal in length:

    a prove that triangles XQR and YQR are congruent

    b prove that triangle PQR is isosceles.

5   In the following, establish that a pair of triangles is similar, and find x:

a
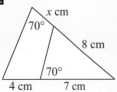

b
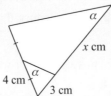

c
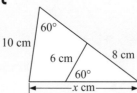

6
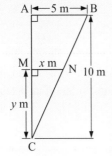

a   Show that Δ's ABC and MNC are similar.

b   Hence, show that $y = 2x$.

c   The volume of a cone is given by $V = \frac{1}{3}\pi r^2 h$.

Find the volume of water in the cone in terms of x.

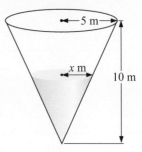

Chapter 10

Univariate data analysis

Contents:

HISTORICAL NOTE

- Florence Nightingale (1820-1910), the famous "lady with the lamp", developed and used graphs to represent data in the areas of hospitals and public health.

- Today about 92% of all nations conduct a census at regular intervals. The UN gives assistance to developing countries to help them with census procedures, so that accurate and comparable worldwide statistics can be collected.

OPENING PROBLEM

Kelly grows pumpkins and wishes to investigate the effect of an organic fertiliser on the number of pumpkins harvested from each plant.

She hopes that the fertiliser will significantly increase the number of pumpkins harvested per plant.

In identical soils she has planted many seeds in two patches, one using the fertiliser and the other not.

All other factors such as watering, have been kept the same for both lots. Random plants are selected and the number of pumpkins counted. The results are:

Without fertiliser			With fertiliser		
4 7 8 3 9	8 6 5 9 7	8 7 8 4 6	8 10 4 10 15	4 9 7 11 10	8 8 6 10 10
7 6 8 6 7	6 6 7 8 8	4 7 7 7 3	9 5 9 6 7	6 6 7 8 8	4 7 7 7 3
5 5 8 9 7	4 9 6 9 7		5 5 8 9 7	4 9 6 9 7	

For you to consider:

- Can you state clearly the problem that Kelly wants to solve?
- How has Kelly tried to make a fair comparison?
- How could Kelly have made sure that her selection was at random?
- What is the best way of organising this data?
- What are suitable methods of display?
- Are there any abnormally high or low results, and how should they be treated?
- How can she best indicate the most typical yield per plant?
- How can we best indicate the spread of the data?
- Can a satisfactory conclusion be made?

TERMINOLOGY FOR THE STUDY OF STATISTICS

STATISTICS

Statistics is the art of solving problems and answering questions by collecting and analysing data.

The facts or pieces of information we collect are called **data**. Data is the plural of the word *datum*, which means a single piece of information.

A list of information is called a **data set** and because it is not in an organised form it is called **raw data**.

THE STATISTICAL METHOD

The process of **statistical enquiry** (or **investigation**) includes the following steps:

Step 1:   Examining a problem which may be solved using data and posing the correct question(s).

Step 2:   Collecting data.

Step 3:   Organising data.

Step 4:   Summarising and displaying data.

Step 5:   Analysing data, making a conclusion in the form of a conjecture.

Step 6:   Writing a report.

VARIABLES

There are two types of variables that we commonly deal with:

- A **categorical variable** is one which describes a particular quality or characteristic. It can be divided into **categories**. The information collected is called **categorical data**.

Examples of categorical variables are:

   Getting to school: the categories could be train, bus, car and walking.
   Colour of eyes: the categories could be blue, brown, hazel, green, grey.

- A **quantitative variable** is one which has a numerical value and is often called a **numerical variable**. The information collected is called **numerical data**.

Quantitative variables can be either discrete or continuous.

A **quantitative discrete variable** takes exact number values and is often a result of **counting**.

Examples of discrete quantitative variables are:

The number of people in a household: the variable could take the values 1, 2, 3, ...
The score out of 30 for a test: the variable could take the values 0, 1, 2, 3, ..., 30.

A **quantitative continuous variable** takes numerical values within a certain continuous range. It is usually a result of **measuring**.

Examples of quantitative continuous variables are:

- *The weight of new-born babies:*   the variable could take any positive value on the number line but is likely to be in the range 0.5 kg to 7 kg.

- *The heights of Year 10 students:*   the variable would be measured in centimetres. A student whose height is recorded as 145 cm could have exact height anywhere between 144.5 cm and 145.5 cm.

CENSUS OR SAMPLE

The two types of data collection are by census or sample.

> A **census** is a method which involves collecting data about every individual in a *whole population*.

The individuals in a population may be people or objects. A census is detailed and accurate but is expensive, time consuming and often impractical.

> A **sample** is a method which involves collecting data about a *part of the population* only.

A sample is cheaper and quicker than a census but is not as detailed or as accurate. Conclusions drawn from samples always involve some error.

A sample must truly reflect the characteristics of the whole population and so it must be **unbiased** and **large enough**.

> A **biased sample** is one in which the data has been unfairly influenced by the collection process and is not truly representative of the whole population.

EXERCISE 10A.1

1   Classify the following variables as either categorical or numerical:
   a   the time taken to travel to school
   b   the number of cousins a person has
   c   voting intention at the next election
   d   the number of cars in a household
   e   the speed of cars on a particular stretch of highway
   f   favourite type of apple
   g   town or city where born
   h   the weight of three-year-old children

2   Write down the possible categories for the following categorical variables:
   a   gender   b   favourite football code
   c   hair colour   d   type of fuel used in a car

3 For each of the following possible investigations, classify the variable as categorical, quantitative discrete or quantitative continuous:

    a the number of goals scored each week by a hockey team

    b the weights of the members of a basketball team

    c the most popular TV station

    d the number of kittens in each litter

    e the number of bread rolls bought each week by a family

    f the pets owned by students in your class

    g the number of leaves on a rose plant stem

    h the number of hours of daylight each day in winter

    i the number of people who die from heart attacks each year in a given city

    j the amount of rainfall in each month of the year

    k the countries of origin of refugees

    l the reasons people use public transport

    m the stopping distances of cars doing 80 km/h

    n the number of cars passing through an intersection per hour

    o the pulse rates of a group of soccer players at rest

4 State whether a census or a sample would be used for these investigations:

    a the reasons for people using taxis

    b the heights of the basketballers at a particular school

    c finding the percentage of people in a city who suffer from asthma

    d the resting pulse rates of members of your favourite sporting team

    e finding the country of origin of immigrants

    f the amount of daylight each month where you live

5 Comment on any possible bias in the following situations:

    a Year 12 students only are interviewed about changes to the school uniform.

    b Motorists stopped in peak hour are interviewed about traffic problems.

    c Real estate agents are interviewed about the prices of houses.

    d A 'who will you vote for' survey at an expensive city restaurant.

STATISTICAL GRAPHS

Two variables under consideration are usually linked by one being *dependent* on the other.

For example,   the *total cost of a dinner* depends on *the number of guests present.*

        We say that   *the total cost of a dinner* is the **dependent variable**, and *the number of guests present* is the **independent variable**.

Generally, when drawing **graphs** involving two variables, the *independent variable* is on the **horizontal axis** and the *dependent variable* is on the **vertical axis**. An exception to this is when we draw a horizontal bar chart.

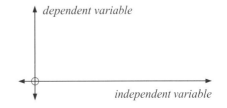

Acceptable graphs to display categorical data are:

Vertical column graph   **Horizontal bar chart**   **Pie chart**   **Segment bar chart**

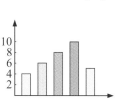
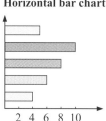
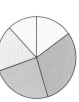

For categorical data, the **mode** is the category which occurs most frequently. In the graphs above, the mode is the green category.

INTERNET STATISTICS

There are thousands of sites worldwide. The following are useful.

- *www.un.org*   for the United Nations
- *www.who.int*   for the World Health Organisation

GRAPHING USING A SPREADSHEET

Suppose you want to draw a frequency column graph of this car colour data:

Colour	white	red	blue	green	other
Frequency	38	27	19	18	11

SPREADSHEET

The following steps using **MS Excel** enable you to do this quickly and easily:

Step 1:   Start a new spreadsheet, type in the table then highlight the area as shown.

Step 2:   Click on from the menu bar.

Step 3:   Choose    This is probably already highlighted. Click [Finish]

You should get:

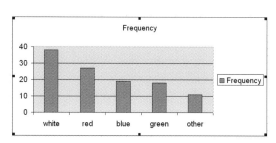

Suppose now you wish to compare two distributions:

Colour	white	red	blue	green	other
Frequency 1	38	27	19	18	11
Frequency 2	15	13	8	11	4

Step 4: Into the C column type the *Frequency 2* data and highlight the three columns as shown.

	A	B	C
1	Colour	Frequency 1	Frequency 2
2	white	38	15
3	red	27	13
4	blue	19	8
5	green	18	11
6	other	11	4

Step 5: Click on 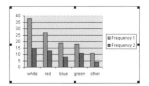 ,

then

Standard Types   Custom Types

Chart type:
- Column
- Bar
- Line
- Pie

Chart sub-type:

then   Finish

Step 6: Experiment with changing the chart type and graph labels.

EXERCISE 10A.2

1 At a school, children were randomly chosen and asked to nominate their favourite fruit. The following data was collected:

Type of fruit	Frequency
Apple	20
Banana	24
Grapes	3
Orange	11
Mandarin	10
Nectarine	7
Pear	2
Peach	3

  a What are the variables in this investigation?

  b What is the dependent variable?

  c If we are trying to find out the favourite fruit of children, is the sample unbiased?

  d If we are only interested in the favourite fruit of 368 children within the school:

     i is the sample unbiased?   **ii** What is the sample size?

  e What is the mode?

  f Construct a vertical column graph to illustrate the data. Use a spreadsheet!

2 55 randomly selected year ten students were asked to nominate their favourite subject studied at school. The results of the survey are displayed in the bar chart shown.

subject: Art, Music, Geography, History, Language, Science, Mathematics, English — frequency axis 0 to 10

  a What are the variables in this investigation?

  b What are the dependent and independent variables?

  c What is the mode?

  d What given information indicates that the sample was unbiased?

  e If there are 173 year 10 students at the school, is the sample size sufficient?

  f Construct a pie chart for the data. If possible, use a spreadsheet.

3 Warren read the following report from the local paper:

OUR CHANGING POPULATION

A spokesperson from the Statistics Bureau reported today that the number of persons per household has reached an all time low. Some of the reasons suggested for this decline were: women having fewer children and at a later stage in their lives because they want to establish their careers, more couples choosing not to have children at all, and it being more expensive than at any time previously to raise children.

In the past large families were common. It was cheaper to raise children as the 'necessities' of life were basic compared with the current times. Few married women had paid employment outside the home.

Whilst there have been fluctuations in family size over the last hundred years, such as the 'baby boom' following World War II, it is now seen as unlikely that we will ever return to the large families of the past.

Warren decided to put this statement to the test in his local town of Boodernut. He applied for and received census data from the Statistics Bureau, a copy of which is given alongside.

a Find the population sizes of the town in:

  i 1935   **ii** 1960   **iii** 1985

b Prepare a table of percentages for the town's population data (correct to 1 decimal place).

Private household size of Boodernut			
Number of persons	*Year*		
	1935	1960	1985
1	9	8	69
2	68	177	184
3	73	162	248
4	109	374	162
5+	178	283	38
Totals			

c From the data, write a brief discussion and conclusion which compares the changes in the household sizes over the 1935 to 1985 period.

B   QUANTITATIVE (NUMERICAL) DATA

Recall that:

> A **quantitative variable** is one which has a numerical value and is often called a **numerical variable**. The information collected is called **numerical data**.

Quantitative variables can be either discrete or continuous and they each have an appropriate way to organise and display the data collected for them.

A **quantitative discrete variable** takes exact number values and is often a result of **counting**.

Some examples are:

- *The number of pets in a household:* the variable could take the values of 0, 1, 2, 3, 4, ...
- *Shoe size:* the variable could take the values of 3, $3\frac{1}{2}$, 4, $4\frac{1}{2}$, 5, $5\frac{1}{2}$, ...

A **quantitative continuous variable** takes numerical values within a certain continuous range. It is usually a result of **measuring**.

Some examples are:

- *The weight of Year 10 students:* the variable can take any value from about 40 kg to 120 kg. Theoretically the variable could take any value on the number line but is very unlikely to take a value outside the range given.
- *The time taken to get to school:* the variable can take any value from about 1 minute to 80 minutes.

ORGANISATION AND DISPLAY OF DISCRETE DATA

In the **Opening Problem**, the **discrete quantitative variable** is: *The number of pumpkins per plant*.

To organise the data a **tally-frequency table** could be used. We count the data systematically and use a '|' to indicate each data value. Remember that ~~||||~~ represents 5.

Below is the table for *Without fertiliser*:

Number of pumpkins/plant	*Tally*	*Frequency*
3	||	2
4	||||	4
5	|||	3
6	~~||||~~ ||	7
7	~~||||~~ ~~||||~~ |	11
8	~~||||~~ |||	8
9	~~||||~~	5

A **column graph** or **dot plot** could be used to display the results.

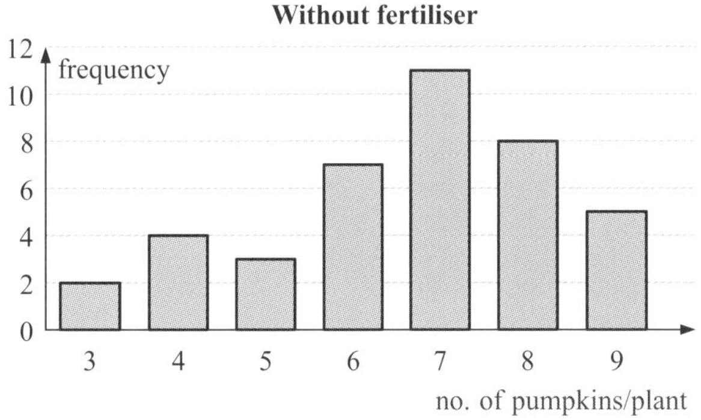

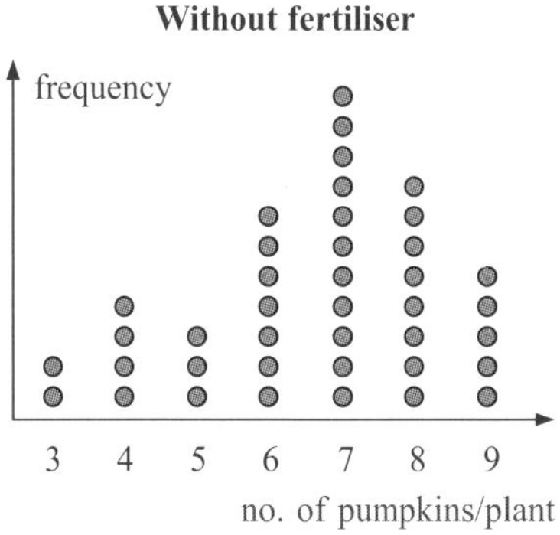

DISCUSSION

Are there any advantages/disadvantages in using a dot plot rather than a column graph?

From both graphs we can make observations and calculations such as:

- 7 pumpkins per plant is the mode of the *Without fertiliser* data.
- 5% of the plants had fewer than 4 pumpkins on them, etc.

DESCRIBING THE DISTRIBUTION OF THE DATA SET

The **mode** of a data set is the most frequently occurring value(s). Many data sets show **symmetry** or **partial symmetry** about the mode.

If we place a curve over the column graph we see that this curve shows symmetry and we say that we have a **symmetrical distribution** of the data.

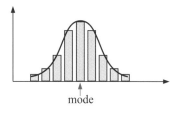

For the *Without fertiliser* data we have the distribution alongside. It is said to be **negatively skewed** as if we compare it with the symmetrical distribution it has been 'stretched' on the left (or negative) side of the mode.

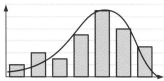

So we have:

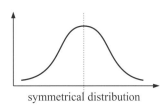

symmetrical distribution

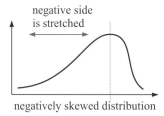

negatively skewed distribution

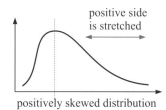

positively skewed distribution

OUTLIERS

Outliers are data values that are either much larger or much smaller than the general body of data. Outliers appear separated from the body of data on a frequency graph.

For example, in the data set: 3, 1, 7, 6, 8, 18, 2, 6, 7, 7,   the data value 18 is an outlier.

Some outliers are genuine and must be included in an analysis of the whole data set. However, other outliers may not reflect the truth and should not be considered. These may be due to human error or some other factor.

EXERCISE 10B

1   State whether the following quantitative (or numerical) variables are discrete or continuous:

  a   the time taken to run 1500 metres

  b   the maximum temperature reached on a March day

   c the weight of cargo taken on a ship

   d the time taken for a battery to run down

   e the number of trips made by a taxi

   f the number of people in a theatre

   g the number of minutes spent sending text messages per day

2 20 students were asked "How many TV sets do you have in your household?" and the following data was collected: 2 1 0 3 1 2 1 3 4 0 0 2 2 0 1 1 0 1 0 1

   a What is the variable in this investigation?

   b Is the data discrete or continuous? Why?

   c Construct a dotplot to display the data. Use a heading for the graph, and scale and label the axes.

   d How would you describe the distribution of the data? (Is it symmetrical, positively skewed or negatively skewed? Are there any outliers?)

   e What percentage of the households had no TV sets?

   f What percentage of the households had three or more TV sets?

3 A randomly selected sample of shoppers was asked, 'How many times did you shop at a supermarket in the past week?' A column graph was constructed for the results.

   a How many shoppers gave data in the survey?

   b How many of the shoppers shopped once or twice?

   c What percentage of the shoppers shopped more than four times?

   d Describe the distribution of the data.

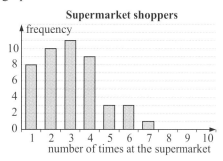

4 Employees of a company were asked to record the number of times they left the company office on business appointments during one week. The following dotplot was constructed from the data:

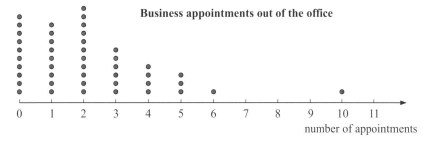

   a What is the variable in this investigation?

   b Explain why the data is discrete numerical data.

   c What percentage of the employees did not leave the office?

   d What percentage of the employees left the office more than 5 times?

   e What was the most frequent number of business appointments out of the office?

   f Describe the distribution of the data.

   g How would you describe the data value '10'?

5 The number of tooth picks in a box is stated as 50 but the actual number of tooth picks has been found to vary. To investigate this, the number of tooth picks in a box has been counted for a sample of 60 boxes:

50 52 51 50 50 51 52 49 50 48 51 50 47 50 52 48 50 49 51 50
49 50 52 51 50 50 52 50 53 48 50 51 50 50 49 48 51 49 52 50
49 49 50 52 50 51 49 52 52 50 49 50 49 51 50 50 51 50 53 48

    a What is the variable in this investigation?

    b Is the data continuous or discrete numerical data?

    c Construct a frequency table for this data.

    d Display the data using a bar chart.

    e Describe the distribution of the data.

    f What percentage of the boxes contained exactly 50 tooth picks?

6 Revisiting the **Opening Problem** data on page **198** for the *With fertiliser* data:

    a Organise the data in a tally-frequency table.

    b Draw a column graph of the data.

    c Are there any outliers?

    d Is the data skewed?

    e What evidence is there that the fertiliser 'increases the number of pumpkins per plant'?

    f Can it be said that the fertiliser will increase the farmer's pumpkin crop and therefore her profits?

C   GROUPED DISCRETE DATA

It is not sensible to organise some discrete data by using a frequency table. Also, graphing by dot plot or column graph is not appropriate.

For example, a local hardware store is concerned about the number of people visiting the store at lunch time.

Over 30 consecutive week days they recorded data.

The results were: 37, 30, 17, 13, 46, 23, 40, 28, 38, 24, 23, 22, 18, 29, 16,
35, 24, 18, 24, 44, 32, 54, 31, 39, 32, 38, 41, 38, 24, 32

In situations like this, grouping the data into **class intervals** is appropriate.

It seems sensible to use class intervals of length 10 in this case.

The tally-frequency table is:

Number of people	Tally	Frequency
10 to 19	‖‖	5
20 to 29	‖‖ ‖‖	9
30 to 39	‖‖ ‖‖ ‖	11
40 to 49	‖‖	4
50 to 59	‖	1
	Total	30

STEM-AND-LEAF PLOTS

A **stem-and-leaf plot** (often called a stem-plot) is a way of writing down the data in groups and is used for small data sets. It shows actual data values and gives a visual comparison of frequencies.

For numbers with two digits, the first digit forms part of the **stem** and the second digit forms a **leaf**.

For example, for the data value 17,   1 is recorded on the stem, 7 is a leaf value.

The **stem-and-leaf plot** is:

Stem	Leaf
1	73868
2	384329444
3	70852192882
4	6041
5	4 **Note:** 1 | 7 means 17

The **ordered stem-and-leaf plot** is

Stem	Leaf
1	36788
2	233444489
3	01222578889
4	0146
5	4

The ordered stemplot arranges all data from smallest to largest.

Notice the following features:

- all the actual data is shown
- the minimum (smallest) data value is 13
- the maximum (largest) data value is 54
- the 'thirties' interval (30 to 39) occurred most often.

EXERCISE 10C

1   The data set below is the test scores (out of 100) for a Science test for 50 students.

92	29	78	67	68	58	80	89	92
69	66	56	88	81	70	73	63	55
67	64	62	74	56	75	90	56	47
59	64	89	39	51	87	89	76	59
72	80	95	68	80	64	53	43	61
71	38	44	88	62				

a   Construct a tally and frequency table for this data using class intervals 0 - 9, 10 - 19, 20 - 29, ..., 90 - 100.

b   What percentage of the students scored 80 or more for the test?

c   What percentage of students scored less than 50 for the test?

d   Copy and complete the following:

More students had a test score in the interval .... than in any other interval.

2   a   Draw a stem-and-leaf plot using stems 2, 3, 4, and 5 for the following data:

29, 27, 33, 30, 46, 40, 35, 24, 21, 58, 27, 34, 25, 36, 57, 34, 42, 51, 50, 48

b   Redraw the stem-and-leaf plot from a so that it is ordered.

3 For the ordered stem-and-leaf plot given, find

Stem	Leaf
0	1 3 7
1	0 3 4 7 8 8 9
2	0 0 1 2 2 3 5 5 6 8 9
3	2 4 4 5 8 9
4	3

  a the minimum value

  b the maximum value

  c the number of data with a value greater than 25

  d the number of data with a value of at least 40

  e the percentage of the data which is less than 15.

4 The test score, out of 60 marks, is recorded for a group of 45 students.

34	37	44	51	53	39	33	58	40	42	43	43	47	37	35
41	43	48	50	55	44	44	52	54	59	39	31	29	44	57
45	34	29	27	18	49	41	42	37	42	43	43	45	34	51

  a Construct a stem-and-leaf plot for this data using 0, 1, 2, 3, 4, and 5 as the stems.

  b Redraw the stem-and-leaf plot so that it is ordered.

  c What advantage does a stem-and-leaf plot have over a frequency table?

  d What is the **i** highest **ii** lowest mark scored for the test?

  e If an 'A' was awarded to students who scored 50 or more for the test, what percentage of students scored an 'A'?

  f What percentage of students scored less than half marks for the test?

  g Describe the distribution of the data.

D ■ CONTINUOUS DATA AND HISTOGRAMS

A **continuous numerical variable** can theoretically take any value on part of the number line. A continuous variable often has to be **measured** so that data can be recorded.

Examples of continuous numerical variables are:

The height of Year 10 students: the variable can take any value from about 120 cm to 200 cm.

The speed of cars on a stretch of highway: the variable can take any value from 0 km/h to the fastest speed that a car can travel, but is most likely to be in the range 30 km/h to 240 km/h.

ORGANISATION AND DISPLAY OF CONTINUOUS DATA

When data is recorded for a continuous variable there are likely to be many different values. This data is therefore organised by grouping into **class intervals**. A special type of graph, called a **histogram**, is used to display the data.

A histogram is similar to a column graph but, to account for the continuous nature of the variable, the 'columns' are joined together.

An example is given alongside:

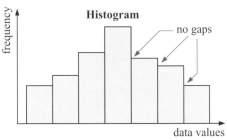

Note: The **modal class** (the class of values that appears most often) is easy to identify from a histogram.

SUMMARY (COLUMN GRAPHS AND HISTOGRAMS)

Column graphs and histograms both have the following features:

- on the **vertical axis** we have the **frequency** of occurrence
- on the **horizontal axis** we have the range of scores
- **column widths are equal** and the height varies according to frequency.

Histograms have no gaps between the columns because they are used for **continuous** data.

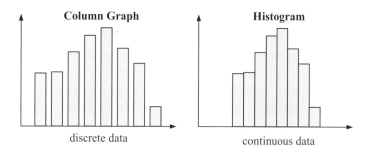

Column Graph	Histogram
discrete data	continuous data

Example 1   ◆》 **Self Tutor**

The weight of parcels sent on a given day from a post office is shown, in kilograms:

2.9, 4.0, 1.6, 3.5, 2.9, 3.4, 3.2, 5.2, 4.6, 3.1, 2.8, 3.7, 4.9, 3.4, 1.3, 2.5, 2.2

Organise the data using a frequency table and graph the data.

The data is *continuous* (as the weight could be any value from 0.1 kg up to 6 kg).

The lowest weight recorded is 1.3 kg and the highest is 5.2 kg so we will use class intervals of 1 kg. The class interval 2- would include all weights from 2 kg up to, but not including 3 kg.

Weight (kg)	Frequency
1 -	2
2 -	5
3 -	6
4 -	3
5 - < 6	1

A histogram is used to graph this continuous data.

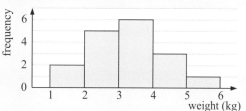

A stemplot could also be used to organise the data:

Note: The modal class is (3- < 4) kg as this occurred most frequently.

Stem	Leaf
1	3 6
2	2 5 8 9 9
3	1 2 4 4 5 7
4	0 6 9
5	2 Scale: 2	9 means 2.9 kg.

EXERCISE 10D

1 A frequency table for the weights of a football squad is given below.

Weight (kg)	Frequency
75 -	2
80 -	5
85 -	8
90 -	7
95 -	5
100 - < 105	1

a Explain why 'weight' is a continuous variable.

b Construct a histogram for the data. The axes should be carefully marked and labelled and include a heading for the graph.

c What is the modal class? Explain what this means.

d Describe the distribution of the data.

2 A school has conducted a survey of 50 students to investigate the time it takes for students to travel to school. The following data gives the travel time to the nearest minute:

```
16   8   10  17  25  34  42  18  24  18  45  33  40
 3  20  12  10  10  27  16  37  45  15  16  26  16
14  18  15  27  19  32   6  12  14  20  10  16
21  25   8  32  46  14  15  20  18   8  10  25
```

a Is travel time a discrete or continuous variable?

b Construct an ordered stemplot for the data using stems 0, 1, 2, ...

c Describe the distribution of the data.

d Copy and complete:

"The modal travelling time was between ..... and ..... minutes."

3 For the following data, state whether a histogram or a column graph should be used and draw the appropriate graph.

a Most appealing car colour data.

Colour	white	red	blue	green	other
Frequency	47	44	31	23	18

b The number of students in classes.

Number of students in a class	21	22	23	24	25	26	27
Frequency	1	4	7	9	15	8	2

c The heights of 25 netball players (to the nearest cm) data.

Height (cm)	140 − 149	150 − 159	160 − 169	170 − 179	180 − 189
Frequency	2	3	7	9	4

d The time taken to make a pizza (to the nearest min.) data.

Time taken (min)	5	6	7	8	9	10	11
Frequency	1	2	3	7	10	8	5

e 45 swimmers have 'best times' as recorded in the given table.

Time (sec)	50 − 59	60 − 69	70 − 79	80 − 89	90 − 99
frequency	8	23	7	4	3

4 A plant inspector takes a random sample of ten week old plants from a nursery and measures their height to the nearest mm.

The results are shown in the table alongside.

height (mm)	frequency
20 - 39	4
40 - 59	17
60 - 79	15
80 - 99	8
100 - 114	2
120 - 139	4

  a Represent the data on a histogram.

  b How many of the seedlings are 40 mm or more?

  c What percentage of the seedlings are between 60 and 79 mm?

  d The total number of seedlings in the nursery is 857. Estimate the number of seedlings which measure   **i** less than 100 mm   **ii** between 40 and 99 mm.

MEASURING THE CENTRE

A better picture of the data in a data set can be seen if we can locate the **middle (centre)** of the data and have an indication of its **spread**. Knowing one of these without the other is often of little use.

There are *three statistics* that are used to measure the **centre** of a data set. These are: the **mean**, the **median** and the **mode**.

THE MEAN

The **mean** of a data set is the statistical name for the arithmetic average,

i.e.,   **mean** $= \dfrac{\textbf{sum of all data values}}{\textbf{the number of data values}}$

or $\overline{x} = \dfrac{\sum x}{n}$ $\{\sum x$ is the sum of the data values$\}$

The mean gives us a single number which indicates a centre of the data set.

For example, a mean test mark of 67% tells us that there are several marks below 67% and several above it with 67% at the centre. 67% does not have to be one of the data set values.

THE MEDIAN

The **median** is the *middle value* of an ordered data set.

An ordered data set is obtained by listing the data, usually from smallest to largest. The median splits the data in halves. Half the data are less than or equal to the median and half are greater than or equal to it.

For example, if the median mark for a test is 67% then you know that half the class scored less than or equal to 67% and half scored greater than or equal to 67%.

Note: For an **odd number** of data, the median is one of the data.

  For an **even number** of data, the median is the average of the two middle values and may not be one of the original data.

Here is a **rule for finding the median** data values:

If there are n data values, find the value of $\dfrac{n+1}{2}$.

The median is the $\left(\dfrac{n+1}{2}\right)$th data value.

For example:

If $n = 13$, $\dfrac{13+1}{2} = 7$.   So, the median $= 7$th ordered data value.

If $n = 14$, $\dfrac{14+1}{2} = 7.5$. So, the median $=$ average of 7th and 8th ordered data values.

THE MODE

The **mode** is the most frequently occurring value in the data set.

Example 2 ◀)) **Self Tutor**

The number of heavy transport vehicles using a road over a 13-day period is 4 6 3 2 7 8 3 5 5 7 6 6 4.   For this data set, find:
a the mean   **b** the median   **c** the mode.

a   mean $= \dfrac{4+6+3+2+7+8+3+5+5+7+6+6+4}{13}$ ◀— sum of the data
 13 ◀———————— 13 data values

$ = \dfrac{66}{13}$

$ \doteqdot 5.08$ trucks

b The ordered data set is: ~~2 3 3 4 4 5 5~~ 5 ~~6 6 6 7 7 8~~ $\{$as $n = 13$, $\frac{n+1}{2} = 7\}$
$\therefore$ median $= 5$ trucks

c 6 is the score which occurs the most often $\therefore$ mode $= 6$ trucks

For the heavy transport vehicle data of **Example 2**, how are the measures of the middle affected if on the 14th day the number of trucks was 7?

We expect the mean to rise as the new data value is greater than the old mean.

In fact,   new mean $= \dfrac{66+7}{14} = \dfrac{73}{14} \doteqdot 5.21$ trucks

The new ordered data set would be: 2 3 3 4 4 5 $\underbrace{5\ 6}$ 6 6 7 7 7 8
 two middle scores

$\therefore$ median $= \dfrac{5+6}{2} = 5.5$ trucks

This new data set has two modes, 6 and 7 trucks, and we say that the data set is **bimodal**.

Note: If a data set has three or more modes, we do not use the mode as a measure of the middle.

Note: Consider the data: 4 2 5 6 7 4 5 3 5 4 7 6 3 5 8 6 5

The dot plot of this data is:

For this data the mean, median and mode are all 5.

Equal or approximately equal values of the mean, mode and median *may* indicate a *symmetrical distribution* of data. However, we should always check using a graph before calling a data set symmetric.

EXERCISE 10E.1

1 Find the **i** mean **ii** median **iii** mode for each of the following data sets:

   a 12, 17, 20, 24, 25, 30, 40

   b 8, 8, 8, 10, 11, 11, 12, 12, 16, 20, 20, 24

   c 7.9, 8.5, 9.1, 9.2, 9.9, 10.0, 11.1, 11.2, 11.2, 12.6, 12.9

   d 427, 423, 415, 405, 445, 433, 442, 415, 435, 448, 429, 427, 403, 430, 446, 440, 425, 424, 419, 428, 441

2 Consider the following two data sets:

   Data set A: 5, 6, 6, 7, 7, 7, 8, 8, 9, 10, 12

   Data set B: 5, 6, 6, 7, 7, 7, 8, 8, 9, 10, 20

   a Find the mean for both *Data set A* and *Data set B*.

   b Find the median of both *Data set A* and *Data set B*.

   c Explain why the mean of *Data set A* is less than the mean of *Data set B*.

   d Explain why the median of *Data set A* is the same as the median of *Data set B*.

3 The selling price of nine houses are: $158 000, $290 000, $290 000, $1.1 million, $900 000, $395 000, $925 000, $420 000, $760 000

   a Find the mean, median and modal selling prices.

   b Explain why the mode is an unsatisfactory measure of the middle in this case.

   c Is the median a satisfactory measure of the middle of this data set?

4 The following raw data is the daily rainfall (to the nearest millimetre) for the month of February 2006 in a city in China:

   0, 4, 1, 0, 0, 0, 2, 9, 3, 0, 0, 0, 8, 27, 5, 0, 0, 0, 0, 8, 1, 3, 0, 0, 15, 1, 0, 0

   a Find the mean, median and mode for the data.

   b Give a reason why the median is not the most suitable measure of centre for this set of data.

   c Give a reason why the mode is not the most suitable measure of centre for this set of data.

   d Are there any outliers in this data set?

   e On some occasions outliers are removed because they are not typical of the rest of the data and are often due to errors in observation and/or calculation. If the outliers in the data set were accurately found, should they be removed before finding the measures of the middle?

5 A basketball team scored 38, 52, 43, 54, 41 and 36 goals in their first six matches.

    a What is the mean number of goals scored for the first six matches?

    b What score will the team need to shoot in the next match so that they maintain the same mean score?

    c The team shoots only 20 goals in the seventh match. What is the mean number of goals scored for the seven matches?

    d The team shoots 42 goals in their eighth and final match. Will this increase or decrease their previous mean score? What is the mean score for all eight matches?

Example 3   ◀) **Self Tutor**

The mean of five scores is 12.2. What is the sum of the scores?

Let S = sum of scores $\therefore$ $\dfrac{S}{5} = 12.2$

$\therefore$ $S = 12.2 \times 5 = 61$

i.e., the sum of the scores is 61.

---

6 The mean of 12 scores is 8.8. What is the sum of the scores?

7 While on a camping holiday, Daffyd drove, on average, 325 km per day for a period of 7 days. How far did Daffyd drive in total while on holiday?

8 The mean monthly sales for a CD store are $216\,000$. Calculate the total sales for the store for the year.

Example 4   ◀) **Self Tutor**

Find x if 10, 7, 3, 6 and x have a mean of 8.

There are 5 scores.

$\therefore$ $\dfrac{10 + 7 + 3 + 6 + x}{5} = 8$

$\therefore$ $\dfrac{26 + x}{5} = 8$

$\therefore$ $26 + x = 40$

$\therefore$ $x = 14$

---

9 Find x if 7, 15, 6, 10, 4 and x have a mean of 9.

10 Find a, given that 10, a, 15, 20, a, a, 17, 7 and 15 have a mean of 12.

11 Over a semester, Jamie did 8 science tests. Each was marked out of 30 and Jamie averaged 25. However, when checking his files, he could only find 7 of the 8 tests. For these he scored 29, 26, 18, 20, 27, 24 and 29. Determine how many marks out of 30 he scored for the eighth test.

12 On the first four days of his holiday Mark drove an average of 424 kilometres per day and on the next three days he drove an average of 544 kilometres per day.
  a What is the total distance that Mark drove in the first four days?
  b What is the total distance that Mark drove in the next three days?
  c What is the mean distance travelled per day, by Mark, over the seven days?

13 A sample of 12 measurements has a mean of 8.5 and a sample of 20 measurements has a mean of 7.5. Find the mean of all 32 measurements.

14 The mean, median and mode of seven numbers are 8, 7 and 6 respectively. Two of the numbers are 8 and 10. If the smallest of the seven numbers is 4, find the largest of the seven numbers.

DISCUSSION

Which of the measures of the middle is more affected by the presence of an outlier? Develop at least two examples to show how the measures of the middle can be altered by outliers.

MEASURES OF THE CENTRE FROM OTHER SOURCES

When the same data appear several times we often summarise the data in table form.

Consider the data in the given table:

We can find the measures of the centre directly from the table.

Data value	Frequency	Product
3	1	$1 \times 3 = 3$
4	2	$2 \times 4 = 8$
5	4	$4 \times 5 = 20$
6	14	$14 \times 6 = 84$
7	11	$11 \times 7 = 77$
8	6	$6 \times 8 = 48$
9	2	$2 \times 9 = 18$
Total	40	258

The mode

There are 14 of data value 6 which is more than any other data value.
The mode is therefore 6.

The mean

Adding a **'Product' column** to the table helps to add all scores.

For example, there are 14 data of value 6 and these add to $14 \times 6 = 84$.

So,   mean $= \dfrac{258}{40} = 6.45$

The median

There are 40 data values, an even number, so there are *two middle* data values. What are they? How do we find them from the table?

Remember that the median is the middle of the *ordered* data set.

As the sample size $n = 40$, $\dfrac{n+1}{2} = \dfrac{41}{2} = 20.5$

$\therefore$ the median is the average of the 20th and 21st data values.

In the table, the blue numbers show us accumulated values.

Data Value	Frequency
3	1
4	2
5	4
6	14
7	11
8	6
9	2
Total	40

1 ——— one number is 3
3 ——— 3 numbers are 4 or less
7 ——— 7 numbers are 5 or less
21 ——— 21 numbers are 6 or less
32 ——— 32 numbers are 7 or less

We can see that the 20th and 21st data values (in order) are both 6's,

$\therefore$ median $= \dfrac{6+6}{2} = 6$

Notice that we have a skewed distribution for which the mean, median and mode are nearly equal. This is why we need to be careful when we use measures of the middle to call distributions symmetric.

Example 5   ◀) Self Tutor

In a class of 20 students the students are assigned a number between 1 and 10 to indicate their fitness.
(10 is the highest score.)

Calculate the   **a**   mean
                b   median
                c   mode

Score	Number of students
5	1
6	2
7	4
8	7
9	4
10	2
Total	20

a

Score	Number of students	Product
5	1	$5 \times 1 = 5$
6	2	$6 \times 2 = 12$
7	4	$7 \times 4 = 28$
8	7	$8 \times 7 = 56$
9	4	$9 \times 4 = 36$
10	2	$10 \times 2 = 20$
Total	20	157

The mean score

$= \dfrac{\text{total of scores}}{\text{number of scores}}$

$= \dfrac{157}{20}$

$= 7.85$

b There are 20 scores, and so the median is the average of the 10th and 11th.

Score	Number of Students
5	1
6	2
7	4
8	7
9	4
10	2

1st student
2nd and 3rd student
4th, 5th, 6th and 7th student
8th, 9th, **10th, 11th,** 12th, 13th, 14th student

STATISTICS PACKAGE

The 10th and 11th students both scored 8 ∴ median = 8.

c Looking down the 'number of students' column, the highest frequency is 7. This corresponds to a score of 8, ∴ mode = 8.

EXERCISE 10E.2

1 The table alongside shows the results when 3 coins were tossed simultaneously 40 times. The number of heads appearing was recorded. Calculate the

   a mode   **b** median   **c** mean.

Number of heads	Number of times occurred
0	6
1	16
2	14
3	4
Total	40

2 The following frequency table records the number of text messages sent in a day by 50 fifteen-year-olds.

No. of messages	Frequency
0	2
1	4
2	7
3	4
4	2
5	0
6	1
7	8
8	13
9	7
10	2

a For this data, find the
   i mean   **ii** median   **iii** mode.

b Construct a column graph for the data and show the position of the measures of centre (mean, median and mode) on the horizontal axis.

c Describe the distribution of the data.

d Why is the mean smaller than the median for this data?

e Which measure of centre would be the most suitable for this data set?

3 The frequency column graph alongside gives the value of donations for an overseas aid organisation, collected in a particular street.

  a Construct a frequency table from the graph.

  b Determine the total number of donations.

  c For the donations find the
    i mean **ii** median **iii** mode.

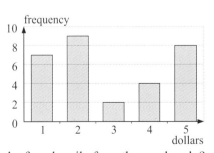

  d Which of the measures of central tendency can be found easily from the graph only?

4 Families at a school were surveyed. The number of children in each family was recorded. The results of the survey are shown alongside:

Number of Children	Frequencies
1	5
2	28
3	15
4	8
5	2
6	1
Total	59

a Calculate the
  i mean **ii** mode **iii** median.

b If the average Canadian family has 2.2 children, how does this school compare to the national average?

c The data set is skewed. Is the skewness positive or negative?

d How has the skewness of the data affected the measures of the middle?

F   CUMULATIVE DATA

Sometimes it is useful to know the number of scores that lie above or below a particular value. In such situations it is convenient to construct a **cumulative frequency distribution table** and a **cumulative frequency graph** to represent the data.

Example 6   ◆)) Self Tutor

The data shown gives the weights of 80 male basketball players.

a Construct a cumulative frequency distribution table.

b Represent the data on a cumulative frequency graph.

c Use your graph to estimate the:
  i median weight
  ii number of men weighing less than 83 kg
  iii number of men weighing more than 92 kg.

Weight (w kg)	frequency
$65 \leqslant w < 70$	1
$70 \leqslant w < 75$	2
$75 \leqslant w < 80$	8
$80 \leqslant w < 85$	16
$85 \leqslant w < 90$	21
$90 \leqslant w < 95$	19
$95 \leqslant w < 100$	8
$100 \leqslant w < 105$	3
$105 \leqslant w < 110$	1
$110 \leqslant w < 115$	1

a

Weight (w kg)	frequency	cumulative frequency
$65 \leqslant w < 70$	1	1
$70 \leqslant w < 75$	2	3 ← this is $1 + 2$
$75 \leqslant w < 80$	8	11 ← this is $1 + 2 + 8$, etc.
$80 \leqslant w < 85$	16	27
$85 \leqslant w < 90$	21	48 ← this 48 means that there are 48 players who weigh less than 90 kg
$90 \leqslant w < 95$	19	67
$95 \leqslant w < 100$	8	75
$100 \leqslant w < 105$	3	78
$105 \leqslant w < 110$	1	79
$110 \leqslant w < 115$	1	80

Note: The cumulative frequency gives a *running total* of the number of players up to certain weights.

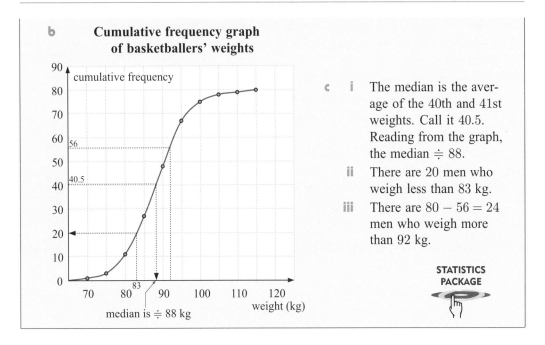

b **Cumulative frequency graph of basketballers' weights**

c **i** The median is the average of the 40th and 41st weights. Call it 40.5. Reading from the graph, the median $\doteqdot$ 88.

ii There are 20 men who weigh less than 83 kg.

iii There are $80 - 56 = 24$ men who weigh more than 92 kg.

STATISTICS PACKAGE

EXERCISE 10F

1 For each of the following distributions:

    i construct a cumulative frequency table

    ii draw a cumulative frequency graph

    iii use your graph to find the median of the data

a

Score	Freq.
0	1
1	3
2	3
3	6
4	12
5	15
6	8
7	5
8	2

b

No. of goals	Freq.
0	7
1	11
2	20
3	22
4	12
5	9
6	5

c

Height	Freq.
$0 \leqslant h < 5$	4
$5 \leqslant h < 10$	8
$10 \leqslant h < 15$	14
$15 \leqslant h < 20$	16
$20 \leqslant h < 25$	10
$25 \leqslant h < 30$	6
$30 \leqslant h < 35$	2

2 The following data shows the lengths of 40 salmon caught in a lake during a fishing competition. Measurements are to the nearest centimetre.

    30 26 38 28 27 31 38 34 40 24 33 30 36 38 32 35 32 36 27 35
    36 37 29 31 33 40 34 37 44 38 36 34 33 31 38 35 36 33 33 28

    a Construct a cumulative frequency table for salmon lengths, x cm, using the following intervals $24 \leqslant x < 27$, $27 \leqslant x < 30$, ... etc.

    b Draw a cumulative frequency graph.

    c Use **b** to find the median length.

    d Use the original data to find its median and compare your answer with **c**. Comment!

3 In an examination the following scores were achieved by a group of students:

Draw a cumulative frequency graph of the data and use it to find:

Score	frequency
$10 \leqslant x < 20$	2
$20 \leqslant x < 30$	6
$30 \leqslant x < 40$	4
$40 \leqslant x < 50$	8
$50 \leqslant x < 60$	12
$60 \leqslant x < 70$	27
$70 \leqslant x < 80$	34
$80 \leqslant x < 90$	18
$90 \leqslant x < 100$	9

  a the median examination mark

  b how many students scored less than 75 marks

  c how many students scored between 60 and 80 marks

  d how many students failed, given that the pass mark was 55

  e the credit mark, given that the top 16% of students were awarded credits.

4 The following frequency distribution was obtained by asking 50 randomly selected people the size of their shoes.

Shoe size	5	$5\frac{1}{2}$	6	$6\frac{1}{2}$	7	$7\frac{1}{2}$	8	$8\frac{1}{2}$	9	$9\frac{1}{2}$	10
frequency	2	0	1	4	6	12	11	7	3	1	1

Draw a cumulative frequency graph of the data and use it to find:

  a the median shoe size

  b how many people had a shoe size of: **i**   7 or more   **ii** $8\frac{1}{2}$ or less.

5 In a cross-country race, the times (in minutes) of 160 competitors were recorded as follows:

Draw a cumulative frequency graph of the data and use it to find:

Time	frequency
$20 \leqslant t < 25$	18
$25 \leqslant t < 30$	45
$30 \leqslant t < 35$	37
$35 \leqslant t < 40$	33
$40 \leqslant t < 45$	19
$45 \leqslant t < 50$	8

  a the median time

  b the approximate number of runners whose time was not more than 32 minutes

  c the approximate time in which the fastest 40 runners competed.

6 The following table is a summary of the distance (to the nearest metre) a cricket ball was thrown by a number of different students.

Distance (m)	$30 \leqslant d < 40$	$40 \leqslant d < 50$	$50 \leqslant d < 60$
frequency	7	17	28

Distance (m)	$60 \leqslant d < 70$	$70 \leqslant d < 80$	$80 \leqslant d < 90$
frequency	15	13	4

Draw a cumulative frequency graph of the data and use it to find:

  a the median distance thrown by the students

  b the number of students who threw the ball less than 45 m

  c the number of students who threw the ball between 55 and 70 m.

  d If only students who threw the ball further than 55 m were considered for further coaching, how many students were considered?

G   MEASURING THE SPREAD (EXTENSION)

Knowing the middle of a data set can be quite useful, but for a more accurate picture of the data set we also need to know its spread.

For example,   2, 3, 4, 5, 6, 7, 8, 9, 10   has a mean value of 6 and so does

                          4, 5, 5, 6, 6, 6, 7, 7, 8.   However, the first data set is more widely spread than the second one.

Three commonly used statistics that indicate the spread of a set of data are the

The range gives us one measure of how the data is spread.

- **range** • **interquartile range** • **standard deviation**.

THE RANGE

The **range** is the difference between the **maximum** (largest) data value and the **minimum** (smallest) data value.

range = maximum data value − minimum data value

Example 7	◄) Self Tutor

Find the range of the data set: 6, 4, 7, 5, 3, 4, 2, 6, 5, 7, 5, 3, 8, 9, 3, 6, 5

range = maximum value − minimum value = $9 - 2 = 7$

THE UPPER AND LOWER QUARTILES AND THE INTERQUARTILE RANGE

The median divides an ordered data set into halves, and these halves are divided in half again by the **quartiles**.

The middle value of the lower half is called the **lower quartile**. One quarter, or 25%, of the data have a value less than or equal to the lower quartile. 75% of the data have values greater than or equal to the lower quartile.

The middle value of the upper half is called the **upper quartile**. One quarter, or 25%, of the data have a value greater than or equal to the upper quartile. 75% of the data have values less than or equal to the upper quartile.

The **interquartile range** is the range of the middle half (50%) of the data.

interquartile range = upper quartile − lower quartile

The data set has been divided into quarters by the lower quartile (Q_1), the median (Q_2) and the upper quartile (Q_3).

So, the interquartile range, $\mathbf{IQR = Q_3 - Q_1}$.

Example 8   ◀◎) **Self Tutor**

For the data set: 6, 4, 7, 5, 3, 4, 2, 6, 5, 7, 5, 3, 8, 9, 3, 6, 5   find the

a median   **b** lower quartile   **c** upper quartile   **d** interquartile range

The ordered data set is:

~~2~~ 3 3 3 4 4 5 5 5 5 6 6 6 7 7 8 ~~9~~ (17 of them)

a   As $n = 17$, $\dfrac{n+1}{2} = 9$

The median = 9th score = 5

b/c As the median is a data value we now ignore it and split the
remaining data into two:

$$\underbrace{2\ 3\ 3\ 3\ 4\ 4\ 5\ 5}_{\text{lower}} \quad \underbrace{5\ 6\ 6\ 6\ 7\ 7\ 8\ 9}_{\text{upper}}$$

Q_1 = median of lower half = $\dfrac{3+4}{2} = 3.5$

Q_3 = median of upper half = $\dfrac{6+7}{2} = 6.5$

d   IQR = $Q_3 - Q_1 = 6.5 - 3.5 = 3$

Example 9   ◀◎) **Self Tutor**

For the data set: 11, 6, 7, 8, 13, 10, 8, 7, 5, 2, 9, 4, 4, 5, 8, 2, 3, 6 find

a   the median   **b**   the lower quartile

c   the upper quartile   **d**   the interquartile range

The ordered data set is:

~~2~~ 2 3 4 4 5 5 6 6 7 7 8 8 8 9 10 11 ~~13~~   (18 of them)

a   As $n = 18$, $\dfrac{n+1}{2} = 9.5$

$\therefore$ median = $\dfrac{\text{9th value} + \text{10th value}}{2} = \dfrac{6+7}{2} = 6.5$

b/c As the median is not a data value we split the data into two:

$$\underbrace{2\ 2\ 3\ 4\ 4\ 5\ 5\ 6\ 6}_{\text{lower}} \quad \underbrace{7\ 7\ 8\ 8\ 8\ 9\ 10\ 11\ 13}_{\text{upper}}$$

$\therefore$ $Q_1 = 4$, $Q_3 = 8$

d   IQR = $Q_3 - Q_1$ **Note:** Some computer packages (for example,
           = $8 - 4$ MS Excel) calculate quartiles in a different
           = 4 way to this example.

EXERCISE 10G

1 For each of the following data sets find:

    i the median (make sure the data is ordered)

    ii the upper and lower quartiles   **iii** the range   **iv** the interquartile range.

  a 5, 6, 6, 6, 7, 7, 7, 8, 8, 8, 8, 9, 9, 9, 9, 9, 10, 10, 11, 11, 11, 12, 12

  b 11, 13, 16, 13, 25, 19, 20, 19, 19, 16, 17, 21, 22, 18, 19, 17, 23, 15

  c 23.8, 24.4, 25.5, 25.5, 26.6, 26.9, 27, 27.3, 28.1, 28.4, 31.5

2 The time spent (in minutes) by 24 people in a queue at a supermarket, waiting to be served at the checkout, has been recorded as follows:

  1.4 5.2 2.4 2.8 3.4 3.8 2.2 1.5

  0.8 0.8 3.9 2.3 4.5 1.4 0.5 0.1

  1.6 4.8 1.9 0.2 3.6 5.2 2.7 3.0

  a Find the median waiting time and the upper and lower quartiles.

  b Find the range and interquartile range of the waiting time.

  c Copy and complete the following statements:

    i "50% of the waiting times were greater than .... minutes."

    ii "75% of the waiting times were less than ...... minutes."

    iii "The minimum waiting time was .... minutes and the maximum waiting time was ..... minutes. The waiting times were spread over ...... minutes."

3

Stem	Leaf
2	0 1 2 2
3	0 0 1 4 4 5 8
4	0 2 3 4 6 6 9
5	1 1 4 5 8

For the data set given, find:

  a the minimum value   **b** the maximum value

  c the median   **d** the lower quartile

  e the upper quartile   **f** the range

  g the interquartile range.

H   BOX-AND-WHISKER PLOTS (EXTENSION)

A **box-and-whisker plot** (or simply a **boxplot**) is a visual display of some of the descriptive statistics of a data set. It shows

- the minimum value
- the lower quartile (Q_1)
- the median (Q_2)
- the upper quartile (Q_3)
- the maximum value

These five numbers form what is known as the **five-number summary** of a data set.

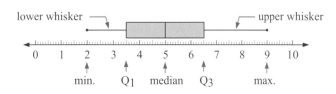

Here is the boxplot for **Example 8**:

The rectangular box represents the 'middle' half of the data set.

The lower whisker represents the 25% of the data with smallest values.

The upper whisker represents the 25% of the data with greatest values.

Example 10   ◀) **Self Tutor**

For the data set: 4 5 9 5 1 7 8 7 3 5 6 3 4 3 2 5

a   construct the five-number summary   b   draw a boxplot
c   find the i range   ii interquartile range
d   find the percentage of data values less than 7.

a   The ordered data set is

1 2 3 3 3 4 4 5 5 5 5 6 7 7 8 9   (16 of them)

$$Q_1 = 3 \qquad \text{median} = 5 \qquad Q_3 = 6.5$$

So the **5-number summary** is:
$$\begin{cases} \text{min. value} = 1 & Q_1 = 3 \\ \text{median} = 5 & Q_3 = 6.5 \\ \text{max. value} = 9 \end{cases}$$

b

c   i   range = max value − min value   ii   IQR = $Q_3 - Q_1$
                = 9 − 1   = 6.5 − 3
                = 8   = 3.5   **STATISTICS PACKAGE**

d   75% of the data values are less than 7.

EXERCISE 10H

1

goals scored by a netball team

a   The boxplot given summarises the goals scored by a netball team. Locate:
   i   the median   ii   the maximum value   iii   the minimum value
   iv the upper quartile v   the lower quartile
b   Calculate: i   the range   ii   the interquartile range

2

scores

The boxplot shown summarises the points scored by a basketball team. Copy and complete the following statements about the test results:

a   The highest score was ...... points.   b   The lowest score was ...... points.
c   Half of the scores were greater than or equal to ..... points.

   d The top 25% of the scores were ..... points.

   e The middle half of the scores were between .... and .... points.

   f Find the range of the data set.

   g Find the interquartile range of the data set.

3 For the following data sets:

      i construct a 5-number summary   **ii** draw a boxplot

      iii find the range   **iv** find the interquartile range

   a 5, 5, 10, 9, 4, 2, 8, 6, 5, 8, 6, 7, 9, 6, 10, 3, 11

   b 7, 0, 4, 6, 8, 8, 9, 5, 6, 8, 8, 8, 9, 8, 1, 8, 3, 7, 2, 7, 4, 5, 9, 4

4 The weight, in kilograms, of a particular brand of bags of firewood is stated to be 20 kg, however some bags weigh more than this and some weigh less. A sample of bags is carefully weighed and their weights are given in the ordered stem-and-leaf plot shown.

Stem	Leaf
18	8
19	5 7 7 8 8 9
20	1 1 1 2 2 5 6 8
21	0 1 1 2 4 6
22	3

20 | 5   represents   20.5 kg

   a Locate the median, upper and lower quartiles and maximum and minimum weights for the sample.

   b Draw a boxplot for the data.

   c Find: **i** the interquartile range   **ii** the range.

   d Copy and complete the following statements about the distribution of weights for the bags of firewood in this sample:

      i Half of the bags of firewood weighed at least .... kg.

      ii .....% of the bags had a weight less than 20 kg.

      iii The weights of the middle 50% of the bags were spread over ...... kg.

      iv The lightest 25% of the bags had a weight of ..... grams or less.

   e Is the distribution of weights in this sample symmetrical or positively or negatively skewed?

PARALLEL BOXPLOTS

Parallel boxplots enable us to make a *visual comparison* of the distributions of two sets of data and their descriptive statistics (e.g., median, range and interquartile range).

Parallel boxplots could be horizontal or vertical.

Example 11   ◀) **Self Tutor**

An office worker has the choice of travelling to work by car or bus and has collected data giving the travel times from recent journeys using both of these types of transport. He is interested to know which type of transport is the quickest to get him to work and which is the most reliable.

Car travel times (m): 13, 14, 18, 18, 19, 21, 22, 22, 24, 25, 27, 28, 30, 33, 43

Bus travel times (m): 16, 16, 16, 17, 17, 18, 18, 18, 20, 20, 21, 21, 23, 28, 30

Prepare parallel boxplots for the data sets and use them to compare the two methods of transport for quickness and reliability.

For car travel: min $= 13$ $Q_1 = 18$ median $= 22$ $Q_3 = 28$ max. $= 43$
For bus travel: min $= 16$ $Q_1 = 17$ median $= 18$ $Q_3 = 21$ max. $= 30$

In the data sets we identify some outliers: 28 and 30 mins by bus and 43 mins by car. They are represented as asterisks on the boxplot, and are not included in the whiskers.

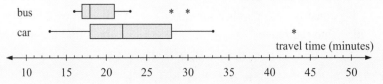

Using the median, 50% of the time, bus travel takes 18 minutes or less, compared with car travel at 22 minutes or less, i.e., bus travel is generally *quicker*.

Comparing spread: range for car $= 43 - 13$ range for bus $= 30 - 16$
$$= 30 \qquad\qquad\qquad = 14$$

$$\text{IQR} = Q_3 - Q_1 \qquad\qquad \text{IQR} = Q_3 - Q_1$$
$$= 28 - 18 \qquad\qquad\qquad = 21 - 17$$
$$= 10 \qquad\qquad\qquad\qquad = 4$$

When comparing these spread measures, they indicate that the bus travel times are less 'spread out' than the car travel times. They are *more predictable or reliable*.

---

5 The following boxplots compare the numbers of students on school buses A and C over a one month period.

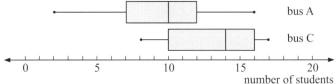

a Find the 5-number summaries for the students on both buses.

b Determine the **i** range **ii** interquartile range   for each group of students.

6 Two classes have completed the same test. Boxplots have been drawn to summarise and display the results. They have been drawn on the same set of axes so that the results can be compared.

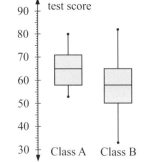

a In which class was:

  i the highest mark   **ii** the lowest mark

  iii there a larger spread of marks?

b Find: **i** the range of marks in class B

    ii the interquartile range for class A.

c If the top 50% of class B passed the test, what percentage of class A passed?

d Describe the distribution of marks in: **i** class A   **ii** class B.

e Copy and complete: The students in class .... generally scored higher marks.
                    The marks in class ...... were more varied.

7 The heights (to the nearest centimetre) of boys and girls in a school year are as follows:

Boys 164 168 175 169 172 171 171 180 168 168 166 168 170 165 171 173 187 179
  181 175 174 165 167 163 160 169 167 172 174 177 188 177 185 167 160

Girls 165 170 158 166 168 163 170 171 177 169 168 165 156 159 165 164 154 170
  171 172 166 152 169 170 163 162 165 163 168 155 175 176 170 166

 a Find the five-number summary for each of the data sets.

 b Compare and comment on the distribution of the data.

STATISTICS FROM TECHNOLOGY

GRAPHICS CALCULATOR

A **graphics calculator** can be used to find descriptive statistics and to draw some types of graphs.

Consider the data set: 5 2 3 3 6 4 5 3 7 5 7 1 8 9 5

No matter what brand of calculator you use you should be able to:

- Enter the data as a list.
- Enter the statistics calculation part of the menu and obtain the descriptive statistics like these shown. $\overline{x}$ is the mean

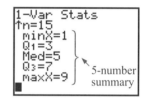

- Obtain a box-and-whisker plot such as:

  These screen dumps are from a TI-83.

- Obtain a vertical barchart if required.

- Enter a second data set into another list and obtain a side-by-side boxplot for comparison with the first one.

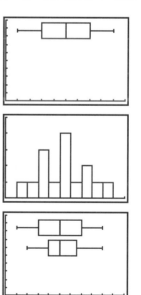

EXERCISE 10I.1

1 For your calculator enter the data set: 5 2 3 3 6 4 5 3 7 5 7 1 8 9 5 and obtain the mean and the 5-number summary. This is the first example above and you should check your results from it.

2 Obtain the boxplot for question **1**.

3 Obtain the vertical bar chart for question **1**.

4 Enter this data set: 9 6 2 3 5 5 7 5 6 7 6 3 4 4 5 8 4 into a second list. Find the mean and 5-number summary. Now create a side-by-side boxplot for both sets of data.

COMPUTER PACKAGE

Various statistical packages are available for computer use, but many are expensive and often not easy to use. Click on the icon to use the statistics package on the CD.

Enter data set 1:   5 2 3 3 6 4 5 3 7 5 7 1 8 9 5

Enter data set 2:   9 6 2 3 5 5 7 5 6 7 6 3 4 4 5 8 4

STATISTICS PACKAGE

Examine the side-by-side column graphs.

Click on the Box & Whisker tab to view the side-by-side boxplots.

Click on the Statistics tab to obtain the descriptive statistics.

Select Print... from the File menu to obtain a print out of all of these on one sheet of paper.

EXERCISE 10I.2

1 Enter the **Opening Problem** data for the *Without fertiliser* data in Set 1 and the *With fertiliser* data in Set 2. Print out the page of graphs, boxplots and descriptive statistics.

2 Enter these grouped continuous data sets:

Set 1:

Value	Frequency
11.6	1
11.7	3
11.8	16
11.9	28
12.0	11
12.1	7
12.2	9

Set 2:

Value	Frequency
11.5	1
11.6	8
11.7	17
11.8	31
11.9	16
12.0	8
12.1	10
12.2	3

Examine the graphs, boxplots and descriptive statistics for each and print the results.

J   STANDARD DEVIATION (EXTENSION)

The problem with the range and the IQR as measures of spread is that both only use two values in their calculation.

Some data sets can have their characteristics hidden when the IQR is quoted. It would be helpful if we could have a measure of spread that used *all* of the data values in its calculation. One such statistic is the **standard deviation**, s.

The **standard deviation** is $s = \sqrt{\dfrac{\sum (x - \overline{x})^2}{n}}$ where $\begin{aligned} & x \text{ is a data value} \\ & \overline{x} \text{ is the mean of the sample} \\ & n \text{ is the sample size.} \end{aligned}$

The **deviation** of a data value x from the mean $\overline{x}$ is given by $x - \overline{x}$.

So, $\dfrac{\sum(x-\overline{x})^2}{n}$ is the average of the sum of the squares of the deviations from the mean.

Notice that in $\dfrac{\sum(x-\overline{x})^2}{n}$ we are squaring the units.

So, by taking the square root we are converting back to the original units.

If we are considering an entire population, we usually call the mean μ (the Greek letter *mu*) and the standard deviation σ (*sigma*).

In general, the population standard deviation σ is unknown, so we use the standard deviation of a sample s as an estimation of σ.

Note: The IQR is a more appropriate tool for measuring spread if the distribution is considerably skewed.

Example 12
🔊 **Self Tutor**

A greengrocer chain is to purchase oranges from two different wholesalers. They take five random samples of 40 oranges to examine them for skin blemishes. The counts for the number of blemished oranges are:

> *Wholesaler Truefruit*   4   16   14   8   8
> *Wholesaler Freshfruit*   9   12   11   10   13

Find the mean and standard deviation for each data set, and hence compare the wholesale suppliers.

Wholesaler Truefruit

x	$x-\overline{x}$	$(x-\overline{x})^2$
4	-6	36
16	6	36
14	4	16
8	-2	4
8	-2	4
50	*Total*	96

$\therefore\ \overline{x}=\dfrac{50}{5}$

$=10$

$s=\sqrt{\dfrac{\sum(x-\overline{x})^2}{n}}$

$=\sqrt{\dfrac{96}{5}}$

$\doteqdot 4.38$

> For TI the standard deviation required is σX. For CASIO the standard deviation is $x\sigma n$.
>
> For the HH statistics package use population standard deviation.

Wholesaler Freshfruit

x	$x-\overline{x}$	$(x-\overline{x})^2$
9	-2	4
12	1	1
11	0	0
10	-1	1
13	2	4
55	*Total*	10

$\therefore\ \overline{x}=\dfrac{55}{5}$

$=11$

$s=\sqrt{\dfrac{\sum(x-\overline{x})^2}{n}}$

$=\sqrt{\dfrac{10}{5}}$

$\doteqdot 1.41$

Clearly, Wholesaler Freshfruit supplied oranges with more blemishes, on average, but with less variability (smaller standard deviation) than for those supplied by Truefruit.

EXERCISE 10J

1 Here are two samples for you to compare.

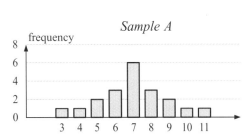

Sample A

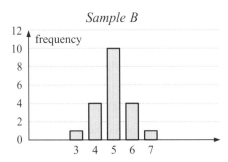

Sample B

  a By looking at the graphs, which distribution appears to have wider spread?
  b Find the mean of each sample.
  c For each sample, find **i** the range **ii** the interquartile range.
  d Calculate the standard deviation, s, for each sample.
  e Explain why s provides a better measure of spread than the other two measures.

2 **a** Find the standard deviation of the data: 3, 4, 5, 6, 7, 20.
  b Recalculate the standard deviation with the outlier removed.
  c What is the effect on the standard deviation if an outlier is removed?

3 Basketballers Andrew and Brad compare their goal throwing scores for the last 8 matches.

Goals by Andrew	23	17	31	25	25	19	28	32
Goals by Brad	9	29	41	26	14	44	38	43

  a Find the mean and standard deviation for the number of goals thrown by each goal shooter for these matches.
  b Which measure is used to determine which of the goal shooters is more consistent?

4 Two baseballers compare their batting performances for a ten game stretch. The number of safe hits per game was recorded as:

Mickey	5	4	1	0	5	4	0	5	4	2
Julio	1	2	3	3	3	4	6	2	3	3

  a Show that each baseballer has the same mean and range.
  b Which performance do you suspect is more variable, Mickey's batting over the period or Julio's?
  c Check your answer to **b** by finding the standard deviation for each distribution.
  d Does the range or the standard deviation give a better indication of variability?

STANDARD DEVIATION FOR GROUPED DATA

For grouped data $s = \sqrt{\dfrac{\sum f(x - \bar{x})^2}{\sum f}}$ where s is the **standard deviation**

x is **any score**

$\bar{x}$ is the **mean**

f is the **frequency** of each score

Example 13   ◀) **Self Tutor**

Find the standard deviation
of the distribution:

score	1	2	3	4	5
frequency	1	2	4	2	1

x	f	fx	$x - \bar{x}$	$(x - \bar{x})^2$	$f(x - \bar{x})^2$
1	1	1	-2	4	4
2	2	4	-1	1	2
3	4	12	0	0	0
4	2	8	1	1	2
5	1	5	2	4	4
Total	10	30			12

$$\bar{x} = \frac{\sum fx}{\sum f} = \frac{30}{10} = 3$$

$$s = \sqrt{\frac{\sum f(x - \bar{x})^2}{\sum f}}$$

$$= \sqrt{\frac{12}{10}}$$

$$\doteqdot 1.10$$

Example 14   ◀) **Self Tutor**

The weights (in kilograms) of 25 calves were
measured and the results placed in a table as
shown alongside.

a Find an estimate of the standard deviation
by using interval midpoints.

b Can the range be found?

Weight (kg)	Frequency
50-	1
60-	3
70-	9
80-	6
90-	4
100- < 110	2

a

Weight class (kg)	Centre of class (x)	Frequency	fx	$f(x - \bar{x})^2$
50-	55	1	55	676
60-	65	3	195	768
70-	75	9	675	324
80-	85	6	510	96
90-	95	4	380	784
100- < 110	105	2	210	1152
	Totals	25	2025	3800

$$\bar{x} = \frac{\sum fx}{\sum f}$$

$$\doteqdot \frac{2025}{25}$$

$$\doteqdot 81$$

$$s = \sqrt{\frac{\sum f(x - \bar{x})^2}{\sum f}}$$

$$\doteqdot \sqrt{\frac{3800}{25}}$$

$$\doteqdot 12.3 \quad \text{(to 3 s.f.)}$$

b As the data has been grouped in classes, we do not know the smallest and
largest data values. Consequently, the range cannot be found.

5 Find the standard deviation of the following test results.

Test score, x	10	11	12	13	14	15
Frequency, f	4	6	7	2	3	2

6 The number of chocolates in 60 boxes was counted and the results tabulated.

Number of chocolates	25	26	27	28	29	30	31	32
Frequency	1	5	7	13	12	12	8	2

Find the mean and standard deviation of the distribution.

7 The lengths of 30 trout were measured to the nearest cm and the following data obtained:

Find estimates of the mean length and the standard deviation of the lengths.

Length (cm)	Frequency
30-	1
32-	1
34-	3
36-	7
38-	11
40-	5
42- <44	2

8 The weekly wages (in dollars) of 90 workers in a steel yard are given alongside:

Find estimates of the mean wage and the standard deviation of the wages.

Wage ($)	Number of Workers
360-369.99	5
370-379.99	16
380-389.99	27
390-399.99	16
400-409.99	12
410-419.99	8
420-429.99	4
430-439.99	2

K | THE NORMAL DISTRIBUTION (EXTENSION)

The normal distribution is the most important distribution for a continuous random variable.

The normal distribution lies at the heart of statistics. Many naturally occurring phenomena have a distribution that is normal, or approximately normal.

Some examples are:
- the heights of 16 year old males
- the distributions of volumes in soft drink cans
- the lengths of adult female tiger sharks
- the lengths of cilia on a cell
- scores on tests taken by a large population
- repeated measurements of the same quantity
- yields of corn or wheat
- life time of batteries

The graphs of the above distributions would be **bell-shaped**, which is an indication of the normal distribution.

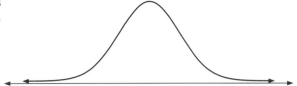

A TYPICAL NORMAL DISTRIBUTION

A large sample of cockle shells was collected and the maximum distance across each shell was measured. Click on the video clip icon to see how a histogram of the data is built up.

Now click on the demo icon to observe the effect of changing the class interval lengths for normally distributed data.

HOW THE NORMAL DISTRIBUTION ARISES

Example 1:

Consider the oranges stripped from an orange tree. They do not all have the same weight. This variation may be due to several factors which could include different genetic factors, different times when the flowers were fertilised, different amounts of sunlight reaching the leaves and fruit, different weather conditions (some may be affected by the prevailing winds more than others), etc.

The result is that much of the fruit could have weights centred about, for example, a mean weight of 214 grams, and there are far fewer oranges that are much heavier or lighter.

Invariably, a bell-shaped distribution of weights would be observed and the normal distribution model fits the data fairly closely.

Example 2:

In manufacturing nails of a given length, say 50 mm, the machines produce nails of average length 50 mm but there is minor variation due to random errors in the manufacturing process. A small standard deviation of 0.3 mm, say, may be observed, but once again a bell-shaped distribution models the situation.

The following bell-shaped curve could represent the distribution of nail lengths.

Once a normal model has been established we can use it to make predictions about the distribution and to answer other relevant questions.

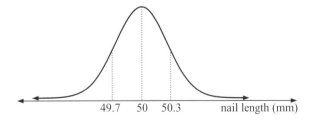

THE SIGNIFICANCE OF STANDARD DEVIATION

If a large sample from a typical bell-shaped data distribution is taken, what percentage of the data values would lie between $\bar{x} - s$ and $\bar{x} + s$?

Click on the icon and try to answer this question. Repeat the sampling many times.

Now try to determine the percentage of data values which would lie between $\bar{x} - 2s$ and $\bar{x} + 2s$ and between $\bar{x} - 3s$ and $\bar{x} + 3s$.

COMPUTER DEMO

It can be shown that for any measured variable from any population that is normally distributed, no matter the values of the mean and standard deviation:

- approximately **68%** of the population will have a measure that falls between **1** standard deviation either side of the mean

- approximately **95%** of the population will have a measure that falls between **2** standard deviations either side of the mean

- approximately **99.7%** of the population will have a measure that falls between **3** standard deviations either side of the mean.

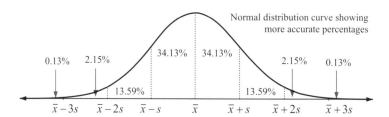

Normal distribution curve showing more accurate percentages

Example 15   ◀)) Self Tutor

A sample of 200 cans of peaches was taken from a warehouse and the contents of each can measured for net weight. The sample mean was 486 g with standard deviation 6.2 g. What proportion of the cans might lie within:

a 1 standard deviation from the mean   **b** 3 standard deviations from the mean?

For a manufacturing process such as this, the distribution of weights in the cans is approximately normal.

a About 68% of the cans would be expected to have contents between 486 ± 6.2 g   i.e.,   479.8 g and 492.2 g.

b Nearly all of the cans would be expected to have contents between $486 \pm 3 \times 6.2$ g   i.e.,   467.4 g and 504.6 g.

EXERCISE 10K

1 Five hundred year 10 students sat for a Mathematics examination. Their marks were normally distributed with a mean of 75 and a standard deviation of 8.

a Copy and complete this bell-shaped curve, assigning scores to the markings on the horizontal axis:

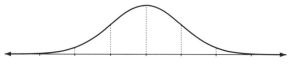

b What was the most likely   **i** maximum score   **ii** minimum score?

c How many students would you expect scored marks

    i more than 83   **ii** less than 59   **iii** between 67 and 91?

2   A sample of 300 bottles of soft drink was taken from a production line and the contents of each bottle measured for net volume. The sample mean was 377 mL with standard deviation 1.5 mL.

   a   Represent this information on a bell-shaped curve.

   b   How many bottles in the sample would you expect to have contents

       i   between 374 and 380 mL   **ii**   more than 375.5 mL?

   c   What proportion of bottles in the production line would you expect to have contents less than 375.5 mL?

3   The mean height of players in a basketball competition is 181 cm. If the standard deviation is 4 cm, what percentage of them are likely to be:

   a   taller than 189 cm   **b**   taller than 177 cm

   c   between 169 cm and 189 cm   **d**   shorter than 185 cm?

4   The mean average rainfall of Charleville for August is 68 mm with a standard deviation of 8 mm. Over a 40 year period, how many times would you expect there to be less than 52 mm of rainfall during August?

REVIEW SET 10A

1   Classify the following variables as either categorical or numerical:

   a   the country of origin of a person

   b   the heights of seedlings after two weeks

   c   the scores of team members in a darts competition.

2   A randomly selected sample of small businesses has been asked, "How many full-time employees are there in your business?". A column graph has been constructed for the results.

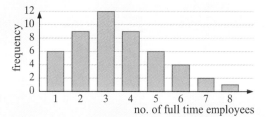

   a   How many small businesses gave data in the survey?

   b   How many of the businesses had only one or two full-time employees?

   c   What percentage of the businesses had five or more full-time employees?

   d   Describe the distribution of the data.

3   A class of 20 students was asked "How many children are there in your household?" and the following data was collected:

       1 2 3 3 2 4 5 4 2 3 8 1 2 1 3 2 1 2 1 2

   a   What is the variable in the investigation?

   b   Is the data discrete or continuous? Why?

   c   Construct a dotplot to display the data showing a heading for the graph, a scale and clearly labelled axes.

   d   How would you describe the distribution of the data? Is it symmetrical, positively or negatively skewed? Are there any outliers?

4 The test score out of 40 marks was recorded for a group of 30 students:

25	18	35	32	34	28	24	39	29	33
22	34	39	31	36	35	36	33	35	40
26	25	20	18	9	40	32	23	28	27

  a Construct a stem-and-leaf plot for this data using 0, 1, 2, 3 and 4 as the stems.

  b Redraw the stem-and-leaf plot so that it is ordered.

  c What advantage does the stem-and-leaf plot have over a frequency table?

  d What was the **i** highest **ii** lowest mark scored for the test?

  e If an 'A' was awarded to students who scored 36 or more for the test, what percentage of students scored an 'A'?

5 Eight scores produce an average of six. Scores of 15 and x increase the average to 7. Find x.

6 For the following sample of weights (in kg) of Year 10 students, find:

  a the minimum weight

  b the maximum weight

  c the number of students with a weight greater than 52 kg

  d the number of students with a weight of at least 70 kg

  e the percentage of students with a weight less than 48 kg.

Stem	Leaf
3	2 4 8
4	0 4 4 7 9 9 9
5	0 0 1 2 2 3 3 5 5 6 8 8
6	0 1 2 4 4 5 7 9
7	0 2 6
8	4
9	1

9 | 1 represents 91

7 A frequency table for the masses of eggs in a carton marked '50 g eggs' is given below.

Mass (g)	Frequency
48 -	1
49 -	1
50 -	16
51 -	4
52 - <55	3

  a Explain why 'mass' is a continuous variable.

  b Construct a histogram for the data. The axes should be carefully marked and labelled and include a heading for the graph.

  c What is the modal class? Explain what this means.

  d Describe the distribution of the data.

8 For the following data set, showing the number of goals scored by a netball team, find:

  a the median
      b the upper and lower quartiles

  c the range
      d the interquartile range.

    28, 24, 16, 6, 46, 34, 43, 16, 36, 49, 30, 28, 4, 31, 47, 41, 26, 25, 20, 29, 42

9

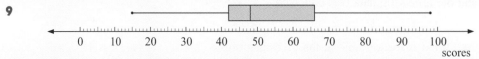

  a From the boxplot that shows the scores out of 100 for an exam, state:

    i the median score
           ii the maximum score

    iii the minimum score
         iv the upper quartile

    v the lower quartile

  b Calculate: **i** the range   **ii** the interquartile range of scores.

10 The weights to the nearest 0.1 kg of a sample of chickens were:

0.8,   0.7,   1.0,   0.9,   0.9,   0.8,   0.9,   1.0,   1.0,   0.8

    a Find the sample mean and standard deviation.

    b In the next 3 months, the weights of the chickens doubled. Find the new sample mean and standard deviation.

    c Comment, in general terms, on your findings from **a** and **b**.

REVIEW SET 10B

1 **a** State whether a census or a survey would be used in this investigation:
      Finding the preferred time of day for shopping at a supermarket.

    b Comment on possible bias when conducting this investigation.

2 The data below is the scores (out of 100) for a Mathematics examination for 45 students.

58	31	80	69	70	71	82	91	94	60	68	58	90	83	72
75	65	76	69	66	64	57	58	77	92	94	49	61	66	91
64	53	89	91	78	61	74	82	97	70	82	66	55	45	63

    a Construct a stem-and-leaf plot for this data using 3, 4, 5, 6, 7, 8 and 9 as the stems.

    b Redraw the stem-and-leaf plot so that it is ordered.

    c What advantages does a stem-and-leaf plot have over a frequency table?

    d What is the **i** highest **ii** lowest   mark scored for the examination?

    e If an 'A' was awarded to students who scored 85 or more for the examination, what percentage of students scored an 'A'?

    f Would you describe this distribution as:

      i symmetric   **ii** skewed   **iii** neither symmetric nor skewed?

3 Find the **a** mean **b** median **c** mode   for the following data set:

13   16   15   17   14   13   13   15   16   14
16   14   15   15   15   13   17   14   12   14

4 A sample of 15 measurements has a mean of 14.2 and a sample of 10 measurements has a mean of 12.6. Find the mean of the total sample of 25 measurements.

5 Determine the mean of the numbers 7, 5, 7, 2, 8 and 7. If two additional numbers, 2 and x, reduce the mean by 1, find x.

6 The given table shows the distribution of scores in a Year 10 spelling test.

    a Calculate the: **i** mean   **ii** mode
                      iii median   **iv** range of the scores

Score	Frequency
6	2
7	4
8	7
9	12
10	5
Total	30

    b The average score for all Year 10 students across Australia in this spelling test was 6.2. How does this class compare to the national average?

    c The data set is skewed. Is the skewness positive or negative?

7 In a one month period at a particular hospital the lengths of newborn babies were recorded to the nearest mm.

The results are shown in the table alongside.

length (cm)	frequency
$48 \leqslant l < 49$	1
$49 \leqslant l < 50$	3
$50 \leqslant l < 51$	9
$51 \leqslant l < 52$	10
$52 \leqslant l < 53$	16
$53 \leqslant l < 54$	4
$54 \leqslant l < 55$	5
$55 \leqslant l < 56$	2

a Represent the data on a histogram.

b How many babies are 52 cm or more?

c What percentage of babies have lengths in the interval 50 cm $\leqslant l < 53$ cm?

d Construct a cumulative frequency distribution table.

e Represent the data on a cumulative frequency graph.

f Use your graph to estimate:

   i the median length

   ii the number of babies whose length is less than 51.5 cm.

8 For the following data set that shows the amount of money spent on lunch by a sample of office workers:

a construct a 5-number summary

b draw a boxplot

c find the range of money spent.

d What was the range of money spent by the middle 50% of office workers surveyed?

Stem	Leaf
8	6
9	0 2 5 5 7
10	0 1 1 1 2 4 4 6
11	3 6 6 8 8
12	0

8 | 6 represents $8.60

9 The given parallel boxplots represent the 100-metre swim times for the members of a swimming squad.

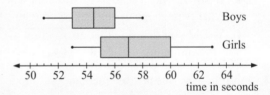

Copy and complete the following:

a Comparing the median swim times for girls and boys shows that, in general, ... swim ...... seconds faster than the ......

b The range of the girls' swim times is ...... seconds compared to the range of ...... seconds for the boys.

c The fastest 25% of the boys swim faster than ......% of the girls.

d ......% of the boys swim faster than 60 seconds whereas ......% of the girls swim faster than 60 seconds.

10 The life of a clock battery is found to be normally distributed with a mean of 35.4 weeks and a standard deviation of 2.8 weeks.

In a batch of 500 batteries, find the number of batteries that probably:

a lasted at least 38.2 weeks

b lasted less than 29.8 weeks

c lasted between 35.4 and 41 weeks.

Chapter 11

Quadratic equations

Contents:

Equations of the form $ax + b = 0$ are called **linear equations** and have *only one* solution.

For example, $3x - 2 = 0$ is a linear equation ($a = 3$ and $b = -2$) and has the one solution, $x = \frac{2}{3}$.

> **Quadratic equations** can be written in the form $ax^2 + bx + c = 0$.

Quadratic equations may have *two*, *one* or *zero* solutions. We can demonstrate this with some examples.

Equation	$ax^2 + bx + c = 0$ form	a	b	c	Solutions	
$x^2 - 4 = 0$	$x^2 + 0x - 4 = 0$	1	0	-4	$x = 2$ or $x = -2$	**two**
$(x - 2)^2 = 0$	$x^2 - 4x + 4 = 0$	1	-4	4	$x = 2$	**one**
$x^2 + 4 = 0$	$x^2 + 0x + 4 = 0$	1	0	4	none as x^2 is always $\geqslant 0$	**zero**

Now consider the example, $x^2 + 3x - 10 = 0$

$$\begin{aligned}\text{if}\quad x = 2,\qquad & x^2 + 3x - 10 \\ &= 2^2 + 3 \times 2 - 10 \\ &= 4 + 6 - 10 \\ &= 0\end{aligned}\qquad\qquad\begin{aligned}\text{and if}\quad x = -5,\qquad & x^2 + 3x - 10 \\ &= (-5)^2 + 3 \times -5 - 10 \\ &= 25 - 15 - 10 \\ &= 0\end{aligned}$$

Because $x = 2$ and $x = -5$ both satisfy the equation $x^2 + 3x - 10 = 0$ we say that they are **solutions** of it.

But, how do we find these solutions without using trial and error?

Diadro Dress Company makes and sells dresses.

If x dresses are made each day their income function is given by $I = 4.2x^2 - 31.6x + 3200$ dollars.

How many dresses must be made and sold each week in order to obtain an income of $6000 each week?

Clearly the equation

$4.2x^2 - 31.6x + 3200 = 6000$ must be solved.

How can we solve this equation?

QUADRATIC EQUATIONS OF THE FORM $x^2 = k$

Consider the equation $x^2 - 7 = 0$

i.e., $x^2 = 7$ (adding 7 to both sides)

Notice that $\sqrt{7} \times \sqrt{7} = 7$,   so $x = \sqrt{7}$ is one solution

and $(-\sqrt{7}) \times (-\sqrt{7}) = 7$,   so $x = -\sqrt{7}$ is also a solution.

Thus,   if $x^2 = 7$,   then $x = \pm\sqrt{7}$.

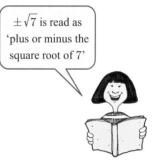

$\pm\sqrt{7}$ is read as 'plus or minus the square root of 7'

SOLUTION OF $x^2 = k$ (REVIEW)

$$\text{If} \quad x^2 = k \quad \text{then} \quad \begin{cases} x = \pm\sqrt{k} & \text{if } k > 0 \\ x = 0 & \text{if } k = 0 \\ \text{there are } \textbf{no real solutions} & \text{if } k < 0 \end{cases}$$

Example 1   ◀» **Self Tutor**

Solve for x: a $2x^2 + 1 = 15$ b $2 - 3x^2 = 8$

a $2x^2 + 1 = 15$

$\therefore \quad 2x^2 = 14$ {take 1 from both sides}

$\therefore \quad x^2 = 7$ {divide both sides by 2}

$\therefore \quad x = \pm\sqrt{7}$

b $2 - 3x^2 = 8$

$\therefore \quad -3x^2 = 6$ {take 2 from both sides}

$\therefore \quad x^2 = -2$ {dividing both sides by -3}

which has no solutions as x^2 cannot be < 0.

EXERCISE 11A

1   Solve for x:

a $x^2 = 100$ b $2x^2 = 50$ c $5x^2 = 20$

d $6x^2 = 54$ e $5x^2 = -45$ f $7x^2 = 0$

g $3x^2 - 2 = 25$ h $4 - 2x^2 = 12$ i $4x^2 + 2 = 10$

Example 2
🔊 **Self Tutor**

Solve for x:

a $(x - 3)^2 = 16$

b $(x + 2)^2 = 11$

> Did you notice that for equations of the form $(x \pm a)^2 = k$ we did not expand the LHS?

a $(x - 3)^2 = 16$
$\therefore \quad x - 3 = \pm\sqrt{16}$
$\therefore \quad x - 3 = \pm 4$
$\therefore \quad x = 3 \pm 4$
$\therefore \quad x = 7 \text{ or } -1$

b $(x + 2)^2 = 11$
$\therefore \quad x + 2 = \pm\sqrt{11}$
$\therefore \quad x = -2 \pm \sqrt{11}$

2 Solve for x:

a $(x - 1)^2 = 9$

b $(x + 4)^2 = 16$

c $(x + 2)^2 = -1$

d $(x - 4)^2 = 5$

e $(x - 6)^2 = -4$

f $(x + 2)^2 = 0$

g $(2x - 5)^2 = 0$

h $(3x + 2)^2 = 4$

i $\frac{1}{3}(2x + 3)^2 = 2$

B   THE NULL FACTOR LAW

When the product of two (or more) numbers is zero, then *at least one* of them must be zero,

i.e.,   if $ab = 0$ then $a = 0$ or $b = 0$.

Example 3
🔊 **Self Tutor**

Solve for x using the Null Factor law:

a $3x(x - 5) = 0$

b $(x - 4)(3x + 7) = 0$

a $3x(x - 5) = 0$
$\therefore \quad 3x = 0 \text{ or } x - 5 = 0$
$\therefore \quad x = 0 \text{ or } 5$

b $(x - 4)(3x + 7) = 0$
$\therefore \quad x - 4 = 0 \text{ or } 3x + 7 = 0$
$\therefore \quad x = 4 \text{ or } 3x = -7$
$\therefore \quad x = 4 \text{ or } -\frac{7}{3}$

EXERCISE 11B

1 Solve for the unknown using the Null Factor law:

a $3x = 0$

b $5y = 0$

c $a \times 8 = 0$

d $b \times -2 = 0$

e $-7y = 0$

f $ab = 0$

g $2xy = 0$

h $abc = 0$

i $x^2 = 0$

j $a^2 = 0$

k $pqrs = 0$

l $a^2 b = 0$

2 Solve for x using the Null Factor law:

a $x(x - 5) = 0$

b $2x(x + 3) = 0$

c $(x + 1)(x - 3) = 0$

d $3x(7 - x) = 0$

e $-2x(x + 1) = 0$

f $4(x + 6)(2x - 3) = 0$

g $x^2 = 0$

h $4(5 - x)^2 = 0$

i $-3(3x - 1)^2 = 0$

To use the **Null Factor law** when solving equations, we must have one side of the equation *equal to zero*.

STEPS FOR SOLVING QUADRATIC EQUATIONS

Step 1:   If necessary rearrange the equation with one side being **zero**.

Step 2:   **Fully factorise** the other side (usually the LHS).

Step 3:   Use the **Null Factor law**.

Step 4:   **Solve** the resulting linear equations.

Step 5:   **Check** at least one of your solutions.

Example 4   ◆) **Self Tutor**

Solve for x: $x^2 = 3x$

$$x^2 = 3x$$
$$\therefore \quad x^2 - 3x = 0 \qquad \{\text{'equating to zero'   i.e.,   RHS} = 0\}$$
$$\therefore \quad x(x-3) = 0 \qquad \{\text{factorising the LHS}\}$$
$$\therefore \quad x = 0 \quad \text{or} \quad x - 3 = 0 \qquad \{\text{Null Factor law}\}$$
$$\therefore \quad x = 0 \quad \text{or} \quad x = 3$$
$$\therefore \quad x = 0 \text{ or } 3$$

If $a \times b = 0$ then either $a = 0$ or $b = 0$.

ILLEGAL CANCELLING

Let us reconsider the equation $x^2 = 3x$ from **Example 4**.

If we cancel x from both sides we have $\dfrac{x^2}{x} = \dfrac{3x}{x}$ and we finish with $x = 3$.

Consequently, we have 'lost' the solution $x = 0$.

From this example we conclude that:

> We must never cancel a variable that is a common factor from both sides of an equation unless we know that the factor cannot be zero.

3   Solve for x:

a	$x^2 - 7x = 0$	**b**	$x^2 - 5x = 0$	**c**	$x^2 = 8x$
d	$x^2 = 4x$	**e**	$3x^2 + 6x = 0$	**f**	$2x^2 + 5x = 0$
g	$4x^2 - 3x = 0$	**h**	$4x^2 = 5x$	**i**	$3x^2 = 9x$

Example 5   ◀) **Self Tutor**

Solve for x: $x^2 + 3x = 28$

$$x^2 + 3x = 28$$
$$\therefore \quad x^2 + 3x - 28 = 0 \qquad \text{\{one side must be 0\}}$$
$$\therefore \quad (x + 7)(x - 4) = 0 \qquad \text{\{as sum} = +3 \text{ and product} = -28$$
$$\text{gives } +7 \text{ and } -4\}$$
$$\therefore \quad x + 7 = 0 \quad \text{or} \quad x - 4 = 0 \qquad \text{\{Null Factor law\}}$$
$$\therefore \quad x = -7 \text{ or } 4 \qquad \text{\{solving linear equations\}}$$

4 Solve for x:

   a $x^2 - 1 = 0$ b $x^2 - 9 = 0$ c $(x - 5)^2 = 0$

   d $(x + 2)^2 = 0$ e $x^2 + 3x + 2 = 0$ f $x^2 - 3x + 2 = 0$

   g $x^2 + 5x + 6 = 0$ h $x^2 - 5x + 6 = 0$ i $x^2 + 7x + 6 = 0$

   j $x^2 + 9x + 14 = 0$ k $x^2 + 11x = -30$ l $x^2 + 2x = 15$

   m $x^2 + 4x = 12$ n $x^2 = 11x - 24$ o $x^2 = 14x - 49$

5 Solve for x:

   a $x^2 + 9x + 14 = 0$ b $x^2 + 11x + 30 = 0$ c $x^2 + 2x = 15$

   d $x^2 + x = 12$ e $x^2 + 6 = 5x$ f $x^2 + 4 = 4x$

   g $x^2 = x + 6$ h $x^2 = 7x + 60$ i $x^2 = 3x + 70$

   j $10 - 3x = x^2$ k $x^2 + 12 = 7x$ l $9x + 36 = x^2$

Example 6   ◀) **Self Tutor**

Solve for x: $5x^2 = 3x + 2$

$$5x^2 = 3x + 2$$
$$\therefore \quad 5x^2 - 3x - 2 = 0 \qquad \text{\{making the RHS} = 0\}$$
$$\therefore \quad 5x^2 - 5x + 2x - 2 = 0 \qquad \text{\{} ac = -10, \quad b = -3$$
$$\therefore \quad 5x(x - 1) + 2(x - 1) = 0 \qquad \therefore \text{ numbers are } -5 \text{ and } +2\}$$
$$\therefore \quad (x - 1)(5x + 2) = 0 \qquad \text{\{factorising\}}$$
$$\therefore \quad x - 1 = 0 \quad \text{or} \quad 5x + 2 = 0 \qquad \text{\{Null Factor law\}}$$
$$\therefore \quad x = 1 \quad \text{or} -\tfrac{2}{5} \qquad \text{\{solving the linear equations\}}$$

6 Solve for x:

   a $2x^2 + 2 = 5x$ b $3x^2 + 8x = 3$ c $3x^2 + 17x + 20 = 0$

   d $2x^2 + 5x = 3$ e $2x^2 + 5 = 11x$ f $2x^2 + 7x + 5 = 0$

   g $3x^2 + 13x + 4 = 0$ h $5x^2 = 13x + 6$ i $2x^2 + 17x = 9$

   j $2x^2 + 3x = 5$ k $3x^2 + 2x = 8$ l $2x^2 + 9x = 18$

Example 7   ◀)) **Self Tutor**

Solve for x: $10x^2 - 13x - 3 = 0$

$$10x^2 - 13x - 3 = 0 \qquad \{ac = -30, \quad b = -13$$
$$\therefore \quad 10x^2 - 15x + 2x - 3 = 0 \qquad \therefore \text{ numbers are } -15 \text{ and } 2\}$$
$$\therefore \quad 5x(2x - 3) + 1(2x - 3) = 0 \qquad \{\text{factorising in pairs}\}$$
$$\therefore \quad (2x - 3)(5x + 1) = 0 \qquad \{\text{common factor factorisation}\}$$
$$\therefore \quad 2x - 3 = 0 \text{ or } 5x + 1 = 0 \qquad \{\text{using the Null Factor law}\}$$
$$\therefore \quad x = \tfrac{3}{2} \text{ or } -\tfrac{1}{5} \qquad \{\text{solving the linear equations}\}$$

7 Solve for x:

   a $6x^2 + 13x = 5$ **b** $6x^2 = x + 2$ **c** $6x^2 + 5x + 1 = 0$

   d $21x^2 = 62x + 3$ **e** $10x^2 + x = 2$ **f** $10x^2 = 7x + 3$

8 Solve for x by first expanding brackets and then equating to zero:

   a $x(x + 5) + 2(x + 6) = 0$ **b** $x(1 + x) + x = 3$

   c $(x - 1)(x + 9) = 8x$ **d** $3x(x + 2) - 5(x - 3) = 17$

   e $4x(x + 1) = -1$ **f** $2x(x - 6) = x - 20$

C   COMPLETING THE SQUARE

Try as much as we like, we will not be able to solve quadratic equations such as $x^2 + 4x - 7 = 0$ by using the factorisation methods already practised. This is because the solutions are not rationals.

To solve this equation we need a different technique.

Consider the solution to the equation $(x + 2)^2 = 11$
$$\therefore \quad x + 2 = \pm\sqrt{11}$$
$$\therefore \quad x = -2 \pm \sqrt{11}$$

$$\text{However, if } (x + 2)^2 = 11$$
$$\text{then } x^2 + 4x + 4 = 11$$
$$\text{and } x^2 + 4x - 7 = 0$$

and so the solutions to $x^2 + 4x - 7 = 0$ are the solutions to $(x + 2)^2 = 11$.

Consequently, an approach for solving such equations could be to reverse the above argument.

$$\text{Consider } x^2 + 4x - 7 = 0$$
$$\therefore \quad x^2 + 4x = 7$$
$$\therefore \quad x^2 + 4x + 4 = 7 + 4$$
$$\therefore \quad (x + 2)^2 = 11$$
$$\therefore \quad x + 2 = \pm\sqrt{11}$$
$$\therefore \quad x = -2 \pm \sqrt{11}$$

Hence the solutions to $x^2 + 4x - 7 = 0$ are $x = -2 \pm \sqrt{11}$.

From the above example it can be seen that a **perfect square** needs to be created on the left hand side. The process used is called **completing the square**.

From our previous study of perfect squares we observe that:

$$(x+3)^2 = x^2 + 2 \times 3 \times x + 3^2 \quad \longleftarrow \quad \text{notice that} \quad 3^2 = \left(\frac{2 \times 3}{2}\right)^2$$

$$(x-5)^2 = x^2 - 2 \times 5 \times x + 5^2 \quad \longleftarrow \quad \text{notice that} \quad 5^2 = \left(\frac{2 \times 5}{2}\right)^2$$

$$(x+p)^2 = x^2 + 2 \times p \times x + p^2 \quad \longleftarrow \quad \text{notice that} \quad p^2 = \left(\frac{2 \times p}{2}\right)^2$$

i.e.,   the constant term is "**the square of half the coefficient of x**".

Example 8   ◄)) **Self Tutor**

To create a perfect square on the LHS, what must be added to both sides of the equation   **a** $x^2 + 8x = -5$ **b** $x^2 - 6x = 13$?

What does the equation become in each case?

a   In $x^2 + 8x = -5$, half the coefficient of x is $\frac{8}{2} = 4$

so, we add 4^2 to both sides

and the equation becomes $x^2 + 8x + 4^2 = -5 + 4^2$

$$(x+4)^2 = -5 + 16$$
$$(x+4)^2 = 11$$

b   In $x^2 - 6x = 13$, half the coefficient of x is $\frac{-6}{2} = -3$

so, we add $(-3)^2 = 3^2$ to both sides

and the equation becomes $x^2 - 6x + 3^2 = 13 + 3^2$

$$(x-3)^2 = 13 + 9$$
$$(x-3)^2 = 22$$

Notice that we keep the equation balanced by adding the same to both sides of the equation.

EXERCISE 11C

1   For each of the following equations:

    i   find what must be added to both sides of the equation to create a perfect square on the LHS

    ii   write each equation in the form $(x+p)^2 = k$

  a $x^2 + 2x = 5$ **b** $x^2 - 2x = -7$ **c** $x^2 + 6x = 2$

  d $x^2 - 6x = -3$ **e** $x^2 + 10x = 1$ **f** $x^2 - 8x = 5$

  g $x^2 + 12x = 13$ **h** $x^2 + 5x = -2$ **i** $x^2 - 7x = 4$

Example 9   ◄)) **Self Tutor**

Solve for x by completing the square, leaving answers in surd form:

a $x^2 + 2x - 2 = 0$ b $x^2 - 4x + 6 = 0$

a $x^2 + 2x - 2 = 0$
∴ $x^2 + 2x \quad = 2$ {move constant term to RHS}
∴ $x^2 + 2x + 1^2 = 2 + 1^2$ {add $(\frac{2}{2})^2 = 1^2$ to both sides}
∴ $(x + 1)^2 = 3$ {factorise LHS, simplify RHS}
∴ $x + 1 = \pm\sqrt{3}$
∴ $x = -1 \pm \sqrt{3}$

So, solutions are $x = -1 + \sqrt{3}$ or $-1 - \sqrt{3}$.

b $x^2 - 4x + 6 = 0$
∴ $x^2 - 4x \quad = -6$ {move the constant term to the RHS}
∴ $x^2 - 4x + 2^2 = -6 + 2^2$ {add $(-\frac{4}{2})^2 = 2^2$ to both sides}
∴ $(x - 2)^2 = -2$ {factorise the LHS, simplify the RHS}

which is impossible as no perfect square can be negative
∴   no real solutions exist.

Remember that if
$x^2 = k$, where $k > 0$
then $x = \pm\sqrt{k}$.

2   If possible, solve for x using 'completing the square', leaving answers in surd form:

a $x^2 - 4x + 1 = 0$ b $x^2 - 2x - 2 = 0$ c $x^2 - 4x - 3 = 0$
d $x^2 + 2x - 1 = 0$ e $x^2 + 2x + 4 = 0$ f $x^2 + 4x + 1 = 0$
g $x^2 + 6x + 3 = 0$ h $x^2 - 6x + 11 = 0$ i $x^2 + 8x + 14 = 0$

3   Using the method of 'completing the square' solve for x, leaving answers in surd form.

a $x^2 + 3x + 2 = 0$ b $x^2 = 4x + 8$ c $x^2 - 5x + 6 = 0$
d $x^2 + x - 1 = 0$ e $x^2 + 3x - 1 = 0$ f $x^2 + 5x - 2 = 0$

4   a   To solve $3x^2 + 6x - 1 = 0$ by 'completing the square' our first step must be to divide both sides by 3, and this results in $x^2 + 2x - \frac{1}{3} = 0$.   Explain why this statement is true.

    b   Use 'completing the square' to solve
       i $2x^2 + 4x - 1 = 0$ ii $3x^2 - 12x + 7 = 0$ iii $5x^2 - 10x + 3 = 0$

PROBLEM SOLVING (QUADRATIC EQUATIONS)

Contained in this section are problems which when converted to algebraic form result in a **quadratic equation**.

It is essential that you are successful at solving these equations using **factorisation** or 'completing the square'.

PROBLEM SOLVING METHOD

Step 1:   Carefully read the question until you understand the problem. A rough sketch may be useful.

Step 2:   Decide on the unknown quantity, calling it x, say.

Step 3:   Find an equation which connects x and the information you are given.

Step 4:   Solve the equation using one of the methods you have learnt.

Step 5:   Check that any solutions satisfy the equation and are realistic to the problem.

Step 6:   Write your answer to the question in sentence form.

Example 10   ◀) Self Tutor

The sum of a number and its square is 42. Find the number.

Let the number be x.   Therefore its square is x^2.

$$x + x^2 = 42$$
$$\therefore \quad x^2 + x - 42 = 0 \qquad \{\text{rearranging}\}$$
$$\therefore \quad (x + 7)(x - 6) = 0 \qquad \{\text{factorising}\}$$
$$\therefore \quad x = -7 \quad \text{or} \quad x = 6$$

Check: If $x = -7$, $-7 + (-7)^2 = -7 + 49 = 42$ ✓
            If $x = 6$, $6 + 6^2 = 6 + 36 = 42$ ✓

So, the number is -7 or 6.

EXERCISE 11D

1   The sum of a number and its square is 90. Find the number.

2   The product of a number and the number decreased by 3 is 108. Find the two possible answers for the number.

3   When 32 is subtracted from the square of a number the result is four times the original number. Find the number.

4   The sum of two numbers is 9 and the sum of their squares is 153. Find the numbers.

5   Two numbers differ by 5 and the sum of their squares is 17. Find the numbers.

Example 11   ◀) **Self Tutor**

A rectangle has length 5 cm greater than its width. If it has an area of 84 cm^2, find the dimensions of the rectangle.

If x cm is the width, then $(x + 5)$ cm is the length.

Now   area $= 84$ cm^2

$\therefore \quad x(x + 5) = 84$

$\therefore \quad x^2 + 5x = 84$

$\therefore \quad x^2 + 5x - 84 = 0$

$\therefore \quad (x + 12)(x - 7) = 0$ {on factorisation}

$\therefore \quad x = -12$ or 7

But $x > 0$ as lengths are positive quantities, $\therefore \quad x = 7$

$\therefore$ the rectangle is 7 cm by 12 cm.

[rectangle diagram: width labelled x cm, length labelled $(x + 5)$ cm]

6   A rectangle has length 5 cm greater than its width. Find its width given that its area is 150 cm^2.

7   A triangle has base 3 cm more than its altitude. If its area is 20 cm^2, find its altitude.

8   A rectangular enclosure is made from 50 m of fencing. The area enclosed is 144 m^2. Find the dimensions of the enclosure.

9   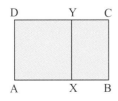   A rectangular garden bed was built against an existing brick wall. 25 m of edging was used to enclose 72 m^2.

Find the dimensions of the garden bed.

10   Use the theorem of Pythagoras to find x given:

a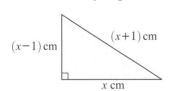

b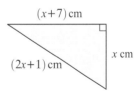

11   A right angled triangle has sides 1 cm and 18 cm respectively less than its hypotenuse. Find the length of each side of the triangle.

12   A forestry worker plants 1500 pine trees. The number of pine trees in each row is 10 less than twice the number of rows. If equal numbers of pine trees were planted in each row, how many rows did the forestry worker plant?

13

[diagram: rectangle ABCD with points D, Y, C across the top and A, X, B across the bottom; square AXYD shaded]

ABCD is a rectangle in which AB $= 21$ cm.

The square AXYD is removed and the remaining rectangle has area 80 cm^2.

Find the length of BC.

14 A, B, C and D are posts on the banks of a 20 m wide canal. A and B are 1 m apart.

If OA is the same length as CD, find how far C and D are apart.

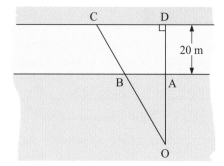

15

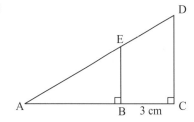

AB is 2 cm longer than BE. DC is 3 cm less than twice BE.

a Explain why triangles ABE and ACD are similar.

b If BE $= x$ cm, show that $x^2 - 4x - 6 = 0$.

c Hence, show that BE $= 2 + \sqrt{10}$ cm.

Example 12 ◀)) **Self Tutor**

The sum of a number and four times its reciprocal is $8\frac{1}{2}$. Find the number.

Let the number be x.   Therefore, its reciprocal is $\dfrac{1}{x}$.

$$x + 4 \times \frac{1}{x} = 8\tfrac{1}{2} \qquad \text{\{as the sum is } 8\tfrac{1}{2}\}$$

$$\therefore \ \frac{x}{1} + \frac{4}{x} = \frac{17}{2} \qquad \text{which has a LCD of } 2x$$

$$\therefore \ \frac{x}{1} \times \frac{2x}{2x} + \frac{4}{x} \times \frac{2}{2} = \frac{17}{2} \times \frac{x}{x} \qquad \text{\{to achieve a common denominator\}}$$

$$\therefore \ 2x^2 + 8 = 17x \qquad \text{\{equating the numerators\}}$$

$$\therefore \ 2x^2 - 17x + 8 = 0 \qquad \text{\{equating to zero\}}$$

$$\therefore \ 2x^2 - x - 16x + 8 = 0 \qquad \text{\{splitting the middle term\}}$$

$$\therefore \ x(2x - 1) - 8(2x - 1) = 0 \qquad \text{\{factorising in pairs\}}$$

$$\therefore \ (2x - 1)(x - 8) = 0 \qquad \text{\{common factor\}}$$

$$\therefore \ 2x - 1 = 0 \ \text{ or } \ x - 8 = 0 \qquad \text{\{Null Factor law\}}$$

$$\therefore \ x = \tfrac{1}{2} \ \text{ or } \ 8$$

So, the number is $\tfrac{1}{2}$ or 8.   *Check:* $\tfrac{1}{2} + 4 \times 2 = 8\tfrac{1}{2}$ ✓ $8 + 4 \times \tfrac{1}{8} = 8\tfrac{1}{2}$ ✓

---

16 The sum of a number and its reciprocal is $2\frac{1}{12}$. Find the number.

17 The sum of a number and twice its reciprocal is $3\frac{2}{3}$. Find the number.

18 A square sheet of cardboard has sides 20 cm long. It is to be made into an open box with a base having an area of 100 cm^2, by cutting out equal squares from the four corners and then bending the edges upwards.

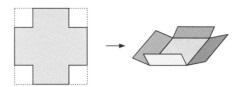

Find the size of the squares cut out.

19 A rectangular swimming pool is 12 m long by 6 m wide. It is surrounded by a pavement of uniform width, the area of the pavement being $\frac{7}{8}$ of the area of the pool.

    a If the pavement is x m wide, show that the area of the pavement is $4x^2 + 36x$ m^2.

    b Hence, show that $4x^2 + 36x - 63 = 0$.

    c How wide is the pavement?

20 A circular magnet has an inner radius x cm, an outer radius 2 cm larger and its depth is the same as the inner radius (as shown).
If the total volume of the magnet is 120π cm^3, find x.

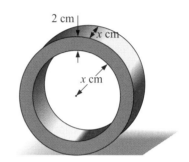

INVESTIGATION   THE QUADRATIC FORMULA (Extension)

What to do:

1 Use factorisation techniques or 'completing the square' where necessary to solve:

   a $x^2 + 3x = 10$ **b** $2x^2 = 7x + 4$ **c** $x^2 = 4x + 3$

   d $4x^2 - 12x + 9 = 0$ **e** $x^2 + 6x + 11 = 0$ **f** $4x^2 + 1 = 8x$

2 A formula for solving $ax^2 + bx + c = 0$ is $x = \dfrac{-b \pm \sqrt{b^2 - 4ac}}{2a}$.

   Check that this formula gives the correct answer for each question in **1**.

3 What is the significance of $b^2 - 4ac$ in determining the solutions of the quadratic equation $ax^2 + bx + c = 0$? You should be able to answer this question from observations in **1** and **2**.

4 Establish the quadratic formula by 'completing the square' on $ax^2 + bx + c = 0$.

   (**Hint:** Do not forget to divide each term by a to start with.)

E ┃ THE QUADRATIC FORMULA (EXTENSION)

Many quadratic equations cannot be solved by factorising, and completing the square is rather tedious. Consequently, the **quadratic formula** has been developed. This formula is:

$$\text{If } \; ax^2 + bx + c = 0, \quad \text{then} \quad x = \frac{-b \pm \sqrt{b^2 - 4ac}}{2a}.$$

Consider the **Opening Problem** involving the Diadro Dress Company. The equation we need to solve is: $4.2x^2 - 31.6x + 3200 = 6000$

   i.e., $4.2x^2 - 31.6x - 2800 = 0$ where $a = 4.2, \; b = -31.6, \; c = -2800$

Using the formula we obtain $x = \dfrac{31.6 \pm \sqrt{48\,038.56}}{8.4}$ which simplifies to $x \doteqdot 29.85$ or -22.33.

But as x needs to be a positive whole number, $x = 30$ would produce income of around $6032 each week.

The following proof of the quadratic formula is worth careful examination.

Proof: If $ax^2 + bx + c = 0$,

   then $x^2 + \dfrac{b}{a}x + \dfrac{c}{a} = 0$ {dividing each term by a, as $a \neq 0$}

   $\therefore \quad x^2 + \dfrac{b}{a}x \quad\quad = -\dfrac{c}{a}$

   $\therefore \quad x^2 + \dfrac{b}{a}x + \left(\dfrac{b}{2a}\right)^2 = -\dfrac{c}{a} + \left(\dfrac{b}{2a}\right)^2$ {completing the square on LHS}

$$\therefore \quad \left(x + \frac{b}{2a}\right)^2 = -\frac{c}{a}\left(\frac{4a}{4a}\right) + \frac{b^2}{4a^2}$$

$$\therefore \quad \left(x + \frac{b}{2a}\right)^2 = \frac{b^2 - 4ac}{4a^2}$$

$$\therefore \quad x + \frac{b}{2a} = \pm\sqrt{\frac{b^2 - 4ac}{4a^2}}$$

$$\therefore \quad x = -\frac{b}{2a} \pm \sqrt{\frac{b^2 - 4ac}{4a^2}}$$

$$\text{i.e.,} \quad x = \frac{-b \pm \sqrt{b^2 - 4ac}}{2a}$$

Example 13 ◀ Self Tutor

Solve for x: **a** $x^2 - 2x - 2 = 0$ **b** $2x^2 + 3x - 4 = 0$

a $x^2 - 2x - 2 = 0$ has $a = 1$, $b = -2$, $c = -2$

$$\therefore \quad x = \frac{-(-2) \pm \sqrt{(-2)^2 - 4(1)(-2)}}{2(1)}$$

$$\therefore \quad x = \frac{2 \pm \sqrt{4 + 8}}{2}$$

$$\therefore \quad x = \frac{2 \pm \sqrt{12}}{2}$$

$$\therefore \quad x = \frac{2 \pm 2\sqrt{3}}{2}$$

$$\therefore \quad x = 1 \pm \sqrt{3}$$

So, the solutions are $1 + \sqrt{3}$ and $1 - \sqrt{3}$.

b $2x^2 + 3x - 4 = 0$ has $a = 2$, $b = 3$, $c = -4$

$$\therefore \quad x = \frac{-3 \pm \sqrt{3^2 - 4(2)(-4)}}{2(2)}$$

$$\therefore \quad x = \frac{-3 \pm \sqrt{9 + 32}}{4}$$

$$\therefore \quad x = \frac{-3 \pm \sqrt{41}}{4}$$

So, the solutions are $\dfrac{-3 + \sqrt{41}}{4}$ and $\dfrac{-3 - \sqrt{41}}{4}$.

EXERCISE 11E.1

1 Use the quadratic formula to solve for x:

a $x^2 - 4x - 3 = 0$ b $x^2 + 6x + 7 = 0$ c $x^2 + 1 = 4x$

d $x^2 + 4x = 1$ e $x^2 - 4x + 2 = 0$ f $2x^2 - 2x - 3 = 0$

g $x^2 - 2\sqrt{2}x + 2 = 0$ h $(3x + 1)^2 = -2x$ i $(x + 3)(2x + 1) = 9$

2 Use the quadratic formula to solve for x:

a $(x+2)(x-1) = 2-3x$ b $(2x + 1)^2 = 3 - x$ c $(x - 2)^2 = 1 + x$

SOLVING USING TECHNOLOGY

A **graphics calculator** or **graphing package** can be used to solve quadratic equations. However, exact solutions in square root form will be lost in most cases. Approximate decimal solutions are usually generated.

In this course we will find solutions using *graphs* of quadratics. We will examine their intersection with the x-axis, giving us zeros, and we will also examine where functions intersect, finding the x-coordinates of the points where they meet.

We have chosen to use this approach, even though it may not be the quickest, so that an understanding of the link between the algebra and the graphics is fully appreciated.

Consider the equation $2x^2 - 3x - 4 = 0$.

Our approach will be:

- draw the graph of $y = 2x^2 - 3x - 4$
- $2x^2 - 3x - 4 = 0$ when $y = 0$
  and this occurs at the x-intercepts of
  the graph.

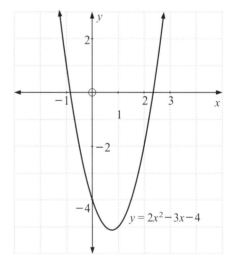

$y = 2x^2 - 3x - 4$

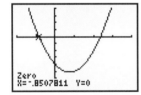
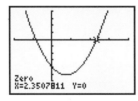

The solutions are: $x \doteq -0.8508$ or 2.351

Click on the appropriate icon for helpful instructions if using a **graphics calculator** and/or **graphing package**.

GRAPHING PACKAGE

EXERCISE 11E.2

1 Use technology to solve:

a $x^2 + 4x + 2 = 0$ b $x^2 + 6x - 2 = 0$ c $2x^2 - 3x - 7 = 0$

d $3x^2 - 7x - 11 = 0$ e $4x^2 - 11x - 13 = 0$ f $5x^2 + 6x - 17 = 0$

To solve a more complicated equation like $(x-2)(x+1) = 2+3x$ we could:

- make the RHS zero   i.e., $(x-2)(x+1) - 2 - 3x = 0$.
  Plot $y = (x-2)(x+1) - 2 - 3x$ and find the x-intercepts.

- Plot $y = (x-2)(x+1)$ and $y = 2+3x$ on the same axes and
  find the x-coordinates where the two graphs meet.

Using a graphics calculator with $Y_1 = (x-2)(x+1)$ and $Y_2 = 2+3x$,   we get

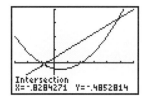

GRAPHING
PACKAGE

So, the solutions are $x \doteqdot -0.8284$ or 4.8284

2 Use technology to solve:

    a $(x+2)(x-1) = 2-3x$ **b** $(2x+1)^2 = 3 - x$ **c** $(x-2)^2 = 1 + x$

QUADRATIC EQUATIONS WITH NO REAL SOLUTIONS

Consider $x^2 + 2x + 5 = 0$.

Using the quadratic formula, the solutions are:

$$x = \frac{-2 \pm \sqrt{4 - 4(1)(5)}}{2(1)}$$

i.e., $$x = \frac{-2 \pm \sqrt{-16}}{2}$$

In the real number system $\sqrt{-16}$ does not exist and so we would say that $x^2 + 2x + 5$ has
no real solutions.

If we graph $y = x^2 + 2x + 5$ we get:

Clearly, the graph does not cut the x-axis and this
further justifies the fact that $x^2 + 2x + 5 = 0$
has no real solutions.

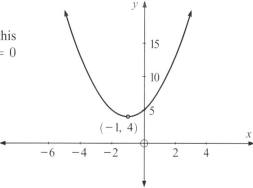

3 Solve for x:

    a $x^2 - 25 = 0$ **b** $x^2 + 25 = 0$ **c** $x^2 - 7 = 0$

    d $x^2 + 7 = 0$ **e** $4x^2 - 9 = 0$ **f** $4x^2 + 9 = 0$

    g $x^2 - 4x + 5 = 0$ **h** $x^2 - 4x - 5 = 0$ **i** $x^2 - 10x + 29 = 0$

    j $x^2 + 6x + 25 = 0$ **k** $2x^2 - 6x + 5 = 0$ **l** $2x^2 + x + 1 = 0$

THE DISCRIMINANT, Δ

In the quadratic formula, $b^2 - 4ac$, which is under the square root sign, is called the **discriminant**.

The symbol **delta** Δ, is used to represent the discriminant,   i.e., $\Delta = b^2 - 4ac$.

The quadratic formula becomes $x = \dfrac{-b \pm \sqrt{\Delta}}{2a}$ if Δ replaces $b^2 - 4ac$.

Notice that

- if $\Delta = 0$, $x = \dfrac{-b}{2a}$ is the **only solution** (a **repeated root**)

- if $\Delta > 0$, $\sqrt{\Delta}$ is a real number and so there are **two distinct real roots**,

  $$\dfrac{-b + \sqrt{\Delta}}{2a} \quad \text{and} \quad \dfrac{-b - \sqrt{\Delta}}{2a}$$

- if $\Delta < 0$, $\sqrt{\Delta}$ does not exist so we have no real solutions.

  Note: If a, b and c are rational and Δ is a **perfect square** then the equation has two rational roots which can be found by factorisation.

4   What is the discriminant of:

   a $x^2 - 2x - 7 = 0$ **b** $2x^2 - 3x + 6 = 0$ **c** $x^2 - 11 = 0$

   d $2x^2 - 6x - 4 = 0$ **e** $3x^2 + 7x - 1 = 0$ **f** $4x^2 - 7x + 11 = 0$

Example 14   ◀)) **Self Tutor**

Use the discriminant to determine the nature of the roots of:

  a $2x^2 - 3x + 4 = 0$ **b** $4x^2 - 4x - 1 = 0$

  a $\begin{aligned} \Delta &= b^2 - 4ac \\ &= (-3)^2 - 4(2)(4) \\ &= -23 \text{ which is } < 0 \end{aligned}$

      $\therefore$ there are no real roots

  b $\begin{aligned} \Delta &= b^2 - 4ac \\ &= (-4)^2 - 4(4)(-1) \\ &= 32 \text{ which is } > 0 \end{aligned}$

      $\therefore$ has 2 distinct real roots

---

5   By using the discriminant only, state the nature of the solutions of:

   a $x^2 + 7x - 2 = 0$ **b** $x^2 + 4\sqrt{2}x + 8 = 0$ **c** $2x^2 + 3x - 1 = 0$

   d $6x^2 + 5x - 4 = 0$ **e** $x^2 + x + 6 = 0$ **f** $9x^2 + 6x + 1 = 0$

6   By using the discriminant only, determine which of the following quadratic equations have rational roots which can be found by factorisation.

   a $2x^2 + 7x - 4 = 0$ **b** $3x^2 - 7x - 6 = 0$ **c** $2x^2 + 6x + 1 = 0$

   d $6x^2 + 19x + 10 = 0$ **e** $4x^2 - 3x + 3 = 0$ **f** $8x^2 - 10x - 3 = 0$

F   MORE DIFFICULT EQUATIONS
(EXTENSION)

Sometimes we need to simplify an equation before we can attempt to solve it.

In the following exercise we have rational equations.

We need to get rid of the algebraic fractions and then convert to a quadratic equation in each case.

EXERCISE 11F

1 Solve for x by first eliminating the algebraic fractions:

    a $\dfrac{x}{3} = \dfrac{2}{x}$
    b $\dfrac{4}{x} = \dfrac{x}{2}$
    c $\dfrac{x}{5} = \dfrac{2}{x}$

    d $\dfrac{x-1}{4} = \dfrac{3}{x}$
    e $\dfrac{x-1}{x} = \dfrac{x+11}{5}$
    f $\dfrac{x}{x+2} = \dfrac{1}{x}$

    g $\dfrac{2x}{3x+1} = \dfrac{1}{x+2}$
    h $\dfrac{2x+1}{x} = 3x$
    i $\dfrac{x+2}{x-1} = \dfrac{x}{2}$

    j $\dfrac{x-1}{2-x} = 2x+1$
    k $x - \dfrac{1}{x} = 1$
    l $2x - \dfrac{1}{x} = 3$

REVIEW SET 11A

1 Solve for x:

    a $2x^2 = 4$
    b $3x^2 + 18 = 0$
    c $5x(x-3) = 0$

    d $x^2 + 24 = 11x$
    e $10x^2 - 11x - 6 = 0$
    f $3x^2 = 2x + 21$

2 Solve for x:

    a $x^2 = x$
    b $(x+3)^2 = -1$
    c $3(x-2)^2 = 15$

3 Solve by 'completing the square':   **a** $x^2 + 8x + 5 = 0$ **b** $x^2 - 14x + 7 = 0$

4 The length of a rectangle is three times its width and its area is 9 cm². Find its dimensions.

5 The sum of a number and its reciprocal is $2\frac{1}{6}$. Find the number.

6 When the square of a number is increased by one the result is four times the original number. Find the number.

7 Solve for x: $x^2 - 5x + 2 = 0$

8 Using the discriminant only, state the nature (how many, if they exist) of the solutions of:

    a $x^2 + 3x - 6 = 0$
    b $2x^2 + 5x + 7 = 0$

REVIEW SET 11B

1 Solve for x:

    a $-2(x-3)^2 = 0$ **b** $(x+5)(x-4) = 0$ **c** $(2-x)^2 = -1$

    d $x^2 - 5x = 24$ **e** $2x^2 = 8$ **f** $6x^2 - x - 2 = 0$

2 Solve by 'completing the square':   **a** $x^2 - 4x = 10$ **b** $x^2 + x - 9 = 0$

3 A rectangle has length 5 cm greater than its width. If it has an area of 84 cm^2, find the dimensions of the rectangle.

4 The sum of a number and five times its square, is equal to four. Find the number.

5 A right angled triangle has its hypotenuse two centimetres less than three times the length of the shortest side, while the other side is 7 cm longer than the shortest side. Find the length of each of the sides of the triangle.

6 Find b and c if $x^2 + bx + c = 0$ has solutions $x = -1$ or $x = 7$.

7 Solve for x: **a** $x^2 - 2x + 7 = 0$ **b** $4x^2 - x + 1 = 0$

8 Using the discriminant only, state the nature (how many, if they exist) of the solutions of:

    a $x^2 + \sqrt{3}x + 1 = 0$ **b** $2x^2 + 5x + 2 = 0$

Chapter 12

Trigonometry

Contents:

Trigonometry is the study of the relationship between lengths and angles of geometrical figures.

We can apply trigonometry in engineering, astronomy, architecture, navigation, surveying, the building industry and in many branches of applied science.

HISTORICAL NOTE

Astronomy leads to the development of trigonometry

The Greek astronomer **Hipparchus** (140 BC) is credited with being the originator of trigonometry. To aid his calculations regarding astronomy, he produced a table of numbers in which the lengths of chords of a circle were related to the length of the radius.

Ptolemy, another great Greek astronomer of the time, extended this table in his major published work *Almagest* which was used by astronomers for the next 1000 years. In fact, much of Hipparchus' work is known through the writings of Ptolemy. These writings found their way to Hindu and Arab scholars.

Aryabhata, a Hindu mathematician in the 6th Century AD, drew up a table of the lengths of half-chords of a circle with radius one unit. After completing this chapter you will see that the length of the half-chord is sine θ. So Aryabhata actually drew up the first table of sine values.

In the late 16th century, **Rhaeticus** produced comprehensive and remarkably accurate tables of all six trigonometric ratios, three of which you will learn about in this chapter. These involved a tremendous number of tedious calculations, all without the aid of calculators or computers!

OPENING PROBLEM

A surveyor is standing on horizontal ground and wishes to find the height of a mountain some distance away on the other side of a fast flowing river. In order to do this he uses a theodolite to accurately measure:

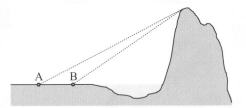

▶   the angle between the horizontal ground at A and the line of sight to the top of the mountain to be 33.7^o

▶   the angle between the horizontal ground at B and the line of sight to the top of the mountain to be 41.6^o

▶   the distance from A to B to be 400 m.

For your consideration:

•   Use this information to draw a scale diagram to estimate the height of the mountain.

•   Comment on the level of accuracy of this estimate.

•   Discuss any limitations of this method which will affect the level of accuracy of your estimate.

- Do you know of any other methods which may be used to determine the height of the mountain?

When you have completed the exercises in this chapter you should be able to accurately calculate the height of the mountain.

The **Opening Problem** is one of many everyday problems. There are a number of ways in which this problem can be solved. Both scale diagrams and trigonometry are appropriate techniques, depending on the level of accuracy required.

The subject of trigonometry uses other branches of mathematics (algebra, arithmetic and geometry) to enable comparisons of similar triangles so that lengths and angles which may be difficult, or perhaps even impossible to measure directly, can be calculated.

  USING SCALE DIAGRAMS

Scale diagrams can be used to find the lengths of sides and angles of geometrical figures.

Example 1   ◀)) **Self Tutor**

From an embankment Fiona measured the angle between the horizontal ground and the line of sight to the top of a tower to be 47°. The embankment is 35.4 m from the centre of the base of the tower. How high is the tower?

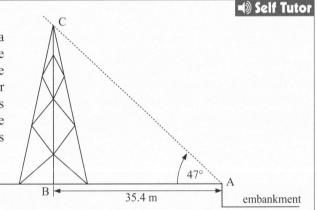

First we choose a suitable *scale* say
$1 \text{ cm} \equiv 10 \text{ m}$ i.e., $1 \text{ mm} = 1 \text{ m}$.

We then draw a horizontal line BA, 35.4 mm long and at the left end draw a vertical line using a set square.

Then we use a protractor to draw a 47° angle at A. Where the two lines meet is C.

Measure BC in mm and use the scale to convert back to metres.

$$BC \doteqdot 38 \text{ mm}$$

$\therefore$ tower is approximately 38 metres high.

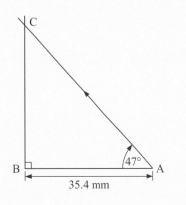

DISCUSSION

Can you think of any factors which would cause errors to be made in scale diagrams?

Comment on the accuracy of answers obtained when using scale diagrams.

EXERCISE 12A

1 Convert this rough sketch into an accurate scale diagram using a scale of 1 cm ≡ 1 m.

Use the scale diagram to find as accurately as you can the length of:

   a QR   **b** PR

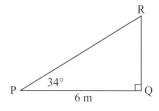

2

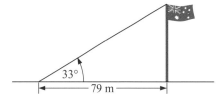

Use a scale diagram to find the height of the flagpole.

3 The triangular garden XYZ has XY = 12 m, YZ = 10.2 m and XZ = 8.4 m. Use a compass and ruler to draw an accurate scale diagram of the garden and hence find the measures of the garden's angles.

4 Revisit the **Opening Problem** on page **262**. A mountain is found on a horizontal plane. A surveyor makes two angle measurements from the plane to the top of the mountain (33.7° and 41.6°) from two points A and B.

A and B are 400 m apart. Use a scale diagram to find the height of the mountain.

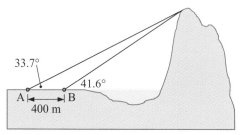

B   THE UNIT CIRCLE

SINE AND COSINE OF AN ANGLE

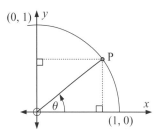

A circle of radius 1 unit with its centre at O is called a **unit circle**.

Suppose OP can rotate about O in the first quadrant and OP makes an angle $\theta°$ with the x-axis as shown.

(θ is a Greek letter, called 'theta'.)

For any sized angle θ we could use an accurate scale diagram to find the coordinates of P.

The x- and y- coordinates of P each have a special name.

- The y-coordinate is called "the sine of angle θ" or $\sin\theta$.
- The x-coordinate is called "the cosine of angle θ" or $\cos\theta$.

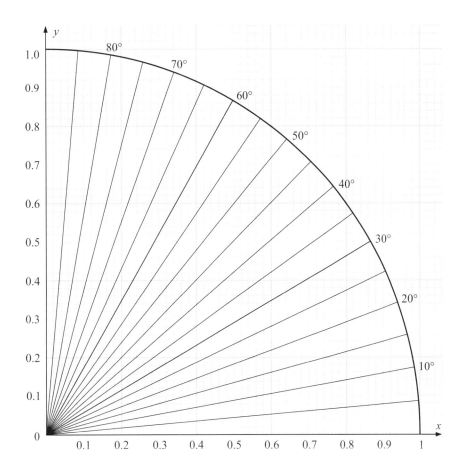

Example 2   ◀) **Self Tutor**

Use the unit circle to find:

a $\sin 40^o$ **b** $\cos 30^o$ **c** the coordinates of P if $\theta = 50^o$

a The y-coordinate at 40° is about 0.64

$\therefore$ $\sin 40^o \doteqdot 0.64$

b The x-coordinate at 30° is about 0.87

$\therefore$ $\cos 30^o \doteqdot 0.87$

c For $\theta = 50^o$,   P is $(\cos 50^o, \sin 50^o) \doteqdot (0.64, 0.77)$

You have probably already noticed the difficulty of obtaining accurate values from the unit circle and the impossibility of estimating beyond 2 decimal places.

EXERCISE 12B.1

1   Use the unit circle to find the value of:

    a $\sin 0^o$ **b** $\sin 15^o$ **c** $\sin 25^o$ **d** $\sin 30^o$

    e $\sin 45^o$ **f** $\sin 60^o$ **g** $\sin 75^o$ **h** $\sin 90^o$

2   Your scientific calculator has a $\boxed{\text{sin}}$ key. To find $\sin 40^o$ you should press $\boxed{\text{sin}}$ 40 $\boxed{)}$ $\boxed{\text{ENTER}}$. The answer $0.642\,787\,609$ can be rounded to whatever accuracy you need.

Use your calculator to check answers to question **1**.

Make sure your calculator is in degree mode.

3   Use the unit circle diagram to find the value of:

    a $\cos 0^o$ **b** $\cos 15^o$ **c** $\cos 25^o$ **d** $\cos 30^o$

    e $\cos 45^o$ **f** $\cos 60^o$ **g** $\cos 75^o$ **h** $\cos 90^o$

4   The calculator key $\boxed{\text{cos}}$ enables you to find cosines of angles. $\cos 40^o$ can be found by pressing $\boxed{\text{cos}}$ 40 $\boxed{)}$ $\boxed{\text{ENTER}}$.

Use your calculator to check answers to question **3**.

5   Use the unit circle diagram to find the coordinates of the point on the unit circle where OP makes an angle of 55° with the x-axis. Use your calculator to check this answer.

6

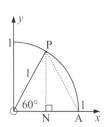

Did you notice that $\cos 60^o = \frac{1}{2}$?

Use the diagram alongside to explain this fact.

THE UNIT CIRCLE AND TANGENTS

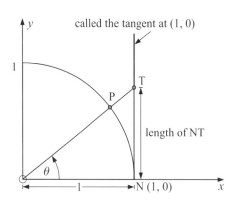

called the tangent at $(1, 0)$

length of NT

Now consider extending OP to meet the tangent at N(1, 0) at T.

The length of the part of the tangent, NT, is called
    'the tangent of angle θ' or $\tan \theta$.

Notice on the following diagram that $\tan 30^o \doteqdot 0.58$ and $\tan 60^o \doteqdot 1.73$.

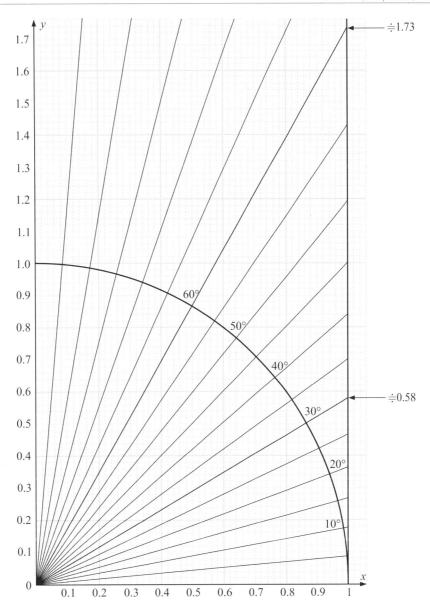

EXERCISE 12B.2

1   Use the unit circle diagram to find the value of:

   a $\tan 0^o$ b $\tan 10^o$ c $\tan 20^o$ d $\tan 35^o$

   e $\tan 40^o$ f $\tan 45^o$ g $\tan 50^o$ h $\tan 55^o$

2   Use your calculator to check your answers to question **1**. $\tan 35^o$ can be found by pressing **tan** 35 **)** **ENTER** .

3   Explain why $\tan 45^o = 1$ exactly.

4   Why have you not been asked to find $\tan 80^o$ using the unit circle diagram? Find $\tan 80^o$ using your calculator.

5

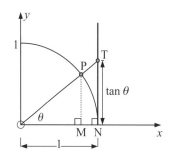

a   What are the coordinates of P?

b   What is the length of:
   i OM   ii PM   iii TN?

c   Use similarity to show that:

$$\tan \theta = \frac{\sin \theta}{\cos \theta}$$

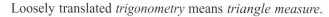

C   LABELLING TRIANGLES

Trigonometry is an important branch of mathematics. It enables us to find lengths and angles to greater accuracy than is possible using scale diagrams, in particular when considering triangles.

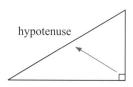

Loosely translated *trigonometry* means *triangle measure*.

In this section we will consider only **right angled triangles**.

The **hypotenuse** is the longest side of the triangle and is opposite the right angle.

For a given angle θ in a triangle, the **opposite** side is opposite the angle θ.

Examples:

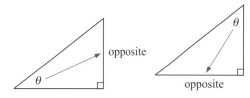   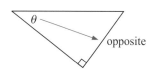   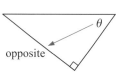

The third side is alongside the angle θ and so is called the **adjacent** side.

Example 3   ◀ **Self Tutor**

In the diagram alongside, find the:
a   hypotenuse
b   side opposite angle A
c   side adjacent to angle A
d   side opposite angle C
e   side adjacent to angle C?

a   The hypotenuse is AC.   b   BC is the side opposite angle A.

c   AB is the side adjacent to angle A.   d   AB is the side opposite angle C.

e   BC is the side adjacent to angle C.

EXERCISE 12C

1 In the diagrams below, name the:

    i hypotenuse   **ii** side opposite the angle marked θ

    iii side adjacent to the angle marked θ

    a 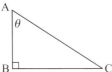   **b** 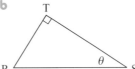   **c**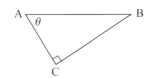

2 The right angled triangle alongside has hypotenuse of length a units and other sides of length b units and c units. θ and ϕ are the two acute angles. Find the length of the side:

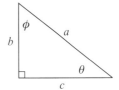

    a opposite θ **b** opposite ϕ

    c adjacent to θ **d** adjacent to ϕ

D   THE TRIGONOMETRIC RATIOS

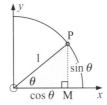   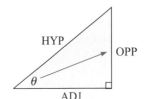

Consider a right angled triangle which is *similar* to $\triangle OMP$ with sides labelled OPP for opposite, ADJ for adjacent and HYP for hypotenuse. Since the ratios of the sides are the same in both triangles,

$$\frac{\sin\theta}{1} = \frac{\text{OPP}}{\text{HYP}}, \quad \frac{\cos\theta}{1} = \frac{\text{ADJ}}{\text{HYP}}, \quad \text{and} \quad \frac{\sin\theta}{\cos\theta} = \frac{\text{OPP}}{\text{ADJ}}$$

So, $\sin\theta = \dfrac{\text{OPP}}{\text{HYP}}, \quad \cos\theta = \dfrac{\text{ADJ}}{\text{HYP}}, \quad \text{and} \quad \tan\theta = \dfrac{\text{OPP}}{\text{ADJ}}$

(In **Exercise 12B.2** question **5 c** we showed that $\dfrac{\sin\theta}{\cos\theta} = \tan\theta$.)

These three formulae are called the **trigonometric ratios** and are the tools we use for finding sides and angles of right angled triangles.

FINDING TRIGONOMETRIC RATIOS

Example 4	◀ Self Tutor

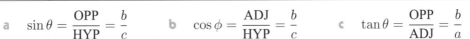

For the following triangle find:

    a $\sin\theta$ **b** $\cos\phi$ **c** $\tan\theta$

    a $\sin\theta = \dfrac{\text{OPP}}{\text{HYP}} = \dfrac{b}{c}$ **b** $\cos\phi = \dfrac{\text{ADJ}}{\text{HYP}} = \dfrac{b}{c}$ **c** $\tan\theta = \dfrac{\text{OPP}}{\text{ADJ}} = \dfrac{b}{a}$

EXERCISE 12D.1

1   For each of the following triangles find:

   i $\sin \theta$ **ii** $\cos \theta$ **iii** $\tan \theta$ **iv** $\sin \phi$ **v** $\cos \phi$ **vi** $\tan \phi$

a
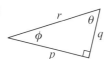

b

c
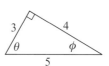

d
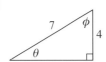

e
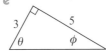

f

INVESTIGATION 1   COMPLEMENTARY ANGLES

37° and 53° are complementary since their sum is 90°.

θ^o and $(90 - \theta)^o$ are therefore **complements** of each other.

PRINTABLE WORKSHEET

Your task is to determine if a relationship exists between the sine and cosine of an angle and its complement.

What to do:

1   Use your calculator to complete a table like the one shown which includes some angles of your choice.

θ	$\sin \theta$	$\cos \theta$	$90 - \theta$	$\sin (90 - \theta)$	$\cos (90 - \theta)$
17			73		
38					
59					

2   Write down your observations from the tabled values.

3   Use the figure alongside to prove that your observations above are true for all angles θ, where $0 < \theta < 90$.

4   Investigate possible connections between $\tan \theta$ and $\tan(90 - \theta)$.

FINDING SIDES

In a right angled triangle, if we are given another angle and a side we can find:

- the third angle using the 'angle sum of a triangle is 180°'
- the other sides using trigonometry.

The method: *Step 1:*   Redraw the figure and mark on it HYP, OPP, ADJ relative to the given angle.

Step 2:   For the given angle choose the correct trigonometric ratio which can be used to set up an equation.

Step 3:   Set up the equation.

Step 4:   Solve to find the unknown.

Example 5   🔊 **Self Tutor**

Find the unknown length in the following (to 2 dec. places):

a
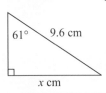

b

7.8 m x m   41°

a

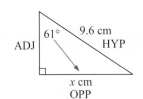

Now $\sin 61^o = \dfrac{x}{9.6}$ $\{\dfrac{OPP}{HYP}\}$

∴ $\sin 61^o \times 9.6 = x$ {mult. both sides by 9.6}

∴ $x \doteqdot 8.40$ {⟨sin⟩ 61 ⟨)⟩ ⟨×⟩ 9.6 ⟨ENTER⟩}

b

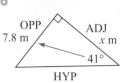

Now $\tan 41^o = \dfrac{7.8}{x}$ $\{\dfrac{OPP}{ADJ}\}$

∴ $x \times \tan 41^o = 7.8$ {mult. both sides by x}

∴ $x = \dfrac{7.8}{\tan 41^o}$ {div. both sides by $\tan 41^o$}

∴ $x \doteqdot 8.97$ {7.8 ⟨÷⟩ ⟨tan⟩ 41 ⟨)⟩ ⟨ENTER⟩}

EXERCISE 12D.2

1   Set up a trigonometric equation connecting the angle and the sides given:

a
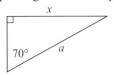

b
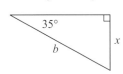

c

d
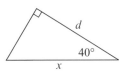

e
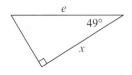

f
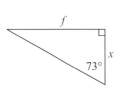

g
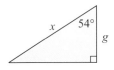

h
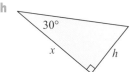

i
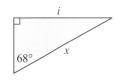

2 Find, to 2 decimal places, the unknown length in:

a
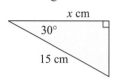

b
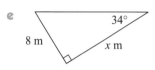

c
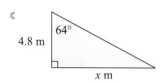

d
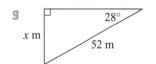

e
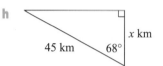

f
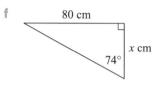

g
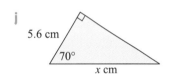

h
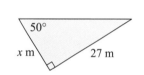

i
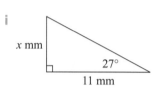

j
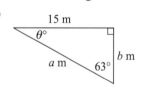

k
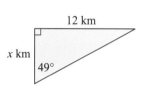

l
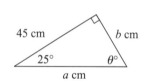

3 Find, to one decimal place, *all* the unknown angles and sides of:

a

b

c

FINDING ANGLES

In the right angled triangle $\sin \theta = \frac{3}{5}$.

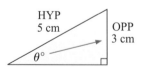

So, we are looking for angle θ with a sine of $\frac{3}{5}$.

If $\sin^{-1}(......)$ reads "the angle with a sine of ......", we can write $\theta = \sin^{-1}\left(\frac{3}{5}\right)$.

Another way of describing this is to say "θ is the *inverse sine* of $\frac{3}{5}$ ".

To find θ press: $\boxed{\text{2nd}}$ $\boxed{\text{sin}^{\text{-1}}}$ 3 $\boxed{\div}$ 5 $\boxed{)}$ $\boxed{\text{ENTER}}$.

With an ordinary scientific calculator you may need to press $\boxed{\text{INV}}$, $\boxed{\text{2nd F}}$ or $\boxed{\text{SHIFT}}$

and then press $\boxed{\text{sin}^{\text{-1}}}$ $\boxed{(}$ 3 $\boxed{\div}$ 5 $\boxed{)}$ $\boxed{=}$.   The answer is $\theta \doteqdot 36.9^{\circ}$.

We can define *inverse cosine* and *inverse tangent* in a similar way.

Example 6   ◀)) **Self Tutor**

Find, to one decimal place, the measure of the angle marked θ in:

a   **b**

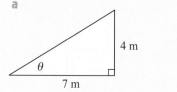

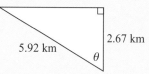

a

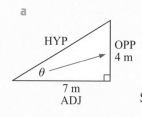

$$\tan\theta = \tfrac{4}{7} \qquad \{\text{as } \tan\theta = \frac{\text{OPP}}{\text{ADJ}}\}$$

$$\therefore \quad \theta = \tan^{-1}\left(\tfrac{4}{7}\right)$$

$$\therefore \quad \theta \doteqdot 29.7 \quad \{\boxed{\text{2nd}}\ \boxed{\text{tan}}\ 4\ \boxed{\div}\ 7\ \boxed{)}\ \boxed{\text{ENTER}}\}$$

So, the angle measure is $29.7°$.

b

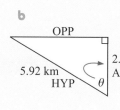

$$\cos\theta = \frac{2.67}{5.92} \qquad \{\text{as } \cos\theta = \frac{\text{ADJ}}{\text{HYP}}\}$$

$$\therefore \quad \theta = \cos^{-1}\left(\frac{2.67}{5.92}\right)$$

$$\therefore \quad \theta \doteqdot 63.2 \quad \{\boxed{\text{2nd}}\ \boxed{\text{cos}}\ 2.67\ \boxed{\div}\ 5.92\ \boxed{)}\ \boxed{\text{ENTER}}\}$$

So, the angle measure is $63.2°$.

EXERCISE 12D.3

1 Find, to one decimal place, the measure of the angle marked θ in:

a   **b**   **c**

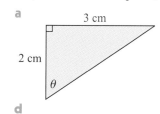

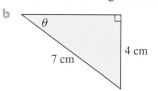

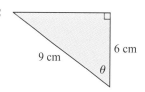

d   **e**   **f**

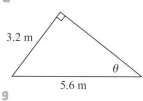

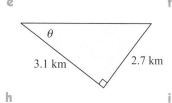

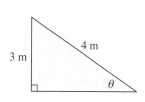

g   **h**   **i**

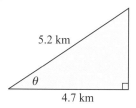

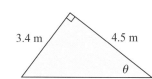

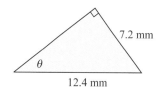

2 Find to 1 decimal place, all the unknown sides and angles of the following:

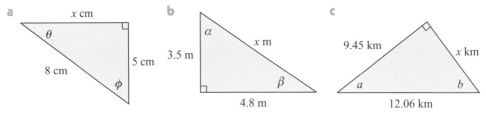

3 Check your answers for x in question **2** using Pythagoras' theorem.

4 Find θ using trigonometry in the following. What conclusions can you draw?

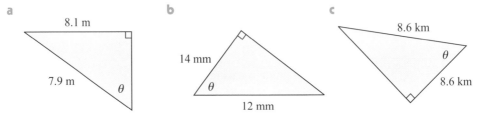

INVESTIGATION 2   **HIPPARCHUS AND THE UNIVERSE**

How Hipparchus measured the distance to the moon.

Think of A and B as two towns on the earth's equator. The moon is directly overhead town A. From B, the moon is just visible (MB is a tangent to the earth and is therefore perpendicular to BC). Angle C is the difference in longitude between towns A and B.

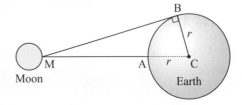

Hipparchus (2nd Century BC) calculated that angle to be approximately 89°.

We know today that the radius of the earth is approximately 6378 km. Hipparchus would have used a less accurate figure probably based on Eratosthenes' measure of the earth's circumference.

What to do:

1 Use $r = 6378$ km and $\angle C = 89^o$ to calculate the distance from the centre of the earth (C) to the moon.

2 Now calculate the distance **between** the earth and the moon (i.e., AM).

3 In calculating just one distance between the earth and the moon, Hipparchus was assuming that the orbit of the moon was circular. In fact it is not. Do some research to find the most up-to-date figure for the shortest and greatest distance to the moon. How were these distances determined? How do they compare to Hipparchus' method?

How Hipparchus measured the radius of the moon.

From town A on the earth's surface, the angle between an imaginary line to the centre of the moon and an imaginary line to the edge of the moon (i.e., a tangent to the moon) is observed to be $0.25°$.

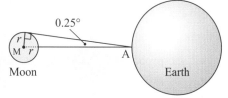

The average distance from the earth to the moon is 384 403 km. (How does this distance compare with the distance you found using Hipparchus' method?)

What to do:

1 Confirm from the diagram that $\sin 0.25° = \dfrac{r}{r + 384\,403}$.

2 Solve this equation to find r, the radius of the moon.

3 Find out the most up-to-date figure for the radius of the moon, and, if possible, find out how it was calculated.

How does your answer to **2** compare?

E   TRIGONOMETRIC PROBLEM SOLVING

The trigonometric ratios discussed in the previous exercises can be used to solve a wide variety of problems involving right angled triangles. It is important to follow the steps below:

Step 1:   **Read** the question carefully.

Step 2:   Draw a **diagram**, not necessarily to scale, with the given information clearly marked.

Step 3:   If necessary, **label** the vertices of triangles in the figure.

Step 4:   State clearly any assumptions you make which will enable you to use **right angled triangles** or properties of other geometric figures.

Step 5:   Choose an appropriate **trigonometric ratio** and substitute into a trigonometric equation connecting the quantities. On some occasions more than one equation may be needed.

Step 6:   **Solve** the equation(s) to find the unknown.

Step 7:   Answer the question that was asked in **words**.

ANGLES OF ELEVATION AND DEPRESSION

The angle between the horizontal and your line of sight is called the **angle of elevation** if you are looking upwards, or the **angle of depression** if you are looking downwards.

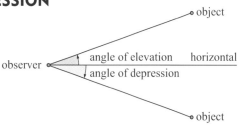

Note: If the angle of elevation from A to B is θ^o, then the angle of depression from B to A is also θ^o. (Can you explain this?)

When using trigonometry to solve problems we often use:

- the properties of isosceles and right angled triangles
- the properties of circles and tangents
- true bearings
- angles of elevation and depression.

Example 7   ◀◎ Self Tutor

Determine the length of the roofing beam required to support a roof of pitch 16° as shown alongside:

$$\therefore \quad \cos 16^o = \frac{x}{9.4} \quad \{\text{as } \cos \theta = \frac{\text{ADJ}}{\text{HYP}}\}$$

$$\therefore \quad x = 9.4 \times \cos 16^o$$

$$\therefore \quad x \doteqdot 9.036$$

{*Calculator:* 9.4 $\boxed{\times}$ $\boxed{\cos}$ 16 $\boxed{)}$ $\boxed{\text{ENTER}}$ }

$$\therefore \quad \text{length of beam} = 2 \times 9.036 \text{ m}$$
$$\doteqdot 18.1 \text{ m}$$

Example 8   ◀◎ Self Tutor

A ladder 4.1 m in length rests against a vertical wall and reaches 3.5 m up from ground level. Find:

a the angle the ladder makes with the ground

b the distance from the foot of the ladder to the wall.

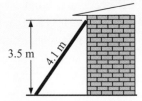

a $\quad \sin \theta = \dfrac{\text{OPP}}{\text{HYP}} = \dfrac{3.5}{4.1}$

$$\therefore \quad \theta = \sin^{-1}\left(\frac{3.5}{4.1}\right)$$

$$\therefore \quad \theta \doteqdot 58.6$$

{ $\boxed{\text{2nd}}$ $\boxed{\text{sin}}$ 3.5 $\boxed{\div}$ 4.1 $\boxed{)}$ $\boxed{\text{ENTER}}$ }

i.e., the ladder makes an angle of about 58.6^o with the ground.

b $\quad \cos \theta = \dfrac{\text{ADJ}}{\text{HYP}}$

$$\therefore \quad \cos 58.61^o = \frac{x}{4.1}$$

$$\therefore \quad 4.1 \times \cos 58.61^o = x$$

$$\therefore \quad 2.14 \doteqdot x$$

i.e., the foot of the ladder is 2.1 m from the wall.
{or use Pythagoras' Thm}

EXERCISE 12E.1

1   Find the height of a vertical cliff if the angle of elevation is 25° to the top from a point which is 235 m from the base of the cliff.

2   What angle will a 5 m ladder make with a wall if it reaches 4.2 m up the wall?

3   The angle of elevation to the top of a lighthouse 25 m above sea-level from a fishing boat is 6°. Calculate the horizontal distance of the boat from the lighthouse.

4   The angle of elevation from point A on horizontal ground to the top of a 20 m high pole is 35°. A rope is attached from A to the top of the pole. Find the length of the rope.

5   A rectangular gate has a diagonal strut of length 3 m and an angle between the diagonal and a side is 28°. Find the length of the longer side of the gate.

6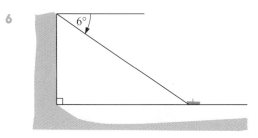
From a vertical cliff 80 m above sea level, a fishing boat is observed at an angle of depression of 6°. How far out to sea is the boat?

7   A railway line goes up an incline of constant angle 4° over a horizontal distance of 4 km. How high is it above the horizontal at the end of the incline?

8   At the entrance to a building there is a ramp for wheelchair access. The length of the ramp is 5 metres, and it rises to a height of 0.6 metres. Find the angle θ that the ramp makes with the ground.

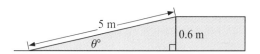

9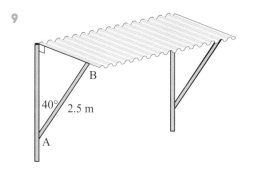
The roof of a bus shelter is supported by a metal strut 2.5 m in length, attached to the back wall of the shelter at an angle of 40°. Calculate how far below the roof of the shelter the strut is attached to the wall.

10   The diagram alongside shows a goalpost which has snapped in two after being hit by lightning. The top of the post is now resting 15 m from its base at an angle of 25°. Find the height of the goal post before it snapped.

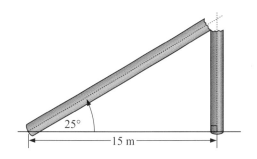

Example 9   ◄)) **Self Tutor**

The angle between a tangent from a point P to a circle and the line from P to the
centre of the circle is $27°$. Determine the length of the line from P to the centre of
the circle if the radius is 3 cm.

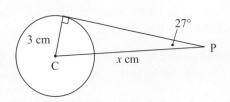

Using $\sin 27° = \dfrac{3}{x}$ $\{$as $\sin\theta = \dfrac{\text{OPP}}{\text{HYP}}\}$

$\therefore$ $x = \dfrac{3}{\sin 27°}$

$\therefore$ $x \doteqdot 6.61$

Thus CP has length   6.61 cm.

11 A tangent from a point P to a circle of radius 4 cm is 10 cm long. Find:
   a the distance of P from the centre of the circle
   b the size of the angle between the tangent and the line joining P to the centre of the
          circle.

12 AB is a chord of a circle, centre O, with radius
        of length 5 cm. AB has length 8 cm. What angle
        does AB subtend at the centre of the circle, i.e.,
        what is the size of angle AOB?

13 A rhombus has sides of length 10 cm, and the angle between two adjacent sides is $76°$.
        Find the length of the longer diagonal of the rhombus.

14

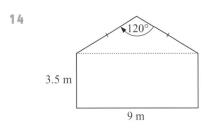

The dimensions of a double garage are as shown
in the diagram alongside. Calculate the height of
the top of the roof above the ground.

15 A tree casts a shadow 6 m long when the sun is at an elevation of $70°$. A gardener
        wishes to fell the tree at ground level and needs to cut the trunk into 4 m lengths to cart
        it away. How many cuts must he make?

16 An aeroplane takes off from the ground at an angle of $27°$ and its average speed in the
        first 10 seconds is 200 km/h. What is the altitude of the plane at the end of this time?

17 An observer notices that an aeroplane flies directly overhead at an altitude of 10 000 m.
        Two minutes later the aeroplane is at an angle of elevation of $27°$. Determine the speed
        of the aeroplane.

18 Determine the measure of the base angles of an isosceles triangle in which the equal
        sides are $\frac{2}{3}$ of the length of the base.

19   An isosceles triangle is drawn with base angles 24° and base 28 cm. Find the base angles of the isosceles triangle with the same base but with treble the area.

20   The angle of elevation from a point on level ground to the top of a building 100 m high is 22°. Find:

   a   the distance of the point from the base of the building

   b   the distance the point must be moved towards the building in order that the angle of elevation becomes 40°.

21   From a point A, 30 m from the base of a building B, the angle of elevation to the top of the building C is 56° and to the top of the flag pole, CD, is 60°.

Find the length of the flag pole.

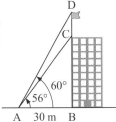

22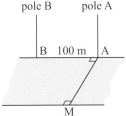

A man, M, positions himself on a river bank, as in the diagram alongside, so he can observe two poles A and B of equal height on the opposite bank of a river.

He finds the angle of elevation to the top of A is 22°, and the angle of elevation to the top of B is 19°. Show how he could use these facts to determine the width of the river, given that A and B are 100 m apart.

23   A surveyor can see a volcano in the distance. Standing on a horizontal plane looking up, the angle of elevation of the top of the volcano is 23°. If the surveyor moves 750 m closer, the angle of elevation is now 37°. Determine the height of the volcano.

24   Find the shortest distance between the two parallel lines.

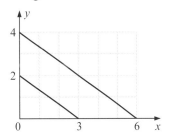

COMPASS BEARINGS

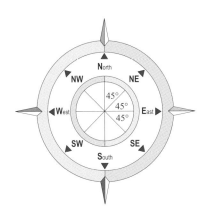

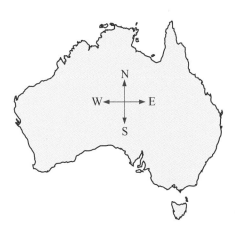

TRUE BEARINGS

One way to measure the direction of travel is by comparing it with the **true north direction**. Measurements are always made in the **clockwise** direction.

The **bearing of A from B** is the measure of the angle between BA and the line through B in the true north direction.

Imagine you are at B, facing north. You turn clockwise through an angle until you face A. The bearing of A from B is the angle through which you have turned.

In the top diagram, the bearing of A from B is 113° from true north, and we write this as 113°T or simply 113°.

The bearing of B from A is 293°.

In the bottom diagram the bearing of A from B is 49°T or simply 049°.

The bearing of B from A is 229°.

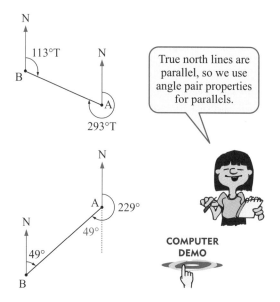

True north lines are parallel, so we use angle pair properties for parallels.

COMPUTER DEMO

Note: • A true bearing is usually given using **3 digits** (for example, 049°).
  • The bearing of A from B and B from A always differ by 180°. Can you explain this?

EXERCISE 12E.2

1   Draw diagrams to represent bearings from O of:
   a   136°   b   240°   c   051°   d   327°

2   Find the bearing of Q from P if the bearing of P from Q is:
   a   054°   b   113°   c   263°   d   304°

3   A, B and C are the checkpoints of a triangular orienteering course. For each of the following, find the bearing of:
   i   B from A   ii   C from B   iii B from C
   iv   C from A   v   A from B   vi   A from C

a
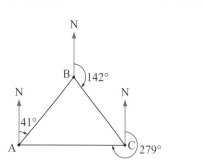

b
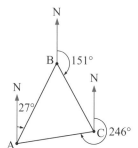

Example 10

🔊 **Self Tutor**

An aeroplane departs A and flies on a course of 143° for 368 km. It then changes direction to a 233° course and flies a further 472 km to town C. Find:

a the distance of C from A   **b** the bearing of C from A.

First, we draw a fully labelled diagram of the flight. On the figure, we show angles found by using parallel lines. Angle ABC measures 90°.

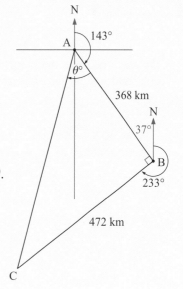

a AC $= \sqrt{368^2 + 472^2}$ {Pythagoras}
$ \doteqdot 598.5$

So, C is 598.5 km from A.

b To find the required angle we first need to find θ.

$$\text{Now} \quad \tan\theta = \frac{472}{368} \quad \left\{ \text{as} \quad \tan\theta = \frac{\text{OPP}}{\text{ADJ}} \right\}$$

$$\therefore \quad \theta = \tan^{-1}\left(\frac{472}{368}\right)$$

$$\therefore \quad \theta \doteqdot 52.06$$

So, the required angle is $143 + 52.06 \doteqdot 195.06$

$\therefore$ the bearing of C from A is 195°.

---

4 A bush-walker walks 14 km east and then 9 km south. Find the bearing of his finishing position from his starting point.

5 Runner A runs at 10 km/h due north. Runner B leaves the same spot and runs at 12 km/h due east. Find the distance and bearing of runner B from runner A after 30 minutes.

6 A hiker walks in a direction of 153° and stops when she is 20 km south of her starting point. How far did she walk?

7 A ship sails for 60 km on a bearing 040°. How far is the ship east of its starting point?

8 An aeroplane travels on a bearing of 295° so that it is 200 km west of its starting point. How far has it travelled on this bearing?

9 A fishing trawler sails in a direction 024° for 30 km from a port P, and then in a direction 114° for 20 km. Calculate:

  a the distance and bearing of the trawler from P

  b the direction in which the trawler must sail in order to return to P.

F   3-DIMENSIONAL PROBLEM SOLVING

Right angled triangles occur frequently in 3-dimensional figures. Consequently, trigonometry can be used to find unknown angles and lengths.

Example 11   ◀) Self Tutor

A cube has sides of length 10 cm. Find the angle between the diagonal AB of the cube and one of the edges at B.

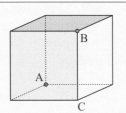

The angle between AB and *any* of the edges at B is the same.
∴ the required angle is ∠ABC.

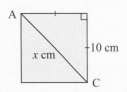   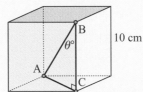

By Pythagoras:

$$x^2 = 10^2 + 10^2$$
$$\therefore \quad x^2 = 200$$
$$\therefore \quad x = \sqrt{200}$$

$$\tan \theta = \frac{\sqrt{200}}{10} \quad \{\text{as } \tan \theta = \frac{\text{OPP}}{\text{ADJ}}\}$$

$$\therefore \quad \theta = \tan^{-1}(\frac{\sqrt{200}}{10})$$

$$\therefore \quad \theta \doteqdot 54.7$$

i.e.,   the required angle is 54.7^o.

EXERCISE 12F.1

1   The figure alongside is a cube with sides of length 15 cm. Find:

    a   EG   **b**   ∠AGE

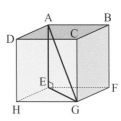

2
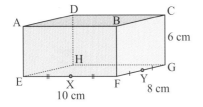

The figure alongside is a rectangular prism with dimensions as shown. X and Y are the midpoints of the edges EF and FG respectively. Find:

    a   HX   **b**   angle DXH

    c   HY   **d**   angle DYH

3   In the triangular prism alongside, find:

    a   DF

    b   angle AFD

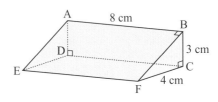

4   AB and BC are wooden support struts on a crate.
Find the total length of wood required to make
the two struts.

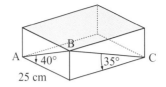

5   All edges of a square-based pyramid are 12 cm in length. Find the angle between a slant
edge and a base diagonal.

SHADOW LINES (PROJECTIONS)

Consider a wire frame in the shape of a cube as shown in
the diagram alongside. Imagine a light source shining down
directly on this cube from above.

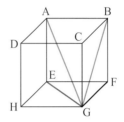

The shadow cast by wire AG would be EG and this is called
the **projection** of AG onto the base plane EFGH. Similarly
the projection of BG onto the base plane is FG.

Example 12	◀)) Self Tutor

Find the shadow (projection) of each of
the following in the base plane if a light
is shone from directly above the figure:

a   UP   b   WP   c   VP   d   XP

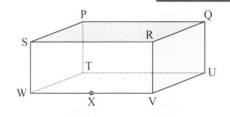

a   The projection of UP onto the base
plane is UT.

b   The projection of WP onto the base
plane is WT.

c   The projection of VP onto the base
plane is VT.

d   The projection of XP onto the base
plane is XT.

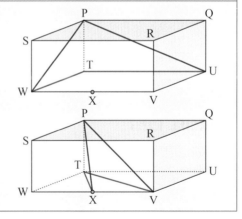

EXERCISE 12F.2

1   Find each of the following projections in the base planes of the given figures:

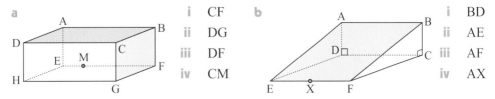

a   i   CF
    ii DG
    iii DF
    iv CM

b   i   BD
    ii AE
    iii AF
    iv AX

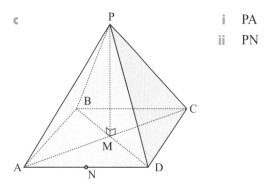

c

i PA
ii PN

THE ANGLE BETWEEN A LINE AND A PLANE

The angle between a line and a plane is the angle between the line and its projection on the plane.

Example 13	🔊 Self Tutor

Name the angle between the following lines and the base plane EFGH:
a AH   **b** AG

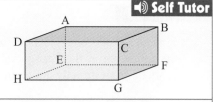

a   The projection of AH onto the base plane EFGH is EH
∴   the required angle is $\angle$AHE.

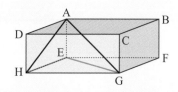

b   The projection of AG onto the base plane EFGH is EG
∴   the required angle is $\angle$AGE.

EXERCISE 12F.3

1   For each of the following figures name the angle between the given line and the base plane:

a i DE   ii CE   **b** i PY   ii QW   **c** i AQ   ii AY
       iii AG iv BX   iii QX iv YQ

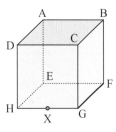

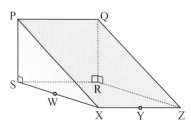

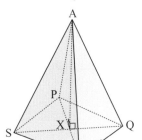

Example 14

🔊 Self Tutor

Find the angle between the following lines
and the base plane EFGH:

a DG   **b** BH

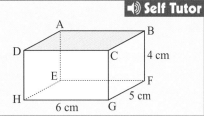

a The required angle is ∠DGH.

$$\therefore \quad \tan \theta = \tfrac{4}{6} \quad \{\text{as } \tan \theta = \frac{\text{OPP}}{\text{ADJ}}\}$$

$$\therefore \quad \theta = \tan^{-1}\left(\tfrac{4}{6}\right)$$

$$\therefore \quad \theta \doteqdot 33.69$$

i.e.,   the angle is 33.7°

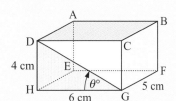

b The required angle is ∠BHF.

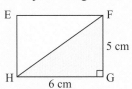

By Pythagoras

$$(HF)^2 = 6^2 + 5^2$$

$$\therefore \quad (HF)^2 = 36 + 25$$

$$\therefore \quad (HF)^2 = 61$$

$$\therefore \quad HF = \sqrt{61} \text{ cm}$$

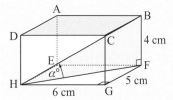

$$\tan \alpha = \frac{\text{OPP}}{\text{ADJ}}$$

$$= \frac{4}{\sqrt{61}}$$

$$\therefore \quad \alpha = \tan^{-1}\left(\frac{4}{\sqrt{61}}\right)$$

$$\therefore \quad \alpha \doteqdot 27.12$$

i.e.,   the angle is 27.1°

2 For each of the following figures find the angle between the given line and the base
plane:

a
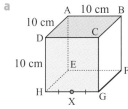

  i   DE
  ii DF
  iii DX
  iv AX

b
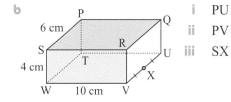

  i   PU
  ii PV
  iii SX

c
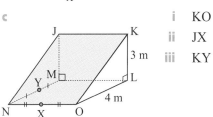

  i   KO
  ii JX
  iii KY

d
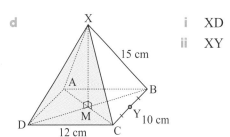

  i   XD
  ii XY

G   # OBTUSE ANGLES

So far in these exercises we have only considered angles between $0°$ and $90°$, which are known as acute angles. **Obtuse angles** have measurement between $90°$ and $180°$. In order to display obtuse angles we can extend the unit circle as seen in the diagram below.

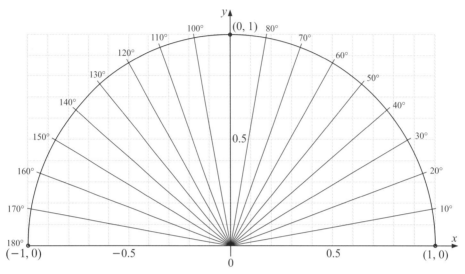

We can now apply the definitions for $\sin\theta$ and $\cos\theta$ to obtuse angles as well as acute angles.

Definition: If P is any point on the unit circle and θ is the angle measured from the positive x-axis then

$\cos\theta$ is the x-coordinate of P and
$\sin\theta$ is the y-coordinate of P.

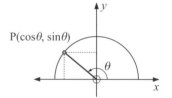

Example 15   ◄⁾ **Self Tutor**

Use the unit circle to find:
a $\sin 140°$ b $\cos 150°$ c   the coordinates of P if $\theta = 160°$

a   The y-coordinate at $140°$ is about 0.64 ∴ $\sin 140° \doteqdot 0.64$

b   The x-coordinate at $150°$ is about -0.87 ∴ $\cos 150° \doteqdot -0.87$

c   For $\theta = 160°$,   P is $(\cos 160°, \sin 160°)$,   i.e., $(-0.94, 0.34)$

EXERCISE 12G

1   Use the unit circle to find the value of:

    a $\sin 110°$ b $\sin 50°$ c $\sin 120°$ d $\sin 60°$

    e $\sin 160°$ f $\sin 30°$ g $\sin 180°$ h $\sin 0°$

2   Use your calculator to check your answers to question 1.

3 **a** Use your results from question **1** to copy and complete: $\sin(180 - \theta)° = \ldots\ldots$

b Justify your answer using the diagram alongside.

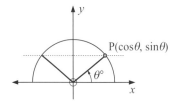

4 Use the unit circle to find the value of:

   a $\cos 100°$ **b** $\cos 60°$ **c** $\cos 120°$ **d** $\cos 80°$

   e $\cos 130°$ **f** $\cos 20°$ **g** $\cos 180°$ **h** $\cos 0°$

5 Use your calculator to check your answers to question **4**.

6 **a** Use your results from question **4** to copy and complete: $\cos(180 - \theta)° = \ldots\ldots$

b Justify your answer using the diagram alongside.

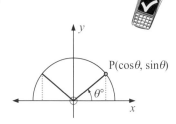

7 Find the obtuse angle which has the same sine as:

   a $26°$ **b** $45°$ **c** $69°$ **d** $86°$

8 Find the acute angle which has the same sine as:

   a $98°$ **b** $127°$ **c** $156°$ **d** $168°$

9 Without using your calculator find:

   a $\sin 112°$ if $\sin 68° \doteqdot 0.9272$ **b** $\sin 26°$ if $\sin 154° \doteqdot 0.4384$

   c $\cos 168°$ if $\cos 12° \doteqdot 0.9781$ **d** $\cos 49°$ if $\cos 131° \doteqdot -0.6561$

   e $\sin 145°$ if $\sin 35° \doteqdot 0.5736$ **f** $\cos 98°$ if $\cos 82° \doteqdot 0.1392$

Having considered $\sin \theta$ and $\cos \theta$ we can now consider $\tan \theta$ for θ being an obtuse angle.

10 Use your calculator to find the value of:

   a $\tan 100°$ **b** $\tan 80°$ **c** $\tan 110°$ **d** $\tan 70°$

   e $\tan 120°$ **f** $\tan 60°$ **g** $\tan 130°$ **h** $\tan 50°$

   i $\tan 140°$ **j** $\tan 40°$ **k** $\tan 150°$ **l** $\tan 30°$

11 **a** Using your results from question **10**,   copy and complete:

   $\tan(180 - \theta)° = \ldots\ldots$

b Use $\tan \theta = \dfrac{\sin \theta}{\cos \theta}$ to justify your answer.

12 Without using your calculator find:

   a $\tan 142°$ given $\tan 38° \doteqdot 0.7813$ **b** $\tan 54°$ given $\tan 126° \doteqdot -1.3764$

   c $\tan 165°$ given $\tan 15° \doteqdot 0.2679$ **d** $\tan 27°$ given $\tan 153° \doteqdot -0.5095$

AREA OF A TRIANGLE USING SINE

Consider the following situation:

In the triangle alongside, the sides opposite angles A, B and C are labelled a, b and c respectively.

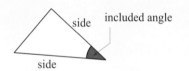

$$\text{Area of triangle ABC} = \tfrac{1}{2}\text{AB} \times \text{CN} = \tfrac{1}{2}ch$$

$$\text{However,} \quad \sin A = \frac{h}{b}$$

$$\therefore \quad h = b \sin A$$

$$\therefore \quad \text{area} = \tfrac{1}{2}c(b \sin A) \qquad \text{So,} \quad \text{area} = \tfrac{1}{2}bc\sin A$$

Similarly, if the altitudes from A and B were drawn, it could be shown that

$$\text{area} = \tfrac{1}{2}ac\sin B = \tfrac{1}{2}ab\sin C. \qquad\qquad \mathbf{area = \tfrac{1}{2}ab\sin C} \quad \text{is worth remembering.}$$

Summary:

The area of a triangle is:

a half of the product of two sides and the sine of the included angle.

Example 16   ◀⑨ **Self Tutor**

Find the area of triangle ABC.

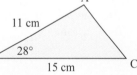

$$\text{Area} = \tfrac{1}{2}ac\sin B$$
$$= \tfrac{1}{2} \times 15 \times 11 \times \sin 28^o$$
$$\doteqdot 38.7 \text{ cm}^2$$

EXERCISE 12H

1   Find the area of:

a
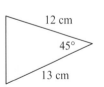

b
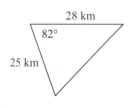

c
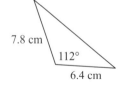

d
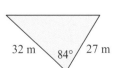

e
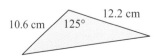

f
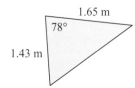

2 Find the area of a parallelogram with sides 6.4 cm and 8.7 cm and one interior angle 64°.
(**Hint:** Divide the parallelogram into two congruent triangles.)

3

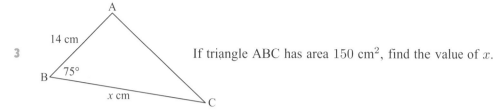

If triangle ABC has area 150 cm^2, find the value of x.

THE FULL UNIT CIRCLE (EXTENSION)

Consider a circle of radius 1 unit with its centre at the origin O. Such a circle is called a **unit circle**.

Suppose P lies on the circle and OP can rotate about O making an angle of θ^o with the positive x-axis.

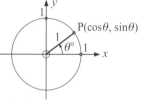

We give the coordinates of P special names:

- The y-coordinate of P is called "the **sine** of angle θ" or $\sin\theta$.
- The x-coordinate of P is called "the **cosine** of angle θ" or $\cos\theta$.

Below is a full unit circle diagram.

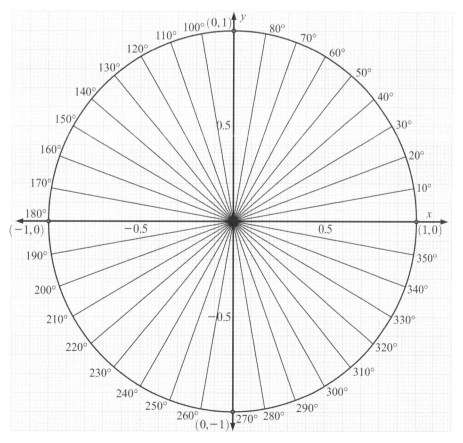

EXERCISE 12I.1

1 Use the unit circle diagram to find:

    a $\cos 0^o$ **b** $\sin 0^o$ **c** $\cos 90^o$ **d** $\sin 90^o$

    e $\sin 180^o$ **f** $\cos 180^o$ **g** $\sin 270^o$ **h** $\cos 270^o$

    i $\cos 360^o$ **j** $\sin 360^o$ **k** $\cos 450^o$ **l** $\sin 450^o$

2 Use the unit circle diagram to estimate, to 2 decimal places:

    a $\cos 50^o$ **b** $\sin 50^o$ **c** $\cos 110^o$ **d** $\sin 110^o$

    e $\sin 170^o$ **f** $\cos 170^o$ **g** $\sin 230^o$ **h** $\cos 230^o$

    i $\cos 320^o$ **j** $\sin 320^o$ **k** $\cos(-30^o)$ **l** $\sin(-30^o)$

3 Check your answers to **2** using your calculator.

4 Explain, using a unit circle diagram, why it is true that:

    a $\sin(180 - \theta) = \sin\theta$ **b** $\cos(180 - \theta) = -\cos\theta$

    c $\cos(-\theta) = \cos\theta$ **d** $\sin(-\theta) = -\sin\theta$

5 Simplify:

    a $\sin(180 + \theta)$ **b** $\cos(180 + \theta)$

TANGENT

Suppose the line OP which makes an angle of θ with the positive x-axis is extended to meet the tangent from the x-axis at point T.

As P moves around the circle, the length of the tangent changes and we define,

"the **tangent** of angle θ" or $\tan\theta$ as the length of the tangent from the x-axis."

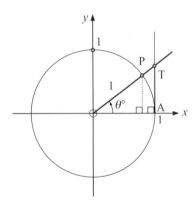

EXERCISE 12I.2

1 Find $\tan\theta$ for:

    a $\theta = 0$ **b** $\theta = 45$ **c** θ acute but very close to 90°

2

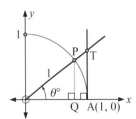

    a For θ any acute angle as shown, find the length of:

        i OQ   **ii** PQ   **iii** AT

    b Deduce that $\tan\theta = \dfrac{\sin\theta}{\cos\theta}$ using similar triangles.

3 By considering $\tan(180 - \theta) = \dfrac{\sin(180 - \theta)}{\cos(180 - \theta)}$ find the connection between $\tan(180 - \theta)$ and $\tan\theta$.

    Check your answer using your calculator with $\theta = 23$, say.

J   TRIGONOMETRIC GRAPHS (EXTENSION)

INTRODUCTION

Periodic phenomena occur in the physical world in:
- seasonal variations in our climate
- variations in the average maximum and minimum monthly temperatures at a place
- the number of daylight hours at a place
- variations in the depth of water in a harbour due to tidal movement, etc.

These phenomena illustrate variable behaviour which is repeated over time. This repetition may be called periodic, oscillatory or cyclic in different situations.

Consider the following:

A Ferris wheel rotates at a constant speed. The wheel's radius is 10 m and the bottom of the wheel is 2 m above ground level. From a point in front of the wheel Andrew is watching a green light on the perimeter of the wheel. Andrew notices that the green light moves in a circle. He then considers how high the light is above ground level at two second intervals and draws a graph of *height* against *time* for his results.

Click on the icon to see a simulation of the Ferris wheel.

You are to view the light on the Ferris wheel:
- from a position in front of the wheel
- from a side-on position
- from above the wheel.

COMPUTER DEMO

Now observe the graph of height above (or below) the wheel's axis over time as the wheel rotates at a constant rate. The motion is *periodic*, repeating again and again.

Now consider the table below which shows the mean monthly maximum temperature (^{o}C) for a city in Brazil.

Month	Jan	Feb	Mar	Apr	May	Jun	Jul	Aug	Sep	Oct	Nov	Dec
Temp	28	27	$25\frac{1}{2}$	22	$18\frac{1}{2}$	16	15	16	18	21	24	26

If this data is graphed, assigning January = 1, February = 2 etc., for a 3 year period, the graph shown is obtained.

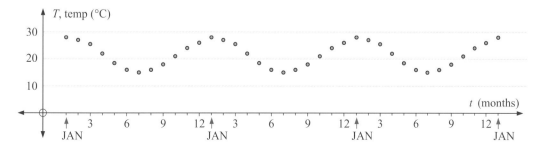

GATHERING PERIODIC DATA

- Maximum and minimum monthly temperatures can be obtained from the internet.
- Tidal details can be obtained from daily newspapers or from the internet.

TERMINOLOGY USED TO DESCRIBE PERIODICITY

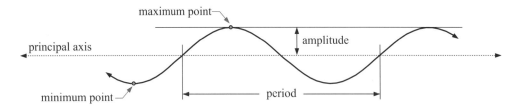

A **periodic function** is one which repeats itself over and over in a horizontal direction.
The **period** of a periodic function is the length of one repetition or cycle.

The wave oscillates about a horizontal line called the **principal axis** (or **mean line**).

A **maximum point** occurs at the top of a crest and a **minimum point** at the bottom of a trough.

The **amplitude** is the distance between a maximum (or minimum) point and the mean line.

EXERCISE 12J

1 **a** Use the unit circle diagram to find the values of $\sin\theta$ for θ values from 0° to 180° at 10° intervals.

  b Now from **a** draw the graph of $y = \sin\theta$ with the θ values on the x-axis, from 0° to 180°.

  c On another set of axes, draw the graph of $y = \cos\theta$ with the θ values on the x-axis, from 0° to 180°.

2 Below is a graph of $y = \sin\theta$. Use the graph to solve these equations (find θ), correct to 1 decimal place:

  a $\sin\theta = 0, \quad 0^o \leqslant \theta \leqslant 720^o$ **b** $\sin\theta = 0.3, \quad 0^o \leqslant \theta \leqslant 720^o$

  c $\sin\theta = 0.8, \quad 0^o \leqslant \theta \leqslant 720^o$ **d** $\sin\theta = -0.4, \quad 0^o \leqslant \theta \leqslant 720^o$

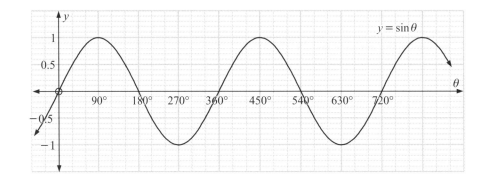

3 Below is a graph of $y = \cos\theta$. Use the graph to solve these equations (find θ), correct to 1 decimal place:

a $\cos\theta = 1$, $0^o \leqslant \theta \leqslant 720^o$

b $\cos\theta = 0.7$, $0^o \leqslant \theta \leqslant 720^o$

c $\cos\theta = 0.2$, $0^o \leqslant \theta \leqslant 720^o$

d $\cos\theta = -0.5$, $0^o \leqslant \theta \leqslant 720^o$

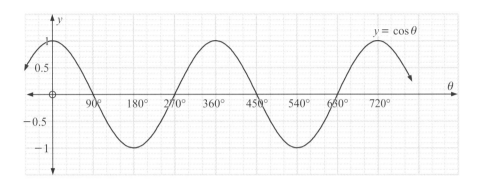

K TRIGONOMETRIC IDENTITIES (EXTENSION)

We have already discovered that $\sin(180 - \theta) = \sin\theta$ and that $\tan\theta = \dfrac{\sin\theta}{\cos\theta}$ and these are *true for all values of* θ.

We call such relationships **trigonometric identities**.

Consider the unit circle again.

Recall that:

If P(x, y) moves around the unit circle such that OP makes an angle of θ with the positive x-axis then

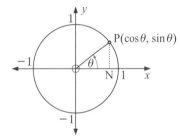

the x-coordinate of P is $\cos\theta$ and

the y-coordinate of P is $\sin\theta$.

GEOMETRY PACKAGE

Notice that: $\cos\theta = \dfrac{\text{ON}}{\text{OP}} = \dfrac{x}{1} = x$

and $\sin\theta = \dfrac{\text{PN}}{\text{OP}} = \dfrac{y}{1} = y$.

Notice also that in $\triangle$ONP, $x^2 + y^2 = 1$ {Pythagoras}

and so $[\cos\theta]^2 + [\sin\theta]^2 = 1$

or $\cos^2\theta + \sin^2\theta = 1$ if we use $\cos^2\theta$ for $[\cos\theta]^2$, etc.

Notice also that as $-1 \leqslant x \leqslant 1$ and $-1 \leqslant y \leqslant 1$ for all points on the unit circle,

hence, $-1 \leqslant \cos\theta \leqslant 1$ and $-1 \leqslant \sin\theta \leqslant 1$ for all θ.

SIMPLIFYING TRIGONOMETRIC EXPRESSIONS

For a given angle θ, $\sin \theta$ and $\cos \theta$ are real numbers, so the algebra of trigonometry is identical to the algebra of real numbers.

Consequently, expressions like $2\sin \theta + 3\sin \theta$ compare with $2x + 3x$ when we wish to do simplification.

$$\text{So,} \quad 2\sin \theta + 3\sin \theta = 5\sin \theta.$$

Example 17　　🔊 **Self Tutor**

Simplify:　　**a**　$3\cos \theta + 4\cos \theta$　　**b**　$\sin \alpha - 3\sin \alpha$

a　　$3\cos \theta + 4\cos \theta$
$= 7\cos \theta$
$\{3x + 4x = 7x\}$

b　　$\sin \alpha - 3\sin \alpha$
$= -2\sin \alpha$
$\{x - 3x = -2x\}$

EXERCISE 12K

1　Simplify:

　　a　$\sin \theta + \sin \theta$　　　　　**b**　$2\cos \theta + \cos \theta$　　　　　**c**　$3\sin \theta - \sin \theta$

　　d　$3\sin \theta - 2\sin \theta$　　　　**e**　$\cos \theta - 3\cos \theta$　　　　**f**　$2\cos \theta - 5\cos \theta$

To simplify more complicated trigonometric expressions involving $\sin \theta$ and $\cos \theta$ we often use $\sin^2 \theta + \cos^2 \theta = 1$

It is worth graphing $y = \sin^2 \theta$, $y = \cos^2 \theta$ and $y = \sin^2 \theta + \cos^2 \theta$ using technology.

Notice that:　　　$\sin^2 \theta + \cos^2 \theta$　could be replaced by　1

　　　　　　　　　　　　　　　　　1　could be replaced by　$\sin^2 \theta + \cos^2 \theta$

　　　　　　　　　　　　　$\sin^2 \theta$　could be replaced by　$1 - \cos^2 \theta$

　　　　　$1 - \cos^2 \theta$　could be replaced by　$\sin^2 \theta$

　　　　　　　　　　　　$\cos^2 \theta$　could be replaced by　$1 - \sin^2 \theta$

　　　　　$1 - \sin^2 \theta$　could be replaced by　$\cos^2 \theta$.

GRAPHING PACKAGE

Example 18　　🔊 **Self Tutor**

Simplify:　　**a**　$2 - 2\cos^2 \theta$　　　　**b**　$\sin^2 \theta \cos \theta + \cos^3 \theta$

a　　$2 - 2\cos^2 \theta$
$= 2(1 - \cos^2 \theta)$
$= 2\sin^2 \theta$
$\{\text{as}\ \cos^2 \theta + \sin^2 \theta = 1\}$

b　　$\sin^2 \theta \cos \theta + \cos^3 \theta$
$= \cos \theta \,(\sin^2 \theta + \cos^2 \theta)$
$= \cos \theta \times 1$
$= \cos \theta$

2　Simplify:

　　a　$3\sin^2 \theta + 3\cos^2 \theta$　　　**b**　$-2\sin^2 \theta - 2\cos^2 \theta$　　　**c**　$-\cos^2 \theta - \sin^2 \theta$

　　d　$3 - 3\sin^2 \theta$　　　　　　　　**e**　$4 - 4\cos^2 \theta$　　　　　　　　**f**　$\sin^3 \theta + \sin \theta \cos^2 \theta$

g $\cos^2\theta - 1$ **h** $\sin^2\theta - 1$ **i** $2\cos^2\theta - 2$

j $\dfrac{1 - \sin^2\theta}{\cos^2\theta}$ **k** $\dfrac{1 - \cos^2\theta}{\sin\theta}$ **l** $\dfrac{\cos^2\theta - 1}{-\sin\theta}$

As with ordinary algebraic expressions we can **expand** trigonometric products.

Sometimes simplication of these expansions is possible.

Example 19 ◀)) **Self Tutor**

Expand and simplify if possible: $(\cos\theta - \sin\theta)^2$

$(\cos\theta - \sin\theta)^2$
$= \cos^2\theta - 2\cos\theta\sin\theta + \sin^2\theta$ {using $(a-b)^2 = a^2 - 2ab + b^2$}
$= \cos^2\theta + \sin^2\theta - 2\cos\theta\sin\theta$
$= 1 - 2\cos\theta\sin\theta$

---

3 Expand and simplify if possible:

a $(1 + \sin\theta)^2$ **b** $(\sin\alpha - 2)^2$ **c** $(\cos\alpha - 1)^2$

d $(\sin\alpha + \cos\alpha)^2$ **e** $(\sin\beta - \cos\beta)^2$ **f** $-(2 - \cos\alpha)^2$

Factorisation of trigonometric expressions is also possible.

Example 20 ◀)) **Self Tutor**

Factorise: **a** $\cos^2\alpha - \sin^2\alpha$ **b** $\sin^2\theta - 3\sin\theta + 2$

a $\cos^2\alpha - \sin^2\alpha$
$= (\cos\alpha + \sin\alpha)(\cos\alpha - \sin\alpha)$ $\{a^2 - b^2 = (a+b)(a-b)\}$

b $\sin^2\theta - 3\sin\theta + 2$
$= (\sin\theta - 2)(\sin\theta - 1)$ $\{x^2 - 3x + 2 = (x-2)(x-1)\}$

Example 21 ◀)) **Self Tutor**

Simplify: **a** $\dfrac{2 - 2\cos^2\theta}{1 + \cos\theta}$ **b** $\dfrac{\cos\theta - \sin\theta}{\cos^2\theta - \sin^2\theta}$

a $\dfrac{2 - 2\cos^2\theta}{1 + \cos\theta}$

$= \dfrac{2(1 - \cos^2\theta)}{1 + \cos\theta}$

$= \dfrac{2(1 + \cos\theta)(1 - \cos\theta)}{(1 + \cos\theta)}$

$= 2(1 - \cos\theta)$

b $\dfrac{\cos\theta - \sin\theta}{\cos^2\theta - \sin^2\theta}$

$= \dfrac{(\cos\theta - \sin\theta)}{(\cos\theta + \sin\theta)(\cos\theta - \sin\theta)}$

$= \dfrac{1}{\cos\theta + \sin\theta}$

4 Factorise:

 a $1 - \sin^2 \theta$ **b** $\sin^2 \alpha - \cos^2 \alpha$ **c** $\cos^2 \alpha - 1$

 d $2 \sin^2 \beta - \sin \beta$ **e** $2 \cos \phi + 3 \cos^2 \phi$ **f** $3 \sin^2 \theta - 6 \sin \theta$

 g $\sin^2 \theta + 5 \sin \theta + 6$ **h** $2 \cos^2 \theta + 7 \cos \theta + 3$ **i** $6 \cos^2 \alpha - \cos \alpha - 1$

5 Simplify: **a** $\dfrac{1 - \sin^2 \alpha}{1 - \sin \alpha}$ **b** $\dfrac{\cos^2 \beta - 1}{\cos \beta + 1}$ **c** $\dfrac{\cos^2 \phi - \sin^2 \phi}{\cos \phi + \sin \phi}$

  d $\dfrac{\cos^2 \phi - \sin^2 \phi}{\cos \phi - \sin \phi}$ **e** $\dfrac{\sin \alpha + \cos \alpha}{\sin^2 \alpha - \cos^2 \alpha}$ **f** $\dfrac{3 - 3 \sin^2 \theta}{6 \cos \theta}$

6 By starting with the left hand side, prove the following identities:

 a $(\cos \theta + \sin \theta)^2 + (\cos \theta - \sin \theta)^2 = 2$

 b $(2 \sin \theta + 3 \cos \theta)^2 + (3 \sin \theta - 2 \cos \theta)^2 = 13$

 c $(1 - \cos \theta)\left(1 + \dfrac{1}{\cos \theta}\right) = \dfrac{\sin^2 \theta}{\cos \theta}$ **d** $\left(1 + \dfrac{1}{\sin \theta}\right)(\sin \theta - \sin^2 \theta) = \cos^2 \theta$

 e $\dfrac{\sin \theta}{1 + \cos \theta} + \dfrac{1 + \cos \theta}{\sin \theta} = \dfrac{2}{\sin \theta}$ **f** $\dfrac{\sin \theta}{1 - \cos \theta} - \dfrac{\sin \theta}{1 + \cos \theta} = \dfrac{2 \cos \theta}{\sin \theta}$

INVESTIGATION 3   SINE AND COSINE RULES

Part A: On page **288** we established that:

the area of a triangle

$= \frac{1}{2}$ the product of 2 sides $\times$ the sine of the included angle.

This can be written in symbolic form as follows:

   Area $\triangle ABC = \frac{1}{2} ab \sin C = \frac{1}{2} ac \sin B = \frac{1}{2} bc \sin A$

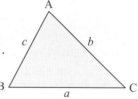

1 Using this relationship, show that $\dfrac{\sin A}{a} = \dfrac{\sin B}{b} = \dfrac{\sin C}{c}$.

This relationship is known as the **sine rule**.

2 Copy and complete the following statement using **1**:

In any triangle the ratio of the sines of angles and their .... sides is constant.

Part B:

1 For the figure alongside, copy and complete the following:

In $\triangle ANC$, $b^2 = ... + ...$ {Pythagoras}

    $\therefore \quad h^2 = ... - .....$ (1)

In $\triangle BNC$, $a^2 = ... + ...$ {Pythagoras}

    $\therefore \quad h^2 = ... - .....$ (2)

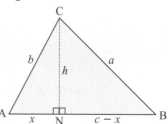

By equating (1) and (2) $a^2 - ...... = b^2 - ......$

Expanding and collecting terms gives $a^2 = ...$

But in $\triangle$ACN, $\cos A = \dfrac{....}{....}$ $\therefore$ $x = ...$

$\therefore$ $a^2 = ...$

$\therefore$ $a^2 = b^2 + c^2 - 2bc \cos A$.

2   Copy and complete the following:

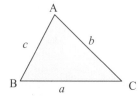

In any triangle with sides a, b and c units and opposite angles A, B and C respectively,

$$a^2 = b^2 + c^2 - ......$$
$$b^2 = a^2 + c^2 - ......$$
$$c^2 = a^2 + b^2 - ......$$

This rule is called the **cosine rule**.

L   THE SINE RULE (EXTENSION)

The **sine rule** is a set of equations which connects the lengths of the sides of any triangle with the sines of the opposite angles.

The triangle does not have to be right angled for the sine rule to be used.

THE SINE RULE

In any triangle ABC with sides a, b and c units in length, and opposite angles A, B and C respectively,

$$\dfrac{\sin A}{a} = \dfrac{\sin B}{b} = \dfrac{\sin C}{c} \quad \text{or} \quad \dfrac{a}{\sin A} = \dfrac{b}{\sin B} = \dfrac{c}{\sin C}.$$

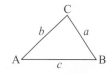

Proof: The area of any triangle ABC is given by $\frac{1}{2}bc \sin A = \frac{1}{2}ac \sin B = \frac{1}{2}ab \sin C$.

Dividing each expression by $\frac{1}{2}abc$ gives $\dfrac{\sin A}{a} = \dfrac{\sin B}{b} = \dfrac{\sin C}{c}$.

Note: The sine rule is used to solve problems involving triangles when angles and sides opposite those angles are to be related.

GEOMETRY PACKAGE

FINDING SIDES

Example 22	◀ﺀ) Self Tutor

Find the length of AC correct to two decimal places.

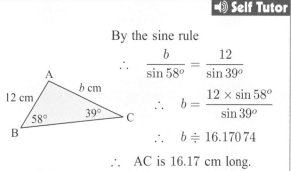

By the sine rule

$\therefore$ $\dfrac{b}{\sin 58^o} = \dfrac{12}{\sin 39^o}$

$\therefore$ $b = \dfrac{12 \times \sin 58^o}{\sin 39^o}$

$\therefore$ $b \doteqdot 16.170\,74$

$\therefore$ AC is 16.17 cm long.

EXERCISE 12L.1

1 Find the value of x:

a
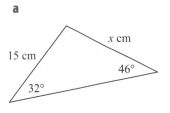

b
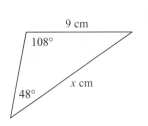

c
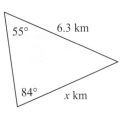

2 In triangle ABC find:

    a a if $A = 63^o$, $B = 35^o$, $b = 18$ cm   **b** b if $A = 82^o$, $C = 25^o$, $c = 24$ cm

    c c if $B = 25^o$, $C = 42^o$, $a = 7.2$ cm.

FINDING ANGLES

The problem of finding angles using the sine rule is more complicated because there may be two possible answers. We discovered this in **Exercise 12G.**

This is because an equation of the form

$$\sin \theta = a \quad \text{produces answers of the form} \quad \theta = \sin^{-1} a \ \ or \ \ (180 - \sin^{-1} a).$$

Example 23 ◀》 **Self Tutor**

Find the measure of angle C in triangle ABC if AC is 7 cm, AB is 11 cm and angle B measures 25°.

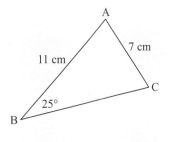

$$\dfrac{\sin C}{c} = \dfrac{\sin B}{b} \quad \{\text{sine rule}\}$$

$$\therefore \quad \dfrac{\sin C}{11} = \dfrac{\sin 25^o}{7}$$

$$\therefore \quad \sin C = \dfrac{11 \times \sin 25^o}{7}$$

This is called the "ambiguous case"!!

$$\text{Now} \quad \sin^{-1}\left(\dfrac{11 \times \sin 25^o}{7}\right) \doteqdot 41.6^o$$

and since the angle at C could be acute or obtuse,

$$\therefore \quad C \doteqdot 41.6^o \text{ or } (180^o - 41.6^o)$$

$$\therefore \quad C \text{ measures } 41.6^o \text{ if it is acute} \quad \text{or} \quad C \text{ measures } 138.4^o \text{ if it is obtuse.}$$

In this case there is insufficient information to determine the actual shape of the triangle.

The validity of the two answers in the above example can be demonstrated by a simple construction.

Step 1: Draw AB of length 11 cm and construct an angle of 25° at B.

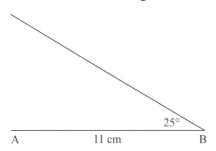

Step 2: From A draw the arc of a circle of radius 7 cm.

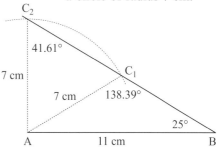

Note: Sometimes there is information given in the question which enables us to **reject** one of the answers.

Example 24   ◀) **Self Tutor**

Find the measure of angle L in triangle KLM given that angle LKM measures 56°, LM $= 16.8$ m and KM $= 13.5$ m.

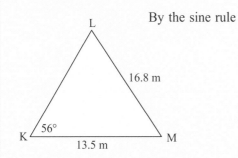

By the sine rule $\dfrac{\sin L}{13.5} = \dfrac{\sin 56^o}{16.8}$

$\therefore \quad \sin L = \dfrac{13.5 \times \sin 56^o}{16.8}$

Now $\sin^{-1}\left(\dfrac{13.5 \times \sin 56^o}{16.8}\right) \doteq 41.8^o$

and since L could be acute or obtuse,

$\therefore \quad L \doteq 41.8^o \quad$ or $\quad (180 - 41.8)^o$

But reject $L = 138.2^o$ as $138.2^o + 56^o > 180^o$ which is impossible.

$\therefore \quad \angle L \doteq 41.8^o.$

EXERCISE 12L.2

1 Find the value of θ:

a

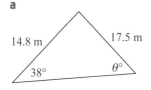

b

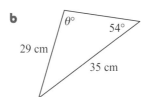

c

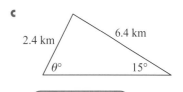

There may be two possible solutions.

2 In triangle ABC, find the measure of:

a angle A if $a = 12.6$ cm, $b = 15.1$ cm and $\angle ABC = 65^o$

b angle B if $b = 38.4$ cm, $c = 27.6$ cm and $\angle ACB = 43^o$

c angle C if $a = 5.5$ km, $c = 4.1$ km and $\angle BAC = 71^o$.

THE COSINE RULE (EXTENSION)

THE COSINE RULE

In any triangle ABC, with sides a, b and c units and opposite angles A, B and C respectively,

$$a^2 = b^2 + c^2 - 2bc \cos A$$
$$b^2 = a^2 + c^2 - 2ac \cos B$$
$$c^2 = a^2 + b^2 - 2ab \cos C.$$

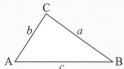

In **Investigation 3** on page **296** and **297** we established the cosine rule by using Pythagoras' Theorem and right angled triangle trigonometry.

Note: The **cosine rule** can be used to solve problems involving triangles given

- **two sides** and the **included angle**   or   - **three sides**.

Example 25 — Self Tutor

Find, correct to 2 decimal places, the length of BC.

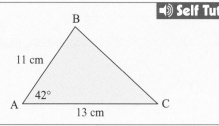

By the cosine rule:
$$a^2 = b^2 + c^2 - 2bc \cos A$$
$\therefore \quad a^2 = 11^2 + 13^2 - 2 \times 11 \times 13 \times \cos 42°$
$\therefore \quad a^2 \doteqdot 77.4605$
$\therefore \quad a \doteqdot 8.80 \qquad \therefore$ BC is 8.80 cm in length.

GEOMETRY PACKAGE

EXERCISE 12M

1 Find the length of the remaining side in the given triangle:

a 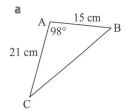   **b** 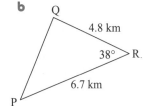   **c**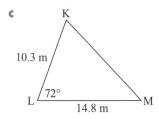

2 Find:

a the smallest angle of a triangle with sides 11 cm, 13 cm and 15 cm

b the largest angle of a triangle with sides 5 cm, 7 cm and 9 cm.

PROBLEM SOLVING WITH THE SINE AND COSINE RULES (EXTENSION)

Whenever there is a choice between using the sine rule or the cosine rule, always use the **cosine rule** to avoid the ambiguous case.

Example 26 ◄)) Self Tutor

An aircraft flies 74 km on a bearing 038° and then 63 km on a bearing 160°. Find the distance of the aircraft from its starting point.

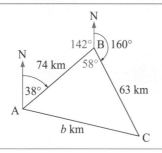

By the cosine rule:

$$b^2 = a^2 + c^2 - 2ac \cos B$$
$$\therefore \quad b^2 = 63^2 + 74^2 - 2 \times 63 \times 74 \times \cos 58^o$$
$$\therefore \quad b^2 \doteqdot 4504.03$$
$$\therefore \quad b \doteqdot 67.1$$

$\therefore$ the aircraft is 67.1 km from its starting point.

EXERCISE 12N

1 Two observation posts are 12 km apart at A and B. From A, a third observation post C is located such that angle CAB is 42° while angle CBA is 67°. Find the distance of C from both A and B.

2 Find the area of quadrilateral PQRS.

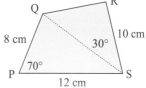

3 An orienteer runs for $4\frac{1}{2}$ km and then turns through an angle of 32° and runs another 6 km. How far is she from her starting point?

4 A yacht sails 6 km on a bearing 127° and then sails 4 km on a bearing 053°. Find:

   a the distance of the yacht from its starting point
   b the bearing of the yacht from its starting point.

5

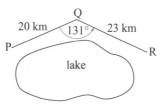

To drive from P to R, alongside a lake, you must drive to Q and then to R as shown.

What is the distance in a straight line from P to R?

6 A golfer played his tee shot a distance of 220 m to a point A. He then played a 165 m six iron to the green. If the distance from tee to green is 340 m, determine the number of degrees the golfer was off line with his tee shot.

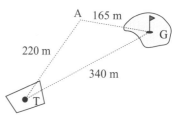

7 Mount X is 9 km from Mount Y on a bearing 146°. Mount Z is 14 km away from Mount X and on a bearing 072° from Mount Y. Find the bearing of X from Z.

REVIEW SET 12A

1 Find $\sin\theta$, $\cos\theta$ and $\tan\theta$ for the triangle:

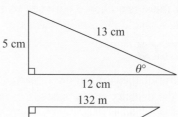

2 Find the value of x:

  a

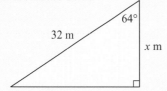

  b

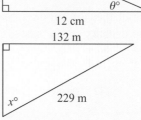

3 Find the measure of all unknown sides and angles in triangle CDE:

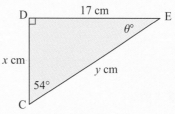

4 From a point 120 m horizontally from the base of a building, the angle of elevation to the top of the building is 34°. Find the height of the building.

5 A flagpole 17 m high is supported by 3 ropes which meet the ground at angles of 55°. Determine the total length of the three ropes.

6 A ship sails 40 km on a bearing 056°. How far is the ship north of its starting point?

7 Find the angle:

  a BG makes with FG

  b AG makes with the base plane EFGH.

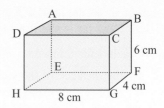

8 Find the area of:

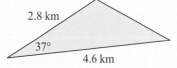

9 Use the diagram alongside, to write in terms of a and b, a value for:

  a $\cos\theta^o$ **b** $\sin\theta^o$

  c $\tan\theta^o$ **d** $\sin(180-\theta)^o$

  e $\cos(180-\theta)^o$

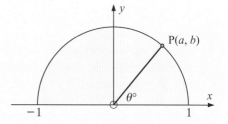

10 **a** Find the obtuse angle with the same sine as 60°.

   b Find the acute angle with the same cosine as 330°.

   c Without using your calculator, find $\tan 300^o$, given that $\tan 60^o \doteqdot 1.732$.

11 Below is a graph of $y = \sin \theta$. Use the graph to solve these equations (find θ), correct to 1 decimal place:

   a $\sin \theta = 0.5$, $0^o \leqslant \theta \leqslant 720^o$ **b** $\sin \theta = -0.7$, $0^o \leqslant \theta \leqslant 720^o$

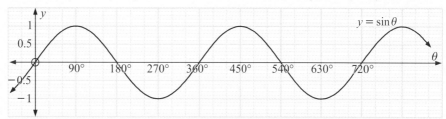

12 Factorise: **a** $\sin^2 \theta - \cos^2 \theta$ **b** $4\cos^2 \theta - 4$

13 Simplify: **a** $\dfrac{\tan^2 \theta - 1}{\tan \theta + 1}$ **b** $\dfrac{2 \sin \theta}{\sin^2 \theta + \cos^2 \theta}$

14 By starting with the left hand side, prove the identity $\dfrac{\sin \theta}{1 - \cos \theta} + \dfrac{1 - \cos \theta}{\sin \theta} = \dfrac{2}{\sin \theta}$

REVIEW SET 12B

1 Use your calculator to find, correct to 4 decimal places:

   a $\cos 74^o$ **b** $\sin 132^o$ **c** $\tan 97^o$

2 Find the value of x in the following:

   a

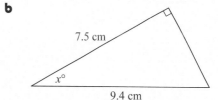

   b

3 Find the measure of all unknown sides and angles in triangle KLM:

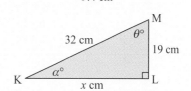

4 A vehicle travels 50 km east and then 40 km south. Determine the distance and bearing of the vehicle from its starting point.

5 The angle of elevation to the top of a vertical cliff from sea level is 17.7^o from a point 2 km from the base of the cliff. Find the height of the cliff, in metres.

6 A tangent to a circle from a point 13 cm from the centre is 11 cm in length. Find the angle between the tangent and the line from the point to the centre of the circle.

7 A ship leaves port P and travels for 50 km in the direction 081°. It then sails 60 km in the direction 171° to an island port Q.

   a How far is Q from P?

   b If the ship wishes to sail back directly to P from Q, in what direction must it sail?

8 The figure alongside is a square-based pyramid in which all edges are 20 cm in length. Find:

   a ∠ADM

   b ∠ACD

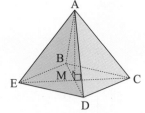

9 If $\sin\theta = \frac{3}{5}$, find the value of $\cos\theta$ and $\tan\theta$, given that θ is acute.

   (**Hint:** Drawing a sketch of a triangle may help.)

10

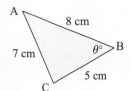

   a Find θ.

   b Hence, find the area of triangle ABC.

11 **a** Find the acute angle with the same sine as 157°.

   b Find the reflex angle with the same cosine as 120°.

   c Find the obtuse angle with the same tangent as 308°.

12 Below is a graph of $y = \cos\theta$. Use the graph to solve these equations (find θ), correct to 1 decimal place:

   a $\cos\theta = 0.5$, $\quad 0° \leqslant \theta \leqslant 720°$ **b** $\cos\theta = -0.7$, $\quad 0° \leqslant \theta \leqslant 720°$

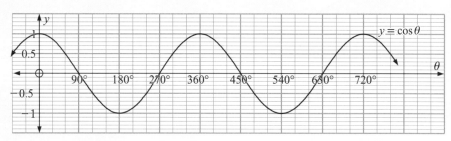

13 By starting with the left hand side, prove the following identities:

   a $(\sin\theta + 2\cos\theta)^2 + (2\sin\theta - \cos\theta)^2 = 5$

   b $(1 + \sin\theta)\left(1 - \dfrac{1}{\sin\theta}\right) = -\dfrac{\cos^2\theta}{\sin\theta}$

Chapter 13

Probability

Contents:

Often we are confronted by situations where we are not sure what outcome will occur.
We hear statements such as:

> "The Wildcats will probably beat the Tigers on Saturday."
> "It is unlikely that it will rain today."
> "I probably will make the team."

Each of these statements indicates a **likelihood** (or **chance**) of a particular event happening.

We can indicate the likelihood of an event happening in the future by using a percentage.

> 0%   indicates we believe the event **will not occur**.
> 100%   indicates we believe the event **is certain to occur**.

All events can therefore be assigned a percentage between 0% and 100% (inclusive).

A number close to 0% indicates the event is **unlikely** to occur, whereas a number close to 100% means that it is **highly likely** to occur.

In mathematics, we usually use either decimals or fractions rather than percentages for probabilities. However, as 100% = 1, comparisons or conversions from percentages to fractions or decimals are very simple.

> An **impossible** event which has 0% chance of happening is assigned a probability of 0.
>
> A **certain** event which has 100% chance of happening is assigned a probability of 1.
>
> All other events can then be assigned a probability between 0 and 1.

The assigning of probabilities is usually based on either

- observing the results of an experiment (experimental probability),   or
- using arguments of symmetry (theoretical probability).

OPENING PROBLEM

When Karla dropped some metal nuts she noticed that they landed either on their ends or on their sides. She then tossed a nut 200 times and it landed on its end 137 times.

Later Sam repeated the experiment and the nut finished on its end 145 times.

side   end

For you to consider:

- What would Karla's best estimate be of the chance that the nut will finish on its end?
- What would Sam's estimate be?
- How can a better estimate of the chance of an end occurring be made?
- Hilda said that the best estimate would be obtained when the nut is tossed thousands of times. Is she correct?

A   PROBABILITY BY EXPERIMENT

In an experiment we should use suitable language to help us describe what we are doing and the results we expect and get.

- The **number of trials** is the total number of times the experiment is repeated.
- The **outcomes** are the different results possible for one trial of the experiment.
- The **frequency** of a particular outcome is the number of times this outcome is observed.
- The **relative frequency** of an outcome is the frequency of that outcome divided by the total number of trials.

So, if we flip a tin can into the air 250 times and if it lands on an end 37 times, then

- the number of trials is 250
- the outcomes are *ends* and *sides*
- the frequency of *ends* is 37 and *sides* is 213
- the relative frequency of *ends* is 0.148 and *sides* is 0.852.

EXPERIMENTAL PROBABILITY

Sometimes the only way of finding the chance of occurrence of a particular event is by experiment.

Tin can flipping is one such example. The chance of a can of this shape finishing on its end is the relative frequency found by experimentation.

We say, the **estimated experimental probability** is the relative frequency of the event.

We write: Experimental P(end) $= 0.148$

Note: •   The larger the number of trials, the more confident we are in the experimental probability obtained.

•   Experimental P(......) = relative frequency of ......

Example 1   ◀ Self Tutor

A marketing company surveys 50 randomly selected people to discover what brand of toothpaste they use. The results are tabulated.

Brand	Frequency	Rel. Freq.
Shine	10	0.20
Starbright	14	0.28
Brite	4	0.08
Clean	12	0.24
No Name	10	0.20

a   Based on these results, what would be the experimental probability of a community member using:
   i   Starbright   ii   Clean?

b   Would you classify the estimate of a to be very good, good, or poor? Why?

a   i   Expt P(Starbright) = 0.28   ii   Expt P(Clean) = 0.24

b· Poor, as the sample size is very small.

EXERCISE 13A

1   A marketing company was commissioned to investigate brands of products usually found in the bathroom. The results of a soap survey are below:

   a   How many people were randomly selected in this survey?

   b   Calculate the relative frequency of use of each brand of soap.

   c   Using these results, what is the experimental probability that the soap used by a randomly selected person is:
      i   Just Soap   ii   Indulgence   iii   Silktouch?

Brand	Count	Relative Frequency
Silktouch	115	
Super	87	
Just Soap	108	
Indulgence	188	
Total		

2   Two coins were tossed 356 times and the *number of heads* occurring at each toss was recorded. The results were:

Outcome	Freq.	Rel. Freq.
0 heads	89	
1 head		
2 heads	95	
Total		

   a   Copy and complete the table given.

   b   What is the best estimate of the chance of the following events occurring from this data?
      i   0 heads   ii   1 head   iii   2 heads

3   At the Annual Show the fairy floss vendor estimated that three times as many people preferred pink fairy floss to white fairy floss.

   a   If 250 people wanted white fairy floss, estimate how many wanted pink.

   b   What is the estimate of the probability that the next customer asks for:
      i   white fairy floss   ii   pink fairy floss?

B   CHANCE INVESTIGATIONS

In experimental probability, the **relative frequency** of an outcome gives us an **estimate** for the **probability** of that outcome.

In general, the greater the number of trials, the more we can rely on our estimate of the probability.

The most commonly used equipment for experimental probability and games of chance is described below:

COINS

When a **coin** is tossed there are two possible sides that could show upwards: the *head* (usually the head of a monarch, president or leader) and the *tail* (the other side of the coin). We would expect a head (H) and a tail (T) to have equal chance of occurring, i.e., we expect each to occur 50% of the time. So,

the probability of obtaining a head is $\frac{1}{2}$, and

the probability of obtaining a tail is $\frac{1}{2}$.

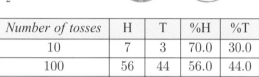

The table alongside shows actual experimental results obtained for tossing a coin:

Number of tosses	H	T	%H	%T
10	7	3	70.0	30.0
100	56	44	56.0	44.0
1000	491	509	49.1	50.9

each is nearly 50%

These experimental results support our expectations and suggest the general rule:

"The more times we repeat an experiment, like tossing a coin, the closer the results will be to the theoretical results we expect to obtain".

DICE

(**Note:**   **Dice** is the plural of **die**.)

The most commonly used dice are small cubes with the numbers 1, 2, 3, 4, 5 and 6 marked on them using dots.

The numbers on the face of a cubic die are arranged such that the sum of each pair of opposite faces is seven.

SPINNERS

A simple **spinner** consists of a regular polygon (or sometimes a circle with equal sectors) with a toothpick or match through its centre.

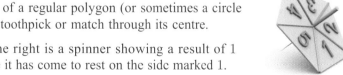

To the right is a spinner showing a result of 1 since it has come to rest on the side marked 1.

A spinner such as the one on the left may be used instead of a die, providing all angles are equal. The result shown is 2, since the pointer came to rest on the sector marked 2.

INVESTIGATION 1   ROLLING A DIE

You will need:

At least one normal six-sided die with numbers 1 to 6 on its faces.
Several dice would be useful to speed up the experiment.

What to do:

1 Examine a die. List the possible outcomes for the uppermost face
when the die is rolled.

2 Consider the possible outcomes when the die is rolled 60 times. Complete a table of
your **expected results** which includes columns of *Outcomes*, *Expected relative
frequency* and *Expected frequency*.

3 Roll the die 60 times and record
the result on the uppermost face in
a table like the one alongside:

4 Pool as much data as you can with
other students.

Outcome	Tally	Frequency	Rel. frequ.
1			
2			
⋮			
6			
	Total	60	

- Look at similarities and differences from one set to another.

- Look at the overall pooled data added into one table.

SIMULATION

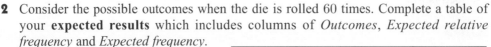

5 How close to your expectation were your results?

6 Use the die rolling simulation from the computer package on the CD to
roll the die 10 000 times and repeat this 10 times. On each occasion, record your
results in a table like that in **3**. Do your results confirm your expected results?

INVESTIGATION 2   TOSSING THREE COINS

You will need:

Three coins. They do not
have to be all the same type.

What to do:

1 List the 8 possible outcomes for tossing 3 coins simultaneously. (Let HHT represent
"a head for the first coin, a head for the second and a tail for the third".)

2 How many of these outcomes could be described as:

   a 'three heads'   **b** 'two heads and a tail'

   c 'one head and two tails'   **d** 'three tails'?

3 Consider the possible outcomes of tossing three coins 80 times. Copy and complete
a table of **expected results**.

Result	Expected relative frequency	Expected frequency
3 heads		
2 heads and 1 tail		
1 head and 2 tails		
3 tails		

4 Now perform the above experiment and record your results in a table such as that which follows:

Result	Tally	Frequency	Relative frequency
3 heads			
2 heads and 1 tail			
1 head and 2 tails			
3 tails			
Total		80	1

5 Pool as much data as you can with other students and find the overall relative frequencies of the results.

SIMULATION
  • Look for similarities and differences from one set to another.
  • Look at the overall pooled data added into one table.

6 Comment on any differences between the observed results and the expected results for your own experiment and the results of the group overall.

7 Use the three coin simulation from the computer package on the CD to toss the coins 5000 times. Repeat this 10 times and on each occasion record your results in a table like that in **4**. Are your results consistent with your expectations?

INVESTIGATION 3　　　　　　　　**ROLLING A PAIR OF DICE**

You will need: 2 normal six-sided dice with numbers 1 to 6 on the faces.

What to do:

1

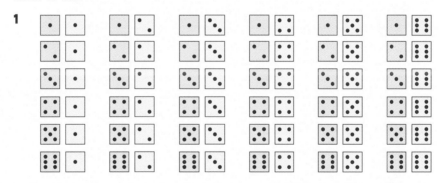

The illustration above shows that when two dice are rolled there are 36 possible outcomes. Of these, {1, 3}, {2, 2} and {3, 1} give a sum of 4.

Using the illustration above, copy and complete the following table of expected (theoretical) results:

Sum	2	3	4	5	· · ·	12
Fraction of total			$\frac{3}{36}$			
Fraction as decimal			0.083			

2 If a pair of dice is rolled 360 times, how many of each result (2, 3, 4, ..., 12) would you expect to get? Extend your table of **1** by adding another row and write your **expected frequencies** within it.

3 Toss the two dice 360 times and record in a table the *sum of the two numbers* for each toss.

SIMULATION

PRINTABLE
WORKSHEET

Sum	Tally	Frequency	Relative Frequency
2			
3			
4			
5			
⋮			
12			
Total		360	1

4 Use the two dice simulation from the computer package on the CD to roll the pair of dice 10 000 times. Repeat this 10 times and on each occasion record your results in a table like that of **3**. Are your results consistent with your expectations?

C   SAMPLE SPACE

A **sample space** is the set of all possible outcomes of an experiment.

There are a variety of ways of representing or illustrating sample spaces.

LISTING OUTCOMES

Example 2   ◀)) Self Tutor

List the sample space for: **a** tossing a coin   **b** rolling a die.

a When a coin is tossed, there are two possible outcomes.
∴ sample space = {H, T}

b When a die is rolled, there are 6 possible outcomes.
∴ sample space = {1, 2, 3, 4, 5, 6}

2-DIMENSIONAL GRIDS

When an experiment involves more than one operation we can still use listing to illustrate the sample space. However, a grid can often be a better way of achieving this.

Example 3   ◀)) Self Tutor

Illustrate the possible outcomes when 2 coins are tossed by using a 2-dimensional grid.

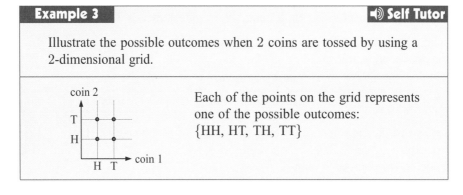

Each of the points on the grid represents one of the possible outcomes:
{HH, HT, TH, TT}

TREE DIAGRAMS

The sample space in **Example 3** could also be represented by a tree diagram.

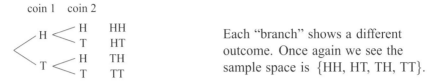

coin 1   coin 2

Each "branch" shows a different outcome. Once again we see the sample space is {HH, HT, TH, TT}.

The advantage of tree diagrams is that they can be used when more than two operations are involved.

Example 4   ◆)) **Self Tutor**

Illustrate, using a tree diagram, the possible outcomes when drawing two marbles from a bag containing a number of red, green and yellow marbles.

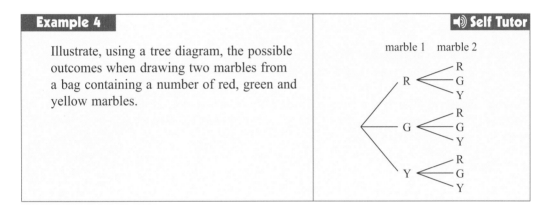

EXERCISE 13C

1   List the sample space for the following:
   a   rolling a six-sided die
   b   the sexes of a 3-child family
   c   the order in which 3 boys can be lined up
   d   the order in which 4 different rowing teams could finish a race.

2   Illustrate on a 2-dimensional grid the sample space for:
   a   rolling a die and tossing a coin simultaneously
   b   rolling two dice
   c   twirling a square spinner labelled A, B, C, D and a pentagonal spinner labelled 1, 2, 3, 4, 5
   d   tossing two coins and rolling a die simultaneously.

3   Illustrate on a tree diagram the sample space for:
   a   tossing a 20-cent and 50-cent coin simultaneously
   b   tossing 3 different coins
   c   the sexes of a 4-child family
   d   two teams, X and Y, play soccer. The team which is first to kick 3 goals wins the match.

D   THEORETICAL PROBABILITY

Consider the *pentagonal* spinner alongside.

Since the spinner is symmetrical, when it is spun the arrowed marker could finish with **equal likelihood** on each of the sections marked 1 to 5.

Therefore, we would say that the likelihood of obtaining a particular number, for example, 4, would be

$\quad$ 1 chance in 5, $\quad \frac{1}{5}$, $\quad$ 20% $\quad$ or $\quad$ 0.2

This is a **mathematical** (or **theoretical**) probability and is based on what we theoretically expect to occur.

> The **theoretical probability** of a particular event is the chance of that event occurring in any trial of the experiment.

Consider the event of getting *a result of 3 or more* from one spin of the pentagonal spinner. There are three favourable outcomes (3, 4 or 5) out of the five possible outcomes, and each of these is equally likely to occur.

So, $\quad$ P(3 or more) $= \frac{3}{5}$

We read $\frac{3}{5}$ as '3 chances in 5'.

In general, $\quad$ for an event E containing **equally likely** possible results:

$$P(E) = \frac{\text{the number of outcomes of the event } E}{\text{the total number of possible outcomes}}.$$

Example 5   ◄») **Self Tutor**

A marble is *randomly selected* from a bag containing 1 green, 4 yellow and 4 red marbles. Determine the probability of getting:

  a   a red marble $\qquad\qquad$ **b**   a green or yellow marble

  c   a blue marble $\qquad\qquad$ **d**   a green, yellow or red marble

---

The sample space is $\quad$ {G, Y, Y, Y, Y, R, R, R, R}
which has $1 + 4 + 4 = 9$ outcomes.

a $\quad$ P(red)

$\quad = \frac{4}{9}$

b $\quad$ P(a green or a yellow) $= \dfrac{1+4}{9}$

$\qquad\qquad\qquad\qquad\qquad = \frac{5}{9}$

c $\quad$ P(blue)

$\quad = \frac{0}{9}$

$\quad = 0$

d $\quad$ P(green, yellow or red) $= \dfrac{1+4+4}{9}$

$\qquad\qquad\qquad\qquad\qquad = \frac{9}{9}$

$\qquad\qquad\qquad\qquad\qquad = 1$

In **Example 5** notice that in c a blue result cannot occur and the calculated probability is 0, which fits the fact that it has *no chance* of occurring.

Also notice in d, a green, yellow or red result is certain to occur. It is 100% likely which is perfectly described using a 1.

The two events of   *no chance of occurring* with probability 0 and
certain to occur with probability 1 are two extremes.

Consequently, for any event E, $0 \leqslant \mathrm{P}(E) \leqslant 1$.

COMPLEMENTARY EVENTS

Example 6	◄) Self Tutor

An ordinary 6-sided die is rolled once. Determine the chance of:

a   getting a 5   b   not getting a 5
c   getting an even number d   getting an odd number

The sample space of possible outcomes is $\{1, 2, 3, 4, 5, 6\}$

a $\mathrm{P}(5)$ b $\mathrm{P}(\text{not getting a } 5)$
$= \frac{1}{6}$ $= \mathrm{P}(1, 2, 3, 4 \text{ or } 6)$
$= \frac{5}{6}$

c $\mathrm{P}(\text{an even number})$ d $\mathrm{P}(\text{an odd number})$
$= \mathrm{P}(2, 4 \text{ or } 6)$ $= \mathrm{P}(1, 3 \text{ or } 5)$
$= \frac{3}{6}$ $= \frac{3}{6}$
$= \frac{1}{2}$ $= \frac{1}{2}$

In **Example 6**, did you notice that

$\mathrm{P}(5) + \mathrm{P}(\text{not getting a } 5) = 1$ and that $\mathrm{P}(\text{an even number}) + \mathrm{P}(\text{an odd number}) = 1$?

This is no surprise as *getting a 5* and *not getting a 5* are **complementary events** where one of them **must occur**.

Likewise *getting an even number* and *getting an odd number* are complementary events.

NOTATION

If E is an event, then E' is the **complementary event** of E.

So, $\mathrm{P}(E) + \mathrm{P}(E') = 1$.

A useful rearrangement is: $\mathrm{P}(E \text{ \textbf{not} occurring}) = 1 - \mathrm{P}(E \text{ occurring})$

EXERCISE 13D

1   A fair die is rolled. Determine the probability of getting:
   a   a 2 or a 3   b   a positive integer   c   a 7
   d   a result greater than 4   e   a non-six

2 A symmetrical octahedral die has numbers 1 to 8 marked on its faces, and it is rolled once. Determine the probability of throwing:

   a   a 2   b   a number less than 4

   c   a number less than 1   d   a number between 1 and 8

3 A regular pentagonal spinner has the numbers 1 to 5 marked on its partitions. Determine the probability that after a spin the result will be:

   a   even

   b   prime

   c   a factor of 6.

4 A bag contains 3 red and 7 blue buttons, and a button is randomly selected from the bag. Determine the probability of getting:

   a   a red   b   a blue   c   a red or a blue   d   a red and a blue.

5 One ticket is chosen in a lottery consisting of 100 tickets numbered 1 to 100 and the choice is made randomly. Determine the probability that the ticket is:

   a   a two digit number   b   a multiple of 12

   c   a multiple of 7 or 11

6 Determine the probability that a person randomly selected in the street has his (or her) birthday in September.

7 List the six different orders in which buses A, B and C can arrive at a bus stop. If the three buses arrive at random at a bus stop, determine the probability that:

   a   bus A arrives first   b   they arrive in alphabetical order

   c   bus B is the second bus to arrive   d   after bus B, bus C will be next to arrive

8 a List the 8 possible 3-child families, according to the gender of the children. For example, GGB means *"the first is a girl, the second is a girl, and the third is a boy"*.

   b   Assuming that each of these is equally likely to occur, determine the probability that a randomly selected 3-child family consists of:

      i   all boys   ii   all girls

      iii   boy, then boy, then girl   iv   two girls and a boy

      v   a boy for the eldest   vi   at least one girl

9 a List, in systematic order, the 24 different orders in which four blocks W, X, Y and Z can be placed one on top of the other.

   b   Hence, determine the probability that when 4 blocks are placed at random on top of one another:

      i   W is at the bottom   ii   X is in one of the two middle positions

      iii   X and Y are placed together

      iv   X, Y and Z are together, not necessarily in that order.

E   USING GRIDS TO FIND PROBABILITIES

Two-dimensional grids give us excellent visual displays of sample spaces. From these we can count favourable outcomes and so calculate probabilities.

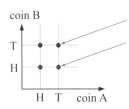

This point represents 'a tail from coin A' and 'a tail from coin B'.

This point represents 'a tail from coin A' and 'a head from coin B'.

There are four members of the sample space.

Example 7   ◀) Self Tutor

Use a two-dimensional grid to illustrate the sample space for tossing a coin and rolling a die simultaneously. From this grid determine the probability of:

a tossing a tail   **b** rolling a 3

c getting a head and a 6   **d** getting a head or a 6

There are 12 members in the sample space.

a $P(\text{tail}) = \frac{6}{12} = \frac{1}{2}$

b $P(3) = \frac{2}{12} = \frac{1}{6}$

c $P(\text{head and a '6'}) = \frac{1}{12}$

d $P(\text{head or a '6'}) = \frac{7}{12}$ {the enclosed points}

Example 8   ◀) Self Tutor

Two circular spinners, each with 1, 2, 3 and 4 on their sectors, are twirled simultaneously. Draw a two-dimensional grid of the possible outcomes.
Use your grid to determine the probability of getting:

a a 2 with each spinner   **b** a 2 and a 4

c an even result for each spinner

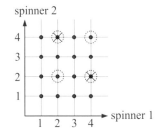

The sample space has 16 members.

a $P(\text{a 2 with each spinner}) = \frac{1}{16}$

b $P(\text{a 2 and a 4}) = \frac{2}{16}$ {crossed points}
$$= \frac{1}{8}$$

c $P(\text{an even result for each spinner})$
$$= \frac{4}{16}   \{\text{circled points}\}$$
$$= \frac{1}{4}$$

EXERCISE 13E

1 Two coins are tossed simultaneously. Use a 2-dimensional grid to illustrate the sample space and hence determine the probability of getting:

a   two heads   b   a head and a tail   c   at least one tail.

2 Draw a 2-dimensional grid to illustrate the sample space when an ordinary die (numbered 1 to 6) is tossed and a square spinner labelled A, B, C and D is spun. Hence, determine the probability of getting:

a   A and 4   b   B and a prime number   c   a consonant and a multiple of 3.

3 A pair of dice is rolled. The 36 different possible 'pair of dice' results are illustrated below on a 2-dimensional grid.

Use the 2-dimensional grid of the 36 possible outcomes to determine the probability of getting:

a   two 6's
b   a 2 and a 3
c   a 2 or a 3
d   at least one 4
e   exactly one 4
f   no fives
g   two even numbers
h   a sum of 8
i   a sum greater than 6
j   a sum of no more than 6.

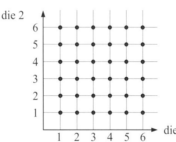

F   MULTIPLYING PROBABILITIES

In the previous section we used two-dimensional grids to represent sample spaces and hence find answers to certain types of probability problems.

Consider again a simple example of tossing a coin and rolling a die simultaneously.

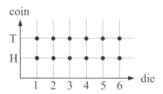

When asked "What is the probability of getting a head and a 5?" we get an answer of $\frac{1}{12}$ from the grid since there are 12 possible outcomes but only one with the property that we want.

But $P(\text{head}) = \frac{1}{2}$ and $P(\text{a '5'}) = \frac{1}{6}$ and $\frac{1}{2} \times \frac{1}{6} = \frac{1}{12}$

This suggests that $P(\text{head and a '5'}) = P(\text{head}) \times P(\text{'5'})$,

i.e., we multiply the separate probabilities.

In general:

If A and B are two events then $P(A \text{ and } B) = P(A) \times P(B)$.

Example 9   ◄ᴺ) **Self Tutor**

Joe has probability $\frac{3}{4}$ of hitting a target and Anne has probability $\frac{4}{5}$.

If they both fire simultaneously at the target, determine the probability that:

| a   they both hit it | b   they both miss it. |

a P(both hit)	b P(both miss)
= P(Joe and Anne hit)	= P(Joe misses and Anne misses)
= P(Joe hits) × P(Anne hits)	= P(Joe misses) × P(Anne misses)
= $\frac{3}{4} \times \frac{4}{5}$	= $\frac{1}{4} \times \frac{1}{5}$
= $\frac{3}{5}$	= $\frac{1}{20}$

EXERCISE 13F

1   Janice and Lee take set shots at a netball goal from 3 m. From past experience Janice throws a goal 2 times in every 3 shots on average whereas Lee throws a goal 4 times in every 7. If they both shoot for goals determine the probability that:

   a   both score a goal

   b   both miss

   c   Janice throws a goal but Lee misses.

2   When a nut was tossed 500 times it finished on its edge 156 times and on its side for the rest. Use this information to estimate the probability that when two identical nuts are tossed:

   a   they both fall on their edges   b   they both fall on their sides.

3   Helena has probability $\frac{1}{3}$ of hitting a target with an arrow, whilst Marco has probability $\frac{2}{5}$.

If they fire at the target, determine the probability that:

   a   both hit the target

   b   both miss the target

   c   Helena hits the target and Marco misses it

   d   Helena misses the target and Marco hits it.

4   A certain brand of drawing pin was tossed into the air 1000 times and it landed on its back ⊥ 375 times and on its side ⋋ for the remainder. Use this information to estimate the probability that:

   a   one drawing pin, when tossed, will fall on its i   back   ii   side

   b   two drawing pins, when tossed, will both fall on their backs

   c   two drawing pins, when tossed, will both fall on their sides.

USING TREE DIAGRAMS

Tree diagrams can be used to illustrate sample spaces provided that the alternatives are not too numerous.

Once the sample space is illustrated, the tree diagram can be used for determining probabilities.

Consider **Example 9** again. The tree diagram for this information is:

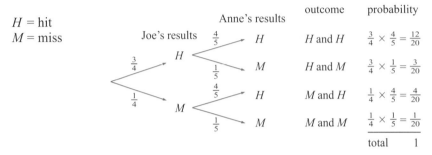

$H = $ hit
$M = $ miss

Notice that:

- The probabilities for hitting and missing are marked on the branches.
- There are *four* alternative paths and each branch shows a particular outcome.
- All outcomes are represented and the probabilities are obtained by **multiplying**.

Example 10   ◀) Self Tutor

Sylke has bad luck with the weather when she takes her summer holidays. She estimates that it rains 60% of the time and it is cold 70% of the time.

a Draw a tree diagram to illustrate this situation.

b Use the tree diagram to determine the chance that for Sylke's holidays:

   i it is cold and raining   **ii** it is fine and cold.

---

a $C = $ the weather is cold $R = $ it is raining

		outcome	probability
	0.6 → R	C and R	$0.7 \times 0.6 = 0.42$
0.7 ← C	0.4 → R′	C and R′	$0.7 \times 0.4 = 0.28$
0.3 ← C′	0.6 → R	C′ and R	$0.3 \times 0.6 = 0.18$
	0.4 → R′	C′ and R′	$0.3 \times 0.4 = 0.12$
		total	1.00

temperature   rain

b **i**   P(it is cold and raining)

     $= \text{P}(C \text{ and } R)$

     $= 0.7 \times 0.6$

     $= 0.42$

  ii   P(it is fine and cold)

     $= \text{P}(R' \text{ and } C)$

     $= 0.4 \times 0.7$

     $= 0.28$

EXERCISE 13G

1   Jar A contains 2 white and 3 red marbles, whereas Jar B contains 4 red and 1 white marble. A jar is randomly selected and one marble is taken from it.

jar   marble

a   Copy and complete the branches on the tree diagram shown.

b   Determine the probability that the marble is red.

2   A square dartboard is made up of nine smaller squares. Five are painted red and the remainder are black.

   R is "landing on red" B is "landing on black"

a   Evaluate: i   P(R)   ii   P(B)

b   Copy and complete the tree diagram illustrating two darts being thrown at the board.

c   Using b, determine the probability that:

   dart 1   dart 2

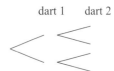

i   both darts land on black

ii   both darts land on red

iii   dart 1 lands on red and dart 2 lands on black

iv   one dart lands on red and the other lands on black.

3   The probability of rain tomorrow is estimated to be $\frac{1}{5}$. If it does rain, the Mudlarks football team will have an 80% probability of winning. If it is fine they have a 50% chance of winning. Display the sample space of possible results of the football match on a tree diagram.

Determine the probability that the Mudlarks will win tomorrow.

4   A factory produces bottles of fruit juice. Machine A fills 60% of the bottles produced and machine B fills the rest. Machine A underfills 1% of the bottles, while Machine B underfills 0.5%. Determine the probability that the next bottle inspected at this factory is underfilled.

Example 11   ◀》 **Self Tutor**

Bag A contains 3 red and 2 yellow tickets. Bag B contains 1 red and 4 yellow tickets. A bag is randomly selected by tossing a coin and one ticket is removed from it. Determine the probability that it is yellow.

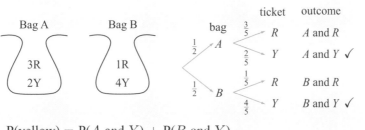

> To get a yellow ticket we take either the first branch marked with a ✓ **or** the second one marked with a ✓ and **add** the probabilities.

P(yellow) = P(A and Y) + P(B and Y)

   $= \frac{1}{2} \times \frac{2}{5} + \frac{1}{2} \times \frac{4}{5}$ {branches marked with a ✓}

   $= \frac{6}{10}$ (or $\frac{3}{5}$)

5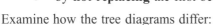

A	B	C
2B 2R	1B 3R	2B 2R

Three bags contain different numbers of blue and red marbles. A bag is selected at random and one marble is then selected from it.

Determine the probability that it is: **a** blue **b** red.

H | SAMPLING WITH AND WITHOUT REPLACEMENT

Consider a box containing 3 red, 2 blue and 1 yellow marble.

Suppose we wish to sample two marbles:

- by **replacement** of the first before the second is drawn
- by **not replacing** the first before the second is drawn.

Examine how the tree diagrams differ:

With replacement   **Without replacement**

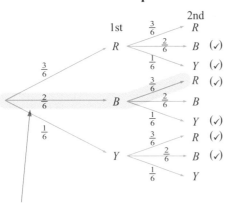   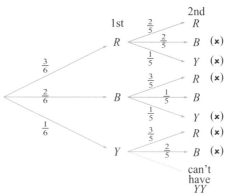

This branch represents Blue with the 1st draw and Red with the second, written as BR.

Notice that:
- with replacement $P(\text{two reds}) = \frac{3}{6} \times \frac{3}{6} = \frac{1}{4}$
- without replacement $P(\text{two reds}) = \frac{3}{6} \times \frac{2}{5} = \frac{1}{5}$

Example 12   ◄🔊 **Self Tutor**

For the example of the box containing 3 red, 2 blue and 1 yellow marble find the probability of getting two different colours:

a   if replacement occurs   **b**   if replacement does not occur.

---

a   P(two different colours)

= P(RB or RY or BR or BY or YR or YB)   {ticked ones}

$= \frac{3}{6} \times \frac{2}{6} + \frac{3}{6} \times \frac{1}{6} + \frac{2}{6} \times \frac{3}{6} + \frac{2}{6} \times \frac{1}{6} + \frac{1}{6} \times \frac{3}{6} + \frac{1}{6} \times \frac{2}{6}$

$= \frac{11}{18}$

> **b**   P(two different colours)
>
> $= P(RB$ or RY or BR or BY or YR or $YB)$ {crossed ones}
>
> $= \frac{3}{6} \times \frac{2}{5} + \frac{3}{6} \times \frac{1}{5} + \frac{2}{6} \times \frac{3}{5} + \frac{2}{6} \times \frac{1}{5} + \frac{1}{6} \times \frac{3}{5} + \frac{1}{6} \times \frac{2}{5}$
>
> $= \frac{11}{15}$

Note:

When using tree diagrams to assist in solving probability questions, the following rules should be used:

- The probability for each branch is calculated by **multiplying** the probabilities along that path.
- If two or more branch paths meet the description of the compound event, the probability of each path is found and then they are **added**.

EXERCISE 13H

1   A box contains 5 red and 2 white tickets. Two tickets are drawn at random (the first being *replaced* before the second is drawn). Draw a tree diagram to represent the sample space and use it to determine the probability that:

    a   both are red   **b**   both are white

    c   the first is red and the second is white   **d**   one is red and the other is white

2   7 tickets numbered 1, 2, 3, 4, 5, 6 and 7 are placed in a hat. Two of the tickets are taken from the hat at random *without replacement.* Determine the probability that:

    a   both are even   **b**   both are odd

    c   the first is odd and the second is even   **d**   one is odd and the other is even

3   Amelie has a bag containing two different varieties of apples. They are approximately the same size and shape, but one variety is red and the other is green. There are 4 red apples and 6 green ones. She selects one apple at random, eats it and then takes another, also at random. Determine the probability that:

    a   both apples were red

    b   both apples were green

    c   the first was red and the second was green

    d   the first was green and the second was red

    Add your answers to **a**, **b**, **c** and **d**. Explain why the answer must be 1.

4   Marjut has a carton containing 10 cans of soup. 4 cans are tomato and the rest are pumpkin. She selects 2 cans at random without looking at the labels.

    a   Let T represent tomato and P represent pumpkin. Draw a tree diagram to illustrate this sampling process.

    b   What is the probability that both cans were tomato soup?

    c   What is the probability that one can was tomato and the other can was pumpkin soup?

5 Box A contains 2 red and 2 green tickets. Box B contains 3 red and 5 green tickets. When a box has been selected at random, two tickets are randomly selected without replacement from it. Determine the probability that:

    a   both are green   **b**   they are different in colour.

6 A bag contains two white and five red marbles. Three marbles are selected simultaneously. Determine the probability that:

    a   all are red   **b**   only two are red   **c**   at least two are red.

7 Bag A contains 3 red and 2 white marbles.
Bag B contains 4 red and 3 white marbles.

One marble is randomly selected from A and its colour noted. If it is red, 2 reds are added to B. If it is white, 2 whites are added to B. A marble is then selected from B.

A   B

What are the chances that the marble selected from B is white?

8 A man holds two tickets in a 100-ticket lottery in which there are two winning tickets. If no replacement occurs, determine the probability that he will win:

    a   both prizes   **b**   neither prize   **c**   at least one prize.

I   PROBABILITIES FROM VENN DIAGRAMS
(EXTENSION)

Example 13   🔊 Self Tutor

If the Venn diagram alongside illustrates the number of passengers on an aeroplane flight who watched television (T) and slept (S), determine the number of passengers:

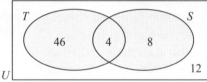

    a on the flight   **b** who watched television
    c who slept or watched television   **d** who neither watched television
    e who did not sleep   nor slept

    a Number on the flight   **b** Number who watched television
        $= 46 + 4 + 8 + 12 = 70$ $= 46 + 4 = 50$
    c Number who slept or watched television
        $= 46 + 4 + 8 = 58$
    d Number who neither watched television nor slept $= 12$
    e Number who did not sleep $= 46 + 12 = 58$

EXERCISE 13I

1 The Venn diagram alongside illustrates the number of students in a particular class who study German (G) and Spanish (S). Determine the number of students:

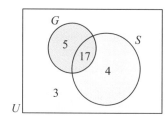

   a in the class   **b** who study both subjects

   c who study at least one of the subjects

   d who only study Spanish.

2 In a survey people were asked if their holidays for the last year had been within their own country (O) or in another country (A). Use the Venn diagram to determine the number of people:

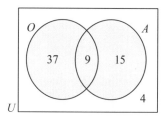

   a in the survey

   b who had holidays in their own country

   c who did not have holidays

   d who only had holidays in another country.

Example 14 ◀)) **Self Tutor**

In a class of 30 students, 19 play sport, 8 play music and 3 play sport and music, in their leisure time. Display this information on a Venn diagram and hence determine the probability that a randomly selected class member plays:

  a both sport and music   **b** at least one of sport and music

  c sport, but not music   **d** exactly one of sport and music

  e neither sport nor music   **f** music if it is known that the student plays sport

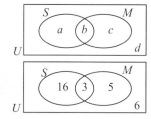

Let S represent the event of 'playing sport', and M represent the event of 'playing music'.

Now $a + b = 19$ {as 19 play sport}

            $b + c = 8$ {as 8 play music}

                $b = 3$ {as 3 play both}

$a + b + c + d = 30$ {as there are 30 in the class}

$\therefore \ b = 3, \quad a = 16, \quad c = 5, \quad d = 6.$

a P(plays both)

$= \frac{3}{30}$ or $\frac{1}{10}$

b P(plays at least one of sport and music)

$= \frac{16+3+5}{30}$

$= \frac{24}{30}$ (or $\frac{4}{5}$)

c P(plays S, but not M)

$= \frac{16}{30}$

$= \frac{8}{15}$

d P(plays exactly one)

$= \frac{16+5}{30}$

$= \frac{7}{10}$

e P(plays neither)

$= \frac{6}{30}$

$= \frac{1}{5}$

f P(plays M if it is known plays S)

$= \frac{3}{16+3}$

$= \frac{3}{19}$

3 In summer, in a class of 35 students, 18 swim, 14 play tennis and 8 do neither of these sports. A student is randomly chosen from the class. Determine the probability that the student:

   a plays tennis   **b** does not swim

   c does at least one of the sports   **d** does exactly one of the sports

   e swims, but does not play tennis

4 On a hot day a group of 50 people at the beach were asked why they had come to the beach. 27 had come to swim, 19 had come to surf, and 3 had come to do both. If one person was chosen at random, determine the probability that he/she had come to:

   a surf but not swim   **b** neither surf nor swim

   c swim, but not surf.

5 From the Venn diagram $\quad P(A) = \dfrac{a+b}{a+b+c+d}$

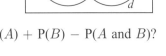

   a Use the Venn diagram to find:

        i $P(B)$ **ii** $P(A \text{ and } B)$ **iii** $P(A \text{ or } B)$

        iv $P(A) + P(B) - P(A \text{ and } B)$

   b What is the connection between $P(A \text{ or } B)$ and $P(A) + P(B) - P(A \text{ and } B)$?

J CONDITIONAL PROBABILITY (EXTENSION)

THE ADDITION LAW

In question **5** of the previous exercise we showed that

$$\text{for two events } A \text{ and } B, \quad P(A \cup B) = P(A) + P(B) - P(A \cap B).$$

This is known as the **addition law of probability**, and can be written as

$$P(\textbf{either } A \textbf{ or } B) = P(A) + P(B) - P(\textbf{both } A \textbf{ and } B)$$

Example 15   ◀》 **Self Tutor**

If $P(A) = 0.6$, $P(A \cup B) = 0.7$ and $P(A \cap B) = 0.3$, find P(B).

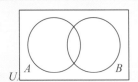

Since $\quad P(A \cup B) = P(A) + P(B) - P(A \cap B)$,
       then $\quad 0.7 = 0.6 + P(B) - 0.3$
       $\therefore \quad P(B) = 0.4$

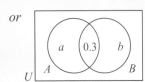

Using a Venn diagram with the probabilities on it,
       $a + 0.3 = 0.6 \qquad \therefore \quad a = 0.3$
       $0.3 + b + 0.3 = 0.7$
            $\therefore \quad b = 0.1$
       $\therefore \quad P(B) = 0.3 + b = 0.4$

or

MUTUALLY EXCLUSIVE EVENTS

If A and B are **mutually exclusive** events then $P(A \cap B) = 0$
and so the addition law becomes

$$P(A \cup B) = P(A) + P(B).$$

In a Venn diagram for mutually exclusive events, the circles for the events do not overlap.

Mutually exclusive events
have no common outcomes.

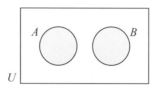

Example 16   ◀) **Self Tutor**

A basket of fruit contains 8 apples (A) and 12 oranges (O).

a   Are the events A and O mutually exclusive?

b   Find   i $P(A)$ ii $P(O)$ iii $P(A \cap O)$ iv $P(A \cup O)$.

---

a   A piece of fruit cannot be an apple and an orange.
∴ A and O are mutually exclusive.

b   i $P(A) = \frac{8}{20}$ ii $P(O) = \frac{12}{20}$ iii $P(A \cap O)$ iv $P(A \cup O)$
          $= \frac{2}{5}$ $= \frac{3}{5}$ $= 0$ $= \frac{20}{20}$
                                                                                                $= 1$

CONDITIONAL PROBABILITY

If we have two events A and B, then

$A \mid B$ is used to represent that 'A occurs knowing that B has occurred'.

Example 17   ◀) **Self Tutor**

In a class of 25 students, 15 like chocolate milk (M) and 17 like iced coffee (C).
Two students like neither and 9 students like both. One student is randomly selected
from the class. What is the probability that the student:

a   likes chocolate milk

b   likes chocolate milk given that he/she likes iced coffee?

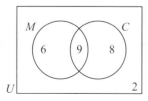

The Venn diagram of the situation is shown.

a   15 of the 25 students like chocolate milk.

∴   P(chocolate milk) $= \frac{15}{25}$

b   Of the 17 who like iced coffee, 9 like chocolate milk.

∴   P(chocolate milk | iced coffee) $= \frac{9}{17}$

If A and B are events then

$$P(A \mid B) = \frac{P(A \cap B)}{P(B)}.$$

Proof:

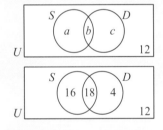

$$P(A \mid B)$$
$$= \frac{b}{b+c} \quad \{\text{Venn diagram}\}$$
$$= \frac{b \div (a+b+c+d)}{(b+c) \div (a+b+c+d)}$$
$$= \frac{P(A \cap B)}{P(B)}$$

It follows that $P(A \cap B) = P(A \mid B)\,P(B)$ or $P(A \cap B) = P(B \mid A)\,P(A)$

Example 18   ◀) Self Tutor

In a library group of 50 readers, 34 like science fiction, 22 like detective stories and 12 dislike both.

If a reader is randomly selected, find the probability that the reader:

a likes science fiction and detective stories

b likes at least one of science fiction and detective stories

c likes science fiction given that he/she likes detective stories

d dislikes detective stories given that he/she likes science fiction.

S represents readers who like science fiction
D represents readers who like detective stories

We are given that $a + b = 34$
$$b + c = 22$$
$$a + b + c = 38$$

$$\therefore \quad c = 38 - 34 \quad \text{and so} \quad b = 18$$
$$= 4 \qquad\qquad \text{and} \quad a = 16$$

a P(likes both)

$= \dfrac{18}{50}$

$= \dfrac{9}{25}$

b P(likes at least one)

$= \dfrac{38}{50}$

$= \dfrac{19}{25}$

c $P(S \mid D)$

$= \dfrac{18}{22}$

$= \dfrac{9}{11}$

d $P(D' \mid S)$

$= \dfrac{16}{34}$

$= \dfrac{8}{17}$

EXERCISE 13J

1 50 students went on a 'thrill seekers' holiday. 40 went white-water rafting, 21 went paragliding and each student did at least one of these activities.

    a From a Venn diagram find how many students did both activities.

    b If a student from this group is randomly selected, find the probability that he/she:

        i went white-water rafting but not paragliding

        ii went paragliding given that he/she went white-water rafting.

2 In a class of 25 students, 19 have fair hair, 15 have blue eyes, and 22 have fair hair, blue eyes or both. A child is selected at random. Determine the probability that the child has:

    a fair hair and blue eyes

    b neither fair hair nor blue eyes

    c fair hair but not blue eyes

    d blue eyes given that the child has fair hair.

3 28 students go tramping. 23 get sunburnt, 8 get blisters and 5 get both sunburnt and blisters. Determine the probability that a randomly selected student:

    a did not get blisters

    b either got blisters or sunburnt

    c neither got blisters nor sunburnt

    d got blisters, given that the student was sunburnt

    e was sunburnt, given that the student did not get blisters.

4 An examination in French has two parts; aural and written. When 30 students sit for the examination, 25 pass aural, 26 pass written and 3 fail both parts. Determine the probability that a student who:

    a passed aural also passed written   **b** passed aural, failed written.

5 In a certain town there are 3 supermarkets, P, Q and R. 60% of the population shop at P, 36% shop at Q, 34% shop at R, 18% shop at P and Q, 15% shop at P and R, 4% shop at Q and R and 2% shop at all 3 supermarkets. A person is selected at random.

Determine the probability that the person shops at:

    a none of the supermarkets   **b** at least one of the supermarkets

    c exactly one of the supermarkets   **d** either P or Q

    e P, given that the person shops at at least one supermarket

    f R, given that the person shops at either P or Q or both.

Example 19   **◀») Self Tutor**

Bin A contains 2 red and 4 white tickets. Bin B contains 3 red and 3 white. A die with four faces marked A and two faces marked B is rolled and used to select bin A or B. A ticket is then selected from this bin. Determine the probability that:

    a the ticket is red   **b** the ticket was chosen from B given it is red.

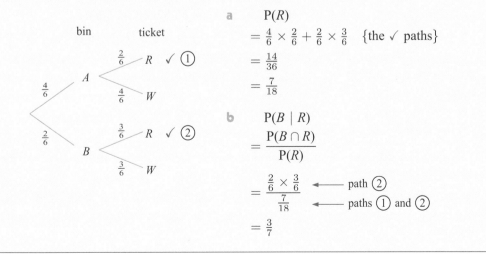

a $P(R)$
$$= \frac{4}{6} \times \frac{2}{6} + \frac{2}{6} \times \frac{3}{6} \quad \{\text{the } \checkmark \text{ paths}\}$$
$$= \frac{14}{36}$$
$$= \frac{7}{18}$$

b $P(B \mid R)$
$$= \frac{P(B \cap R)}{P(R)}$$
$$= \frac{\frac{2}{6} \times \frac{3}{6}}{\frac{7}{18}} \quad \begin{matrix} \longleftarrow \text{ path ②} \\ \longleftarrow \text{ paths ① and ②} \end{matrix}$$
$$= \frac{3}{7}$$

6 Marius has 2 bags of peaches. Bag A has 4 ripe and 2 unripe peaches, and bag B has 5 ripe and 1 unripe peaches. Ingrid selects a bag by tossing a coin, and takes a peach from that bag.

    a Determine the probability that the peach is ripe.

    b Given that the peach is ripe, what is the probability it came from B?

7 When Sophia goes to the local shopping centre on Monday to Thursday the probability that she finds a carpark is 95%. When she goes on Friday or Saturday the probability of finding a carpark is 70%. Assuming that she is equally likely to shop on any day from Monday to Saturday, determine the probability that on any trip:

    a she finds a carpark   **b** it is Saturday, given that she finds a carpark.

8 On a given day, Claude's car has an 80% chance of starting first time and André's car has a 70% chance of the same. Given that at least one of the cars has started first time, what is the chance that André's car started first time?

REVIEW SET 13A

1 Donna keeps records of the number of clients she interviews over a consecutive period of days.

    a For how many days did the survey last?

    b Estimate Donna's chances of interviewing:

        i no clients on a day

        ii four or more clients on a day

        iii less than three clients on a day.

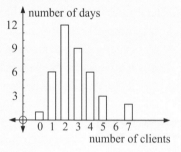

2 Illustrate on a 2-dimensional grid the possible outcomes when a coin and a pentagonal spinner with sides labelled A, B, C, D and E are tossed and spun.

3 What is meant by saying that two events are "independent"?

4 Use a tree diagram to illustrate the sample space for the possible four-child families and hence determine the probability that a randomly chosen four-child family:

    a is all boys   **b** has exactly two boys   **c** has more girls than boys.

5 In a shooting competition, Louise has 80% chance of hitting her target and Kayo has 90% chance of hitting her target. If they both have a single shot, determine the probability that:

    a both hit their targets   **b** neither hits her target

    c at least one hits her target   **d** only Kayo hits her target

6 Two fair six-sided dice are rolled simultaneously. Determine the probability that the result is a double.

7 A bag contains 4 green and 3 red marbles. Two marbles are randomly selected from the bag, the first being replaced before the drawing of the second. Determine the probability that:

    a both are green   **b** they are different in colour.

8 A circle is divided into 5 sectors with congruent angles at the centre and a spinner is constructed. The sectors are numbered 1, 2, 3, 4, and 5. A coin is tossed and the spinner is spun.

    a Use a 2-dimensional grid to show the sample space.

    b What is the chance of getting: **i** a head and a 5   **ii** a head or a 5?

9 Bag X contains three white and two red marbles. Bag Y contains one white and three red marbles. A bag is randomly chosen and two marbles are drawn from it. Illustrate the given information on a tree diagram and hence determine the probability of drawing two marbles of the same colour.

10 At a local girls' school, 65% of the students play netball, 60% play tennis and 20% play neither sport. Display this information on a Venn diagram and hence determine the likelihood that a randomly chosen student plays:

    a netball
                          b netball but not tennis

    c at least one of these two sports
        d exactly one of these two sports

    e tennis, given that she plays netball

REVIEW SET 13B

1 Pierre conducted a survey to determine the ages of people walking through a shopping mall. The results are shown in the table alongside. Find, correct to 3 decimal places, the estimated probability that the next person Pierre meets in the shopping mall is:

Age	Frequency
0 - 19	22
20 - 39	43
40 - 59	39
60+	14

    a between 20 and 39 years of age

    b less than 40 years of age   **c** at least 20 years of age.

2 **a** List, in set notation, the sample space of possible results when a tetrahedral die with four faces labelled A, B, C and D is rolled and a 20-cent coin are tossed simultaneously.

    b Use a tree diagram to illustrate the sample space for the following:

       Bags A, B and C contain green or yellow tickets. A bag is selected and then a ticket taken from it.

3 Use a tree diagram to illustrate the following sample space: Martina and Justine play tennis. The first to win three sets wins the match.

4 When a box of drawing pins dropped onto the floor it was observed that 49 landed on their backs and 32 landed on their sides. Find, correct to 2 decimal places, the estimated probability of a drawing pin landing:

back   side

    a on its back
                 b on its side.

5 The letters A, B, C, D, ... N are put in a hat.

  a Determine the probability of drawing a vowel (A, E, I, O or U) if one of the letters is chosen at random.

  b If two letters are drawn without replacement, copy and complete the following tree diagram including all probabilities where appropriate:

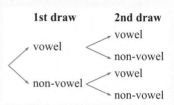

  c Use your tree diagram to determine the probability of drawing:

   i a vowel and a non-vowel

   ii at least one vowel.

6 A farmer fences his rectangular property, as shown alongside, into 9 rectangular paddocks:

If a paddock is selected at random, what is the probability that

  a it has no fences on the boundary of the property

  b it has one fence on the boundary of the property

  c it has two fences on the boundary of the property?

7 If $P(A) = \frac{7}{12}$, find $P(A')$.   (**Recall**: A' is the complement of A.)

8 Bag X contains 3 black and 2 red marbles. Bag Y contains 4 black and 1 red marble. A bag is selected at random and then two marbles are selected without replacement. Determine the probability that:

  a both marbles are red   **b** two black marbles are picked from Bag Y.

9 Two dice are rolled simultaneously. Illustrate this information on a 2-dimensional grid. Determine the probability of getting:

  a a double 5   **b** at least one 4   **c** a sum greater than 9

  d a sum of 7 or 11

10 A class consists of 25 students, 15 have blue eyes, 9 have fair hair and 3 have both blue eyes and fair hair. Represent this information on a Venn diagram and hence find the probability that a randomly selected student from the class:

  a has neither blue eyes nor fair hair   **b** has blue eyes, but not fair hair

  c has fair hair given that he or she has blue eyes

  d does not have fair hair given that he or she does not have blue eyes.

Chapter **14**

Further algebra

Contents:

ALGEBRAIC FRACTIONS

Algebraic fractions are fractions which contain at least one pronumeral (unknown).

The pronumeral(s) may be in the numerator (top), or denominator (bottom), or in both the numerator and denominator.

For example, $\dfrac{x}{7}, \quad \dfrac{-2}{5-y}, \quad \dfrac{x+2y}{1-y}$ are algebraic fractions.

Algebraic fractions are sometimes called **rational expressions**.

A   EVALUATING FRACTIONS

To **evaluate** an algebraic expression we replace the pronumerals with known values and then simplify the expression giving our answer in simplest form.

Example 1   ◆) **Self Tutor**

If $a = 2$, $b = -3$ and $c = -5$, evaluate: **a** $\dfrac{a-b}{c}$ **b** $\dfrac{a-c-b}{b-a}$

a $\dfrac{a-b}{c}$

$= \dfrac{2-(-3)}{(-5)}$

$= \dfrac{2+3}{-5}$

$= \dfrac{5}{-5}$

$= -1$

b $\dfrac{a-c-b}{b-a}$

$= \dfrac{2-(-5)-(-3)}{(-3)-2}$

$= \dfrac{2+5+3}{-3-2}$

$= \dfrac{10}{-5}$

$= -2$

EXERCISE 14A

1 If $a = 3$, $b = 2$, $c = 6$, evaluate:

a $\dfrac{c}{2}$ **b** $\dfrac{c}{a}$ **c** $\dfrac{a}{c}$ **d** $\dfrac{c}{b-a}$ **e** $\dfrac{a+c}{b}$

f $\dfrac{ab}{c}$ **g** $\dfrac{a^2}{b}$ **h** $\dfrac{c^2}{a}$ **i** $\dfrac{ab^2}{c}$ **j** $\dfrac{(ab)^2}{c}$

2 If $a = 2$, $b = -3$ and $c = -4$, evaluate:

a $\dfrac{c}{a}$ **b** $\dfrac{a}{c}$ **c** $\dfrac{-1}{b}$ **d** $\dfrac{c^2}{a}$ **e** $\dfrac{c}{a+b}$

f $\dfrac{a-c}{2b}$ **g** $\dfrac{b}{c-a}$ **h** $\dfrac{a-c}{a+c}$ **i** $\dfrac{c-a}{b^2}$ **j** $\dfrac{a^2}{c-b}$

B   SIMPLIFYING ALGEBRAIC FRACTIONS

CANCELLATION

If the numerator and denominator of an algebraic fraction are both written in factored form and common factors are found, we can simplify by **cancelling the common factors**.

This process was observed when we cancelled number fractions such as $\frac{12}{28}$.

i.e., $\frac{12}{28} = \frac{4 \times 3}{4 \times 7} = \frac{3}{7}$ where the common factor 4 was cancelled.

Similarly, algebraic fractions can be simplified by cancelling common factors if they exist.

For example,

$$\frac{4ab}{2a} = \frac{2 \times \cancel{2}^1 \times \cancel{a}^1 \times b}{{}_1\cancel{2} \times \cancel{a}_1} \quad \{\text{fully factorised}\}$$

$$= \frac{2b}{1} \quad \{\text{after cancellation}\}$$

$$= 2b$$

For algebraic fractions:

Check both numerator and denominator to see if they can be expressed as the product of factors then look for common factors which can be cancelled.

When cancelling in algebraic fractions, only factors can be cancelled, not terms.

ILLEGAL CANCELLATION

Take care with fractions such as $\dfrac{a+3}{3}$.

The expression in the numerator, $a + 3$, cannot be written as the product of factors other than $1 \times (a + 3)$ as a and 3 are terms of the expression not factors.

A typical error in illegal cancellation is: $\dfrac{a + \cancel{3}^1}{\cancel{3}_1} = \dfrac{a+1}{1} = a + 1.$

You can check that this cancellation of terms is not correct by substituting a value for a.

For example,   if $a = 3$,   LHS $= \dfrac{a+3}{3} = \dfrac{3+3}{3} = 2,$

whereas   RHS $= a + 1 = 4.$

EXERCISE 14B

1 Joe Lin says that you should always check algebraic simplification by using substitution.

For example, Wei Soong suggested that $\dfrac{2x+6}{3} = 2x + 2$.

However,   when $x = 3$, $\dfrac{2x+6}{3} = \dfrac{6+6}{3} = \dfrac{12}{3} = 4$,

whereas, $2x + 2 = 6 + 2 = 8 \neq 4$.

This one example shows that $\dfrac{2x+6}{3} \neq 2x + 2$ on simplifying.

Check the following simplifications with the given substitutions:

a $\dfrac{3x+8}{4} = 3x + 2$ (substituting $x = 4$)

b $\dfrac{4x+2}{2} = 2x + 1$ (substituting $x = 1$, 2 and 3)

c $\dfrac{4x+3}{2} = 2x + 3$ (substituting $x = 3$)

d $\dfrac{2a+b+10}{5} = 2a + b + 2$ (substituting $a = 2$ and $b = 1$)

Example 2 🔊 **Self Tutor**

Simplify: **a** $\dfrac{a^2}{2a}$ **b** $\dfrac{6a^2 b}{3b}$

a $\dfrac{a^2}{2a}$

$= \dfrac{a \times \cancel{a}^{1}}{2 \times \cancel{a}^{1}}$

$= \dfrac{a}{2}$

b $\dfrac{6a^2 b}{3b}$

$= \dfrac{{}^{2}\cancel{6} \times a \times a \times \cancel{b}^{1}}{{}_{1}\cancel{3} \times \cancel{b}_{1}}$

$= \dfrac{2 \times a \times a}{1}$

$= 2a^2$

---

2 Simplify:

a $\dfrac{2a}{4}$		**b** $\dfrac{4m}{2}$		**c** $\dfrac{6a}{a}$		**d** $\dfrac{6a}{2a}$		**e** $\dfrac{2a^2}{a}$
f $\dfrac{2x^3}{2x}$		**g** $\dfrac{2x^3}{x^2}$		**h** $\dfrac{2x^3}{x^3}$		**i** $\dfrac{2a^2}{4a^3}$		**j** $\dfrac{8m^2}{4m}$
k $\dfrac{4a^2}{a^2}$		**l** $\dfrac{6t}{3t^2}$		**m** $\dfrac{4d^2}{2d}$		**n** $\dfrac{ab^2}{2ab}$		**o** $\dfrac{4ab^2}{6a^2 b}$

Example 3   ◀)) **Self Tutor**

Simplify: **a** $\dfrac{(-4b)^2}{2b}$ **b** $\dfrac{3(x+4)^2}{x+4}$

a $\dfrac{(-4b)^2}{2b}$

$= \dfrac{(-4b) \times (-4b)}{2 \times b}$

$= \dfrac{^8\cancel{16} \times b \times \cancel{b}^{\,1}}{_1\cancel{2} \times \cancel{b}_{\,1}}$

$= 8b$

b $\dfrac{3(x+4)^2}{x+4}$

$= \dfrac{3(x+4)\cancel{(x+4)}^{\,1}}{_1\cancel{x+4}}$

$= 3(x+4)$

3 Simplify:

a $\dfrac{(2a)^2}{a^2}$ **b** $\dfrac{(4n)^2}{8n}$ **c** $\dfrac{(-a)^2}{a}$ **d** $\dfrac{a^2}{(-a)^2}$

e $\dfrac{(-2a)^2}{4}$ **f** $\dfrac{(-3n)^2}{6n}$ **g** $\dfrac{(x+y)^2}{x+y}$ **h** $\dfrac{2(x+2)}{(x+2)^2}$

Example 4   ◀)) **Self Tutor**

Simplify:

a $\dfrac{(2x+3)(x+4)}{5(2x+3)}$ **b** $\dfrac{4(x+2)(x-1)}{2(x-1)}$

a $\dfrac{^1\cancel{(2x+3)}(x+4)}{5\cancel{(2x+3)}^{\,1}}$

$= \dfrac{(x+4)}{5}$

$= \dfrac{x+4}{5}$

b $\dfrac{^2\cancel{4}(x+2)\cancel{(x-1)}^{\,1}}{_1\cancel{2}\cancel{(x-1)}_{\,1}}$

$= \dfrac{2(x+2)}{1}$

$= 2(x+2)$

4 Simplify:

a $\dfrac{2(a+3)}{2}$ **b** $\dfrac{4(x+2)}{2}$ **c** $\dfrac{6(c+3)}{3}$

d $\dfrac{2(d-3)}{6}$ **e** $\dfrac{4}{2(x+1)}$ **f** $\dfrac{12}{4(2-x)}$

g $\dfrac{3(x+4)}{9(x+4)}$ **h** $\dfrac{12(a-3)}{6(a-3)}$ **i** $\dfrac{(x+y)(x-y)}{3(x-y)}$

j $\dfrac{2xy(x-y)}{6x(x-y)}$ **k** $\dfrac{5(y+2)(y-3)}{15(y+2)}$ **l** $\dfrac{x(x+1)(x+2)}{3x(x+2)}$

Example 5		◄⑴ **Self Tutor**

Simplify if possible: **a** $\dfrac{4(x+8)}{2}$ **b** $\dfrac{x+8}{2}$

a $\dfrac{4(x+8)}{2}$

$= \dfrac{2 \times \overset{1}{2} \times (x+8)}{\underset{1}{2}}$

$= 2(x+8)$

b $\dfrac{x+8}{2}$

cannot be simplified {Since the coefficient of x is not a multiple of 2, we cannot cancel the denominator.}

5   Simplify if possible:

a $\dfrac{3(x+2)}{6}$ **b** $\dfrac{6(x+2)}{3}$ **c** $\dfrac{x+6}{3}$ **d** $\dfrac{x-4}{2}$

e $\dfrac{2(x-1)}{4(x+1)}$ **f** $\dfrac{2x+5}{10}$ **g** $\dfrac{2x+6}{10}$ **h** $\dfrac{3}{3a+9}$

C   ADDING AND SUBTRACTING ALGEBRAIC FRACTIONS

Pronumerals are used in algebraic fractions to represent unknown numbers. So we can treat algebraic fractions in the same way that we treat numerical fractions, as they are in fact representing numerical fractions.

The rules for addition and subtraction of algebraic fractions are identical to those used with numerical fractions.

These are:

To add two or more fractions we obtain the *lowest common denominator* then add the resulting numerators.

Since $\dfrac{2}{5} + \dfrac{4}{5} = \dfrac{2+4}{5}$,

$\dfrac{a}{c} + \dfrac{b}{c} = \dfrac{a+b}{c}$.

To subtract two or more fractions we obtain the *lowest common denominator* and then subtract the resulting numerators.

Since $\dfrac{7}{9} - \dfrac{5}{9} = \dfrac{7-5}{9}$,

$\dfrac{a}{c} - \dfrac{d}{c} = \dfrac{a-d}{c}$.

To find the lowest common denominator, we look for the **lowest common multiple of the denominators**.

For example, when adding $\frac{3}{2} + \frac{5}{3}$ the lowest common denominator is 6,

when adding $\frac{5}{6} + \frac{4}{9}$, the lowest common denominator is 18.

The same method is used when there are pronumerals in the denominator, i.e., we find the lowest common multiple of the denominators.

For example, when adding $\dfrac{2}{a} + \dfrac{3}{b}$, the lowest common denominator is ab,

when adding $\dfrac{2}{x} + \dfrac{4}{5x}$, the lowest common denominator is $5x$,

when adding $\dfrac{5}{6x} + \dfrac{4}{9y}$, the lowest common denominator is $18xy$.

To find $\dfrac{x}{3} + \dfrac{5x}{4}$ we find the LCD and then proceed in the same manner as for ordinary fractions.

So, $\dfrac{x}{3} + \dfrac{5x}{4}$

$= \dfrac{x \times 4}{3 \times 4} + \dfrac{5x \times 3}{4 \times 3}$ {as LCD of 3 and 4 is 12}

$= \dfrac{4x}{12} + \dfrac{15x}{12}$

$= \dfrac{19x}{12}$

Example 6   ◀) Self Tutor

Simplify:

a $\dfrac{x}{2} + \dfrac{3x}{4}$

b $\dfrac{a}{3} - \dfrac{2a}{5}$

a $\dfrac{x}{2} + \dfrac{3x}{4}$ {has LCD of 4}

$= \dfrac{x \times 2}{2 \times 2} + \dfrac{3x}{4}$

$= \dfrac{2x}{4} + \dfrac{3x}{4}$

$= \dfrac{2x + 3x}{4}$

$= \dfrac{5x}{4}$

b $\dfrac{a}{3} - \dfrac{2a}{5}$ {has LCD of 15}

$= \dfrac{a \times 5}{3 \times 5} - \dfrac{2a \times 3}{5 \times 3}$

$= \dfrac{5a}{15} - \dfrac{6a}{15}$

$= \dfrac{-a}{15}$ or $-\dfrac{a}{15}$

EXERCISE 14C

1 Simplify, i.e., write as a single fraction:

  a $\dfrac{a}{2} + \dfrac{a}{3}$ **b** $\dfrac{b}{5} - \dfrac{b}{10}$ **c** $\dfrac{c}{4} + \dfrac{3c}{2}$ **d** $\dfrac{x}{7} - \dfrac{x}{2}$

  e $\dfrac{a}{3} + \dfrac{b}{4}$ **f** $\dfrac{t}{3} - \dfrac{5t}{9}$ **g** $\dfrac{m}{7} + \dfrac{2m}{21}$ **h** $\dfrac{5d}{6} - \dfrac{d}{3}$

  i $\dfrac{3p}{5} - \dfrac{2p}{7}$ **j** $\dfrac{m}{2} + \dfrac{m}{3} + \dfrac{m}{6}$ **k** $\dfrac{a}{2} - \dfrac{a}{3} + \dfrac{a}{4}$ **l** $\dfrac{x}{4} - \dfrac{x}{3} + \dfrac{x}{6}$

Example 7   ◀》 Self Tutor

Simplify: **a** $\dfrac{4}{a} + \dfrac{3}{b}$ **b** $\dfrac{5}{x} - \dfrac{4}{3x}$

a $\dfrac{4}{a} + \dfrac{3}{b}$ {has LCD of ab}

    $= \dfrac{4 \times b}{a \times b} + \dfrac{3 \times a}{b \times a}$

    $= \dfrac{4b}{ab} + \dfrac{3a}{ab}$

    $= \dfrac{4b + 3a}{ab}$

b $\dfrac{5}{x} - \dfrac{4}{3x}$ {has LCD of $3x$}

    $= \dfrac{5 \times 3}{x \times 3} - \dfrac{4}{3x}$

    $= \dfrac{15}{3x} - \dfrac{4}{3x}$

    $= \dfrac{11}{3x}$

---

2 Simplify:

  a $\dfrac{7}{a} + \dfrac{3}{b}$ **b** $\dfrac{3}{a} + \dfrac{2}{c}$ **c** $\dfrac{4}{a} + \dfrac{5}{d}$ **d** $\dfrac{2a}{m} - \dfrac{a}{m}$

  e $\dfrac{a}{x} + \dfrac{b}{2x}$ **f** $\dfrac{3}{a} - \dfrac{1}{2a}$ **g** $\dfrac{4}{x} - \dfrac{1}{xy}$ **h** $\dfrac{a}{b} + \dfrac{c}{d}$

  i $\dfrac{a}{b} - \dfrac{x}{y}$ **j** $\dfrac{2}{3} + \dfrac{a}{2}$ **k** $\dfrac{x}{3} + \dfrac{3}{4}$ **l** $\dfrac{x}{y} + \dfrac{2}{3}$

Example 8   ◀》 Self Tutor

Simplify: **a** $\dfrac{b}{3} + 1$ **b** $\dfrac{a}{4} - a$

a $\dfrac{b}{3} + 1$

    $= \dfrac{b}{3} + \dfrac{3}{3}$

    $= \dfrac{b + 3}{3}$

b $\dfrac{a}{4} - a$

    $= \dfrac{a}{4} - \dfrac{a \times 4}{1 \times 4}$

    $= \dfrac{a}{4} - \dfrac{4a}{4}$

    $= \dfrac{-3a}{4}$ or $-\dfrac{3a}{4}$

3 Simplify:

a $\dfrac{x}{2} + 1$ b $\dfrac{y}{3} - 1$ c $\dfrac{a}{2} + a$ d $\dfrac{b}{4} - 3$

e $\dfrac{x}{2} - 4$ f $2 + \dfrac{a}{3}$ g $3 - \dfrac{x}{5}$ h $2 + \dfrac{1}{x}$

i $5 - \dfrac{2}{x}$ j $a + \dfrac{2}{a}$ k $\dfrac{3}{b} + b$ l $\dfrac{x}{3} - 2x$

4 Simplify: (miscellaneous)

a $\dfrac{x}{2} + \dfrac{2x}{5}$ b $\dfrac{4x}{5} - \dfrac{3x}{2}$ c $\dfrac{3}{a} + \dfrac{2}{3a}$ d $\dfrac{4}{y} - \dfrac{3}{2y}$

e $\dfrac{5}{a} + \dfrac{3}{b}$ f $\dfrac{4}{3a} - \dfrac{5}{b}$ g $\dfrac{x}{7} + 2$ h $3 - \dfrac{x}{4}$

D — MULTIPLYING AND DIVIDING ALGEBRAIC FRACTIONS

The rules for multiplying and dividing algebraic fractions are identical to those with numerical fractions. These are:

To multiply two or more fractions we multiply the numerators to form the new numerator and we multiply the denominators to form the new denominator.

i.e., $\dfrac{a}{b} \times \dfrac{c}{d} = \dfrac{a \times c}{b \times d} = \dfrac{ac}{bd}$.

To divide by a fraction we multiply by its reciprocal.

i.e., $\dfrac{a}{b} \div \dfrac{c}{d} = \dfrac{a}{b} \times \dfrac{d}{c} = \dfrac{ad}{bc}$.

MULTIPLICATION

The method to follow when **multiplying** algebraic fractions is the same method used for numerical fractions, but take care to check if the algebraic fraction formed can be simplified by cancelling common factors.

The method is: *step 1:*   Multiply numerators, multiply denominators.
   step 2:   Separate the factors.
   step 3:   Cancel any common factors.
   step 4:   Write in simplest form.

For example, $\dfrac{a^2}{2} \times \dfrac{4}{a}$ $= \dfrac{a^2 \times 4}{2 \times a}$ {step 1}

$= \dfrac{a \times \overset{1}{\cancel{a}} \times 2 \times \overset{1}{\cancel{2}}}{\underset{1}{\cancel{2}} \times \underset{1}{\cancel{a}}}$ {step 2 and 3}

$= \dfrac{2a}{1}$

$= 2a$ {step 4}

DIVISION

The method is:

step 1:   To divide by a fraction, we instead multiply by its reciprocal.

step 2:   Multiply numerators, multiply denominators.

step 3:   Cancel common factors.

step 4:   Write in simplest form.

For example, $\dfrac{a}{2} \div \dfrac{b}{4} = \dfrac{a}{2} \times \dfrac{4}{b}$ {step 1}

$$= \dfrac{a \times 4}{2 \times b} \quad \text{{step 2}}$$

$$= \dfrac{a \times \cancel{4}^{\,2}}{_{1}\cancel{2} \times b} \quad \text{{step 3}}$$

$$= \dfrac{2a}{b} \quad \text{{step 4}}$$

Example 9   ◀◎ **Self Tutor**

Simplify: **a** $\dfrac{3}{m} \times \dfrac{m}{6}$ **b** $\dfrac{3}{m} \times m^2$

a $\dfrac{3}{m} \times \dfrac{m}{6}$

$= \dfrac{^{1}\cancel{3} \times \cancel{m}^{\,1}}{_{1}\cancel{m} \times \cancel{6}_{\,2}}$

$= \dfrac{1}{2}$

b $\dfrac{3}{m} \times m^2$

$= \dfrac{3}{m} \times \dfrac{m^2}{1}$

$= \dfrac{3m^2}{m}$

$= \dfrac{3 \times m \times \cancel{m}^{\,1}}{\cancel{m}_{\,1}}$

$= \dfrac{3m}{1}$

$= 3m$

EXERCISE 14D

1 Simplify:

a $\dfrac{x}{2} \times \dfrac{y}{5}$ **b** $\dfrac{a}{2} \times \dfrac{3}{a}$ **c** $\dfrac{a}{2} \times a$ **d** $\dfrac{a}{4} \times \dfrac{2}{3a}$

e $\dfrac{c}{5} \times \dfrac{1}{c}$ **f** $\dfrac{c}{5} \times \dfrac{c}{2}$ **g** $\dfrac{a}{b} \times \dfrac{c}{d}$ **h** $\dfrac{a}{b} \times \dfrac{b}{a}$

i $\dfrac{1}{m^2} \times \dfrac{m}{2}$ **j** $\dfrac{m}{2} \times \dfrac{4}{m}$ **k** $\dfrac{a}{x} \times \dfrac{x}{b}$ **l** $m \times \dfrac{4}{m}$

m $\dfrac{3}{m^2} \times m$ **n** $\left(\dfrac{a}{b}\right)^2$ **o** $\left(\dfrac{2}{x}\right)^2$ **p** $\dfrac{1}{a} \times \dfrac{a}{b} \times \dfrac{b}{c}$

Example 10	◀) Self Tutor

Simplify: **a** $\dfrac{4}{n} \div \dfrac{2}{n^2}$ **b** $\dfrac{3}{a} \div 2$

a
$$\dfrac{4}{n} \div \dfrac{2}{n^2}$$

$$= \dfrac{4}{n} \times \dfrac{n^2}{2}$$

$$= \dfrac{4 \times n^2}{n \times 2}$$

$$= \dfrac{2 \times \cancel{2}^1 \times \cancel{n}^1 \times n}{{}^1\cancel{n} \times \cancel{2}^1}$$

$$= 2n$$

b
$$\dfrac{3}{a} \div 2$$

$$= \dfrac{3}{a} \times \dfrac{1}{2}$$

$$= \dfrac{3 \times 1}{a \times 2}$$

$$= \dfrac{3}{2a}$$

2 Simplify:

a $\dfrac{a}{2} \div \dfrac{a}{3}$ **b** $\dfrac{2}{a} \div \dfrac{2}{3}$ **c** $\dfrac{3}{4} \div \dfrac{4}{x}$ **d** $\dfrac{3}{x} \div \dfrac{4}{x}$

e $\dfrac{2}{n} \div \dfrac{1}{n}$ **f** $\dfrac{c}{5} \div 5$ **g** $\dfrac{c}{5} \div c$ **h** $m \div \dfrac{2}{m}$

i $m \div \dfrac{m}{2}$ **j** $1 \div \dfrac{m}{n}$ **k** $\dfrac{3}{g} \div 4$ **l** $\dfrac{3}{g} \div \dfrac{9}{g^2}$

3 Simplify: (miscellaneous)

a $\dfrac{2a}{3} \times \dfrac{6}{4a}$ **b** $\dfrac{2}{9} \div \dfrac{b}{3}$ **c** $\dfrac{2c}{5} + \dfrac{3c}{4}$ **d** $\dfrac{a}{c} - \dfrac{b}{2}$

e $\dfrac{7}{b} \times \dfrac{3a}{2b}$ **f** $\dfrac{8}{3a} - \dfrac{2}{a}$ **g** $\dfrac{ab}{cd} \div \dfrac{ab}{cd}$ **h** $\dfrac{a}{3b} + \dfrac{5}{2b}$

E   FURTHER SIMPLIFICATION (EXTENSION)

The **distributive law** is used to **expand** algebraic expressions.

For example, $a(x + y) = ax + ay$.

The **distributive law** is also used, in reverse, to **factorise** algebraic expressions.

For example, $ax + ay = a(x + y)$.

Algebraic **fractions** may contain expressions which can be factorised using the distributive law.

For example,   the fraction $\dfrac{3x + 3y}{6x + 6y}$ can be simplified by factorising the numerator and

denominator **separately** using the distributive law, and **then** cancelling common factors:

So, $\dfrac{3x+3y}{6x+6y} = \dfrac{3(x+y)}{6(x+y)}$ {factorising separately}

$= \dfrac{^1\cancel{3}\cancel{(x+y)}^1}{_2\cancel{6}\cancel{(x+y)}^1}$ {cancelling common factors}

$= \dfrac{1}{2}$ {simplifying}

Example 11   ◀ Self Tutor

Simplify: **a** $\dfrac{3a+9}{3}$ **b** $\dfrac{4a+12}{8}$

a $\dfrac{3a+9}{3}$

$= \dfrac{^1\cancel{3}(a+3)}{_1\cancel{3}}$

$= a+3$

b $\dfrac{4a+12}{8}$

$= \dfrac{^1\cancel{4}(a+3)}{\cancel{8}_2}$

$= \dfrac{a+3}{2}$

EXERCISE 14E

1 Simplifying by removing common factors:

a $\dfrac{4}{2(x+1)}$ **b** $\dfrac{12}{4(2-x)}$ **c** $\dfrac{2x+4}{2}$ **d** $\dfrac{3x+6}{3}$

e $\dfrac{3x+6}{6}$ **f** $\dfrac{4x+20}{8}$ **g** $\dfrac{4y+12}{12}$ **h** $\dfrac{ax+bx}{x}$

i $\dfrac{ax+bx}{cx+dx}$ **j** $\dfrac{(a+2)^2}{2(a+2)}$ **k** $\dfrac{3(b-4)}{6(b-4)^2}$ **l** $\dfrac{8(p+q)^2}{12(p+q)}$

Example 12   ◀ Self Tutor

Simplify by factorising: **a** $\dfrac{ab+ac}{b+c}$ **b** $\dfrac{6x^2-6xy}{3x-3y}$

a $\dfrac{ab+ac}{b+c} = \dfrac{a(b+c)}{b+c}$ {remove HCF a from numerator}

$= \dfrac{a\cancel{(b+c)}^1}{\cancel{(b+c)}^1}$

$= a$

b $\dfrac{6x^2-6xy}{3x-3y} = \dfrac{6x(x-y)}{3(x-y)}$ ⟵ HCF is $6x$

⟵ HCF is 3

$= \dfrac{^2\cancel{6} \times x \times \cancel{(x-y)}^1}{_1\cancel{3} \times \cancel{(x-y)}^1}$

$= 2x$

2 Simplify by factorising:

a $\dfrac{3x+6}{4x+8}$ **b** $\dfrac{ax+bx}{2x}$ **c** $\dfrac{ax+bx}{a+b}$ **d** $\dfrac{x^2+2x}{x+2}$

e $\dfrac{x}{ax+bx}$ **f** $\dfrac{a+b}{ay+by}$ **g** $\dfrac{ax+bx}{ay+by}$ **h** $\dfrac{x^3+2x^2}{x+2}$

i $\dfrac{4x^2+8x}{x+2}$ **j** $\dfrac{3x^2+9x}{x+3}$ **k** $\dfrac{4x^3+12x^2}{x^2+3x}$ **l** $\dfrac{ax^2+bx}{b+ax}$

A useful rule for reversing terms in a subtraction is $\quad b-a = -1(a-b)$.

Example 13   Self Tutor

Simplify, if possible: **a** $\dfrac{6a-6b}{b-a}$ **b** $\dfrac{xy^2-xy}{1-y}$

a $\dfrac{6a-6b}{b-a} = \dfrac{6(a-b)}{-1(a-b)} = -6$

b $\dfrac{xy^2-xy}{1-y} = \dfrac{xy(y-1)}{-1(y-1)} = -xy$

3 Simplify, if possible:

a $\dfrac{2x-2y}{y-x}$ **b** $\dfrac{3x-3y}{2y-2x}$ **c** $\dfrac{m+n}{n-m}$ **d** $\dfrac{m-n}{n-m}$

e $\dfrac{r-2s}{4s-2r}$ **f** $\dfrac{3r-6s}{2s-r}$ **g** $\dfrac{2x-2}{x-x^2}$ **h** $\dfrac{ab^2-ab}{2-2b}$

i $\dfrac{4x^2-4x}{2-2x}$ **j** $\dfrac{4x+6}{2}$ **k** $\dfrac{4x+6}{3}$ **l** $\dfrac{4x+6}{4}$

m $\dfrac{4x+6}{5}$ **n** $\dfrac{4x+6}{6}$ **o** $\dfrac{6a+1}{2}$ **p** $\dfrac{6a+1}{3}$

q $\dfrac{6a+2}{4}$ **r** $\dfrac{3b+9}{2}$ **s** $\dfrac{3b+9}{6}$ **t** $\dfrac{4x-2}{2-x}$

4 Simplify:

a $\dfrac{x^2-1}{x-1}$ **b** $\dfrac{x^2-1}{x+1}$ **c** $\dfrac{x^2-1}{1-x}$ **d** $\dfrac{x+2}{x^2-4}$

e $\dfrac{a^2-b^2}{a+b}$ **f** $\dfrac{a^2-b^2}{b-a}$ **g** $\dfrac{2x+2}{x^2-1}$ **h** $\dfrac{9-x^2}{3x-x^2}$

i $\dfrac{3x^2-3y^2}{2xy-2y^2}$ **j** $\dfrac{2b^2-2a^2}{a^2-ab}$ **k** $\dfrac{4xy-y^2}{16x^2-y^2}$ **l** $\dfrac{4x(x-4)}{16-x^2}$

5 Simplify by factorising and cancelling common factors:

a $\dfrac{x^2 - x - 2}{x - 2}$

b $\dfrac{x + 3}{x^2 - 2x - 15}$

c $\dfrac{2x^2 + 2x}{x^2 - 4x - 5}$

d $\dfrac{x^2 - 4}{x^2 + 4x + 4}$

e $\dfrac{x^2 - x - 12}{x^2 - 5x + 4}$

f $\dfrac{x^2 + 2x + 1}{1 - x^2}$

g $\dfrac{x^2 - x - 20}{x^2 + 7x + 12}$

h $\dfrac{2x^2 + 5x + 2}{2x^2 + 7x + 3}$

i $\dfrac{3x^2 + 7x + 2}{6x^2 - x - 1}$

j $\dfrac{8x^2 + 2x - 1}{4x^2 - 5x + 1}$

k $\dfrac{12x^2 - 5x - 3}{6x^2 + 5x + 1}$

l $\dfrac{15x^2 + 17x - 4}{5x^2 + 9x - 2}$

F   MORE COMPLICATED FRACTIONS
(EXTENSION)

Addition and subtraction of more complicated algebraic fractions is relatively straight forward if we adopt a consistent approach.

For example, consider simplifying $\dfrac{x + 2}{3} + \dfrac{5 - 2x}{2}$.

$$\dfrac{x + 2}{3} + \dfrac{5 - 2x}{2} \qquad \text{\{has LCD of 6\}}$$

$$= \dfrac{2}{2}\left(\dfrac{x + 2}{3}\right) + \dfrac{3}{3}\left(\dfrac{5 - 2x}{2}\right) \qquad \text{\{achieves a common denominator of 6\}}$$

$$= \dfrac{2(x + 2)}{6} + \dfrac{3(5 - 2x)}{6} \qquad \text{\{simplify each fraction\}}$$

..... etc

Example 14
🔊 **Self Tutor**

Write as a single fraction: **a** $\dfrac{x}{12} + \dfrac{x - 1}{4}$ **b** $\dfrac{x - 1}{3} - \dfrac{x + 2}{7}$

a
$$\dfrac{x}{12} + \dfrac{x - 1}{4}$$
$$= \dfrac{x}{12} + \dfrac{3}{3}\left(\dfrac{x - 1}{4}\right)$$
$$= \dfrac{x + 3(x - 1)}{12}$$
$$= \dfrac{x + 3x - 3}{12}$$
$$= \dfrac{4x - 3}{12}$$

b
$$\dfrac{x - 1}{3} - \dfrac{x + 2}{7}$$
$$= \dfrac{7}{7}\left(\dfrac{x - 1}{3}\right) - \dfrac{3}{3}\left(\dfrac{x + 2}{7}\right)$$
$$= \dfrac{7(x - 1)}{21} - \dfrac{3(x + 2)}{21}$$
$$= \dfrac{7(x - 1) - 3(x + 2)}{21}$$
$$= \dfrac{7x - 7 - 3x - 6}{21}$$
$$= \dfrac{4x - 13}{21}$$

EXERCISE 14F

1 Write as a single fraction:

    a $\dfrac{x}{4} + \dfrac{x-1}{5}$
    b $\dfrac{2x+5}{3} + \dfrac{x}{6}$
    c $\dfrac{x}{7} + \dfrac{2x-1}{6}$

    d $\dfrac{a+b}{2} + \dfrac{b-a}{3}$
    e $\dfrac{x-1}{4} + \dfrac{2x-1}{5}$
    f $\dfrac{x+1}{2} + \dfrac{2-x}{7}$

    g $\dfrac{x}{5} - \dfrac{x-3}{6}$
    h $\dfrac{x-1}{6} - \dfrac{x}{7}$
    i $\dfrac{x}{10} - \dfrac{2x-1}{5}$

    j $\dfrac{x}{6} - \dfrac{1-x}{12}$
    k $\dfrac{x-1}{3} - \dfrac{x-2}{5}$
    l $\dfrac{2x+1}{3} - \dfrac{1-3x}{8}$

Example 15
🔊 **Self Tutor**

Write as a single fraction: **a** $\dfrac{2}{x} + \dfrac{1}{x+2}$ **b** $\dfrac{5}{x+2} - \dfrac{1}{x-1}$

a $\dfrac{2}{x} + \dfrac{1}{x+2}$

$= \dfrac{2}{x}\left(\dfrac{x+2}{x+2}\right) + \left(\dfrac{1}{x+2}\right)\dfrac{x}{x}$ {as LCD is $x(x+2)$}

$= \dfrac{2(x+2) + x}{x(x+2)}$

$= \dfrac{2x + 4 + x}{x(x+2)}$

$= \dfrac{3x + 4}{x(x+2)}$

b $\dfrac{5}{x+2} - \dfrac{1}{x-1}$

$= \left(\dfrac{5}{x+2}\right)\left(\dfrac{x-1}{x-1}\right) - \left(\dfrac{1}{x-1}\right)\left(\dfrac{x+2}{x+2}\right)$ {as LCD is $(x+2)(x-1)$}

$= \dfrac{5(x-1) - 1(x+2)}{(x+2)(x-1)}$

$= \dfrac{5x - 5 - x - 2}{(x+2)(x-1)}$

$= \dfrac{4x - 7}{(x+2)(x-1)}$

---

2 Write as a single fraction:

    a $\dfrac{2}{x+1} + \dfrac{3}{x-2}$
    b $\dfrac{5}{x+1} + \dfrac{7}{x+2}$
    c $\dfrac{5}{x-1} - \dfrac{4}{x+2}$

d $\dfrac{2}{x+2} - \dfrac{4}{2x+1}$

e $\dfrac{3}{x-1} + \dfrac{4}{x+4}$

f $\dfrac{7}{1-x} - \dfrac{8}{x+2}$

g $\dfrac{1}{x+1} + \dfrac{3}{x}$

h $\dfrac{5}{x} - \dfrac{2}{x+3}$

i $\dfrac{x}{x+2} + \dfrac{3}{x-4}$

j $2 + \dfrac{4}{x-3}$

k $\dfrac{3x}{x+2} - 1$

l $\dfrac{x}{x+3} + \dfrac{x-1}{x+2}$

m $\dfrac{2}{x(x+1)} + \dfrac{1}{x+1}$

n $\dfrac{1}{x-1} - \dfrac{1}{x} + \dfrac{1}{x+1}$

o $\dfrac{2}{x+1} - \dfrac{1}{x-1} + \dfrac{3}{x+2}$

p $\dfrac{x}{x-1} - \dfrac{1}{x} + \dfrac{x}{x+1}$

Example 16 🔊 **Self Tutor**

Write as a single fraction:

a $\dfrac{3}{(x+2)(x-1)} + \dfrac{x}{x-1}$

b $\dfrac{-3}{(x+2)(x-1)} + \dfrac{x}{x-1}$

a
$$\dfrac{3}{(x+2)(x-1)} + \dfrac{x}{x-1}$$

$$= \dfrac{3}{(x+2)(x-1)} + \left(\dfrac{x}{x-1}\right)\left(\dfrac{x+2}{x+2}\right) \quad \{\text{as LCD is } (x+2)(x-1)\}$$

$$= \dfrac{3 + x(x+2)}{(x+2)(x-1)}$$

$$= \dfrac{x^2 + 2x + 3}{(x+2)(x-1)} \quad \{\text{we cannot simplify further as}$$
$$x^2 + 2x + 3 \text{ has no simple factors}\}$$

b
$$\dfrac{-3}{(x+2)(x-1)} + \dfrac{x}{x-1}$$

$$= \dfrac{-3}{(x+2)(x-1)} + \left(\dfrac{x}{x-1}\right)\left(\dfrac{x+2}{x+2}\right) \quad \{\text{as LCD is } (x+2)(x-1)\}$$

$$= \dfrac{-3 + x(x+2)}{(x+2)(x-1)}$$

$$= \dfrac{x^2 + 2x - 3}{(x+2)(x-1)}$$

$$= \dfrac{(x+3)(x-1)^{\,1}}{(x+2)(x-1)^{\,1}}$$

$$= \dfrac{x+3}{x+2} \qquad \textbf{Note:} \quad x \neq -2 \text{ or } 1$$

3 Write as a single fraction:

a $\dfrac{2}{x(x+1)} + \dfrac{1}{x+1}$

b $\dfrac{2}{x(x+1)} + \dfrac{x}{x+1}$

c $\dfrac{2x}{x-3} + \dfrac{4}{(x+2)(x-3)}$

d $\dfrac{2x}{x-3} - \dfrac{30}{(x+2)(x-3)}$

e $\dfrac{3}{(x-2)(x+3)} + \dfrac{x}{x+3}$

f $\dfrac{x}{x+3} - \dfrac{15}{(x-2)(x+3)}$

g $\dfrac{2x}{x+4} - \dfrac{40}{(x-1)(x+4)}$

h $\dfrac{x+5}{x-2} - \dfrac{63}{(x-2)(x+7)}$

4 a Write $\dfrac{2}{(x+2)(x-3)} + \dfrac{2x}{x-3}$ as a single fraction.

b Hence, find x when $\dfrac{2}{(x+2)(x-3)} + \dfrac{2x}{x-3}$ is   **i** undefined   **ii** zero.

G   FURTHER EXPANSION (EXTENSION)

To expand expressions like $x^{\frac{1}{2}}(2x^{\frac{1}{2}} - 3x^{-\frac{1}{2}})$, $(3^x + 1)(3^x - 2)$ and $(2^x + 5)^2$ we can use the same expansion laws, as done in previous algebra.

Recall the following expansion laws:
- $a(b+c) = ab + ac$
- $(a+b)(c+d) = ac + ad + bc + bd$
- $(a+b)(a-b) = a^2 - b^2$
- $(a+b)^2 = a^2 + 2ab + b^2$
- $(a-b)^2 = a^2 - 2ab + b^2$

Example 17   ◀)) Self Tutor

Expand and simplify: $x^{\frac{1}{2}}(2x^{\frac{1}{2}} - 3x^{-\frac{1}{2}})$

$x^{\frac{1}{2}}(2x^{\frac{1}{2}} - 3x^{-\frac{1}{2}})$
$= x^{\frac{1}{2}}2x^{\frac{1}{2}} - x^{\frac{1}{2}}3x^{-\frac{1}{2}}$ {each term in the bracket is × by $x^{\frac{1}{2}}$}
$= 2x^1 - 3x^0$ {adding indices}
$= 2x - 3$ {simplifying}

EXERCISE 14G

1 Expand and simplify:

a $x(x^2 + 3x + 1)$

b $x^2(x^3 + 3x - 2)$

c $x^{\frac{1}{2}}(x^{\frac{1}{2}} - x^{-\frac{1}{2}})$

d $x^{-\frac{1}{2}}(x^{\frac{1}{2}} - 2x^{-\frac{1}{2}})$

e $x^{\frac{3}{2}}(2x^{\frac{1}{2}} - x^{-\frac{1}{2}})$

f $2^x(2^x + 1)$

g $3^x(1 - 3^{-x})$

h $2^{-x}(2^x + 3)$

i $5^{-x}(5^{2x} + 5^x)$

Example 18

Self Tutor

Expand and simplify: **a** $(2^x + 3)(2^x + 5)$ **b** $(3^x - 3^{-x})^2$

a $\quad (2^x + 3)(2^x + 5)$
$= (2^x)^2 + 5(2^x) + 3(2^x) + 15 \quad$ {using FOIL}
$= 2^{2x} + 8(2^x) + 15$
$= 4^x + 2^{3+x} + 15$

b $\quad (3^x + 3^{-x})^2$
$= (3^x)^2 + 2(3^x)(3^{-x}) + (3^{-x})^2 \quad$ {as $(a+b)^2 = a^2 + 2ab + b^2$}
$= 3^{2x} + 2(3^0) + 3^{-2x}$
$= 3^{2x} + 2 + 3^{-2x}$

Note: 5×2^x is written conveniently as $5(2^x)$.

2 Expand and simplify:

a $(3^x + 1)(3^x + 2)$ **b** $(2^x + 1)(2^x + 5)$ **c** $(5^x - 2)(5^x - 7)$

d $(2^x + 1)^2$ **e** $(3^x + 2)^2$ **f** $(4^x - 7)^2$

g $(3^x + 1)^2$ **h** $(3^x - 8)^2$ **i** $(5^x - 3)^2$

j $(x^{\frac{1}{2}} + 3)(x^{\frac{1}{2}} - 3)$ **k** $(2^x + 5)(2^x - 5)$ **l** $(x^{\frac{1}{2}} + x^{-\frac{1}{2}})(x^{\frac{1}{2}} - x^{-\frac{1}{2}})$

m $(x + \dfrac{3}{x})^2$ **n** $(e^x - e^{-x})^2$ **o** $(3 - 2^{-x})^2$

H   FURTHER FACTORISATION (EXTENSION)

We first look for **common factors** and then for other forms such as **perfect squares**, **difference of two squares**, etc.

Example 19

Self Tutor

Factorise: **a** $3^{n+3} + 3^n$ **b** $2^{n+2} + 8$ **c** $5^{3n} + 5^{2n}$

a $\quad 3^{n+3} + 3^n$
$= 3^n 3^3 + 3^n$
$= 3^n(3^3 + 1)$
$= 3^n \times 28$

b $\quad 2^{n+2} + 8$
$= 2^n 2^2 + 8$
$= 4(2^n) + 8$
$= 4(2^n + 2)$

c $\quad 5^{3n} + 5^{2n}$
$= 5^{2n} 5^n + 5^{2n}$
$= 5^{2n}(5^n + 1)$

EXERCISE 14H

1 Factorise:

a $3^{2x} + 3^x$ **b** $2^{n+2} + 2^n$ **c** $4^n + 4^{3n}$

d $6^{n+1} - 6$ **e** $7^{n+2} - 7$ **f** $3^{n+2} - 9$

g $5(2^n) + 2^{n+2}$ **h** $3^{n+2} + 3^{n+1} + 3^n$ **i** $2^{n+1} + 3(2^n) + 2^{n-1}$

Example 20

Factorise: **a** $9^x - 4$ **b** $25^x + 4(5^x) + 4$

a $\quad 9^x - 4$
$= (3^x)^2 - 2^2$ {difference of two squares, $a^2 - 2^2$}
$= (3^x + 2)(3^x - 2)$ {as $a^2 - 2^2 = (a+2)(a-2)$}

b $\quad 25^x + 4(5^x) + 4$
$= (5^x)^2 + 4(5^x) + 4$ {compare $a^2 + 4a + 4$}
$= (5^x + 2)^2$ {as $a^2 + 4a + 4 = (a+2)^2$}

2 Factorise:

a $4^x - 9$ **b** $9^x - 25$ **c** $64 - 9^x$

d $16 - 25^x$ **e** $4^x - 9^x$ **f** $4^x + 6(2^x) + 9$

g $9^x + 10(3^x) + 25$ **h** $4^x - 14(2^x) + 49$ **i** $25^x - 4(5^x) + 4$

Example 21

Factorise: $\quad 4^x - 9(2^x) + 20$

$\quad 4^x - 9(2^x) + 20$
$= (2^x)^2 - 9(2^x) + 20$ {compare $a^2 - 9a + 20$}
$= (2^x - 4)(2^x - 5)$ {as $a^2 - 9a + 20 = (a-4)(a-5)$}

3 Factorise:

a $4^x + 11(2^x) + 18$ **b** $4^x - 2^x - 20$ **c** $9^x + 9(3^x) + 14$

d $9^x + 4(3^x) - 5$ **e** $25^x + 5^x - 2$ **f** $49^x - 7^{x+1} + 12$

Example 22

Simplify: **a** $\dfrac{12^n}{3^n}$ **b** $\dfrac{4^n}{8^n}$

a $\quad \dfrac{12^n}{3^n}$ **or** $\dfrac{12^n}{3^n}$ **b** $\quad \dfrac{4^n}{8^n}$ **or** $\dfrac{4^n}{8^n}$

$= \dfrac{4^n 3^n}{3^n}$ $= \left(\dfrac{12}{3}\right)^n$ $= \dfrac{4^n}{2^n 4^n}$ $= \left(\dfrac{4}{8}\right)^n$

$= 4^n$ $= 4^n$ $= \dfrac{1}{2^n}$ $= \left(\dfrac{1}{2}\right)^n$

4 Simplify:

a $\dfrac{18^n}{6^n}$ **b** $\dfrac{20^a}{5^a}$ **c** $\dfrac{6^b}{3^b}$ **d** $\dfrac{4^n}{24^n}$

e $\dfrac{36^x}{6^x}$ **f** $\dfrac{6^a}{10^a}$ **g** $\dfrac{3^{n+1}}{3^n}$ **h** $\dfrac{4^{n+1}}{4}$

Example 23   ◀) **Self Tutor**

Simplify: **a** $\dfrac{3^n + 6^n}{3^n}$ **b** $\dfrac{2^{m+2} - 2^m}{2^m}$ **c** $\dfrac{2^{m+3} + 2^m}{9}$

a $\dfrac{3^n + 6^n}{3^n}$

$= \dfrac{3^n + 2^n 3^n}{3^n}$

$= \dfrac{{}^1 \cancel{3^n}(1 + 2^n)}{{}_1 \cancel{3^n}}$

$= 1 + 2^n$

b $\dfrac{2^{m+2} - 2^m}{2^m}$

$= \dfrac{2^m 2^2 - 2^m}{2^m}$

$= \dfrac{2^m(2^2 - 1)}{2^m}$

$= \dfrac{3 (\cancel{2^m})^1}{{}_1 \cancel{2^m}}$

$= 3$

c $\dfrac{2^{m+3} + 2^m}{9}$

$= \dfrac{2^m 2^3 + 2^m}{9}$

$= \dfrac{2^m(2^3 + 1)}{9}$

$= \dfrac{{}^1 \cancel{9}(2^m)}{\cancel{9}\, 1}$

$= 2^m$

5 Simplify:

a $\dfrac{6^m + 2^m}{2^m}$ **b** $\dfrac{2^n + 12^n}{2^n}$ **c** $\dfrac{5^a + 15^a}{5^a}$

d $\dfrac{8^n + 4^n}{2^n}$ **e** $\dfrac{6^n + 12^n}{1 + 2^n}$ **f** $\dfrac{8^m + 2^m}{1 + 4^m}$

g $\dfrac{5^{n+1} - 5^n}{4}$ **h** $\dfrac{6^{n+2} - 6^n}{35}$ **i** $\dfrac{5^{n+1} - 5^n}{5^n}$

j $\dfrac{2^{n+2} + 2^n}{2^n}$ **k** $\dfrac{2^n - 2^{n-1}}{2^n}$ **l** $\dfrac{2^{n+2} - 2^n}{2^{n+1}}$

m $\dfrac{2^n + 2^{n-1}}{2^n + 2^{n+1}}$ **n** $\dfrac{3^{n+1} - 3^n}{3^n + 3^{n-1}}$ **o** $\dfrac{5^{x+y} + 5^x}{5^x}$

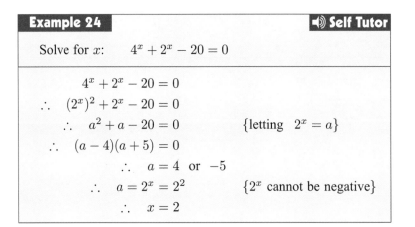

Example 24   ◀) **Self Tutor**

Solve for x: $4^x + 2^x - 20 = 0$

$$4^x + 2^x - 20 = 0$$
$$\therefore \quad (2^x)^2 + 2^x - 20 = 0$$
$$\therefore \quad a^2 + a - 20 = 0 \qquad \{\text{letting} \;\; 2^x = a\}$$
$$\therefore \quad (a - 4)(a + 5) = 0$$
$$\therefore \quad a = 4 \;\; \text{or} \;\; -5$$
$$\therefore \quad a = 2^x = 2^2 \qquad \{2^x \text{ cannot be negative}\}$$
$$\therefore \quad x = 2$$

6 Solve for x:

a $4^x - 6(2^x) + 8 = 0$ **b** $4^x - 2^x - 2 = 0$ **c** $9^x - 12(3^x) + 27 = 0$

d $9^x = 3^x + 6$ **e** $25^x - 23(5^x) - 50 = 0$ **f** $49^x + 8(7^x) + 7 = 0$

REVIEW SET 14A

1 Simplify:

    a $\dfrac{6x^2}{2x}$
    b $6 \times \dfrac{n}{2}$
    c $\dfrac{x}{2} \div 3$
    d $\dfrac{8x}{(2x)^2}$

2 If $a = 2$, $b = -3$ and $c = -6$ find the value of:

    a $\dfrac{c}{b}$
    b $b - \dfrac{c}{a}$
    c $\dfrac{b+c}{b-c}$
    d $\dfrac{ab^2}{c}$

3 Simplify, if possible:

    a $\dfrac{8}{4(c+3)}$
    b $\dfrac{3x+8}{4}$
    c $\dfrac{4x+8}{4}$
    d $\dfrac{x(x+1)}{3(x+1)(x+2)}$

4 Write as a single fraction:

    a $\dfrac{2x}{3} + \dfrac{3x}{5}$
    b $\dfrac{2x}{3} \times \dfrac{3x}{5}$
    c $\dfrac{2x}{3} \div \dfrac{3x}{5}$
    d $\dfrac{2x}{3} - \dfrac{3x}{5}$

5 Simplify by factorising:

    a $\dfrac{4x+8}{x+2}$
    b $\dfrac{5-10x}{2x-1}$
    c $\dfrac{4x^2+6x}{2x+3}$

6 Write as a single fraction:

    a $\dfrac{x+3}{4} + \dfrac{2x-2}{3}$
    b $\dfrac{x-1}{7} - \dfrac{1-2x}{2}$
    c $\dfrac{2}{x+2} + \dfrac{1}{x}$

7 Simplify by factorising:

    a $\dfrac{8-2x}{x^2-16}$
    b $\dfrac{x^2+7x+12}{x^2+4x}$
    c $\dfrac{2x^2-3x-2}{3x^2-4x-4}$

8 **a** Write $\dfrac{3x}{x-4} - \dfrac{60}{(x+1)(x-4)}$ as a single fraction.

    b Hence, find x when $\dfrac{3x}{x-4} - \dfrac{60}{(x+1)(x-4)}$ is **i** undefined **ii** zero.

9 Expand and simplify:

    a $2^x(2^x - 2^{-x})$
    b $(3^x + 2)(3^x - 1)$
    c $(5^x - 2)^2$

10 Fully factorise:

    a $5^{n+2} - 5^n$
    b $25 - 16^x$
    c $4^x - 6(2^x) + 8$

11 Solve for x: $9^x - 2(3^x) - 3 = 0$

REVIEW SET 14B

1 Simplify:

   a $\dfrac{4a}{6a}$ **b** $\dfrac{x}{3} \times 6$ **c** $3 \div \dfrac{1}{n}$ **d** $\dfrac{12x^2}{6x}$

2 If $x = 4$, $y = 3$ and $z = -2$ find the value of:

   a $\dfrac{x+y}{x-y}$ **b** $\dfrac{x-z}{y}$ **c** $\dfrac{yz^2}{x}$ **d** $\dfrac{x+2y}{z}$

3 Simplify, if possible:

   a $\dfrac{3x+15}{5}$ **b** $\dfrac{3x+15}{3}$ **c** $\dfrac{2(a+4)}{(a+4)^2}$ **d** $\dfrac{abc}{2ac(b-a)}$

4 Write as a single fraction:

   a $\dfrac{3x}{4} + 2x$ **b** $\dfrac{3x}{4} - 2x$ **c** $\dfrac{3x}{4} \times 2x$ **d** $\dfrac{3x}{4} \div 2x$

5 Simplify by factorising:

   a $\dfrac{3-x}{x-3}$ **b** $\dfrac{5x+10}{2x+4}$ **c** $\dfrac{3x^2-9x}{ax-3a}$

6 Write as a single fraction:

   a $\dfrac{x}{5} + \dfrac{2x-1}{3}$ **b** $\dfrac{x}{7} - \dfrac{1-2x}{2}$ **c** $\dfrac{3}{2x} - \dfrac{1}{x+2}$

7 Simplify by factorising:

   a $\dfrac{2x^2-8}{x+2}$ **b** $\dfrac{x^2-5x-14}{x^2-4}$ **c** $\dfrac{3x^2-5x-2}{4x^2-7x-2}$

8 **a** Write $\dfrac{2x}{x+5} - \dfrac{70}{(x+5)(x-2)}$ as a single fraction.

   b Hence, find x when $\dfrac{2x}{x+5} - \dfrac{70}{(x+5)(x-2)}$ is **i** zero **ii** undefined.

9 Expand and simplify:

   a $2x^{\frac{1}{2}}(3x^{\frac{3}{2}} - 4x^{-\frac{1}{2}})$ **b** $(5 - 2^x)^2$ **c** $(\sqrt{x} + 2)^2$

10 Simplify:

   a $\dfrac{3^{n+1} - 3^n}{3^n}$ **b** $\dfrac{3^{n+1} - 3^n}{2}$ **c** $\dfrac{2^{n+1} + 2^n}{2^n + 2^{n-1}}$

11 Solve for x: $4^x - 9(2^x) + 8 = 0$

Chapter 15

Formulae

Contents:

The **formula** $s = \dfrac{d}{t}$ relates the three variable quantities: speed (s), distance travelled (d) and time taken (t).

> A **formula** is an equation which connects two or more variables.

The plural of formula is **formulae** or **formulas**.

A   FORMULA SUBSTITUTION

We usually write formulae with one variable on its own on the left hand side. The other variable(s) and constants are written on the right hand side.

The variable on its own is called the **subject** of the formula.

If a formula contains two or more variables and we know the value of all but one of them, we can use the formula to find the value of the unknown variable.

The Method: *Step 1:*   Write down the formula.

Step 2:   State the values of the known variables.

Step 3:   Substitute into the formula to form a one variable equation.

Step 4:   Solve the equation for the unknown variable.

Example 1
◀) **Self Tutor**

When a stone is dropped from a cliff into the sea the total distance fallen, D metres, is given by the formula $D = \frac{1}{2}gt^2$ where t is the time of fall (in seconds) and g is the gravitational constant of 9.8 . Find:

a   the distance fallen after 4 seconds

b   the time (to the nearest $\frac{1}{100}$th second) taken for the stone to fall 200 metres.

a
$$D = \tfrac{1}{2}gt^2 \text{ where } g = 9.8 \text{ and } t = 4$$

$$\therefore \quad D = \tfrac{1}{2} \times 9.8 \times 4^2$$

$$= 78.4$$

∴ the stone has fallen 78.4 metres.

Calculator:

$0.5 \boxed{\times} \; 9.8 \; \boxed{\times} \; 4 \; \boxed{x^2} \; \boxed{=}$

b $D = \tfrac{1}{2}gt^2$ where $D = 200,\quad g = 9.8$

$$\therefore \quad \tfrac{1}{2} \times 9.8 \times t^2 = 200$$

$$\therefore \quad 4.9t^2 = 200$$

$$\therefore \quad t^2 = \frac{200}{4.9}$$

$$\therefore \quad t = \pm\sqrt{\frac{200}{4.9}}$$

$$\therefore \quad t = 6.39 \qquad \{\text{as } t > 0\}$$

∴ time taken is approx. 6.39 seconds.

Remember that if $x^2 = k$, then $x = \pm\sqrt{k}$.

Calculator:

$\boxed{\sqrt{}} \; \boxed{(\!(} \; 200 \; \boxed{\div} \; 4.9 \; \boxed{)\!)} \; \boxed{=}$

EXERCISE 15A

In this exercise, unless it is otherwise stated, give your answer correct to 1 decimal place where necessary.

1 The formula for finding the circumference, C, of a circle of radius r, is $C = 2\pi r$ where π is the constant with value approximately 3.14159. Find:

   a the circumference of a circle of radius 4.2 cm

   b the radius of a circle with circumference 112 cm

   c the diameter of a circle of circumference 400 metres.

2

When a stone is dropped from the top of a cliff the total distance fallen is given by the formula $D = \frac{1}{2}gt^2$ where D is the distance in metres and t is the time taken in seconds. Given that $g = 9.8$, find:

   a the total distance fallen in the first 2 seconds of fall

   b the height of the cliff, to the nearest metre, when the time of fall to hit the ground is 4.8 seconds.

3 When a car travels a distance d kilometres in time t hours, the average speed s km/h for the journey is given by the formula $s = \dfrac{d}{t}$. Find:

   a the average speed of a car which travels 250 km in $3\frac{1}{2}$ hours

   b the distance travelled by a car in $2\frac{3}{4}$ hours if its average speed is 80 km/h

   c the time taken, to the nearest minute, for a car to travel 790 km at an average speed of 95 km/h.

4 A circle's area A, is given by $A = \pi r^2$ where r is its radius length. Find:

   a the area of a circle of radius 6.4 cm

   b the radius of a circular swimming pool which must have an area of 160 m².

5 A cylinder of radius r, and height h, has volume given by $V = \pi r^2 h$. Find:

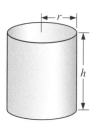

   a the volume of a cylindrical tin can of radius 8 cm and height 21.2 cm

   b the height of a cylinder of radius 6 cm and volume 120 cm³

   c the radius, in mm, of a copper pipe of volume 470 cm³ and length 6 m.

6

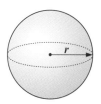

The formula for calculating the total surface area of a sphere of radius r is given by $A = 4\pi r^2$. Find:

   a the total surface area of a sphere of radius 7.5 cm

   b the radius (in cm) of a spherical balloon which is to have a surface area of 2 m².

7   The formula $D = 3.56\sqrt{h}$ gives the approximate distance (D km) to the horizon which can be seen by a person with eye level h metres above the level of the sea. Find:

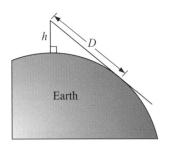

    a   the distance to the horizon when a person's eye level is 20 m above sea level

    b   how far above sea level a person's eye must be if the person wishes to see the horizon at a distance of 25 km.

8

point of support

l

pendulum

The time taken for one complete swing of a simple pendulum is given approximately by $T = \frac{1}{5}\sqrt{l}$ where l is the length of the pendulum (in cm) and T is the time (called the *period*) in seconds. Find:

    a   the time for one complete swing of the pendulum if its length is 45 cm

    b   the length of a pendulum if it is to have a period of exactly 1.8 seconds.

INVESTIGATION 1   PIZZA PRICING

Lou E Gee's Pizza Parlour has a 'Seafood Special' pizza advertised this week.

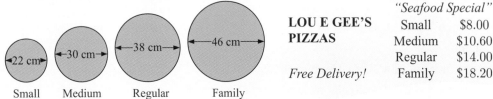

LOU E GEE'S	"Seafood Special"	
PIZZAS	Small	$8.00
	Medium	$10.60
	Regular	$14.00
Free Delivery!	Family	$18.20

Sasha, Enrico and Bianca decide to find Lou's formula for determining his prices (P). Letting r cm be the radius of a pizza dish, the formulae they worked out were:

    Sasha: $P = \dfrac{17r - 27}{20}$ Enrico: $P = \sqrt{\dfrac{33r - 235}{2}}$ Bianca: $P = 5 + \dfrac{r^2}{40}$.

What to do:

1   Investigate the suitability of each formula.

2   Lou is thinking about introducing a Party size pizza of diameter 54 cm. What do you think his price will be?

B   FORMULA REARRANGEMENT

For the formula $D = xt + p$ we say that D is the **subject**. This is because D is expressed in terms of the other variables, x, t and p.

We can rearrange formulae to make one of the other variables the subject.

> We **rearrange** formulae using the same processes we use to solve equations. Anything we do to one side we must also do to the other.

Example 2   ◀) Self Tutor

Make y the subject of $2x + 3y = 12$.

$$2x + 3y = 12$$
$$\therefore \quad 3y = 12 - 2x \quad \text{\{subtract } 2x \text{ from both sides\}}$$
$$\therefore \quad y = \frac{12 - 2x}{3} \quad \text{\{divide both sides by 3\}}$$
$$\therefore \quad y = \frac{12}{3} - \frac{2x}{3} = 4 - \tfrac{2}{3}x$$

EXERCISE 15B

1 Make y the subject of:

    a $2x + 5y = 10$ **b** $3x + 4y = 20$ **c** $2x - y = 8$

    d $2x + 7y = 14$ **e** $5x + 2y = 20$ **f** $2x - 3y = -12$

Example 3   ◀) Self Tutor

Make x the subject of $D = xt + p$.

$$\text{If} \quad D = xt + p$$
$$\text{then} \quad xt + p = D$$
$$\therefore \quad xt + p - p = D - p \quad\quad\quad \text{\{subtract } p \text{ from both sides\}}$$
$$\therefore \quad xt = D - p$$
$$\therefore \quad \frac{xt}{t} = \frac{D - p}{t} \quad\quad\quad \text{\{divide both sides by } t\text{\}}$$
$$\therefore \quad x = \frac{D - p}{t}$$

2 Make x the subject of:

    a $p + x = r$ **b** $xy = z$ **c** $3x + a = d$

    d $5x + 2y = d$ **e** $ax + by = p$ **f** $y = mx + c$

    g $2 + tx = s$ **h** $p + qx = m$ **i** $6 = a + bx$

Example 4

Self Tutor

Make y the subject of $x = 5 - cy$.

$$x = 5 - cy$$
$$\therefore \quad x + cy = 5 - cy + cy \quad \text{\{add } cy \text{ to both sides\}}$$
$$\therefore \quad x + cy = 5$$
$$\therefore \quad x + cy - x = 5 - x \quad \text{\{subtract } x \text{ from both sides\}}$$
$$\therefore \quad cy = 5 - x$$
$$\therefore \quad \frac{cy}{c} = \frac{5 - x}{c} \quad \text{\{divide both sides by } c\}$$
$$\therefore \quad y = \frac{5 - x}{c}$$

3 Make y the subject of:

   a $mx - y = c$ **b** $c - 2y = p$ **c** $a - 3y = t$

   d $n - ky = 5$ **e** $a - by = n$ **f** $p = a - ny$

Example 5

Self Tutor

Make z the subject of $c = \dfrac{m}{z}$.

$$c = \frac{m}{z}$$
$$c \times z = \frac{m}{z} \times z \quad \text{\{multiply both sides by } z\}$$
$$\therefore \quad cz = m$$
$$\therefore \quad \frac{cz}{c} = \frac{m}{c} \quad \text{\{divide both sides by } c\}$$
$$\therefore \quad z = \frac{m}{c}$$

4 Make z the subject of:

   a $az = \dfrac{b}{c}$ **b** $\dfrac{a}{z} = d$ **c** $\dfrac{3}{d} = \dfrac{2}{z}$

   d $\dfrac{z}{2} = \dfrac{a}{z}$ **e** $\dfrac{b}{z} = \dfrac{z}{n}$ **f** $\dfrac{m}{z} = \dfrac{z}{a - b}$

5 Make:

   a a the subject of $F = ma$ **b** r the subject of $C = 2\pi r$

   c d the subject of $V = ldh$ **d** K the subject of $A = \dfrac{b}{K}$

   e h the subject of $A = \dfrac{bh}{2}$ **f** T the subject of $I = \dfrac{PRT}{100}$

C SUBSTITUTION AFTER REARRANGEMENT

In the previous section on formula substitution, the pronumerals were replaced by numbers and then the equation was solved. However, in those situations where repeated substitutions for given unknowns is required, it is quicker to **rearrange** the formula **before substituting**.

Example 6	◀) Self Tutor

The formula for the circumference of a circle is given by $C = 2\pi r$. Rearrange this formula to make r the subject and then find the radius (to 2 d.p.) when the circumference is: **a**   10 cm   **b**   20 cm   **c**   50 cm

$$2\pi r = C \quad \therefore \quad r = \frac{C}{2\pi} \quad \{\text{dividing both sides by } 2\pi\}$$

a When $C = 10$, $\quad r = \dfrac{10}{2\pi} \doteqdot 1.59$, $\therefore$ the radius is 1.59 cm.

b When $C = 20$, $\quad r = \dfrac{20}{2\pi} \doteqdot 3.18$, $\therefore$ the radius is 3.18 cm.

c When $C = 50$, $\quad r = \dfrac{50}{2\pi} \doteqdot 7.96$ $\therefore$ the radius is 7.96 cm.

EXERCISE 15C

1 The equation of a straight line is $\;5x + 3y = 18$. Rearrange this formula into the form $y = mx + c$.

Hence, state the value of   **a**   the slope, m **b**   the y-intercept c.

2 **a** Given the formula $\;K = \dfrac{d^2}{2ab}$,   make a the subject of the formula.

  b Find the value for a when:

  i $K = 112$, $\;d = 24$, $\;b = 2$ **ii** $K = 400$, $\;d = 72$, $\;b = 0.4$

3 When a car travels a distance d kilometres in time t hours, the average speed s km/h for the journey is given by the formula $\;s = \dfrac{d}{t}$.

  a Make d the subject of the formula and hence find the distance travelled by the car when:

  i   the speed is 60 km/h and the time travelled is 3 hours

  ii   the speed is 80 km/h and the time travelled is $1\frac{1}{2}$ hours

  iii the speed is 95 km/h and the time travelled is 1 h 20 min.

  b Make t the subject of the formula and hence find the time taken by the car to travel:

  i   180 km at a speed of 60 km/h

  ii   140 km at a speed of 35 km/h

  iii 220 km at a speed of 100 km/h.

4   The simple interest (I) paid on an investment of P is determined by the annual rate of interest ($R\%$) and the time of the investment, T years, and is given by $I = \dfrac{PRT}{100}$.

    a   Make T the subject of the formula.

    b   **i**   Find the time taken, correct to 2 decimal places, which would produce interest of $1050 on an investment of $6400 at an interest rate of 8% per annum.

        ii Find the time taken, correct to 2 decimal places, for an investment of $1000 to double at an interest rate of 10% per annum.

D   FORMULA CONSTRUCTION

Formulae are often constructed as the generalisation of numerical observations. To construct a formula, we reduce the problem to a specific numeric situation to understand it, and then generalise the result.

For example,   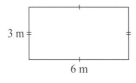   the perimeter of the rectangle is given by
$$P = 3 + 6 + 3 + 6 \text{ metres,}$$
i.e., $P = (2 \times 3) + (2 \times 6)$ metres,
i.e.,   double the width plus double the length.

Thus for    $$P = 2a + 2b,$$
or $P = 2(a + b)$.

Example 7   ◀) Self Tutor

Write the formula for the total cost C of a taxi trip given a fixed charge of:

    a $3 and $0.55 per km for 12 km
    b $3 and $0.55 per km for k km
    c $3 and d per km for k km
    d F and d per km for k km

    a $C = 3 + (0.55 \times 12)$

    b $C = 3 + (0.55 \times k)$
        i.e., $C = 3 + 0.55k$

    c $C = 3 + d \times k$
       i.e., $C = 3 + dk$

    d $C = F + dk$

EXERCISE 15D

1   Write a formula for the amount A, in a new savings account given monthly deposits of:

    a $200 over 17 months   **b** $200 over m months   **c** D over m months

2   Write a formula for the amount A, in a bank account if initially the balance was:

    a $2000, and then $150 was deposited each week for 8 weeks

    b $2000, and then $150 was deposited each week for w weeks c $2000, and then $d was deposited each week for w weeks

d $P and $d was deposited each week for w weeks.

3 Write the formula for the total cost $C of hiring a plumber given a fixed call out fee of:

    a $40 and $60 per hour for 5 hours work

    b $40 and $60 per hour for t hours work

    c $40 and $x per hour for t hours work

    d $F and $x per hour for t hours work.

Example 8 ◀)) Self Tutor

Write the formula for the amount $A, in a person's bank account if initially the balance was:

a $5000 and $200 was withdrawn each week for 10 weeks

b $5000 and $200 was withdrawn each week for w weeks

c $5000 and $x was withdrawn each week for w weeks

d $B and $x was withdrawn each week for w weeks.

a $A = 5000 - 200 \times 10$

b $A = 5000 - 200 \times w$
   i.e., $A = 5000 - 200w$

c $A = 5000 - x \times w$
   i.e., $A = 5000 - xw$

d $A = B - x \times w$
   i.e., $A = B - xw$

---

4 Write the formula for the amount $A, in Leon's wallet if initially he had:

    a $200 and he bought 8, $5 presents   b $200 and he bought x, $5 presents

    c $200 and he bought x, $b presents   d $P and he bought x, $b presents

5 Write a formula for the capacity, C litres, of a tank if initially the tank held:

    a 5000 litres and 10 litres per minute for 200 minutes have run out of it through a tap

    b 5000 litres and r litres per minute for 200 minutes have run out of it through a tap

    c 5000 litres and r litres per minute for m minutes have run out of it through a tap

    d L litres and r litres per minute for m minutes have run out of it.

E   FORMULAE BY INDUCTION (EXTENSION)

Induction is the method of determining a formula for the general situation by looking at the simplest cases where $n = 1, 2, 3, 4, \ldots$ etc.

Consider the set of even numbers: 2, 4, 6, 8, 10, 12, ... etc.

Notice that

$2 = 2 \times 1$ is the 1st

$4 = 2 \times 2$ is the 2nd

$6 = 2 \times 3$ is the 3rd

$8 = 2 \times 4$ is the 4th, etc.

We see from this pattern that   the 10th   even number is 2×10,   i.e.,   20

and   the 37th   even number is 2×37,   i.e.,   74   etc.

So we **generalise** by saying that: the nth even number is $2 \times n$,   i.e., $2n$.

Example 9   ◀) **Self Tutor**

Examine the following figures made from matches:

1st: ☐   can be constructed from 4 matches.

2nd: ☐☐   can be constructed from 7 matches.

3rd: ☐☐☐   can be constructed from 10 matches.

How many matches M, are required for the:
a   8th figure   **b** nth figure?

---

a   1st $4 = 1 + 3$ | + ☐

2nd $7 = 1 + 2 \times 3$ | + ☐ + ☐

3rd $10 = 1 + 3 \times 3$ | + ☐ + ☐ + ☐

⋮

8th $= 1 + 8 \times 3$ $= 25$ matches

b $M = 1 + n \times 3$ continuing the pattern

i.e., $M = 1 + 3n$

EXERCISE 15E

1   Consider the matchstick pattern: △ , △▽ , △▽△ , ...

How many matchsticks M, are required to make the:
a   1st, 2nd and 3rd figures   **b**   4th and 5th figures
c   10th figure   **d** nth figure?

2   For the following matchstick pattern, how many matches M, are required to make the: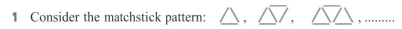

a   4th and 5th figures   **b**   20th figure   **c** nth figure?

3   For the following matchstick pattern, how many matches M, are required to make the: ☐ , ☐◪ , ☐◪☐ , ...

a   8th figure   **b** nth figure?

4   If $S_1 = \dfrac{1}{1 \times 2}$, $S_2 = \dfrac{1}{1 \times 2} + \dfrac{1}{2 \times 3}$, $S_3 = \dfrac{1}{1 \times 2} + \dfrac{1}{2 \times 3} + \dfrac{1}{3 \times 4}$, ..., etc.,

a   find the values of S_1, S_2, S_3, and S_4 and hence
b   write down the value of: **i** S_{10} **ii** S_n.

5 $S_1 = 1^2,$ $S_2 = 1^2 + 2^2,$ $S_3 = 1^2 + 2^2 + 3^2,$ ......, etc.

    a Check that the formula $S_n = \dfrac{n(n+1)(2n+1)}{6}$ is correct for $n = 1, 2, 3$ and 4.

    b Assuming the formula in **a** is always true, find the sum of

        $1^2 + 2^2 + 3^2 + 4^2 + 5^2 + \ldots\ldots + 100^2,$ i.e.,   the sum of the squares of the first one hundred integers.

F   MORE DIFFICULT REARRANGEMENTS (EXTENSION)

Example 10   ◀)) Self Tutor

Make x the subject of $ax + 3 = bx + d.$

$$ax + 3 = bx + d$$
$$\therefore \quad ax + 3 - bx - 3 = bx + d - bx - 3 \qquad \{\text{subtract } bx \text{ and } 3 \text{ from both sides}\}$$
$$\therefore \quad ax - bx = d - 3 \qquad \{\text{terms containing } x \text{ on LHS}\}$$
$$\therefore \quad x(a - b) = d - 3 \qquad \{x \text{ is a common factor on LHS}\}$$
$$\therefore \quad \frac{x(a-b)}{(a-b)} = \frac{d-3}{(a-b)} \qquad \{\text{divide both sides by } a - b\}$$
$$\therefore \quad x = \frac{d-3}{a-b}$$

Example 11   ◀)) Self Tutor

Make t the subject of $s = \frac{1}{2}gt^2$ where $t > 0.$

$$\frac{1}{2}gt^2 = s \qquad \{\text{rewrite with } t^2 \text{ on LHS}\}$$
$$\therefore \quad 2 \times \tfrac{1}{2}gt^2 = 2 \times s \qquad \{\text{multiply both sides by } 2\}$$
$$\therefore \quad gt^2 = 2s$$
$$\therefore \quad \frac{gt^2}{g} = \frac{2s}{g} \qquad \{\text{divide both sides by } g\}$$
$$\therefore \quad t^2 = \frac{2s}{g}$$
$$\therefore \quad t = \sqrt{\frac{2s}{g}} \qquad \{\text{as } t > 0\}$$

EXERCISE 15F

1 Make x the subject of:

   a $3x + a = bx + c$ **b** $ax = c - bx$ **c** $mx + a = nx - 2$

   d $8x + a = -bx$ **e** $a - x = b - cx$ **f** $rx + d = e - sx$

2 Make:

   a r the subject of $A = \pi r^2, \; (r > 0)$ **b** x the subject of $N = \dfrac{x^5}{a}$

   c r the subject of $V = \frac{4}{3}\pi r^3$ **d** x the subject of $D = \dfrac{n}{x^3}$

   e x the subject of $y = 4x^2 - 7$ **f** Q the subject of $P^2 = Q^2 + R^2$

Example 12   ◀) **Self Tutor**

Make x the subject of $T = \dfrac{a}{\sqrt{x}}$.

$$T = \frac{a}{\sqrt{x}}$$

$$\therefore \quad T^2 = \left(\frac{a}{\sqrt{x}}\right)^2 \qquad \{\text{squaring both sides}\}$$

$$\therefore \quad T^2 = \frac{a^2}{x}$$

$$\therefore \quad T^2 \times x = \frac{a^2}{x} \times x \qquad \{\text{multiplying both sides by } x\}$$

$$\therefore \quad T^2 x = a^2$$

$$\therefore \quad \frac{T^2 x}{T^2} = \frac{a^2}{T^2} \qquad \{\text{dividing both sides by } T^2\}$$

$$\therefore \quad x = \frac{a^2}{T^2}$$

---

3 Make:

   a a the subject of $d = \dfrac{\sqrt{a}}{n}$ **b** l the subject of $T = \frac{1}{5}\sqrt{l}$

   c a the subject of $c = \sqrt{a^2 - b^2}$ **d** d the subject of $\dfrac{k}{a} = \dfrac{5}{\sqrt{d}}$

   e l the subject of $T = 2\pi\sqrt{\dfrac{l}{g}}$ **f** b the subject of $A = 4\sqrt{\dfrac{a}{b}}$

4 The formula for determining the volume of a sphere is $V = \frac{4}{3}\pi r^3$ where r is the radius.

   a Make r the subject of the formula.

   b Find the radius of a sphere having a volume of:

      i 40 cm^3 **ii** 1 000 000 cm^3.

5 The distance (S cm) travelled by an object accelerating from a stationary position is given by the formula $S = \frac{1}{2}at^2$ where a is the acceleration (cm/sec^2) and t is the time (seconds).

   a Make t the subject of the formula. (Consider only $t > 0$.)

   b Find the time taken for an object accelerating at 8 cm/sec^2 to travel a distance of:

      i 40 cm   **ii** 10 m.

6 According to the theory of relativity by Einstein, the mass of a particle is given by the

   formula $m = \dfrac{m_0}{\sqrt{1 - (\frac{v}{c})^2}}$, where m_0 is the mass of the particle at rest, v is the velocity of the particle and c is the velocity of light.

   a Make v the subject of the formula, (for $v > 0$).

   b Find the velocity necessary to increase the mass of a particle to three times its rest mass, i.e., $m = 3m_0$. Give the value for v as a fraction of c.

   c A cyclotron increased the mass of an electron to $30m_0$. With what velocity must the electron have been travelling? (**Note:** $c = 3 \times 10^8$ m/s)

REVIEW SET 15A

1 The formula for finding the density, D, of a substance with mass M and volume V is $D = \dfrac{M}{V}$.

   a Find the density of lead if 350 g of lead occupies 30.7 cm^3.

   b Find the mass of a lump of uranium with density 18.97 g/cm^3 and volume 2 cm^3.

   c Find the volume of a piece of pine timber with mass 6 kg and density 0.65 g/cm^3.

2 The period of a pendulum (the time for one complete swing) is approximately given by $T = \frac{1}{5}\sqrt{l}$ seconds where l cm is the length of the pendulum. Find:

   a the period if the pendulum has length 74 cm

   b the length of the pendulum if its period is 2.5 seconds.

3 Make x the subject of the formula   **a** $mx + c = y$ **b** $ax = \dfrac{2}{x}$

4 **a** Write a formula for the volume of water V in a trough if it is empty initially, then:

      i 6, 8 litre buckets of water are poured into it

      ii n, 8 litre buckets of water are poured into it

      iii n, l-litre buckets of water are poured into it.

   b Write a formula for the volume of water V in a trough that initially contained 25 litres, if n buckets of water containing l litres are poured into it.

5 For the following matchstick pattern, how many matches M are required to make the:

    a 10th figure   **b** nth figure?

6 Make p the subject of the formula: **a** $r = \dfrac{p+q}{3}$ **b** $y = \sqrt{p^3 + 3}$.

REVIEW SET 15B

1 The volume of a cylinder is given by the formula $V = \pi r^2 h$, where r is its radius and h is its height. Find:

    a the volume, in cm^3, of a cylinder of height 23 cm and base radius 10 cm

    b the height of a cylinder of base radius 12 m and volume 426.4 m^3.

2 Make x the subject of the formula: **a** $y = 3q - 2x$ **b** $3y = \dfrac{4}{x}$

3 Write a formula for the total cost C of packing parcels of books for despatch if there is a fixed charge of:

    a $2 per parcel plus $1.20 for one book

    b $2 per parcel plus $1.20 per book for 5 books

    c p per parcel plus $1.20 per book for b books

    d p per parcel plus x per book for b books.

4 The equation of a straight line is $2x - 3y = 4$. Rearrange this formula into the form $y = mx + c$. Hence, state the value of the   **a** slope, m **b** y-intercept, c.

5 For the following matchstick pattern, how many matches M are required to make the:

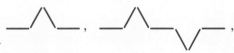 , 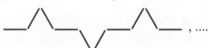 , ...

    a 8th figure   **b** nth figure?

6 Make y the subject of the formula: $\dfrac{x}{2} = \dfrac{4}{\sqrt{y}}$

7 The formula for calculating the area A of the curved surface of a sphere of radius r is $A = 4\pi r^2$.

    a Make r the subject of the formula.

    b Find the radius of a sphere whose surface area is 1.5 m^2.

Chapter 16

Deductive geometry

Contents:

The geometry of triangles, quadrilaterals and circles has been used for at least 3000 years in art, design and architecture. Simple geometrical figures often have very interesting and useful properties.

Deductive geometry, which uses special results called **theorems**, also uses highly developed logical reasoning to prove that certain observations about geometrical figures are indeed true.

Many amazing, yet sometimes quite useless, discoveries have been made by mathematicians and non-mathematicians who were simply drawing figures with straight edges and compasses.

For example: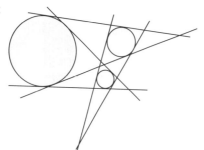

This figure consists of three circles of unequal radii. Common external tangents are drawn between each pair of circles and extended until they meet.

Click on the icon to see what interesting fact emerges.

GEOMETRY PACKAGE

HISTORICAL NOTE

Euclid was one of the great mathematical thinkers of ancient times. It is known that he was the founder of a school in Alexandria during the reign of Ptolemy I, which lasted from 323 BC to 284 BC.

Euclid's most famous mathematical writing is the *Elements*. This work is the most complete study of geometry ever written and has been a major source of information for the study of geometric techniques, logic and reasoning. Despite writing a large number of books on various mathematical topics, Euclid's fame is still for geometry.

A large proportion of the information in the *Elements* was derived from previously written works but the organisation of the material and the discovery of new proofs is credited to Euclid.

The importance of his contribution is emphasized by the fact that his *Elements* was used as a text book for 2000 years until the middle of the 19th century. At this time a number of other texts adapting Euclid's original ideas began to appear. After that, the study and teaching of geometry began to follow a variety of paths.

Like many of the great mathematicians and philosophers, Euclid believed in study and learning for its own merit rather than for the rewards it may bring.

OPENING PROBLEM

Market gardener Joe has four long straight pipes not necessarily of equal length. He places the pipes on the ground and joins them with rubber hose to form a garden bed in the shape of a quadrilateral. A sprinkler which sprinkles in semi-circles of diameter equal to that of the length of a pipe is placed at the midpoint of each pipe.

Joe draws a rough sketch of the watering system. His son Clinton is rather sceptical of his father's idea and draws his own sketch which seems to indicate that his father's reasoning is incorrect.

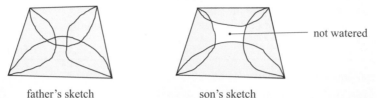

father's sketch   son's sketch

Can you:

1   draw any quadrilateral and use a compass to find the midpoint of each side
2   draw an accurate diagram of the four semi-circles using a compass
3   make a conjecture as to who you think is correct; father or son
4   prove that your conjecture is true using the theorems of deductive geometry?

A   REVIEW OF FACTS AND THEOREMS

In previous years the following **theorems** should have been established. These theorems can be used to prove new theorems and help solve other geometrical problems.

GEOMETRY PACKAGE

Below is a list of **theorems** previously established.

Name	Statement	Figure
Angles on a line	The sum of the sizes of the angles on a line is $180°$.	$a°$ $b°$ i.e., $a + b = 180$
Angles at a point	The sum of the sizes of the angles at a point is $360°$.	$b°$ $a°$ $c°$ i.e., $a + b + c = 360$
Vertically opposite angles	Vertically opposite angles are equal.	$a°$ $b°$ i.e., $a = b$
Corresponding angles	When two **parallel** lines are cut by a third line, then angles in corresponding positions are equal.	$a°$ $b°$ e.g., $a = b$

Name	Statement	Figure
Alternate angles	When two **parallel** lines are cut by a third line, then angles in alternate positions are equal.	e.g., $a = b$
Co-interior angles (Allied angles)	When two **parallel** lines are cut by a third line, then angles in co-interior positions are supplementary.	e.g., $a + b = 180$
Angles of a triangle	The sum of the sizes of the interior angles of a triangle is 180°.	i.e., $a + b + c = 180$
Exterior angle of a triangle	The size of the exterior angle of a triangle is equal to the sum of the interior opposite angles.	i.e., $c = a + b$
Isosceles triangle	In an isosceles triangle: • base angles are equal • the line joining the apex to the midpoint of the base is perpendicular to the base and bisects the angle at the apex.	
Equal angles of a triangle	If a triangle has two equal angles, then the triangle is isosceles.	
Parallelogram	In a parallelogram: • opposite sides are equal • opposite angles are equal.	
Diagonals of a parallelogram	The diagonals of a parallelogram bisect each other.	
Diagonals of a rhombus	The diagonals of a rhombus: • bisect each other at right angles • bisect the angles of the rhombus.	

In geometrical figures where one or more angles (or lengths) are unknown we can use the **theorems** to find the value of the unknowns. We can also use the theorems to solve other geometrical problems.

When using a theorem it is the accepted practice to state the theorem's name as a reason to justify a particular step in the argument.

Theorems are special results. You should learn all of the given geometric theorems.

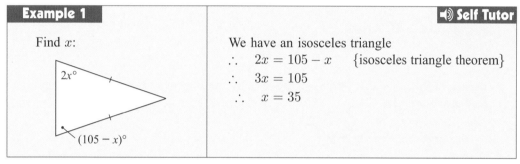

Example 1	◀)) **Self Tutor**

Find x:

$2x°$

$(105 - x)°$

We have an isosceles triangle

$\therefore \quad 2x = 105 - x \quad$ {isosceles triangle theorem}

$\therefore \quad 3x = 105$

$\therefore \quad \ \ x = 35$

EXERCISE 16A

1 Find, giving reasons, the unknown values in the given figures:

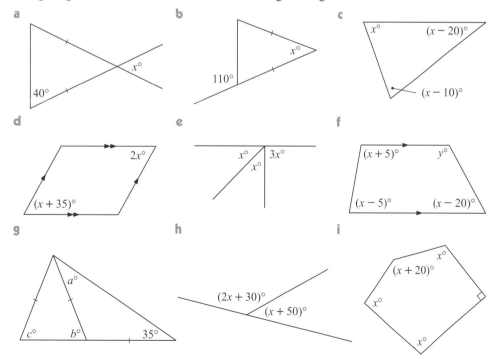

Sometimes we need to draw an additional line (or lines) so that we can solve a problem. These lines are often called **constructions**.

Example 2
🔊 **Self Tutor**

Find a, stating appropriate reasons:

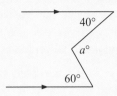

Notice that we label the figure and
draw a construction line CX.

$\angle BXD = \angle XDE$ \qquad {alternate angles}

$\therefore \quad \angle BXD = 60^o$

$\therefore \quad a = 60 + 40$ \qquad {exterior angle of Δ}

$\therefore \quad a = 100$

 2 In each of the following, find a, giving reasons. Adding an additional line to each figure may prove useful.

a

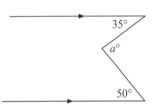

b

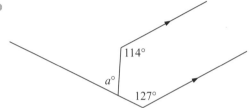

Example 3
🔊 **Self Tutor**

Prove that the angle bisectors of angles
ABD and CBD form a right angle.

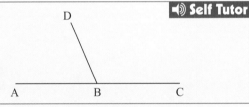

Draw angle bisectors BE and BF

$\therefore \quad \alpha_1 = \alpha_2 \quad$ and $\quad \beta_1 = \beta_2$

but $\quad 2\alpha + 2\beta = 180^o \quad$ {sum of angles on a line}

$\therefore \quad \alpha + \beta = 90^o$

$\therefore \quad \angle EBF = 90^o$

3

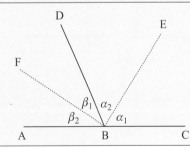

In the given figure we have two isosceles triangles,
PQS and SQR. $\angle QPS = a^o$ and $\angle QRS = b^o$.

a State, with reasons, the sizes of angles PSQ and QSR.

b What is the value of $2a + 2b$?

c Deduce that $\angle PSR$ is a right angle.

4 Alongside is a quadrilateral which has not been drawn accurately. However, its opposite angles are equal in size as shown.

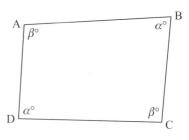

    a What is the value of $2\alpha + 2\beta$? Give a reason.

    b What is the value of $\alpha + \beta$?

    c Give reasons why AB is parallel to DC and AD is parallel to BC.

    d Copy and complete: "If opposite angles of a quadrilateral are equal, then .... "

5

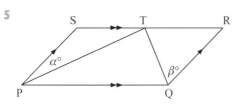

PQRS is a parallelogram. The angle bisectors of $\angle$SPQ and $\angle$PQR meet at T on side SR. $\angle$SPT $= \alpha^o$ and $\angle$RQT $= \beta^o$.

    a What are the sizes of angles TPQ and TQP?

    b What is the value of $2\alpha + 2\beta$? Give a reason.

    c Explain why angle PTQ must be a right angle.

6 ABCD is a rhombus. M is a point on AD such that CM bisects angle ACD.

Show that angle DMC is 3 times larger than angle ACM.

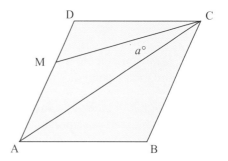

7 AB is the diameter of a semi-circle with centre O. P is any point on the semi-circle. Prove that angle POB is twice as large as angle PAB.

8 Triangle ABC is isosceles with AB = AC. CB is extended to D, and AB is extended to E so that BE = DE. Show that DE and AC are parallel.

9

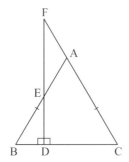

ABC is an isosceles triangle in which AB and AC are equal in length. DE is perpendicular to BC and is produced (extended) to meet CA produced at F.

Show that triangle AEF is also isosceles.

B | CIRCLE THEOREMS

A list of the common features of the circle is given below.

The circle also has some interesting **properties** which we will explore.

DEFINITIONS

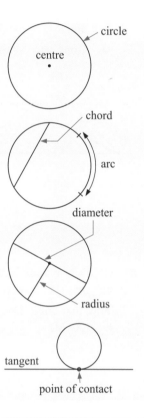

- A **circle** is the set of all points which are equidistant from a fixed point called the **centre**.

- The **circumference** is the distance around the entire circle boundary.

- An **arc** of a circle is any continuous part of the circle.

- A **chord** of a circle is a line segment joining any two points on the circle.

- A **semi-circle** is a half of a circle.

- A **diameter** of a circle is any chord passing through its centre.

- A **radius** of a circle is any line segment joining its centre to any point on the circle.

- A **tangent** to a circle is any line which touches the circle in exactly one point.

INVESTIGATION 1 | PROPERTIES OF CIRCLES

Your task is to investigate properties of circles. This investigation is best attempted using a **computer package** such as that on the CD. Click on an icon to find each activity.

However, each part of this investigation can be done using *compass*, *ruler* and *protractor*.

Part 1: The angle in a semi-circle

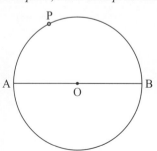

What to do:

1 Draw a circle and construct a diameter. Label as shown.

2 Mark any point P (not at A or B) on the circle. Now draw AP and PB.

3 Measure angle APB.

4 Repeat for different positions of P and for different circles. What do you notice?

5 Copy and complete: *The angle in a semi-circle is ......*

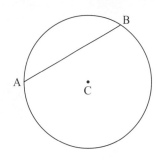

GEOMETRY
PACKAGE

Part 2:   Chords of a circle theorem

What to do:

1 Draw a circle with centre C and on it draw a chord AB.

2 Construct the perpendicular from C to AB, cutting the chord at M.

3 Measure the lengths of AM and BM. What do you notice?

4 Repeat the procedure above with another circle and chord.

5 Copy and complete:
The perpendicular from the centre of a circle to a chord ......

GEOMETRY
PACKAGE

Part 3:   Radius-tangent theorem

What to do:

1 With a compass, draw a circle, centre O, and mark point A on it.

2 At A, draw as accurately as possible a tangent TA.

3 Draw the radius OA.

4 Measure the angle OAT with a protractor.

5 Repeat the procedure above with another circle and tangent.

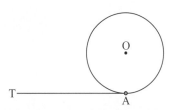

GEOMETRY
PACKAGE

6 Copy and complete: *The tangent to a circle is ...... to the radius at the point ......*

Part 4:   Tangents from an external point

What to do:

1 Use your compass to draw a circle, centre O.

2 From an external point P draw as accurately as possible the two tangents to the circle to meet it at A and B.

3 Measure AP and BP.

4 Repeat with another circle of different size.

5 Copy and complete: *Tangents from an external point to a circle are ......*

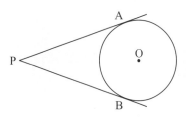

GEOMETRY
PACKAGE

From the investigation you should have discovered that:

Name of theorem	Statement	Diagram
Angle in a semi-circle	The angle in a semi-circle is a right angle.	If [diagram with B at top, A, O, C on base] then $\angle ABC = 90°$.
Chords of a circle	The perpendicular from the centre of a circle to a chord bisects the chord.	If [diagram with circle, O, A, M, B] then $AM = BM$.
Radius-tangent	The tangent to a circle is perpendicular to the radius at the point of contact.	If [diagram with circle, O, A, T] then $\angle OAT = 90°$.
Tangents from an external point	Tangents from an external point are equal in length.	If [diagram with circle, O, A, B, P] then $AP = BP$.

Two useful **converses** are:

- If line segment AB subtends a right angle at C then the circle through A, B and C has diameter AB.

- The perpendicular bisector of a chord of a circle passes through its centre.

Example 4   ◄》 **Self Tutor**

Find x, giving brief reasons.

[diagram: semi-circle with A, B, C; angle at A is $(x+10)°$, angle at C is $3x°$]

$\angle ABC$ measures $90°$ {angle in semi-circle}

$\therefore \quad (x+10) + 3x + 90 = 180$ {angles in triangle}

$\therefore \quad 4x + 100 = 180$

$\therefore \quad 4x = 80$

$\therefore \quad x = 20$

EXERCISE 16B

1 Find x giving brief reasons:

a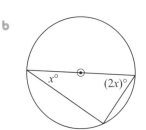

b

c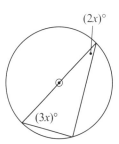

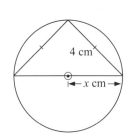

d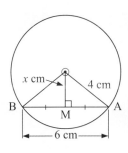

e

f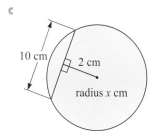

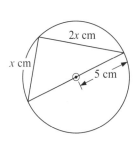

Example 5   🔊 **Self Tutor**

A circle has radius 4 cm and a chord of length 6 cm. Find the shortest distance from the circle's centre to the chord.

The shortest distance is the perpendicular distance.

$\therefore$ M is the midpoint of AB   {chord of a circle}

$\therefore$ AM $= 3$ cm

In $\triangle$OMA, $x^2 + 3^2 = 4^2$ {Pythagoras}

$\therefore$ $x^2 + 9 = 16$

$\therefore$ $x^2 = 7$

$\therefore$ $x = \pm\sqrt{7}$

$\therefore$ $x = \sqrt{7}$ {as $x > 0$}

So,   the shortest distance is $\sqrt{7}$ cm.

---

2 Find x in the following giving brief reasons:

a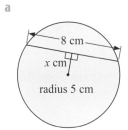

b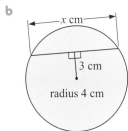

c

3 Solve the following problems:

    a A circle has a chord of length 8 cm and the shortest distance from the centre of the circle to the chord is 2 cm. Find the radius of the circle.

    b The shortest distance from the centre of a circle to a chord is 2 cm. Find the length of the chord given that the radius has length 5 cm.

Example 6   ◀) **Self Tutor**

The tangent from point M to a circle of radius 5 cm is 12 cm long. Find the distance from M to the centre of the circle.

$\angle$OTM $= 90^o$ {radius-tangent theorem}

    OM^2 = OT^2+ TM^2 {Pythagoras}

$\therefore$ OM$^2 = 5^2 + 12^2$

$\therefore$ OM$^2 = 169$

$\therefore$ OM $= 13$ {OM > 0}

Hence, M is 13 cm from the centre of the circle.

---

4 C is the centre of the circle and XY is a tangent in each of the following questions:

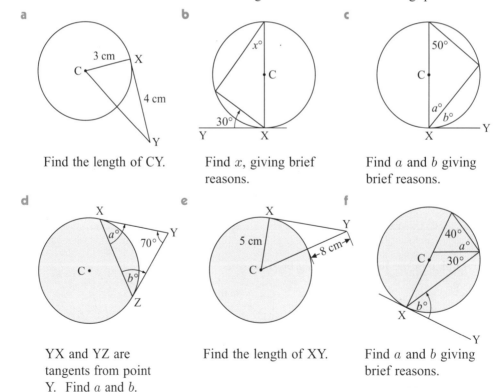

a Find the length of CY.

b Find x, giving brief reasons.

c Find a and b giving brief reasons.

d YX and YZ are tangents from point Y. Find a and b.

e Find the length of XY.

f Find a and b giving brief reasons.

5 A point P is 10 cm from the centre of a circle of radius 6 cm. A tangent is drawn from P to touch the circle at Q. Find the length of PQ.

6 Find x giving reasons:

a

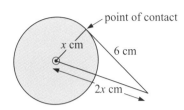

b

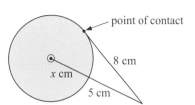

7

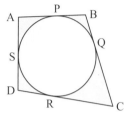

A circle is drawn and four tangents are drawn as shown.

Deduce that   AB + CD = BC + AD.

8 Find the radius of the circle which touches the three sides of the triangle.

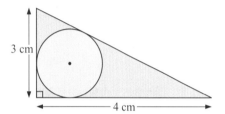

C   FURTHER CIRCLE THEOREMS

Any continuous part of a circle is called an **arc**. If the arc is less than half the circle it is called a **minor arc**; if it is greater than half the circle it is called a **major arc**.

a minor arc BC   a major arc BC

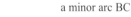

A chord divides the interior of a circle into two regions called **segments**. The larger region is called a **major segment** and the smaller region is called a **minor segment**.

In the diagram opposite:

- the minor arc BC **subtends the angle** BAC, where A is on the circle
- the minor arc BC also subtends angle BOC at the centre of the circle

The following investigation will give you the opportunity to discover more properties of circles.

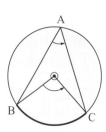

INVESTIGATION 2   MORE CIRCLE THEOREMS

Once again, the use of the **geometry package** on the CD is recommended. Otherwise, use a ruler, compass and protractor.

Part 1:   Angle at the centre theorem

What to do:

1   Use a compass to draw a large circle, centre O, and mark on it points A, B and P.

2   Join AO, BO, AP and BP with a ruler.
    Now measure angles AOB and APB.

3   What do you notice about the measured angles?

4   Repeat the above steps with another circle.

5   Copy and complete: *"The angle at the centre of a circle is ...... the angle on the circle when subtended by the same arc."*

GEOMETRY PACKAGE

Part 2:   Angles subtended by the same arc theorem

What to do:

1   Use a compass to draw a circle, centre O, and mark on it points A, B, C and D.

2   Draw angles ACB and ADB with a ruler.

3   Measure angles ACB and ADB. What do you notice?

4   Repeat the above steps with another circle.

5   Copy and complete: *"Angles subtended by an arc on the circle are ...... in size."*

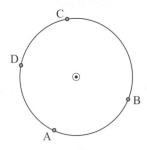

GEOMETRY PACKAGE

Part 3:   Angle between a tangent and a chord theorem

What to do:

1   Use a compass to draw a circle and mark on it points A, B and C.

2   Draw carefully tangent TAS at A and join AB, BC and CA.

3   Measure angles BAS and ACB.
    What do you notice?

4   Repeat with another circle.

5   Copy and complete: *"The angle between a tangent and a chord at the point of contact is ...... to the angle subtended by the chord in the alternate ......"*

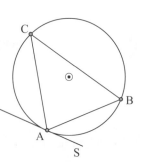

GEOMETRY PACKAGE

From the investigation you should have discovered that:

Name of theorem	Statement	Diagram
Angle at the centre	The angle at the centre of a circle is twice the angle on the circle subtended by the same arc.	If ... then $\angle AOB = 2\angle ACB$.
Angles subtended by the same arc	Angles subtended by an arc on the circle are equal in size.	If ... then $\angle ADB = \angle ACB$.
Angle between a tangent and a chord	The angle between a tangent and a chord at the point of contact is equal to the angle subtended by the chord in the alternate segment.	If ... then $\angle BAS = \angle BCA$.

Note:
- The following diagrams show other cases of **the angle at the centre theorem**. These cases can be easily shown using the **geometry package**.

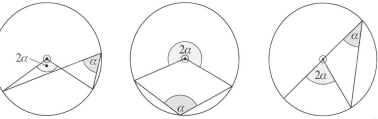

- The **angle in a semi-circle theorem** is a special case of the angle at the centre theorem.

Example 7   ◀)) **Self Tutor**

Find x:

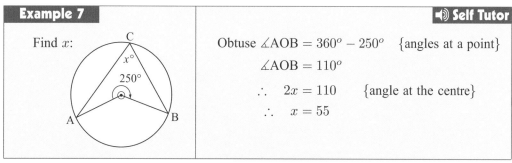

Obtuse $\angle AOB = 360° - 250°$ {angles at a point}

$\angle AOB = 110°$

$\therefore \quad 2x = 110$ {angle at the centre}

$\therefore \quad x = 55$

EXERCISE 16C

1 Find, giving reasons, the value of x in each of the following:

a

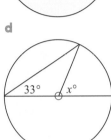

b

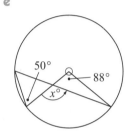

c

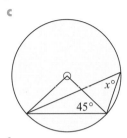

d

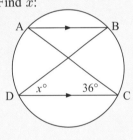

e

f

Example 8   ◄)) **Self Tutor**

Find x:

$\angle ABD = \angle ACD = 36^o$ {angles on the same arc}

$\angle ABD = \angle BDC$ {equal alternate angles}

$\therefore \quad x = 36$

---

2 Find, giving reasons, the value of the pronumerals in each of the following:

a

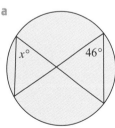

b

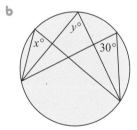

c

d

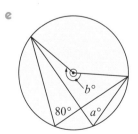

e

f

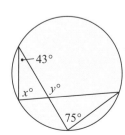

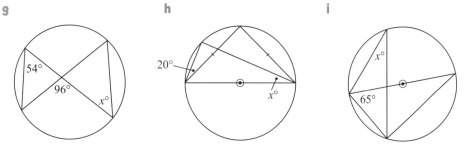

Example 9

Find x if AT is a tangent and A is the point of contact.

◀ᴺ Self Tutor

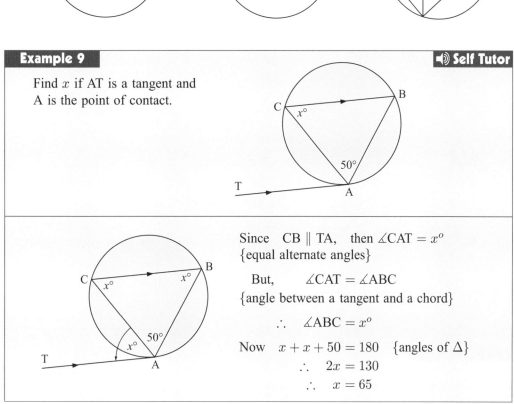

Since   CB ∥ TA,   then ∠CAT = $x°$
{equal alternate angles}

  But,   ∠CAT = ∠ABC
{angle between a tangent and a chord}

      ∴   ∠ABC = $x°$

Now $x + x + 50 = 180$ {angles of Δ}
      ∴ $2x = 130$
      ∴ $x = 65$

3   In each diagram C is the point of contact of tangent CT. Find x, giving reasons:

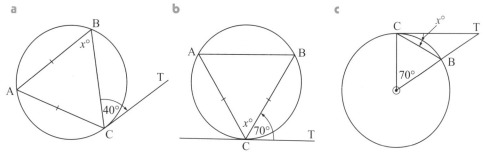

GEOMETRIC PROOF (EXTENSION)

The circle theorems and other geometric facts can be formally **proved**.

To do this we use previously proven theorems such as the isosceles triangle theorem and congruence.

 ◀🔊 **Self Tutor**

Use the given figure to prove the *angle in a semi-circle theorem*.

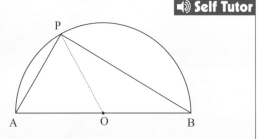

Proof:

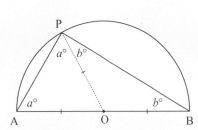

Let $\angle PAO = a^\circ$ and $\angle PBO = b^\circ$

Now OA = OP = OB   {equal radii}

$\therefore$ Δ's OAP and OBP are isosceles.

So $\angle OPA = a^\circ$ and $\angle BPO = b^\circ$ {isosceles Δ}

Now $a + (a + b) + b = 180$ {angles of $\triangle APB$}

$\therefore$ $2a + 2b = 180$

$\therefore$ $a + b = 90$

So, $\angle APB$ is a right angle.

EXERCISE 16D

1   In this question we prove the *chords of a circle* theorem.

   a   For the given figure join OA and OB and classify $\triangle$OAB.

   b   Apply the isosceles triangle theorem to triangle OAB. What geometrical fact(s) result?

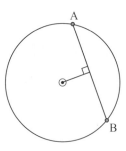

2   In this question we prove the *tangents from an external point* theorem.

   a   Join OP, OA and OB.

   b   Assuming the *tangent-radius* theorem, prove that Δ's POA and POB are congruent.

   c   What are the consequences of the congruence in **b**?

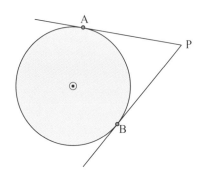

3 In this question we prove the *angle at the centre* theorem.

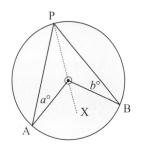

a Explain why $\triangle$'s OAP and OBP are isosceles.

b Find the measure of the following angles in terms of a^o and b^o:

  i $\angle$APO   **ii** $\angle$BPO   **iii** $\angle$AOX
  iv $\angle$BOX   **v** $\angle$APB   **vi** $\angle$AOB

c What can be deduced from **b v** and **b vi**?

4 In this question we prove the *angles in the same segment* theorem.

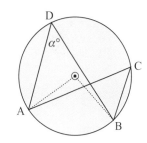

a Using the results of question **3**, find the size of $\angle$AOB in terms of α.

b Now find the size of $\angle$ACB in terms of α.

c State the relationship between $\angle$ADB and $\angle$ACB.

5 In this question we prove the *angle between a tangent and a chord* theorem.

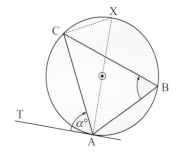

a We draw diameter AOX and join CX. Find the size of **i** $\angle$TAX **ii** $\angle$ACX

b If $\angle$TAC $= \alpha^o$, find in terms of α:
  i $\angle$CAX **ii** $\angle$CXA **iii** $\angle$CBA

Give reasons for your answers.

6 AB is the diameter of a circle, centre O. X is a point on the circle and AX is produced to Y such that OX = XY.

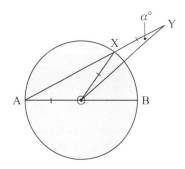

a If $\angle$XYO $= \alpha^o$, find in terms of α:
  i $\angle$XOY   **ii** $\angle$AXO
  iii $\angle$XAO   **iv** $\angle$XOB
  v $\angle$BOY

b What is the relationship between $\angle$BOY and $\angle$YOX?

7 Revisit the **Opening Problem** (pages **370** and **371**). Consider the two semi-circles shown in the figure alongside.

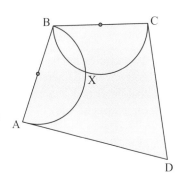

a Determine the measure of $\angle$BXA and $\angle$BXC

b What does **a** tell us about the points A, X and C?

c Do the two illustrated sprinklers water on one side of the diagonal AC?

d Will the four sprinklers water the whole garden? Why?

Example 11   ◀ **Self Tutor**

△ABC is isosceles and is inscribed in a circle.
TC is a tangent to the circle.
Prove that AC bisects angle ∠BCT.

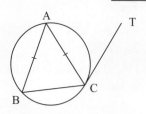

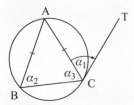

Now $\alpha_1 = \alpha_2$ {tangent and chord theorem}
also $\alpha_2 = \alpha_3$ {isosceles △ theorem}
∴ $\alpha_1 = \alpha_3$
Thus AC bisects ∠BCT.

8 AB is a diameter of a circle, centre O. CD
is a chord parallel to AB.

Prove that BC bisects angle DCO.

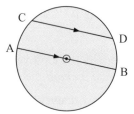

9 P is any point on a circle. QR is a chord of the circle parallel to the tangent at P. Prove
that triangle PQR is isosceles.

10 Two circles intersect at A and B.

Straight lines PQ and XY are drawn
through A to meet the circles as shown.

Show that ∠XBP = ∠YBQ.

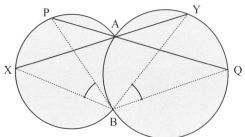

11 A, B and C are three points on a circle. The bisector of angle BAC cuts BC at P and
the circle at Q. Prove that ∠APC = ∠ABQ.

12 Triangle ABC is inscribed in a circle and AB = AC. The bisector of angle ACB meets
the tangent from A at D. Prove that AD and BC are parallel.

13 Two circles intersect at A and B. AX
and AY are diameters as shown. Prove
that X, B and Y are collinear (i.e., lie
on a straight line).

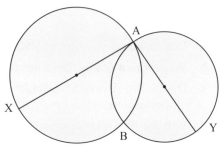

14 Two circles touch at A. O is the centre of the larger circle. The smaller circle passes through O. Prove that any chord AB of the larger circle is bisected by the smaller circle.

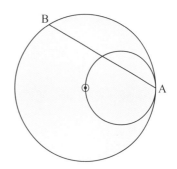

E ▏ THE MIDPOINT THEOREM

 Your task is to investigate the line joining the midpoints of two sides of a triangle. Once again the use of the **geometry package** on the CD is recommended. Otherwise, use a ruler and protractor.

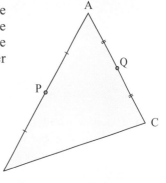

What to do:

1 Construct a large triangle and label it like the triangle alongside.

2 As accurately as you can, mark the midpoints P and Q of AB and AC respectively.

3 Join PQ and QB.

4 Measure the lengths of PQ and BC. What do you notice?

GEOMETRY PACKAGE

5 Measure ∠PQB and ∠QBC. What conclusion can be drawn about PQ and BC?

6 Repeat the procedure with different sized triangles.

7 Copy and complete: *"The line joining the midpoints of two sides of a triangle is ...... to the third side and ...... its length."*

From the investigation you should have discovered:

THE MIDPOINT THEOREM

The line joining the midpoints of two sides of a triangle is parallel to the third side and half its length,

i.e., given 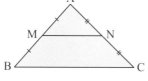 then • MN is parallel to BC, and
• MN = $\frac{1}{2}$(BC).

CONVERSE OF MIDPOINT THEOREM

The line drawn from the midpoint of one side of a triangle, parallel to a second side, bisects the third side,

i.e.,   given 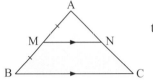   then   AN = NC.

GEOMETRY PACKAGE

EXERCISE 16E

1 Find the unknowns in the following: (Give reasons)

a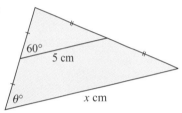

b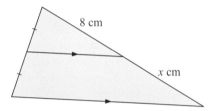

2 ABCD is a parallelogram and its diagonals meet at E. M is the midpoint of AD. Show that ME is parallel to AB and half its length.

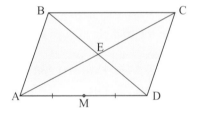

Example 12   ◀) **Self Tutor**

ABCD is a parallelogram. AB is produced to E such that AB = BE.
AD is produced to meet EC produced at F. Prove that EC = CF.

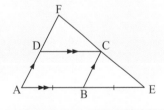

In △AEF,
BC is parallel to AF   {as ABCD is a parallelogram}

and as   B is the midpoint of AE,
        using the midpoint theorem converse
        C is the midpoint of EF,   i.e.,   EC = CF.

---

3 ABC is a triangle and D, E and F are the midpoints of its sides as shown. Show that DFEB is a parallelogram.

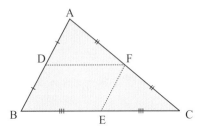

4 A and B are the midpoints of sides PQ and PR of $\triangle$PQR. Y is any point on QR. Prove that X is the midpoint of PY.

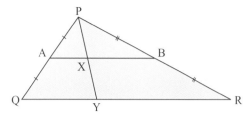

5 Stacey says "I have drawn dozens of different quadrilaterals, and when I have joined the midpoints of adjacent sides of each one of them, the figure formed appears to be a parallelogram."

  a Draw two quadrilaterals of your own choosing to check Stacey's suspicion.

  b By drawing one diagonal of a labelled quadrilateral, show that Stacey's suspicion is correct.

6 To **prove** *the midpoint theorem* in $\triangle$BAC we extend PQ to meet a line from C which is parallel to BA at R. Copy and complete the proof:

In $\triangle$'s APQ, CRQ

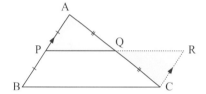

  •   AQ = CQ   {..........} (1)
  • $\angle$APQ = $\angle$CRQ   {..........} (2)
  •   .... = ...   {vertically opposite} (3)

$\therefore$ the triangles are congruent   {........} (4)

Consequently, AP = CR, and as AP = BP, then CR = ... (5)

So, BP and CR are parallel and equal in length and this is sufficient to deduce that BCRP is a .... (6) $\therefore$ PQ is parallel to ......(7) and PR = BC.

But, from the congruence,   PQ = QR,   and so   PQ = $\frac{1}{2}$BC.

F   EULER'S RULES

Euler, pronounced 'oiler' was one of the greatest mathematicians of all time. He made numerous interesting observations in geometry. Following is one of them:

INVESTIGATION 4   VERTICES, EDGES AND REGIONS

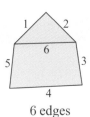

In these identical figures there are:

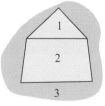

| 5 vertices | 6 edges | 3 regions | (outside the figure counts as a region) |

What to do:

1 Consider the following figures:

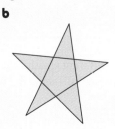

a

b

c

d

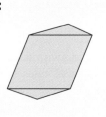

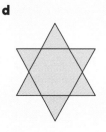

2 Copy and complete where **e** to **h** are for four diagrams like those above, but of your choice.

Figure	Vertices (V)	Regions (R)	Edges (E)	V + R − 2
given example	5	3	6	6
a				
b				
c				
d				
e				
f				
g				
h				

3 What is the most likely relationship (rule) between V, R and E?

From the previous investigation you should have discovered one of **Euler's rules**.

> In any closed figure, the number of edges is always two less than the sum of the number of vertices and regions, i.e., $\boldsymbol{E = V + R - 2}$.

Note: Euler's rule applies even if the edges are *not straight lines*.

For example, 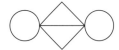 has $V = 4$, $R = 5$ and $E = 7$

and $V + R - 2 = 9 - 2 = 7$ which checks.

EXERCISE 16F.1

1 Using Euler's rule, determine the number of:

   a vertices of a figure with 7 edges and 3 regions

   b edges for a figure with 5 vertices and 4 regions

   c regions for a figure with 10 edges and 8 vertices.

2 Draw a possible figure for each of the cases in **1**.

3 Draw two *different* figures which have 5 vertices and 7 edges.

INVESTIGATION 5   VERTICES, EDGES AND FACES

The diagrams of four *polyhedra* are shown below. There is a relationship between the number of edges, the number of faces and the number of vertices for all solids bounded by planes.

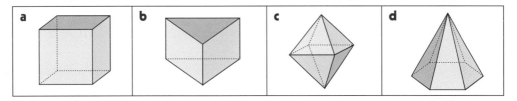

In the table which follows:

  E represents the number of **edges**,

  F represents the number of **faces,** and

  V represents the number of **vertices**.

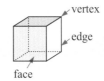

What to do:

1 Copy and complete the following table for the solids labelled **a**, **b**, **c** and **d**.

  e and **f** are for solids of your choosing.

Figure	F	V	F + V	E
a				
b				
c				
d				
e				
f				

2 Look carefully at the last two columns of your table.

Can you see the relationship?

This is **Euler's rule** for polyhedra.

3 Does Euler's rule apply for a solid with cut off corners?

From the previous investigation you should have discovered:

For any polyhedron, the sum of the number of faces and vertices is two more than the number of edges, i.e., $F + V = E + 2$.

EXERCISE 16F.2

1 Use Euler's rule for polyhedra $(F + V = E + 2)$ to determine the number of:

  a vertices if there are 9 edges and 5 faces

  b edges if there are 8 faces and 12 vertices.

2 Draw a possible figure for each case in question **1**.

3 **a** Explain why $F \geqslant 4$ for all polyhedra.

  b Dan has discovered a polyhedron which has 8 vertices and 9 edges. Show that Dan has made an error in counting.

G NETS OF SOLIDS

Click on the icon for printable nets of the Platonic Solids. Make the solids from light card. Research the significance of these solids.

PRINTABLE WORKSHEET

INVESTIGATION 6   CYCLIC QUADRILATERALS

A **cyclic quadrilateral** is a quadrilateral whose vertices (corner points) lie on a circle, i.e., ABCD is a cyclic quadrilateral.

Notice that angles at A and C are opposite angles of the cyclic quadrilateral, as are the angles at B and D.

The use of the **geometry package** on the CD is recommended. Otherwise, use a ruler, compass and protractor.

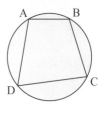
GEOMETRY PACKAGE

What to do:

1 Draw several circles with diameters at least 10 cm and inscribe cyclic quadrilaterals within them. Label each cyclic quadrilateral ABCD.

2 Measure the angles at A, B, C and D and record your results in a table like the one below.

Circle	$m\angle A$	$m\angle B$	$m\angle C$	$m\angle D$	$m\angle A + m\angle C$	$m\angle B + m\angle D$
a						
b						
c						
⋮						

3 What do you propose from your tabled calculations? Write your proposition in sentence form.

4 Use the figure alongside to prove your proposition of **3**.

(**Hint:** What sort of triangles are OAB, OBC, OCD, ODA? Find all angles of these triangles.)

You must write out a detailed **proof**, giving all reasons for statements made.

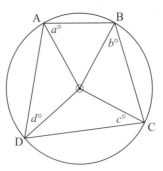

REVIEW SET 16A

1 Find the value of x giving reasons:

a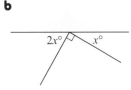

b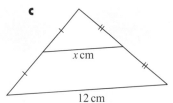

c

2 Find the value of a giving reasons:

a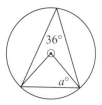

b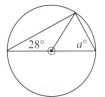

c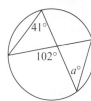

d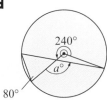

e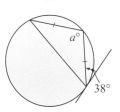

f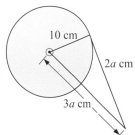

3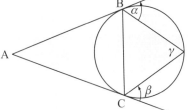

AB and AC are tangents to the circle.
Find an equation connecting α, β and γ.

4 AB is the diameter of a circle, centre O.
AC and BD are any two chords.
If $\angle BDO = \alpha^o$:

   a find $\angle DBO$

   b show that $\angle BDO = \angle ACD$.

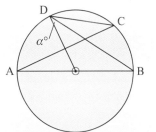

5 AB and CM are common tangents to two circles.
Show that:

   a M is the midpoint of AB

   b $\angle ACB$ is a right angle.

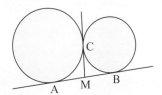

6 **a** Use Euler's rule $V + R - 2 = E$ for the vertices, edges and regions of closed figures, to determine the number of vertices of a figure with 8 edges and 4 regions.

   b Draw a possible figure for **a**.

REVIEW SET 16B

1 Find the value of a, giving reasons:

a

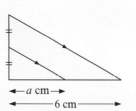

$\leftarrow a$ cm $\rightarrow$

$\longleftarrow$ 6 cm $\longrightarrow$

b

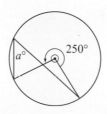

$a°$ 250°

c

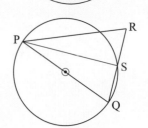

T

A

$a°$ 20°

C

2 In triangle PQR, PQ = PR. A circle is drawn using PQ as diameter and the circle cuts QR at S. Show that S is the midpoint of QR.

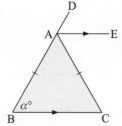

3

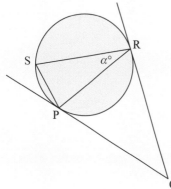

S   R $\alpha°$

P

Q

QP and QR are tangents to a circle. S is a point on the circle such that angles PSR and PQR are equal and both are double angle PRS.

Let angle PRS be $\alpha°$.

a Find in terms of α:
  i ∠PSR **ii** ∠PQR
  iii ∠PRQ **iv** ∠QPR

b Use triangle PQR to show that $\alpha = 30$.

c Find the measure of ∠QRS.

d What can you conclude about RS?

4 Triangle ABC is isosceles with AB = AC.

BA is produced to D and AE is drawn parallel to BC.

Given that ∠ABC = $\alpha°$:

a find ∠ACB in terms of α

b hence show that AE bisects ∠DAC.

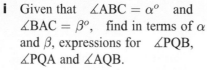

D

A $\rightarrow$ E

$\alpha°$

B   C

5 **a** Copy and complete: *"The angle between a tangent and a chord through the point of contact is equal to ......"*

b Two circles intersect at points P and Q. Any line APB is drawn through P and the tangents at A and B meet at C.

  i Given that ∠ABC = $\alpha°$ and ∠BAC = $\beta°$, find in terms of α and β, expressions for ∠PQB, ∠PQA and ∠AQB.

  ii Now show that ∠ACB + ∠AQB = 180°.

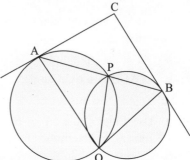

C

A

P

B

Q

Chapter 17

Relations, functions and sequences

Contents:

OPENING PROBLEM

A piece of paper measures 30 cm by 21 cm. If squares of equal size are cut from its corners, the shape remaining can be formed into an open box.

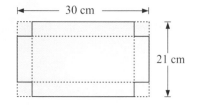

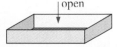

For you to consider:

1 If 3 cm squares are removed, what is the box's
   a height   **b** length   **c** width   **d** capacity?

2 If 5 cm squares are removed, what is the box's
   a height   **b** length   **c** width   **d** capacity?

3 Does the capacity of the box depend on the size of the squares removed?

4 Is there a formula which allows us to connect the capacity of the box with the size of the cut out squares (x cm)?

5 If the equation does exist, how can it be used to answer questions like:
    "What sized squares should be removed to create the box of maximum capacity?"

A | RELATIONS AND FUNCTIONS

The charges for parking a car in a long-term car park are given in the table alongside. There is an obvious relationship between time spent and the charge. The charge is dependent on the length of time the car is parked.

Car park charges	
Period	*Charge*
0 - 1 days	$10.00
1 - 2	$18.00
2 - 4	$30.00
5 - 7	$40.00
8 - 12	$50.00
13 - 19	$60.00
20 - 30	$75.00

Looking at this table we might ask: "How much would be charged for exactly one day? Would it be $10 or $18?"

To make the situation clear, and to avoid confusion, we could adjust the table and draw a graph. We need to indicate that 2-4 days really means for time over 2 days up to and including 4 days, i.e., $2 < t \leqslant 4$.

So, we now have:

Car park charges	
Period	*Charge*
$0 < t \leqslant 1$ days	$10.00
$1 < t \leqslant 2$ days	$18.00
$2 < t \leqslant 4$ days	$30.00
$4 < t \leqslant 7$ days	$40.00
$7 < t \leqslant 12$ days	$50.00
$12 < t \leqslant 19$ days	$60.00
$19 < t \leqslant 30$ days	$75.00

In mathematical terms, we have a relationship between two variables, time and charge, so the schedule of charges is an example of a **relation**.

A relation may consist of a finite number of ordered pairs, such as $\{(1, 5), (2, 3), (3, 3), (4, 2)\}$ or an infinite number of ordered pairs.

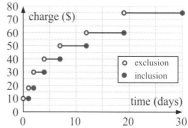

The parking charges example is clearly the latter as any real value of time (t days) in the interval $0 < t \leqslant 30$ is represented.

The set of possible values of the variable on the horizontal axis is called the **domain** of the relation.

For example:
- $\{t: \ 0 < t \leqslant 30\}$ is the domain for the car park relation
- $\{1, 2, 3, 4\}$ is the domain of $\{(1, 5), (2, 3), (3, 3), (4, 2)\}$.

The set which describes the possible y-values is called the **range** of the relation.

For example:
- the range of the car park relation is $\{10, 18, 30, 40, 50, 60, 75\}$
- the range of $\{(1, 5), (2, 3), (3, 3), (4, 2)\}$ is $\{2, 3, 5\}$.

RELATIONS

A **relation** is any set of points on the Cartesian plane.

A relation is often expressed in the form of an **equation** connecting the **variables** x and y.

For example $y = x + 5$ and $y = x^2$ are the equations of two relations.

Their graphs are:

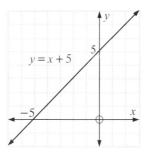

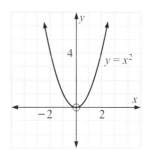

However, a relation may not be able to be defined by an equation. Below are two examples which show this:

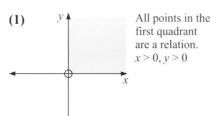

All points in the first quadrant are a relation. $x > 0, y > 0$

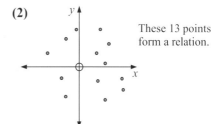

These 13 points form a relation.

FUNCTIONS

A **function** is a relation in which no two different ordered pairs have the same x-coordinate (first member).

GEOMETRIC TEST FOR FUNCTIONS: "VERTICAL LINE TEST"

If we draw all possible vertical lines on the graph of a relation:
- the relation is a function if each line cuts the graph no more than once
- the relation is *not* a function if *any* line cuts the graph more than once.

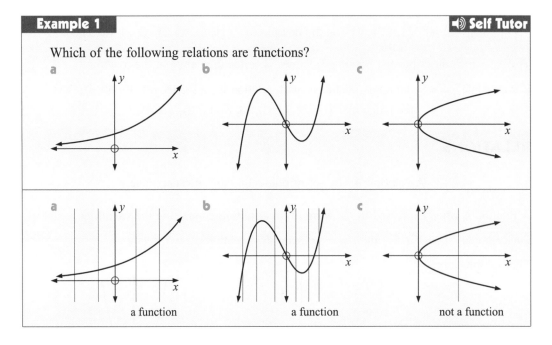

GRAPHICAL NOTE

- If a graph contains a small **open circle** end point such as ——o , the end point is **not included**.

- If a graph contains a small **filled-in circle** end point such as ——• , the end point **is included**.

- If a graph contains an **arrow head** at an end such as ——► then the graph continues indefinitely in that general direction, or the shape may repeat as it has done previously.

EXERCISE 17A

1 Which of the following sets of ordered pairs are functions? Give reasons.

a (1, 1), (2, 2), (3, 3), (4, 4)   b (−1, 2), (−3, 2), (3, 2), (1, 2)

c (2, 5), (−1, 4), (−3, 7), (2, −3)   d (3, −2), (3, 0), (3, 2), (3, 4)

e (−7, 0), (−5, 0), (−3, 0), (−1, 0)   f (0, 5), (0, 1), (2, 1), (2, −5)

2 Use the vertical line test to determine which of the following relations are functions:

a
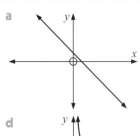

b
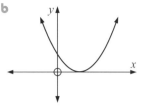

c
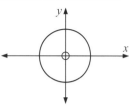

d
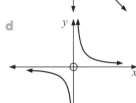

e
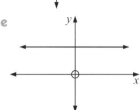

f
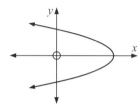

g
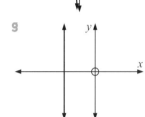

h
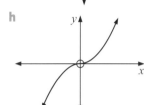

i
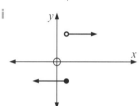

3 Will the graph of a straight line always be a function? Give evidence.

B | INTERVAL NOTATION, DOMAIN AND RANGE

DOMAIN AND RANGE

The **domain** of a relation is the set of permissible values that x may have.

The **range** of a relation is the set of permissible values that y may have.

The domain and range of a relation are best described using **interval notation**.

For example:

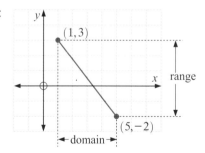

The domain consists of all real x such that $1 \leqslant x \leqslant 5$ and we write this as

$$\{x : \ 1 \leqslant x \leqslant 5\}$$

the set of all ⌐ such that

The range is $\{y : \ -2 \leqslant y \leqslant 3\}$

Note:

for numbers *between* a and b we write $a < x < b$

for numbers '*outside*' a and b we write $x < a$ or $x > b$

For example:

(1)

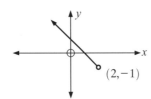

All values of $x < 2$ are permissible.

∴ the domain is $\{x:\ x < 2\}$.

All values of $y > -1$ are permissible.

∴ the range is $\{y:\ y > -1\}$.

(2)

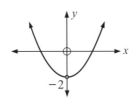

x can take any value.

∴ the domain is $\{x:\ x$ is in $\mathbb{R}\}$.

y cannot be < -2

∴ range is $\{y:\ y \geqslant -2\}$.

(3)

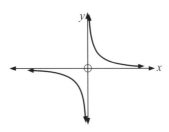

x can take all values except $x = 0$.

∴ the domain is $\{x:\ x \neq 0\}$.

y can take all values except $y = 0$.

∴ the range is $\{y:\ y \neq 0\}$.

Example 2   ◀) **Self Tutor**

For each of the following graphs state the domain and range:

a

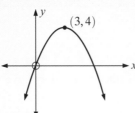

b

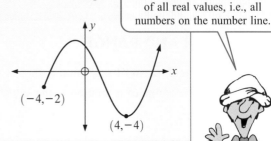

> Notice that $\mathbb{R}$ represents the set of all real values, i.e., all numbers on the number line.

a Domain is $\{x:\ x$ is in $\mathbb{R}\}$.   **b** Domain is $\{x:\ x \geqslant -4\}$.

Range is $\{y:\ y \leqslant 4\}$.   Range is $\{y:\ y \geqslant -4\}$.

EXERCISE 17B

1 For each of the following graphs find the domain and range:

a

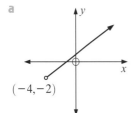

b

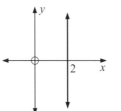

c

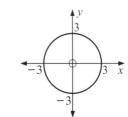

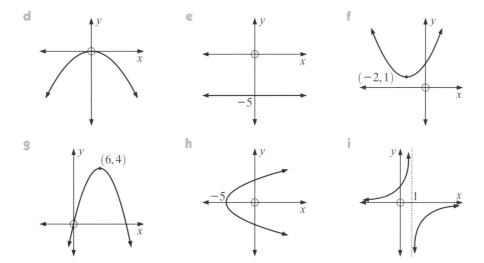

C   FUNCTION NOTATION

We sometimes use a 'function machine' to illustrate how functions behave.

For example:

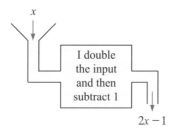

So, if 3 is fed into the machine, $2(3) - 1 = 5$ comes out.

The above 'machine' has been programmed to perform a particular function.

If f is used to represent that particular function we can write:

'f is the function that will convert x into $2x - 1$.'

So, f converts 2 into $2(2) - 1 = 3$ and
    -4 into $2(-4) - 1 = -9$.

This function can be written as: $\boldsymbol{f : x \longmapsto 2x - 1}$

$\boldsymbol{f}$	$\boldsymbol{:}$	$\boldsymbol{x}$	$\boldsymbol{\longmapsto}$	$\boldsymbol{2x - 1}$
↑	↑	↑	↑	↑
function f	such that	x	is converted into	$2x - 1$

Another way to write this function is: $f(x) = 2x - 1$

> If $f(x)$ is the value of y for a given value of x, then $y = f(x)$.

Notice that for $f(x) = 2x - 1,$ $f(2) = 2(2) - 1 = 3$ and
                $f(-4) = 2(-4) - 1 = -9.$

Since $y = f(x)$, $f(2) = 3$ indicates that the point (2, 3) lies on the graph of the function.

Likewise $f(-4) = -9$ indicates that the point $(-4, -9)$ also lies on the graph.

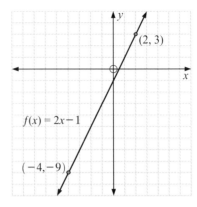

Note:
- $f(x)$ is read as "f of x" and is the value of the function at any value of x.
- If (x, y) is any point on the graph then $y = f(x)$.
- f is the function which converts x into $f(x)$, i.e., $f : x \longmapsto f(x)$.
- $f(x)$ is sometimes called the **image** of x.

Example 3   ◄ŷ **Self Tutor**

If $f : x \longmapsto 3x^2 - 4x$, find the value of: **a** $f(2)$ **b** $f(-5)$

$f(x) = 3x^2 - 4x$

a $f(2) = 3(2)^2 - 4(2)$ {replacing x by (2)}
$\quad\quad = 3 \times 4 - 8$
$\quad\quad = 4$

b $f(-5) = 3(-5)^2 - 4(-5)$ {replacing x by (-5)}
$\quad\quad = 3(25) + 20$
$\quad\quad = 95$

Example 4   ◄ŷ **Self Tutor**

If $f(x) = 4 - 3x - x^2$, find in simplest form: **a** $f(-x)$ **b** $f(x+2)$

a $f(-x) = 4 - 3(-x) - (-x)^2$ {replacing x by $(-x)$}
$\quad\quad = 4 + 3x - x^2$

b $f(x+2) = 4 - 3(x+2) - (x+2)^2$ {replacing x by $(x+2)$}
$\quad\quad = 4 - 3x - 6 - [x^2 + 4x + 4]$
$\quad\quad = -2 - 3x - x^2 - 4x - 4$
$\quad\quad = -x^2 - 7x - 6$

EXERCISE 17C

1 If $f : x \longmapsto 2x + 3$, find the value of:

    a $f(0)$ **b** $f(2)$ **c** $f(-1)$ **d** $f(-5)$ **e** $f(-\frac{1}{2})$

2 If $g : x \longmapsto x + \dfrac{2}{x}$, find the value of:

    a $g(1)$ **b** $g(4)$ **c** $g(-1)$ **d** $g(-4)$ **e** $g(-\tfrac{1}{2})$

3 If $f : x \longmapsto 2x^2 - 3x + 2$, find the value of:

    a $f(0)$ **b** $f(3)$ **c** $f(-3)$ **d** $f(-7)$ **e** $f(\tfrac{1}{2})$

4 If $f(x) = 5 - 2x$, find in simplest form:

    a $f(a)$ **b** $f(-a)$ **c** $f(a+1)$ **d** $f(x-3)$ **e** $f(2x)$

5 If $P(x) = x^2 + 4x - 3$, find in simplest form:

    a $P(x+2)$ **b** $P(1-x)$ **c** $P(-x)$ **d** $P(x^2)$ **e** $P(x^2+1)$

6 If $R(x) = \dfrac{2x-3}{x+2}$:   **a** evaluate **i** $R(0)$ **ii** $R(1)$ **iii** $R(-\tfrac{1}{2})$

    b find a value of x where $R(x)$ does not exist

    c find $R(x-2)$ in simplest form

    d find x if $R(x) = -5$.

7 If the value of a car t years after purchase is given by $V(t) = 28\,000 - 4000t$ dollars:

    a find $V(4)$ and state what $V(4)$ means

    b find t when $V(t) = 8000$ and explain what this represents

    c find the original purchase price of the car.

INVESTIGATION 1   FLUID FILLING FUNCTIONS

When water is added to a container, the depth of water is given by a function of time.

DEMO

If the water is added at a *constant* rate, the volume of water added is directly proportional to the time taken to add it.

If the container has a uniform cross-section, for example, a cylinder, then the graph of depth against time is a straight line, or *linear*. The depth-time graph for the cylinder is shown alongside:

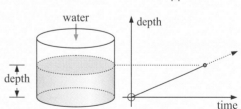

The question arises:

'What changes in appearance of the graph occur for different shaped containers?'

For example, consider the graph shown for a vase of conical shape.

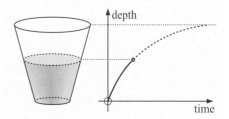

What to do:

1 For each of the following containers, draw a 'depth v time' graph as water is added:

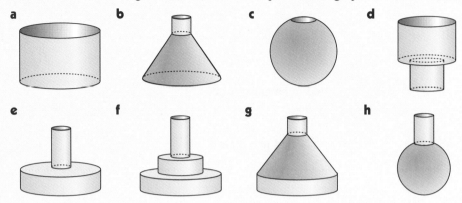

2 Use the water filling demonstration to check your answers to question **1**.

 LINEAR FUNCTIONS

When a quantity changes we say that it shows **variation**. Variation could mean *getting larger* as in growth, *getting faster*, *decreasing in price*, etc.

Some variation will be regular and predictable and some will not. The variation in one quantity may **depend** on the variation in another.

For example:
- Does variation in *a company's profit* depend on *its sales*, or vice versa?
- Does *blood pressure* depend on *blood alcohol level*, or vice versa?

A variable which depends on another is called the **dependent** variable and the other variable is called the **independent** variable.

In the examples above, a *company's profit* is the **dependent** variable as it depends on the company's *sales*. Also *blood pressure* depends on *blood alcohol level* (amongst other things). So, blood pressure is the **dependent** variable.

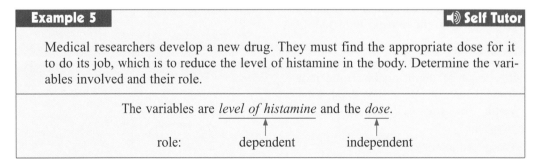

In graphing functions involving dependent and independent variables, the independent variable is placed on the horizontal axis.

In this section we are interested in problems involving **exact linear relationships**.

Example 6   ◀)) **Self Tutor**

Below are diagrams for the first four polygons. The sum of the interior angles of each polygon is shown in the table which follows.

Number of sides (n)	3	4	5	6	7	8
Angle sum (A)	180	360	540	720	900	1080

a Name the dependent and independent variables.

b Graph the tabled information.

c What is the slope of the imagined line through the points?

d Find the linear model which connects the variables.

e What is the interpretation of the slope?

f What, if anything, do the axis intercepts represent?

a The *angle sum* depends on the *number of sides*. So, *the number of sides* is the independent variable and *the angle sum* is the dependent variable.

b

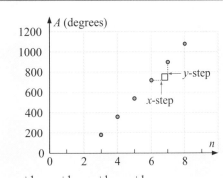

c

	+1	+1	+1	+1	+1	
Number of sides (n)	3	4	5	6	7	8
Angle sum (A)	180	360	540	720	900	1080
	+180	+180	+180	+180	+180	

From the graph or from the table, the slope is $m = 180$.

This can be seen from the **constant adder** (for every increase of 1 in n, A increases by 180) or by using $m = \dfrac{y\text{-step}}{x\text{-step}}$.

d   Our linear model is $y = mx + c$ where $y = A$ and $x = n$.

So, $A = 180n + c$

But when $n = 3$, $A = 180$ $\therefore$ $180 = 180 \times 3 + c$ $\therefore$ $c = -360$

Hence, $A = 180n - 360$.

e   *Slope interpretation:* an increase in 1 of the number of sides produces an increase of 180° in the angle sum.

f   Clearly $n \geqslant 3$,   as no polygons exist for smaller values of n

$\therefore$ axis intercepts are meaningless.

EXERCISE 17D

1   'Pavers for all' sell a certain type of paver for $800 per thousand with a fixed delivery fee of $50 regardless of the number ordered.

We define two variables, A as the number of pavers purchased ($\times 1000$) and P as the price of pavers plus delivery.

  a State the role of each variable, that is, which is the independent variable and which is the dependent variable.

  b Copy and complete the following table:

A ($\times 1000$)	0	1	2	3	4	5
P ($)						

  c Explain why the relationship between these variables is 'linear'.

  d Produce a graphical model of the relationship between P and A.

  e Write down an algebraic relationship that links P to A (or the function for P in terms of A).

  f Determine the price of purchasing and delivery of 5500 pavers.

  g Determine the number of pavers that could be purchased and delivered for $3200.

2   Temperatures can be expressed in a variety of units. Consider the following table:

temperature (T_C, $^\circ C$)	10	20	30	40
temperature (T_F, $^\circ F$)	50	68	86	104

  a Show that the relationship between degrees T_F and degrees T_C is linear.

  b Find the *constant addition* in degrees T_F per unit increase in degrees T_C.

  c Write down the function for degrees T_F in terms of degrees T_C.

  d Convert $100^\circ F$ to $^\circ C$.   **e** Convert $32^\circ F$ to $^\circ C$.

3   A storage bin for chicken food contains 1000 kg of food pellets.
Exactly 13 kg of food is removed each day for the chickens.

  a Copy and complete the following table:

Days elapsed (t)	0	1	2	3	4
Pellets in bin (F, kg)	1000	987			

  b What is the dependent variable? What is the independent variable?

  c If a graph was to be drawn, what axis should F be plotted on? Why?

  d Produce a graphical model of the relationship between F and t.

  e What is the slope of the line that could be drawn through these points? Write down the function for F in terms of t.

  f Interpret the slope and the vertical intercept.

  g Using the function from **e**, determine the amount of food left after a fortnight.

  h Determine when the food supply will run out.

INVESTIGATION 2   **THE FARMYARD PROBLEM**

 There are ducks and cows in a farmyard. Altogether there are 9 heads and 22 legs. How many ducks and how many cows are there?

What to do:

1 Copy and complete the following table:

Number of ducks	0	1	2	3	4	5	6	7	8	9
Number of legs										
Number of cows	9	8								
Number of legs										
Total legs (cows & ducks)										

2 Use the table to find the solution to the problem.

3 Suppose there were x ducks and y cows in the farmyard.

    a By considering the number of heads seen, explain why $x + y = 9$.

    b By considering the total number of legs seen, explain why $2x + 4y = 22$.

4 You should have found that there were seven ducks and two cows in the farmyard.

    a Substitute $x = 7$ and $y = 2$ into $x + y = 9$. What do you notice?

    b Substitute $x = 7$ and $y = 2$ into $2x + 4y = 22$. What do you notice?

We say that $x = 7$, $y = 2$ is the only solution to the **simultaneous equations**

$$\begin{cases} x + y = 9 \\ 2x + 4y = 22. \end{cases}$$

We found the solution to the problem by trial and error. However, the solution can also be found by algebraic means.

E   LINEAR SIMULTANEOUS EQUATIONS

Simultaneous equations are two equations containing two unknowns, e.g., $\begin{cases} x + y = 5 \\ 4x - 3y = 6. \end{cases}$

When we solve these problems we are trying to find the solution which is common to both equations.

Notice that if $x = 3$ and $y = 2$ then:

   • $x + y = 3 + 2 = 5$ ✓   i.e., the equation is satisfied

   • $4x - 3y = 4 \times 3 - 3 \times 2 = 12 - 6 = 6$ ✓   i.e., the equation is satisfied.

So, $x = 3$ and $y = 2$ is the **solution** to the simultaneous equations $\begin{cases} x + y = 5 \\ 4x - 3y = 6 \end{cases}$.

The solutions to **linear simultaneous equations** can be found by **trial and error** (a little tedious) or **graphically** (which can be inaccurate if solutions are not integers).

Due to these limitations, it is preferable to solve equations algebraically.

SOLUTION BY SUBSTITUTION

The method of **solution by substitution** is used when at least one equation is given with either x or y as the **subject** of the formula.

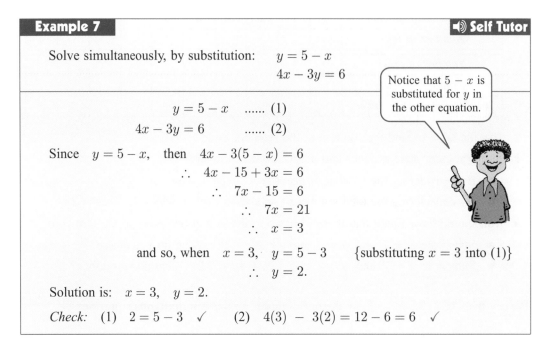

Example 7   🔊 **Self Tutor**

Solve simultaneously, by substitution: $y = 5 - x$
$4x - 3y = 6$

Notice that $5 - x$ is substituted for y in the other equation.

$$y = 5 - x \quad \text{...... (1)}$$
$$4x - 3y = 6 \quad \text{...... (2)}$$

Since $y = 5 - x$, then $4x - 3(5 - x) = 6$
$$\therefore \quad 4x - 15 + 3x = 6$$
$$\therefore \quad 7x - 15 = 6$$
$$\therefore \quad 7x = 21$$
$$\therefore \quad x = 3$$

and so, when $x = 3$, $y = 5 - 3$ {substituting $x = 3$ into (1)}
$$\therefore \quad y = 2.$$

Solution is: $x = 3$, $y = 2$.

Check: (1) $2 = 5 - 3$ ✓   (2) $4(3) - 3(2) = 12 - 6 = 6$ ✓

Example 8   🔊 **Self Tutor**

Solve simultaneously, by substitution: $2y + x = 2$
$x = 1 - 3y$

$2y + x = 2$ ...... (1)
$x = 1 - 3y$ ...... (2)   Substituting (2) into (1) gives $2y + (1 - 3y) = 2$
$$\therefore \quad 2y + 1 - 3y = 2$$
$$\therefore \quad -y + 1 = 2$$
$$\therefore \quad -y = 1$$
$$\therefore \quad y = -1.$$

Substituting $y = -1$ into (2) gives
$$x = 1 - 3(-1) = 4.$$

The solution is $x = 4$, $y = -1$.

Check: (1) $2(-1) + 4 = -2 + 4 = 2$ ✓
(2) $1 - 3(-1) = 1 + 3 = 4$ ✓

EXERCISE 17E.1

1   Solve simultaneously, using substitution:

    a $y = 2 - x$
          $3x + 4y = 0$

    b $x = 7 - 2y$
          $3x - 5y = 10$

    c $y = x + 3$
          $3x + 7y = 1$

    d $x = 3 - y$
          $x = -7 + y$

    e $3x - 2y = 8$
          $x = 3y + 12$

    f $x + y + 1 = 0$
          $y = 2x + 5$

2   **a**   Use the method of substitution to try to solve the equations $y = 2x - 5$ and $y = 2x + 1$.

    b   What is the simultaneous solution for the equations in **a**?

3   **a**   Use the method of substitution to try to solve the equations $y = 4x - 3$ and $2y = 8x - 6$.

    b   How many simultaneous solutions do the equations in **a** have?

SOLUTION BY ELIMINATION

In many problems which require the simultaneous solution of linear equations, each equation will be of the form $ax + by = c$.   Solution by substitution is often tedious in such situations and the method of elimination of one of the variables is preferred.

In the method of **elimination**, we make the coefficients of x (or y) the **same size** but **opposite in sign**. We then **add** the equations to **eliminate** one of the variables.

Example 9	◀ Self Tutor

Solve simultaneously, by elimination: $2x + 3y = 1$ ...... (1)
                                   $5x - 3y = 13$ ...... (2)

We **sum** the LHS's and the RHS's to get an equation which contains x only.

$$2x + 3y = 1$$
$$+ \quad 5x - 3y = 13$$
$$\overline{ 7x = 14} \qquad \text{\{on adding the equations\}}$$
$$\therefore \quad x = 2 \qquad \text{\{dividing both sides by 7\}}$$

Let $x = 2$ in (1) $\therefore$ $2 \times 2 + 3y = 1$
$$\therefore \quad 4 + 3y = 1$$
$$\therefore \quad 3y = 1 - 4 \quad \text{\{subtracting 4 from both sides\}}$$
$$\therefore \quad 3y = -3$$
$$\therefore \quad y = -1 \quad \text{\{dividing by 3 on both sides\}}$$

i.e., $x = 2$ and $y = -1$

Check: in (2): $5(2) - 3(-1) = 10 + 3 = 13$ ✓

The method of elimination uses the fact that: If $a = b$ and $c = d$ then $a + c = b + d$.

EXERCISE 17E.2

1 What equation results when the following are added vertically?

a $4x + 3y = 15$
    $5x - 3y = -6$

b $8x + 5y = -4$
    $-8x - 6y = 3$

c $4x - 2y = 9$
    $x + 2y = -4$

d $4x + 5y = 11$
    $-6x - 5y = -21$

e $3x + 6y = 16$
    $-3x + 2y = -8$

f $-9x + 2y = -5$
    $9x - 3y = -4$

2 Solve the following using the method of elimination:

a $2x + y = 6$
    $3x - y = 9$

b $4x + 3y = 13$
    $6x - 3y = -3$

c $x + 5y = 4$
    $-x - 7y = -6$

d $3x + 5y = 6$
    $-3x + 2y = 8$

e $4x - 2y = 21$
    $3x + 2y = -7$

f $-4x + 3y = -25$
    $4x - 5y = 31$

In problems where the coefficients of x (or y) are **not** the **same size** or **opposite in sign**, we may have to **multiply** each equation by a number to enable us to **eliminate** one variable.

Example 10   ◀ᴗ **Self Tutor**

Solve simultaneously, by elimination: $3x + 2y = 5$
                                          $2x - 5y = 16$

$$3x + 2y = 5 \quad ...... \ (1)$$
$$2x - 5y = 16 \quad ...... \ (2)$$

We can eliminate y by multiplying (1) by 5 and (2) by 2.

$$\therefore \quad 15x + 10y = 25$$
$$+ \quad 4x - 10y = 32$$
$$\overline{}$$
$$\therefore \quad 19x = 57 \qquad \{\text{on adding the equations}\}$$
$$\therefore \quad x = 3 \qquad \{\text{dividing both sides by 19}\}$$

Substituting $x = 3$ into equation (1) gives

$$3(3) + 2y = 5$$
$$\therefore \quad 9 + 2y = 5$$
$$\therefore \quad 2y = -4$$
$$\therefore \quad y = -2$$

So, the solution is: $x = 3, \ y = -2$.   *Check:* $3(3) + 2(-2) = 9 - 4 = 5$ ✓
                                                      $2(3) - 5(-2) = 6 + 10 = 16$ ✓

EXERCISE 17E.3

1 Give the equation that results when both sides of the equation:

a $2x + 5y = 1$ is multiplied by 3

b $3x - y = 4$ is multiplied by -2

c $7x - y = 9$ is multiplied by 5

d $2x + 3y = -1$ is multiplied by -3

e $2x - 3y = 6$ is multiplied by -4

f $4x - 7y = -8$ is multiplied by -1

Example 11

🔊 **Self Tutor**

Solve by elimination: $3x + 4y = 6$
$4x + 5y = 7$

$$3x + 4y = 6 \quad ...... \ (1)$$
$$4x + 5y = 7 \quad ...... \ (2)$$

To eliminate x, multiply both sides of
(1) by 4: $12x + 16y = 24 \quad ...... \ (3)$
(2) by -3: $\underline{-12x - 15y = -21} \quad ...... \ (4)$
$$y = 3 \quad \{\text{on adding (3) and (4)}\}$$

and substituting $y = 3$ into (2) gives

$$4x + 5(3) = 7$$
$$\therefore \quad 4x + 15 = 7$$
$$\therefore \quad 4x = -8$$
$$\therefore \quad x = -2$$

Thus $x = -2$ and $y = 3$.

Check: (1) $3(-2) + 4(3) = (-6) + 12 = 6$ ✓
(2) $4(-2) + 5(3) = (-8) + 15 = 7$ ✓

WHAT TO ELIMINATE

There is always a choice whether to eliminate x or y, so our choice depends on which variable is easier to eliminate.

In **Example 11**, try to solve by multiplying (1) by 5 and (2) by -4. This eliminates y rather than x. The final solutions should be the same.

EXERCISE 17E.3 (continued)

2 Solve the following using the method of elimination:

a $4x - 3y = 5$
$-2x + y = 5$

b $2x - y = -10$
$3x + 4y = 7$

c $3x + 4y = -2$
$x - 3y = 8$

d $5x + 3y = 10$
$3x - 5y = -28$

e $4x - 3y = 2$
$3x + 4y = 39$

f $7x - 3y = 33$
$3x + 4y + 7 = 0$

g $2x + 5y = 5$
$3x + 2y = 13$

h $3x - 2y = -13$
$4x + 3y = 11$

i $3x + 5y + 32 = 0$
$5x + 6y + 44 = 0$

3 Use the method of elimination to attempt to solve:

a $x + 3y = 4$
$3x + 9y = 12$

b $5x - 2y = 3$
$10x - 4y = 7$

Comment?

PROBLEM SOLVING

Many problems can be described mathematically by **linear simultaneous equations**, i.e., two equations of the form $ax + by = c$, where x and y are the two variables (unknowns).

We have already seen an example of this in the **Investigation** on page **409**.

Once the equations are formed, they can then be solved simultaneously and the original problem can be solved. The following method is recommended:

Step 1: Decide on the two unknowns. Call them x and y, say. Do not forget the units.

Step 2: Write down **two** equations connecting x and y.

Step 3: Solve the equations simultaneously.

Step 4: Check your solutions with the original data given.

Step 5: Give your answer in sentence form.

> When solving problems with simultaneous equations we must find two equations containing two unknowns.

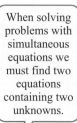

Note: The form of the original equations will help you decide whether to use the substitution method or the elimination method.

Example 12   ◄)) **Self Tutor**

2 icecreams and 3 burgers cost \$17.30, and 3 icecreams and 2 burgers cost \$14.70. Find the cost of each icecream and each burger.

Let each icecream cost \$$x$ and each burger cost \$$y$.

$$\therefore \quad 2x + 3y = 17.30 \quad \text{...... (1)}$$
$$3x + 2y = 14.70 \quad \text{...... (2)}$$

To eliminate x, we multiply (1) by 3 and (2) by -2.

$$\therefore \quad 6x + 9y = 51.90 \quad \text{...... (3)}$$
$$-6x - 4y = -29.40 \quad \text{...... (4)}$$

adding (3) and (4) $\qquad 5y = 22.50$

$$\therefore \quad y = 4.50 \quad \text{\{dividing both sides by 5\}}$$

and substituting in (2)

$$3x + 2(4.50) = 14.70$$
$$\therefore \quad 3x + 9 = 14.70$$
$$\therefore \quad 3x = 5.70$$
$$\therefore \quad x = 1.9 \qquad \text{\{dividing both sides by 3\}}$$

Icecreams cost \$1.90 and burgers cost \$4.50 each.

Check: $\quad 2(1.90) + 3(4.50) = 3.80 + 13.50 = 17.30 \quad \checkmark$

$\qquad\qquad 3(1.90) + 2(4.50) = 5.70 + 9.00 = 14.70 \quad \checkmark$

EXERCISE 17F

1 The sum of two numbers is 53 and their difference is 19. Find the numbers.

2 Find two numbers whose sum is 28, and half their difference is 4.

3 The larger of two numbers is three times the smaller, and their sum is 56. Find the two numbers.

4 Four pencils and 6 biros cost a total of $8.90, whereas 3 pencils and 5 biros cost a total of $7.20. Find the cost of each item.

5 Seven oranges and four apples cost a total of $2.05, whereas four oranges and three apples cost a total of $1.35. Find the cost of an orange and the cost of an apple.

6 Jessie saves $1 and $2 coins. He has 57 of these coins and their total value is $95. How many of each coin type does he have?

7 Anya and Michelle have $34.50 between them and Anya's money is two thirds of Michelle's. How much money does each have?

8 Cheese is sold in either 200 g or 350 g blocks. A supermarket manager ordered 17.4 kg of cheese and received 60 blocks. How many of each type did the manager receive?

9 Given that the triangle alongside is equilateral, find a and b.

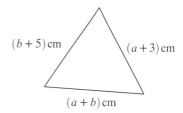

$(b+5)$ cm $(a+3)$ cm

$(a+b)$ cm

10 A rectangle has perimeter 36 cm. If 5 cm is taken from the length and added to the width, the rectangle becomes a square. Find the dimensions of the original rectangle.

HARDER PROBLEMS (EXTENSION)

11 A motor boat travels 12 km/h upstream against the current and 18 km/h downstream with the current. Find the speed of the current and the speed of the motor boat in still water.

12 A jet plane made a 4000 km trip with the wind, in 4 hours, but required 5 hours to make the return trip. Given that the speed of the wind was constant throughout the entire trip, what was the speed of the wind and what was the average speed of the plane in still air?

13 A man on foot covers the 25 km between two towns in $3\frac{3}{4}$ hours. He walks at 4 km/h for the first part of the journey and runs at 12 km/h for the remaining part.

   a How far did he run?   **b** For how long was he running?

14 Explain why any two digit number can be written in the form $10a+b$. Hence, solve the following problem:

   A number consists of two digits which add up to 9. When the digits are reversed, the original number is decreased by 45. What was the original number?

G   SIMPLE RATIONAL FUNCTIONS

A function of the form $y = \dfrac{k}{x}$ where k is a constant is called a **simple rational function**.

If $y = \dfrac{k}{x}$, then y and x are said to vary *inversely* and form a *reciprocal relationship*.

There are many situations in real life where two quantities vary inversely.

For example, the pressure and volume of a gas at room temperature vary inversely with the equation $P = \dfrac{77.4}{V}$.

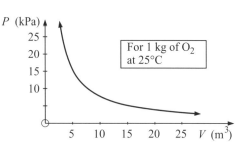

For 1 kg of O_2 at 25°C

If P is graphed against V the curve is one branch of a *hyperbola*. Note that it is not physically possible to have negative pressures and volumes.

INVESTIGATION 3   THE FAMILY OF CURVES $y = \frac{k}{x}$

The use of a **graphing package** or **graphics calculator** is recommended.

What to do:

1   On the same set of axes draw the graphs $y = \dfrac{1}{x}$, $y = \dfrac{4}{x}$, $y = \dfrac{8}{x}$.

2   Describe the effect changes in the k values have on the graphs for $k > 0$.

3   Repeat **1** for $y = \dfrac{-1}{x}$, $y = \dfrac{-4}{x}$, $y = \dfrac{-8}{x}$.

GRAPHING PACKAGE

4   Comment on shape changes in **3**.

5   Explain why there is no point on the graphs corresponding to $x = 0$.

EXERCISE 17G

1   Consider the function $y = \dfrac{10}{x}$.

   a   Find y values for $x = 1000, 100, 10, 5, 2, 1, 0.5, 0.1, 0.01$

   b   Find y values for $x = -1000, -100, -10, -5, -2, -1, -0.5, -0.1, -0.01$

   c   Draw a sketch graph of $y = \dfrac{10}{x}$.

   d   Without calculating new values, sketch the graph of $y = \dfrac{-10}{x}$.

2   Sam has to type an assignment which is 400 words in length. How fast he can type (in words per minute) will affect how long the job takes him (in minutes).

   a   Complete the following table of values:

Words per minute (n)	10	20	30	....
Time taken (t)				

b Draw a graph of n versus t with n on the horizontal axis.

c Is it reasonable to draw a smooth curve through the points plotted in **b**? What shape is the curve?

d State the formula for the relationship between n and t.

3 Determine the equations of the following rational functions:

a

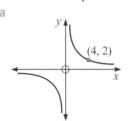

b

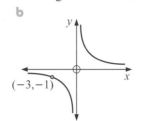

c

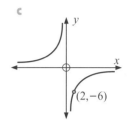

4 Find the axes of symmetry for functions of the form $y = \dfrac{k}{x}$ where:

a $k < 0$ **b** $k > 0$

H   NUMBER SEQUENCES

INTRODUCTION

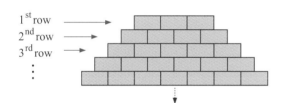

1st row
2nd row
3rd row

Consider the illustrated tower of bricks. The top row, or first row, has three bricks. The second row has four bricks. The third row has five, etc.

If u_n represents the number of bricks in row n (from the top) then

$$u_1 = 3, \quad u_2 = 4, \quad u_3 = 5, \quad u_4 = 6, \quad ......$$

The number pattern: 3, 4, 5, 6, ... is called a **sequence** of numbers.

This sequence can be specified by:

- **Using words**   The top row has three bricks and each successive row under it has one more brick.

- **Using an explicit formula** $u_n = n + 2$ is the **general term** (or **nth term**) formula for $n = 1, 2, 3, 4, 5, ...$ etc.

  Check: $u_1 = 1 + 2 = 3$ ✓
  $u_2 = 2 + 2 = 4$ ✓
  $u_3 = 3 + 2 = 5$ ✓ etc.

- **Using a recursive formula** $u_1 = 3$ and $u_{n+1} = u_n + 1$ for $n \geqslant 1$

  Check: $u_1 = 3$
  $u_2 = u_1 + 1 = 3 + 1 = 4$ ✓
  $u_3 = u_2 + 1 = 4 + 1 = 5$ ✓ etc.

NUMBER SEQUENCES

A **number sequence** is a function whose domain is the set of all positive integers.

u_n, T_n, t_n, A_n, etc. are all used to represent the **general term** (or **nth term**) of a sequence and are defined for $n = 1, 2, 3, 4, 5, 6, ...$

ARITHMETIC SEQUENCES

An **arithmetic sequence** is a sequence in which each term differs from the previous one by the same fixed number.

For example: $1, 5, 9, 13, 17, ...$ is arithmetic as $5 - 1 = 9 - 5 = 13 - 9 = 17 - 13$, etc.

Likewise, $42, 37, 32, 27, ...$ is arithmetic as $42 - 37 = 37 - 32 = 32 - 27$, etc.

Algebraic definition:

Notice in the sequence $1, 5, 9, 13, 17, ...$ that

$$u_1 = 1$$
$$u_2 = 1 + 4 = 1 + 1(4)$$
$$u_3 = 1 + 4 + 4 = 1 + 2(4)$$
$$u_4 = 1 + 4 + 4 + 4 = 1 + 3(4) \quad \text{etc}$$

This suggests that   if u_n is arithmetic then the nth term is $\boldsymbol{u_n = u_1 + (n-1)d}$

where u_1 is the first term and d is the constant **common difference**.

Example 13 ◀) **Self Tutor**

Consider the sequence $3, 9, 15, 21, 27, ...$
a   Show that the sequence is arithmetic.
b   Find the formula for the general term u_n.
c   Find the 100th term of the sequence.
d   Is   i   489   ii   1592   a member of the sequence?

a $9 - 3 = 6, \quad 15 - 9 = 6, \quad 21 - 15 = 6, \quad 27 - 21 = 6$
        So, assuming that the pattern continues, consecutive terms differ by 6
        ∴ the sequence is arithmetic with $u_1 = 3, \quad d = 6$.

b $u_n = u_1 + (n-1)d$ ∴ $u_n = 3 + 6(n - 1)$ i.e., $u_n = 6n - 3$

c   If $n = 100, \quad u_{100} = 6(100) - 3 = 597$.

d   i   Let $u_n = 489$ ii   Let $u_n = 1592$
        ∴ $6n - 3 = 489$ ∴ $6n - 3 = 1592$
        ∴ $6n = 492$ ∴ $6n = 1595$
        ∴ $n = 82$ ∴ $n = 265\frac{5}{6}$

        ∴   489 is a term of the sequence.   which is not possible as n is an
        In fact it is the 82nd term.   integer. ∴ 1592 cannot be a term.

EXERCISE 17H.1

1 Consider the sequence   4, 11, 18, 25, 32, ...
  a Show that the sequence is arithmetic. b Find the formula for its general term.
  c Find its 50th term.   d Is 325 a member?
  e Is 761 a member?

2 Consider the sequence   67, 63, 59, 55, ...
  a Show that the sequence is arithmetic. b Find the formula for its general term.
  c Find its 40th term.   d Is -143 a member?
  e Is 761 a member?

3 An arithmetic sequence is defined by $u_n = 11n - 7$.
  a Find u_1 and d.   b Find the 57th term.
  c What is the least term of the sequence which is greater than 450?

4 A sequence is defined by $u_n = \dfrac{21 - 4n}{2}$.
  a Prove that the sequence is arithmetic. b Find u_1 and d. c Find u_{75}.
  d For what values of n are the terms of the sequence less than -200?

Example 14   ◀)) Self Tutor

Find k given that $k + 5$, -1 and $2k - 1$ are consecutive terms of an arithmetic sequence, and hence find the terms.

Since the terms are consecutive,
$$-1 - (k + 5) = (2k - 1) - (-1) \quad \text{\{equating common differences\}}$$
$$\therefore \quad -1 - k - 5 = 2k - 1 + 1$$
$$\therefore \quad -k - 6 = 2k$$
$$\therefore \quad -6 = 3k$$
$$\therefore \quad k = -2$$
$$\therefore \quad \text{the terms are } 3, -1, -5.$$

5 Find k given the consecutive arithmetic terms:
  a   31, k, 3   b k, 8, $k + 11$ c $k + 2$, $2k + 3$, 17

Example 15   ◀)) Self Tutor

Find the general term u_n for an arithmetic sequence given that $u_3 = 4$ and $u_7 = -24$.

$$u_7 - u_3 = u_1 + 6d - (u_1 + 2d)$$
$$= u_1 + 6d - u_1 - 2d$$
$$= 4d$$
But $u_7 - u_3 = -24 - 4 = -28$
$$\therefore \quad 4d = -28$$
$$\therefore \quad d = -7$$

Now $u_n = u_1 + (n-1)d$ *Check:*

$\therefore$ $u_3 = u_1 + (2)(-7)$ $u_3 = 25 - 7(3)$

$\therefore$ $4 = u_1 - 14$ $= 25 - 21$

$\therefore$ $u_1 = 18$ $= 4$ ✓

$\therefore$ $u_n = 18 + (n-1)(-7)$

$\therefore$ $u_n = 18 - 7n + 7$ $u_7 = 25 - 7(7)$

$\therefore$ $u_n = 25 - 7n$ $= 25 - 49$

                                                            $= -24$ ✓

6 Find the general term u_n for an arithmetic sequence given that:

   a $u_4 = 37$ and $u_{10} = 67$ **b** $u_5 = -10$ and $u_{12} = -38$

   c   the fourth term is -4 and the fifteenth term is 29

   d   the tenth and sixth terms are -16 and -13 respectively.

7 Consider the finite arithmetic sequence $3, 2\frac{1}{2}, 2, ..., -6$.

   a   Find u_1 and d.   **b**   How many terms does the sequence have?

8 An arithmetic sequence starts 17, 24, 31, 38, ...   What is the first term of the sequence to exceed 40 000?

GEOMETRIC SEQUENCES

A sequence is **geometric** if each term can be obtained from the previous one by multiplying by the same non-zero constant.

For example: 2, 6, 18, 54, ...   is a geometric sequence as

   $2 \times 3 = 6$ and $6 \times 3 = 18$ and $18 \times 3 = 54$.

Notice that $u_2 = u_1 \times 3$ and $u_3 = u_2 \times 3 = u_1 \times 3 \times 3 = u_1 \times 3^2$,

                                    $u_4 = u_3 \times 3 = u_1 \times 3^2 \times 3 = u_1 \times 3^3$,

                                    $u_5 = u_4 \times 3 = u_1 \times 3^3 \times 3 = u_1 \times 3^4$,

which suggests the following **algebraic definition**:

   If u_n is geometric, then $\boldsymbol{u_n = u_1 \times r^{n-1}}$

   where u_1 is the **first term** and r is a **constant common ratio**.

Notice: • r is called the common ratio because $\dfrac{u_{n+1}}{u_n} = r$ for all n.

   •   2, 6, 18, 54, ...   is geometric with $r = 3$.

   •   2, -6, 18, -54, ...   is geometric with $r = -3$.

Example 16   ◀)) **Self Tutor**

For the sequence   16, 8, 4, 2, 1, ...

a   Show that the sequence is geometric.   b   Find the general term u_n.

c   Hence, find the 10th term as a fraction.

a $\dfrac{8}{16} = \dfrac{1}{2}, \quad \dfrac{4}{8} = \dfrac{1}{2}, \quad \dfrac{2}{4} = \dfrac{1}{2}, \quad \dfrac{1}{2} = \dfrac{1}{2}$

So, assuming the pattern continues, consecutive terms have a common ratio of $\frac{1}{2}$.

$\therefore$ the sequence is geometric with $u_1 = 16$ and $r = \frac{1}{2}$.

b $u_n = u_1 r^{n-1} \qquad\qquad \therefore \quad u_n = 16 \times \left(\tfrac{1}{2}\right)^{n-1} \qquad or \quad u_n = 2^4 \times (2^{-1})^{n-1}$

$$= 2^4 \times 2^{-n+1}$$
$$= 2^{5-n}$$

c $u_{10} = 16 \times \left(\tfrac{1}{2}\right)^9 = \dfrac{2^4}{2^9} = \dfrac{1}{2^5} = \tfrac{1}{32}$

EXERCISE 17H.2

1   For the geometric sequence with first two terms given, find b and c:

   a   3, 6, b, c, ...   b   8, 2, b, c, ...   c   15, -5, b, c, ...

2   a   Show that the sequence   1, 3, 9, 27, ...   is geometric.

   b   Find u_n and hence find the 10th term.

3   a   Show that the sequence   40, -20, 10, -5, ...   is geometric.

   b   Find u_n and hence find the 12th term (as a fraction).

4   Show that the sequence   16, -4, 1, -0.25, ...   is geometric and hence find the 8th term as a decimal.

Example 17   ◀)) **Self Tutor**

$k - 1$, $2k$ and $21 - k$ are consecutive terms of a geometric sequence. Find k.

Since the terms are geometric

$$\dfrac{2k}{k-1} = \dfrac{21-k}{2k} \qquad\qquad \text{\{equating common ratios\}}$$

$$\therefore \quad 4k^2 = (21-k)(k-1)$$
$$\therefore \quad 4k^2 = 21k - 21 - k^2 + k$$
$$\therefore \quad 5k^2 - 22k + 21 = 0$$
$$\therefore \quad (5k - 7)(k - 3) = 0$$
$$\therefore \quad k = \tfrac{7}{5} \ \text{ or } \ 3$$

5 Find k given that the following are consecutive terms of a geometric sequence:

 a $3, k, 27$ **b** $k, 3k, 10k + 7$ **c** $k, k + 4, 8k + 2$

Example 18   ◀» **Self Tutor**

A geometric sequence has $u_2 = -5$ and $u_5 = 40$. Find its general term.

$$u_2 = u_1 r = -5 \quad \dots\dots (1) \quad \{\text{using } u_n = u_1 r^{n-1} \text{ with } n = 2\}$$

$$\text{and} \quad u_5 = u_1 r^4 = 40 \quad \dots\dots (2)$$

$$\text{So,} \quad \frac{u_1 r^4}{u_1 r} = \frac{40}{-5} \quad \{(2) \div (1)\}$$

$$\therefore \quad r^3 = -8$$

$$\therefore \quad r = \sqrt[3]{-8}$$

$$\therefore \quad r = -2$$

$$\text{and so in (1)} \quad u_1(-2) = -5$$

$$\therefore \quad u_1 = \tfrac{5}{2}$$

$$\text{Thus} \quad u_n = \tfrac{5}{2} \times (-2)^{n-1}.$$

---

6 Find the general term u_n, of the geometric sequence which has:

 a $u_3 = 16$ and $u_8 = 512$ **b** $u_3 = 32$ and $u_6 = -4$

 c $u_7 = 24$ and $u_{15} = 384$ **d** $u_3 = 3$ and $u_9 = \tfrac{3}{8}$

I   RECURRENCE RELATIONSHIPS

Perhaps the simplest example of a recurrence relationship is the **Fibonacci sequence** for the pattern:

$1, 1, 2, 3, 5, 8, 13, 21, 34, 55, \dots\dots$

The pattern starts with two 1s, and after this each term is obtained by adding the two terms preceding it,

i.e., $1 + 1 = 2$
    $1 + 2 = 3$
    $2 + 3 = 5$
    $3 + 5 = 8$
    $\vdots$ etc.

We can hence write down a **recurrence relationship**:

$u_1 = u_2 = 1$ and $u_{n+2} = u_{n+1} + u_n$ for $n = 1, 2, 3, 4, 5, 6, 7, \dots\dots$

Check: If $n = 1$, $u_3 = u_2 + u_1 = 1 + 1 = 2$ ✓

     If $n = 2$, $u_4 = u_3 + u_2 = 2 + 1 = 3$ ✓

     If $n = 3$, $u_5 = u_4 + u_3 = 3 + 2 = 5$ ✓   etc.

Leonardo Fibonacci noticed that this sequence frequently occurred in natural circumstances.

For example, he noticed that flowers of a particular species have the same number of petals and that these numbers are members of the Fibonacci sequence.

3 petals	lily, iris
5 petals	buttercup
8 petals	delphinium
13 petals	cineraria
21 petals	aster
34 petals	pyrethrum

Fibonacci observed the number sequence in:

- the number of leaves arranged about the stem in plants
- the seed patterns of the sunflower
- the seed pattern on the pine cone.

The explicit formula for the Fibonacci sequence is very complicated. In fact it is

$$u_n = \tfrac{1}{\sqrt{5}}\left[\left(\frac{1+\sqrt{5}}{2}\right)^n - \left(\frac{1-\sqrt{5}}{2}\right)^n\right] \quad \text{for} \quad n = 1, 2, 3, 4, 5, \ldots$$

ARITHMETIC SEQUENCES

The sequence   4, 7, 10, 13, ...   can be generated using $u_n = 3n + 1$ or by using the recurrence relationship:

"$u_1 = 4$ and $u_{n+1} = u_n + 3$ where n is a positive integer".

This is easily seen as $u_1 = 4$ and $u_2 = u_1 + 3 = 4 + 3 = 7$
and $u_3 = u_2 + 3 = 7 + 3 = 10$
and $u_4 = u_3 + 3 = 10 + 3 = 13$ etc.

In general,   if $\boldsymbol{u_n = u_1 + (n-1)d}$ where a and d are constants

then $\boldsymbol{u_{n+1} = u_n + d}$.

GEOMETRIC SEQUENCES

The sequence   3, 6, 12, 24, ...   can be generated from the general term formula, $u_n = 3 \times 2^{n-1}$ where n is a positive integer.

Notice that the same sequence can be generated from the recurrence relationship:

"$u_1 = 3$ and $u_{n+1} = 2u_n$ where n is a positive integer".

We have $u_1 = 3$ and $u_2 = 2u_1 = 2 \times 3 = 6$ {letting $n = 1$}
and $u_3 = 2u_2 = 2 \times 6 = 12$ {letting $n = 2$}

etc.

In general,   if $u_n = u_1 r^{n-1}$ where u_1 and r are constants

then $u_{n+1} = r u_n$.

Example 19   ◆)) **Self Tutor**

Find the next 3 members of the sequence given by:

a $u_1 = 7$ and $u_{n+1} = u_n - 2$ **b** $u_1 = 24$ and $u_{n+1} = \frac{1}{2} u_n$

a   If $n = 1$, $u_2 = u_1 - 2$ **b**   If $n = 1$, $u_2 = \frac{1}{2} u_1$

$\qquad\qquad\qquad\quad = 7 - 2$ $\qquad\qquad\qquad\quad = \frac{1}{2} \times 24$

$\qquad\qquad\qquad\quad = 5$ $\qquad\qquad\qquad\quad = 12$

$\quad\;$ If $n = 2$, $u_3 = u_2 - 2$ $\quad\;$ If $n = 2$, $u_3 = \frac{1}{2} u_2$

$\qquad\qquad\qquad\quad = 5 - 2$ $\qquad\qquad\qquad\quad = \frac{1}{2} \times 12$

$\qquad\qquad\qquad\quad = 3$ $\qquad\qquad\qquad\quad = 6$

$\quad\;$ If $n = 3$, $u_4 = u_3 - 2$ $\quad\;$ If $n = 3$, $u_4 = \frac{1}{2} u_3$

$\qquad\qquad\qquad\quad = 3 - 2$ $\qquad\qquad\qquad\quad = \frac{1}{2} \times 6$

$\qquad\qquad\qquad\quad = 1$ $\qquad\qquad\qquad\quad = 3$

EXERCISE 17I

1   Find the next *three* members of the sequence defined by:

a $u_1 = 2$ and $u_{n+1} = u_n + 3$ **b** $u_1 = 11.7$ and $u_{n+1} = u_n - 2.1$

c $u_1 = 1268$ and $u_{n+1} = u_n + 23.9$ **d** $u_1 = 4$ and $u_{n+1} = 3 u_n$

e $u_1 = 1000$ and $u_{n+1} = \frac{1}{10} u_n$ **f** $u_1 = 128$ and $u_{n+1} = -\frac{1}{2} u_n$

Example 20   ◆)) **Self Tutor**

Find the explicit formula for u_n if:

a $u_{n+1} = u_n + 7$ and $u_1 = 5$ **b** $u_{n+1} = 0.4 u_n$ and $u_1 = 100$

a   We identify this sequence as arithmetic   Now $u_n = u_1 + (n-1)d$
$\quad$ with $d = 7$ $\quad\therefore\quad u_n = 5 + (n-1)7$

$\qquad\qquad\qquad\qquad\qquad\qquad\qquad$ i.e., $u_n = 7n - 2$

b   We identify this sequence as geometric   Now $u_n = u_1 r^{n-1}$
$\quad$ with $r = 0.4$ $\quad\therefore\quad u_n = 100 \times (0.4)^{n-1}$

---

2   Find the explicit formula for u_n if:

a $u_1 = 41$ and $u_{n+1} = u_n + 5$ **b** $u_1 = 11.8$ and $u_{n+1} = u_n - 1.7$

c $u_1 = 12$ and $u_{n+1} = \frac{1}{3} u_n$ **d** $u_1 = 36$ and $u_{n+1} = -\frac{1}{2} u_n$

Sequences do not have to be arithmetic or geometric.

For example, the Fibonacci sequence is neither arithmetic nor geometric.

Example 21   ◀)) **Self Tutor**

Given "$u_1 = 1$ and $u_{n+1} = 2u_n + 3$", for all positive integers n, find the next three terms of the sequence.

Letting $n = 1$, $u_2 = 2u_1 + 3 = 2(1) + 3 = 5$

Letting $n = 2$, $u_3 = 2u_2 + 3 = 2(5) + 3 = 13$

Letting $n = 3$, $u_4 = 2u_3 + 3 = 2(13) + 3 = 29$

---

3 Find the next three members of the sequences defined by:

    a $u_1 = 1$ and $u_{n+1} = 2u_n - 1$ **b** $u_{n+1} = 3 - u_n$ and $u_1 = 2$

    c $u_{n+1} = \frac{1}{3}u_n - 1$ and $u_1 = 3$ **d** $u_{n+1} = u_n^2 - 1$ and $u_1 = 1$

Some recurrence relationships relate any term to the previous *two* terms.

For example, "$u_1 = 1$, $u_2 = 3$ and $u_{n+2} = u_{n+1} - u_n$ for all positive integers n".

  Here   letting $n = 1$, $u_3 = u_2 - u_1 = 3 - 1 = 2$

           letting $n = 2$, $u_4 = u_3 - u_2 = 2 - 3 = -1$

           letting $n = 3$, $u_5 = u_4 - u_3 = -1 - 2 = -3$

4 Find the next four terms of the sequences defined by:

    a $u_1 = 1$, $u_2 = 0$ and $u_{n+2} = u_{n+1} - u_n$

    b $u_1 = u_2 = 1$ and $u_{n+2} = 2u_{n+1} + 3u_n$

5 Consider the sequence "$u_1 = 5$ and $u_{n+1} = \frac{1}{2}(u_n + \frac{2}{u_n})$ for positive integers n".

    a Use your calculator to find in decimal form u_2, u_3, u_4, u_5 and u_6.

    b Find $\sqrt{2}$ using your calculator. What do you notice?

    c Now use $u_1 = 10$ with the given recursive formula and repeat **a**.

    d Repeat again with $u_1 = 2$.

    e Comment on your findings from **c** and **d**.

6 Can you prove that "$u_1 = a$ and $u_{n+1} = \frac{1}{2}(u_n + \frac{2}{u_n})$" is a recursive formula for finding $\sqrt{2}$?

Sally thought this was easy and her starting comment was:

"As n gets larger, successive terms are virtually equal so we let u_n and u_{n+1} both be x say."

Complete Sally's argument.

INVESTIGATION 4   SEQUENCES IN FINANCE

Arithmetic and **geometric sequences** are observed in many financial calculations.

What to do:

1 $1000 is invested at a simple interest rate of 7% per year with the interest paid at the end of each year.

After 1 year, its value is 1000×1.07 {to increase by 7% we multiply by 107%}

After 2 years, its value is 1000×1.14 {an increase of 14% on the original}

   a Find the amount of the investment at the end of:

     i 3 years   **ii** 4 years   **iii** 5 years

   b Do the amounts form an arithmetic or geometric sequence (or neither of these)? Give reasons for your answer.

   c Give an explicit formula for finding any term u_n of the sequence being generated.

   d Give a recursive formula for the sequence.

2 Consider investing $6000 at a fixed rate of 7% p.a. compound interest over a lengthy period. The initial investment of $6000 is called the principal.

After 1 year, its value is 6000×1.07

After 2 years, its value is $(\$6000 \times 1.07) \times 1.07 = \$6000 \times (1.07)^2$

   a Explain why the amount after 3 years is given by $\$6000 \times (1.07)^3$.

   b Write down, in the same form, the amount after:

     i 4 years   **ii** 5 years   **iii** 6 years

   c Do the amounts at the end of each year form an arithmetic or geometric sequence (or neither of these)?

   d Give an explicit formula for finding any term u_n of the sequence being generated.

   e Give a recursive formula for the sequence.

3 A photocopier originally cost $12 000 and it depreciates in value (loses value) by 20% each year.

   a Find its value at the end of:

     i one year   **ii** two years   **iii** three years.

   b Do the resulting annual values form an arithmetic or geometric sequence?

   c If the answer to **b** is yes, find:

     i an explicit formula for finding its value at the end of the nth year

     ii a recursive formula for value determination.

J   WHERE FUNCTIONS MEET (EXTENSION)

Consider the graphs of a quadratic function and a linear function on the same set of axes.

Notice that we could have:

cutting
(2 points of intersection)

touching
(1 point of intersection)

missing
(no points of intersection)

If the graphs meet, the coordinates of the point(s) of intersection can be found by solving the two equations *simultaneously*.

Example 22   ◄) Self Tutor

Find the coordinates of the points of intersection of the graphs with equations
$y = x^2 - x - 18$ and $y = x - 3$.

$y = x^2 - x - 18$ meets $y = x - 3$ where

$$x^2 - x - 18 = x - 3$$
$$\therefore \quad x^2 - 2x - 15 = 0 \qquad \{\text{RHS} = 0\}$$
$$\therefore \quad (x - 5)(x + 3) = 0 \qquad \{\text{factorising}\}$$
$$\therefore \quad x = 5 \text{ or } -3$$

Substituting into $y = x - 3$,   when $x = 5$, $y = 2$ and when $x = -3$, $y = -6$.
$\therefore$ graphs meet at $(5, 2)$ and $(-3, -6)$.

EXERCISE 17J

1 Find the coordinates of the point(s) of intersection of the graphs with equations:

   a $y = x^2 - 2x + 8$ and $y = x + 6$
   b $y = \dfrac{2}{x}$ and $y = x - 1$

   c $y = -x^2 + 3x + 9$ and $y = 2x - 3$
   d $y = \dfrac{1}{x}$ and $y = 5x - 4$

   e $y = x^2 - 4x + 3$ and $y = 2x - 6$

2 Use a **graphing package** or a **graphics calculator** to find the coordinates of the points of intersection (to two decimal places) of the graphs with equations:

   a $y = x^2 - 3x + 7$ and $y = x + 5$

   b $y = x^2 - 5x + 2$ and $y = \dfrac{3}{x}$

   c $y = -x^2 - 2x + 4$ and $y = x^2 + 8$

   d $y = -x^2 + 4x - 2$ and $y = x^3$

REVIEW SET 17A

1 For the following graphs, determine:

      i the range and domain   **ii** whether the relation is a function

a
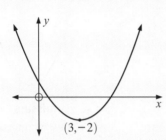

b
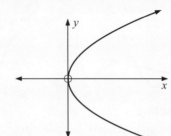

c
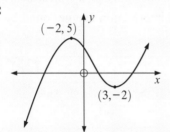

d
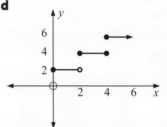

2 If $f(x) = 3x - x^2$, find: **a** $f(2)$ **b** $f(-1)$ **c** $f(\frac{1}{2})$

3 If $g : x \longmapsto x^2 - 3x$, find in simplest form: **a** $g(-x)$ **b** $g(x+2)$

4 A plumber charges a \$60 call out fee and \$48 per hour.

    a Copy and complete the following table:

hours (h)	0	1	2	3	4
Cost \$C					

    b Name the dependent and independent variables.

    c Graph C against h.

    d Find the linear model that connects the variables.

    e Find the cost of a plumbing job that took $6\frac{1}{4}$ hours.

5 The sum of two numbers is 57. Twice the larger number minus the smaller number is 36. Find the numbers.

6 Determine the equation of the rational function with the graph:

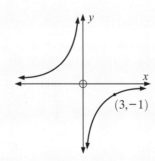

7 Consider the sequence $-6, -2, 2, 6, \ldots\ldots$

    a Show that the sequence is arithmetic.

    b Find a formula for the general term u_n.

    c Find the 100th term of the sequence.

    d Find the largest term that is less than 500.

8 Find the general term u_n of the geometric sequence which has $u_4 = 24$ and $u_7 = -192$.

9 Find the next three members of the sequence defined by $u_1 = 2$ and $u_{n+1} = 2u_n + 4$.

10 Find the coordinates of the points of intersection of the graphs with equations
$y = x^2 + 4x - 2$ and $y = 2x + 1$.

<h2 style="background:gray;color:white;">REVIEW SET 17B</h2>

1 For the following graphs, determine:

    i   the range and domain   **ii**   whether the relation is a function

a

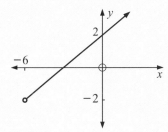

b

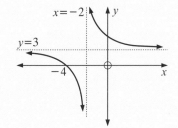

c

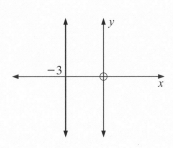

d

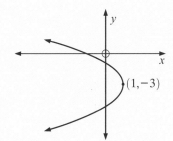

2 If $h(x) = 7 - 2x$,   find the value of:

    a $h(0)$ **b** $h(2)$ **c** $h(-3)$

3 If $f : x \longmapsto 5x - x^2$,   find in simplest form:

    a $f(-x)$ **b** $f(x+1)$

4 A company embroiders logos on clothing. The charge is a $40 set-up fee for the logo, and $5 for each logo sewn.

   a Copy and complete the following table:

number of logos (n)	0	1	2	3	4
Cost $C					

   b Name the dependent and independent variables.

   c Graph C against n.

   d Write down an algebraic relationship between C and n.

   e If a customer paid $430 for logos on business shirts, how many shirts were there?

5 Sam is having a barbeque. He finds that 3 chops and 2 sausages cost $7.80, but 2 chops and 5 sausages cost $7.40. Find the cost each of a sausage and a chop.

6 Find the general term u_n for an arithmetic sequence given that the third term is 24 and the 11th term is -36.

7 Show that the sequence $64, -32, 16, -8, 4, \ ......$ is geometric and hence find the 16th term (as a fraction).

8 $2k + 7$, $1 - k$ and $k - 7$ are the consecutive terms of a geometric sequence. Find k and hence find the three terms given.

9 Find the explicit formula for u_n if:

   a $u_{n+1} = u_n - 3$ and $u_1 = 7$
      b $u_1 = 24$ and $u_{n+1} = -\frac{2}{3}u_n$

10 Find the coordinates of the points of intersection of the graphs with equations $y = \dfrac{3}{x}$ and $y = 2x - 1$.

Chapter 18

Vectors

Contents:

OPENING PROBLEM

An aeroplane in calm conditions is flying due east. A cold wind suddenly blows in from the south west. The aeroplane, cruising at 800 km/h, is blown slightly off course by the 35 km/h wind.

- What effect does the wind have on the speed and direction of the aeroplane?
- How can we accurately determine the new speed and direction using mathematics?
- How much of the force of the wind operates in the direction of the aeroplane, and how does this affect fuel consumption and the time of the flight?

VECTORS AND SCALARS

In order to handle the **Opening Problem** and problems similar to it we need to examine the **size** or **magnitude** of the quantities under consideration as well as the direction in which they are acting.

For example, the effect of the wind on an aeroplane would be different if the wind was against the plane rather than behind it.

To handle these situations we need to consider quantities called vectors which have both size (magnitude) and direction.

Quantities which have only magnitude are called **scalars**.

Quantities which have both magnitude and direction are called **vectors**.

For example, *velocity* is a vector since it deals with speed (a scalar) in a particular direction.

Some other examples of vector quantities are: *acceleration, force* and *displacement*.

A   DIRECTED LINE SEGMENT REPRESENTATION

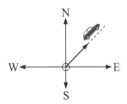

Consider the example where a car is travelling at 100 km/h in a NE direction.

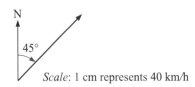

Scale: 1 cm represents 40 km/h

One good way of representing this is to use an arrow on a scale diagram.

The **length of the arrow** represents the size (magnitude) of the velocity and the **arrowhead** shows the direction of travel.

Consider the vector represented by the line segment from O to A.

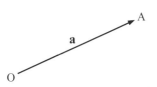

- This **vector** could be represented by

  $\overrightarrow{OA}$ or   **a**   or $\underline{a}$

                    ↑   ↑
              bold used   used by
              in text books   students

- The **magnitude** (**length**) could be represented by

  $|\overrightarrow{OA}|$ or   OA   or $|\mathbf{a}|$ or $|\underline{a}|$

For   the vector which **emanates** at A and **terminates** at B,

$\overrightarrow{AB}$ is the **position vector** of B relative to A.

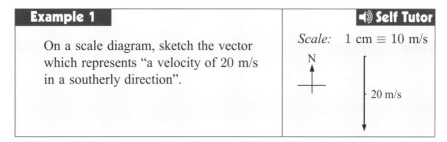

Example 1   ◀) **Self Tutor**

On a scale diagram, sketch the vector which represents "a velocity of 20 m/s in a southerly direction".

Scale: 1 cm ≡ 10 m/s

Example 2   ◀) **Self Tutor**

Draw a scaled arrow diagram representing '40 m/s on a bearing 115°'.

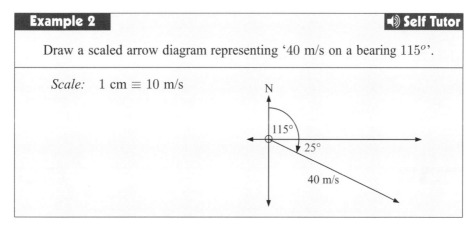

EXERCISE 18A.1

1   Using a scale of 1 cm represents 10 units, sketch a vector to represent:
    a   40 km/h in a SW direction
    b   35 m/s in a northerly direction
    c   a displacement of 25 m in a direction 120°
    d   an aeroplane taking off at an angle of 12° to the runway with a speed of 60 m/s.

2   If ⟶ represents a velocity of 30 m/s due east, draw a directed line segment representing a velocity of:
    a   90 m/s due west   b   75 m/s south west.

3 Draw a scaled arrow diagram representing the following vectors:

    a a velocity of 30 km/h in the SE direction

    b a velocity of 40 m/s in the direction $250°$

    c a displacement of 25 km in the direction N55°E

    d an aeroplane taking off at an angle of $10°$ to the runway at a speed of 180 km/h.

VECTOR EQUALITY

> Two vectors are **equal** if they have the same magnitude *and* direction.

So, if arrows are used to represent vectors, then equal vectors are **parallel** and **equal in length**.

This means that equal vector arrows are translations of one another.

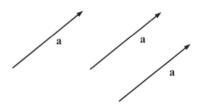

NEGATIVE VECTORS

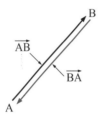

Notice that $\overrightarrow{AB}$ and $\overrightarrow{BA}$ have the same length but have opposite directions.

We say that $\overrightarrow{BA}$ is *the negative of* $\overrightarrow{AB}$ and write $\overrightarrow{BA} = -\overrightarrow{AB}$.

Also, given the vector **a** shown, we can draw the vector $-\mathbf{a}$.

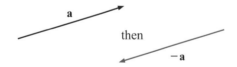

Notice the two vectors are parallel, equal in length, but opposite in direction.

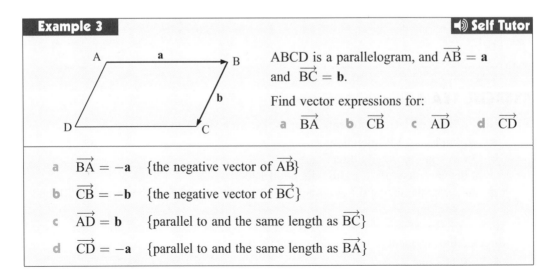

EXERCISE 18A.2

1   State the vectors which are:

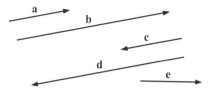

   a   equal in magnitude

   b   parallel

   c   in the same direction

   d   equal

   e   negatives of one another.

2   The figure alongside consists of 2 isosceles
triangles where $PQ \parallel SR$ and $\overrightarrow{PQ} = \mathbf{p}$, $\overrightarrow{PS} = \mathbf{q}$.

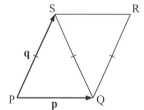

Which of the following statements are true?

   a $\overrightarrow{RS} = \mathbf{p}$ **b** $\overrightarrow{QR} = \mathbf{q}$ **c** $\overrightarrow{QS} = \mathbf{q}$

   d $|\overrightarrow{QS}| = |\overrightarrow{PS}|$ **e** $\overrightarrow{PS} = -\overrightarrow{RQ}$

DISCUSSION

Could we have a zero vector? What would its length be? What direction?

B   OPERATIONS WITH VECTORS

We have already been operating with vectors without realising it.

Bearing problems are an example of this. The vectors in this case are **displacements**.

A typical problem could be, "A girl runs from A in
an easterly direction for 4 km and then in a southerly
direction for 2 km to B.

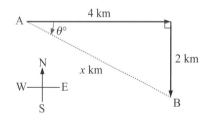

How far is she from her starting point and in what
direction?"

Notice that trigonometry and Pythagoras' theorem are used to answer such problems as we
need to find θ and x.

DISPLACEMENT VECTORS

Suppose we have three towns P, Q and R.

A trip from P to Q followed by a trip from Q to R is
equivalent to a trip from P to R.

This can be expressed in a vector form as

$\overrightarrow{PQ} + \overrightarrow{QR} = \overrightarrow{PR}$ where the $+$ sign
could mean '*followed by*'.

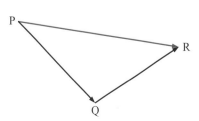

This triangular
diagram could take
all sorts of shapes.
For example

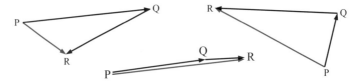

VECTOR ADDITION

After considering displacements in diagrams like those above, we define vector addition
geometrically as:

To add **a** and **b**   *Step 1:*   first draw **a**, then
                           Step 2:   at the arrowhead end of **a** draw **b**, and then
                           Step 3:   join the beginning of **a** to the arrowhead end
                                         of **b** and this is vector   **a** + **b**.

So given   we have   **a**+**b**

COMPUTER
DEMO

Example 4   ◀ͮ) **Self Tutor**

Find a single vector which is equal to:

a $\overrightarrow{AB} + \overrightarrow{BE}$ **b** $\overrightarrow{DC} + \overrightarrow{CA} + \overrightarrow{AE}$

c $\overrightarrow{CB} + \overrightarrow{BD} + \overrightarrow{DC}$

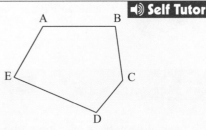

a $\overrightarrow{AB} + \overrightarrow{BE} = \overrightarrow{AE}$ {as shown}

b $\overrightarrow{DC} + \overrightarrow{CA} + \overrightarrow{AE} = \overrightarrow{DE}$

c $\overrightarrow{CB} + \overrightarrow{BD} + \overrightarrow{DC} = \overrightarrow{CC} = \mathbf{0}$ {zero vector}

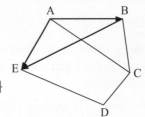

EXERCISE 18B.1

1 Copy the given vectors **p** and **q** and hence show how to find   **p** + **q**:

a 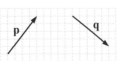   **b** 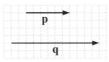   **c**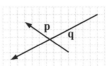

d 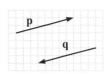   **e** 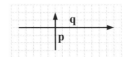   **f**

2 Find a single vector which is equal to:

    a $\overrightarrow{QR} + \overrightarrow{RS}$ **b** $\overrightarrow{PQ} + \overrightarrow{QR}$

    c $\overrightarrow{PS} + \overrightarrow{SR} + \overrightarrow{RQ}$ **d** $\overrightarrow{PR} + \overrightarrow{RQ} + \overrightarrow{QS}$

3 **a** Use vector diagrams to find **i** **p** + **q**   **ii** **q** + **p** given that

    p is   and **q** is 

    b For any two vectors **p** and **q**, is **p** + **q** = **q** + **p**?

Example 5   **◆⦂ Self Tutor**

Jason walks for 3.8 km in a direction 110° and then 2.7 km in a direction 020°. Find his distance and bearing from his starting position.

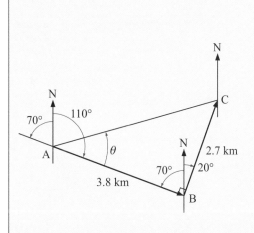

Angle ABC is $70^o + 20^o = 90^o$

Using Pythagoras' theorem:

$$AC^2 = 3.8^2 + 2.7^2$$

$$\therefore \quad AC = \sqrt{3.8^2 + 2.7^2}$$

$$\therefore \quad AC \doteqdot 4.66 \text{ km}$$

Using the tangent rule:

$$\tan\theta = \frac{2.7}{3.8}$$

$$\therefore \quad \theta = \tan^{-1}\left(\frac{2.7}{3.8}\right)$$

$$\therefore \quad \theta \doteqdot 35.4^o$$

and $110^o - 35.4^o \doteqdot 74.6^o$

So, Jason is 4.66 km from his starting point at a bearing of 074.6^o.

---

4 Paolo rides for 20 km in a direction 310° and then for 15 km in a direction 040°. Find Paolo's displacement from his starting point.

5 Gina drives along a straight highway for 42 km in a north-westerly direction and then along another road for 53 km in a north-easterly direction. Find her displacement from her starting position.

Another example of a vector is **velocity**.

When an object moves in a particular direction at a given speed we are describing its velocity.

| Example 6 | ◀)) Self Tutor |

Sonya can swim at 3 km/h in calm water. She swims in a river where the current is 1 km/h in an easterly direction. Find Sonya's resultant velocity if she swims
a   with the current   b   against the current   c   northwards, across the river.

Scale: 1 cm ≡ 1 km/h

Velocity vector of the river is

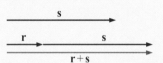

a   <u>With the current:</u>

Sonya's velocity vector is

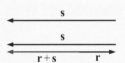

The net result is   **r** + **s**,   i.e.,

∴   Sonya swims at 4 km/h in the direction of the current.

b   <u>Against the current:</u>

Sonya's velocity vector is

The net result is   **r** + **s**

∴   Sonya swims at 2 km/h against the current.

c   <u>Northwards across the river:</u>

Sonya's velocity vector is   and the net result is   **r** + **s**

$\tan \theta = \frac{1}{3}$ ∴ $\theta = \tan^{-1}(\frac{1}{3}) \doteqdot 18.4^o$

∴ $|\mathbf{r} + \mathbf{s}| = \sqrt{10} \doteqdot 3.16$

∴   Sonya swims at about 3.16 km/h in the direction 018.4°.

6   Consider an aeroplane trying to fly at 500 km/h due north. Find the actual speed and direction of the aeroplane if a gale of 100 km/h is blowing:
   a   from the south   b   from the north   c   from the west.

7   If a vessel is trying to travel east at 10 km/h, what will be its actual speed and direction if there is a current of 10 km/h:
   a   from the east   b   from the west   c   from the south?

8   An aircraft flying at 400 km/h aiming due east encounters a 60 km/h wind from the north. Find the actual speed and direction of the aircraft.

9 A ship is travelling at 23 knots heading on a course 124° across a current of 4 knots in the direction 214°. Find the actual speed and direction of the ship.

Before defining vector subtraction it is necessary to look again at what we mean by **negative vectors**.

NEGATIVE VECTORS

$-\mathbf{a}$ is the **negative** of $\mathbf{a}$.

Notice that $-\mathbf{a}$ has the same magnitude as $\mathbf{a}$ but is in the opposite direction.

ZERO VECTOR

The **zero vector** is written as $\mathbf{0}$ and for any vector $\mathbf{a}$, $\mathbf{a} + (-\mathbf{a}) = (-\mathbf{a}) + \mathbf{a} = \mathbf{0}$.

VECTOR SUBTRACTION

To subtract one vector from another, we simply **add its negative**, i.e., $\mathbf{a} - \mathbf{b} = \mathbf{a} + (-\mathbf{b})$.

Geometrically:

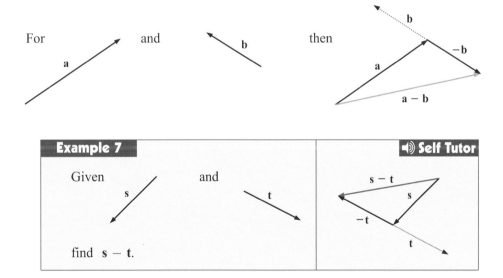

Example 7	◀ Self Tutor
Given $\mathbf{s}$ and $\mathbf{t}$ find $\mathbf{s} - \mathbf{t}$.	

EXERCISE 18B.2

1 For the following vectors $\mathbf{p}$ and $\mathbf{q}$ show how to construct $\mathbf{p} - \mathbf{q}$:

a
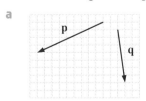

b
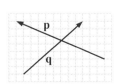

c
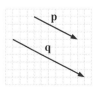

d
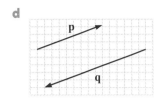

e
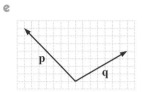

f
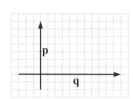

Vector subtraction is used in problem solving involving displacement, velocity and force.

Consider the following velocity application:

An aeroplane needs to fly due east from one city to another at a speed of 400 km/h. However a 50 km/h wind blows constantly from the north.

In what direction must the aeroplane head and at what speed must it travel?

Notice that on this occasion we know:

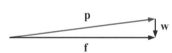

We also know that the aeroplane would have to head a little north of its final destination as the northerly wind would blow it back to its final direction.

So

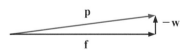

Even though the plane moves in the **f** direction it is actually lined up in the **p** direction.

Notice that $\mathbf{p} + \mathbf{w} = \mathbf{f}$ and   so $\mathbf{p} + \mathbf{w} + (-\mathbf{w}) = \mathbf{f} + (-\mathbf{w})$

$$\therefore \quad \mathbf{p} + \mathbf{0} = \mathbf{f} - \mathbf{w}$$

$$\text{i.e.,} \quad \mathbf{p} = \mathbf{f} - \mathbf{w}$$

The solution:

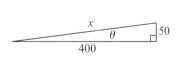

By Pythagoras' theorem,

$x^2 = 50^2 + 400^2$

gives $x = \sqrt{50^2 + 400^2} \doteqdot 403$

and

$\tan \theta = \dfrac{50}{400}$ gives $\theta = \tan^{-1}\left(\dfrac{50}{400}\right) \doteqdot 7.13^o$

Consequently, the aeroplane must fly 7.13^o north of east at 403 km/h.

2 An aeroplane needs to fly due north at a speed of 500 kmph. However, it is affected by a 40 kmph wind blowing constantly from the west. What direction must it head towards and at what speed?

3 A motor boat wishes to travel NW towards a safe haven at a speed of 30 kmph before an electrical storm arrives. However, a strong current is flowing at 10 kmph from the north east. In what direction and at what speed must the boat head?

Example 8 🔊 **Self Tutor**

For points P, Q, R and S, simplify the following vector expressions:

a $\overrightarrow{QR} - \overrightarrow{SR}$ **b** $\overrightarrow{QR} - \overrightarrow{SR} - \overrightarrow{PS}$

a $\overrightarrow{QR} - \overrightarrow{SR}$
$= \overrightarrow{QR} + \overrightarrow{RS}$ {as $\overrightarrow{RS} = -\overrightarrow{SR}$}
$= \overrightarrow{QS}$

b $\overrightarrow{QR} - \overrightarrow{SR} - \overrightarrow{PS}$
$= \overrightarrow{QR} + \overrightarrow{RS} + \overrightarrow{SP}$
$= \overrightarrow{QP}$

---

4 For points P, Q, R and S, simplify the following vector expressions:

a $\overrightarrow{QR} + \overrightarrow{RS}$ **b** $\overrightarrow{PS} - \overrightarrow{RS}$ **c** $\overrightarrow{RS} + \overrightarrow{SR}$

d $\overrightarrow{RS} + \overrightarrow{SP} + \overrightarrow{PQ}$ **e** $\overrightarrow{QP} - \overrightarrow{RP} + \overrightarrow{RS}$ **f** $\overrightarrow{RS} - \overrightarrow{PS} - \overrightarrow{QP}$

C VECTORS IN COMPONENT FORM

So far we have examined vectors from their geometric representation.

We have used arrows where:

- the **length** of the arrow represents size (magnitude)
- the **arrowhead** indicates direction.

Consider a car travelling at 100 km/h in a NE direction.

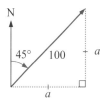

The velocity vector could be represented by using the x and y-steps which are necessary to go from the start to the finish.

In this case the ordered pair [70.7, 70.7] gives these x and y-steps.

$a^2 + a^2 = 100^2$
$\therefore\ 2a^2 = 10\,000$
$\therefore\ a^2 = 5000$
$\therefore\ a \doteqdot 70.7$

Note: **Arrows** (or **directed line segments**) and **ordered pairs** are interchangeable.

Writing a vector as an ordered pair is called **component form**,   i.e., $\begin{bmatrix} x\text{-component} \\ y\text{-component} \end{bmatrix}$.

For example,   given $\begin{bmatrix} -1 \\ 2 \end{bmatrix}$ we could draw   and vice versa.

-1 is the horizontal step and 2 is the vertical step.

EXERCISE 18C.1

1   Draw arrow diagrams to represent the vectors:

a $\begin{bmatrix} 4 \\ 2 \end{bmatrix}$

b $\begin{bmatrix} 0 \\ 3 \end{bmatrix}$

c $\begin{bmatrix} -2 \\ 5 \end{bmatrix}$

d $\begin{bmatrix} 3 \\ 4 \end{bmatrix}$

2   Write the illustrated vectors in component form:

a

b

c

d

e

f

Example 9   ◀》 **Self Tutor**

A car travels at a speed of 20 m/s in the direction 125°.
Write this as a vector in component form.

Sketch: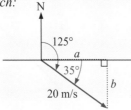

As $\cos 35^o = \dfrac{a}{20}$, $a = 20 \times \cos 35^o \doteqdot 16.4$

and $\sin 35^o = \dfrac{b}{20}$, $b = 20 \times \sin 35^o \doteqdot 11.5$

$\therefore$ the vector is $\begin{bmatrix} a \\ -b \end{bmatrix} \doteqdot \begin{bmatrix} 16.4 \\ -11.5 \end{bmatrix}$

---

3   Draw an arrow diagram representing the following vectors and hence write as an ordered pair:

a   a velocity of 60 m/s in the direction 120°

b   a displacement of 15 km in the direction 221°

c   an aeroplane on the runway taking off at an angle of 9° and a speed of 160 km/h.

VECTOR ADDITION

Consider adding vectors $\mathbf{a} = \begin{bmatrix} a_1 \\ a_2 \end{bmatrix}$ and $\mathbf{b} = \begin{bmatrix} b_1 \\ b_2 \end{bmatrix}$.

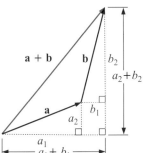

Notice that the

horizontal step for $\mathbf{a} + \mathbf{b}$ is $a_1 + b_1$ and the

vertical step for $\mathbf{a} + \mathbf{b}$ is $a_2 + b_2$.   So,

if $\mathbf{a} = \begin{bmatrix} a_1 \\ a_2 \end{bmatrix}$ and $\mathbf{b} = \begin{bmatrix} b_1 \\ b_2 \end{bmatrix}$ then $\mathbf{a} + \mathbf{b} = \begin{bmatrix} a_1 + b_1 \\ a_2 + b_2 \end{bmatrix}$.

Example 10   ◀) **Self Tutor**

If $\mathbf{a} = \begin{bmatrix} 2 \\ 5 \end{bmatrix}$ and $\mathbf{b} = \begin{bmatrix} 1 \\ -3 \end{bmatrix}$

find $\mathbf{a} + \mathbf{b}$.

Check graphically.

$\mathbf{a} + \mathbf{b} = \begin{bmatrix} 2 \\ 5 \end{bmatrix} + \begin{bmatrix} 1 \\ -3 \end{bmatrix} = \begin{bmatrix} 3 \\ 2 \end{bmatrix}$

> Start at the non-arrow end and move horizontally then vertically to the arrow end.

NEGATIVE VECTORS

Consider the vector $\mathbf{a} = \begin{bmatrix} 5 \\ 2 \end{bmatrix}$.

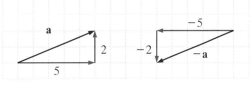

Notice that $-\mathbf{a} = \begin{bmatrix} -5 \\ -2 \end{bmatrix}$.

In general,   if $\mathbf{a} = \begin{bmatrix} a_1 \\ a_2 \end{bmatrix}$ then $-\mathbf{a} = \begin{bmatrix} -a_1 \\ -a_2 \end{bmatrix}$.

ZERO VECTOR

The zero vector is $\mathbf{0} = \begin{bmatrix} 0 \\ 0 \end{bmatrix}$ and for any vector $\mathbf{a}$, $\mathbf{a} + (-\mathbf{a}) = (-\mathbf{a}) + \mathbf{a} = \mathbf{0}$.

VECTOR SUBTRACTION

To subtract one vector from another, we simply **add its negative**,   i.e., $\mathbf{a} - \mathbf{b} = \mathbf{a} + (-\mathbf{b})$.

Notice that, if $\quad \mathbf{a} = \begin{bmatrix} a_1 \\ a_2 \end{bmatrix} \quad$ and $\quad \mathbf{b} = \begin{bmatrix} b_1 \\ b_2 \end{bmatrix}$

then $\quad \mathbf{a} - \mathbf{b} = \mathbf{a} + (-\mathbf{b}) = \begin{bmatrix} a_1 \\ a_2 \end{bmatrix} + \begin{bmatrix} -b_1 \\ -b_2 \end{bmatrix} = \begin{bmatrix} a_1 - b_1 \\ a_2 - b_2 \end{bmatrix}$

i.e., $\qquad$ if $\quad \mathbf{a} = \begin{bmatrix} a_1 \\ a_2 \end{bmatrix} \quad$ and $\quad \mathbf{b} = \begin{bmatrix} b_1 \\ b_2 \end{bmatrix} \quad$ then $\quad \mathbf{a} - \mathbf{b} = \begin{bmatrix} a_1 - b_1 \\ a_2 - b_2 \end{bmatrix}$.

THE LENGTH OF A VECTOR

By the theorem of Pythagoras, the **length** of $\begin{bmatrix} a_1 \\ a_2 \end{bmatrix}$ is $\sqrt{a_1^2 + a_2^2}$.

For example,   • the length of $\begin{bmatrix} 5 \\ 2 \end{bmatrix}$ is $\sqrt{5^2 + 2^2} = \sqrt{25 + 4} = \sqrt{29}$ units

• the length of $\begin{bmatrix} -4 \\ 3 \end{bmatrix}$ is $\sqrt{(-4)^2 + 3^2} = \sqrt{16 + 9} = 5$ units

EXERCISE 18C.2

1 If $\quad \mathbf{a} = \begin{bmatrix} 2 \\ -3 \end{bmatrix}, \quad \mathbf{b} = \begin{bmatrix} 3 \\ -1 \end{bmatrix}, \quad \mathbf{c} = \begin{bmatrix} -2 \\ -3 \end{bmatrix} \quad$ find:

a $\mathbf{a} + \mathbf{b}$ $\qquad$ b $\mathbf{b} + \mathbf{a}$ $\qquad$ c $\mathbf{b} + \mathbf{c}$ $\qquad$ d $\mathbf{c} + \mathbf{b}$

e $\mathbf{a} + \mathbf{c}$ $\qquad$ f $\mathbf{c} + \mathbf{a}$ $\qquad$ g $\mathbf{a} + \mathbf{a}$ $\qquad$ h $\mathbf{b} + \mathbf{a} + \mathbf{c}$

Example 11 ◀)) **Self Tutor**

Given $\quad \mathbf{p} = \begin{bmatrix} 3 \\ -2 \end{bmatrix} \quad$ and $\quad \mathbf{q} = \begin{bmatrix} 1 \\ 4 \end{bmatrix} \quad$ find: $\quad$ a $\mathbf{p} - \mathbf{q}$ $\quad$ b $\mathbf{q} - \mathbf{p}$

a $\quad \mathbf{p} - \mathbf{q}$

$= \begin{bmatrix} 3 \\ -2 \end{bmatrix} - \begin{bmatrix} 1 \\ 4 \end{bmatrix}$

$= \begin{bmatrix} 2 \\ -6 \end{bmatrix}$

b $\quad \mathbf{q} - \mathbf{p}$

$= \begin{bmatrix} 1 \\ 4 \end{bmatrix} - \begin{bmatrix} 3 \\ -2 \end{bmatrix}$

$= \begin{bmatrix} -2 \\ 6 \end{bmatrix}$

---

2 Given $\quad \mathbf{p} = \begin{bmatrix} -1 \\ 3 \end{bmatrix}, \quad \mathbf{q} = \begin{bmatrix} -2 \\ -3 \end{bmatrix} \quad$ and $\quad \mathbf{r} = \begin{bmatrix} 3 \\ -4 \end{bmatrix} \quad$ find:

a $\mathbf{p} - \mathbf{q}$ $\qquad$ b $\mathbf{q} - \mathbf{r}$ $\qquad$ c $\mathbf{p} + \mathbf{q} - \mathbf{r}$

d $\mathbf{p} - \mathbf{q} - \mathbf{r}$ $\qquad$ e $\mathbf{q} - \mathbf{r} - \mathbf{p}$ $\qquad$ f $\mathbf{r} + \mathbf{q} - \mathbf{p}$

3 Find the length of these vectors:

a $\begin{bmatrix} 1 \\ 4 \end{bmatrix}$ $\quad$ b $\begin{bmatrix} 6 \\ 0 \end{bmatrix}$ $\quad$ c $\begin{bmatrix} 3 \\ -2 \end{bmatrix}$ $\quad$ d $\begin{bmatrix} -1 \\ -5 \end{bmatrix}$ $\quad$ e $\begin{bmatrix} -4 \\ 2 \end{bmatrix}$ $\quad$ f $\begin{bmatrix} -6 \\ -1 \end{bmatrix}$

D FURTHER PROBLEM SOLVING (EXTENSION)

Example 12   ◄) **Self Tutor**

An aeroplane heads in the direction 148° at a speed of 200 km/h. A wind blows from the direction 123° at a constant speed of 35 km/h.

a Write the aeroplane's velocity vector in component form.

b Write the wind's velocity vector in component form.

c Find the resulting velocity vector of the aeroplane.

d Hence find the actual speed and direction of the aeroplane.

a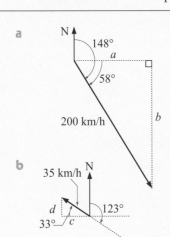

As $\cos 58^o = \dfrac{a}{200}$, $a = 200 \times \cos 58^o \doteqdot 106.0$

and $\sin 58^o = \dfrac{b}{200}$, $b = 200 \times \sin 58^o \doteqdot 169.6$

$\therefore$ the plane's vector is $\begin{bmatrix} a \\ -b \end{bmatrix} \doteqdot \begin{bmatrix} 106.0 \\ -169.6 \end{bmatrix}$

b

As $\cos 33^o = \dfrac{c}{35}$, $c = 35 \times \cos 33^o \doteqdot 29.4$

and $\sin 33^o = \dfrac{d}{35}$, $d = 35 \times \sin 33^o \doteqdot 19.1$

$\therefore$ the wind's vector is $\begin{bmatrix} -c \\ d \end{bmatrix} \doteqdot \begin{bmatrix} -29.4 \\ 19.1 \end{bmatrix}$

c The resultant velocity vector is $\begin{bmatrix} 106.0 \\ -169.6 \end{bmatrix} + \begin{bmatrix} -29.4 \\ 19.1 \end{bmatrix} = \begin{bmatrix} 76.6 \\ -150.5 \end{bmatrix}$

d The length of $\begin{bmatrix} 76.6 \\ -150.5 \end{bmatrix}$ is $\sqrt{(76.6)^2 + (-150.5)^2} \doteqdot 169.$

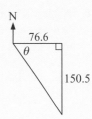

Since $\tan \theta = (\dfrac{150.5}{76.6})$ we find $\theta \doteqdot 63.0^o.$

Hence the plane's direction is $(90 + \theta)^o \doteqdot 153^o.$

So, the aeroplane is travelling at 169 km/h in the direction 153°

EXERCISE 18D

1 An aeroplane heads in the direction 48° at a speed of 300 km/h. A wind blows from the direction 167° at a constant speed of 45 km/h.

a Write the aeroplane's velocity vector in component form.

b Write the wind's velocity vector in component form.

c Find the resulting velocity vector of the aeroplane.

d Hence find the actual speed and direction of the aeroplane.

2 Use the Cosine and Sine rules to redo **Example 12**.

3 Use the Cosine and Sine rules to redo question **1**.

4 When would the component vector method be preferable to use over the Cosine/Sine rule method?

REVIEW SET 18

1 Using a scale of 1 cm represents 10 units, sketch a vector to represent:

    a an aeroplane taking off at an angle of 8° to the runway with a speed of 60 m/s

    b a displacement of 45 m in a direction 060°.

2 For the following vectors **p**, **q** and **r**, show how to construct:

    a $\mathbf{p} - \mathbf{q} + \mathbf{r}$ **b** $\mathbf{r} - \mathbf{q} - \mathbf{p}$

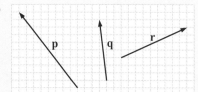

3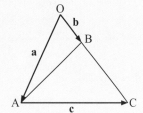

In the figure alongside, $\overrightarrow{OA} = \mathbf{a}$, $\overrightarrow{OB} = \mathbf{b}$, and $\overrightarrow{AC} = \mathbf{c}$.

Find in terms of **a**, **b** and **c**:

    a $\overrightarrow{CA}$ **b** $\overrightarrow{AB}$ **c** $\overrightarrow{OC}$ **d** $\overrightarrow{BC}$

4 For points A, B, C and D, simplify the following vector expressions:

    a $\overrightarrow{AB} + \overrightarrow{BD}$ **b** $\overrightarrow{BC} - \overrightarrow{DC}$ **c** $\overrightarrow{AB} - \overrightarrow{CB} + \overrightarrow{CD} - \overrightarrow{AD}$

5 A yacht is moving at 10 km/h in a south easterly direction and encounters a 3 km/h current from the north. Find the actual speed and direction of the yacht.

6 A pilot wishes to fly his aeroplane due east at a speed of 200 km/h. However, he is hampered by a wind blowing constantly at 40 km/h from the north-east. In what direction must he head and at what speed?

7 If $\mathbf{p} = \begin{bmatrix} 4 \\ 3 \end{bmatrix}$, $\mathbf{q} = \begin{bmatrix} 3 \\ -5 \end{bmatrix}$ and $\mathbf{r} = \begin{bmatrix} 0 \\ -4 \end{bmatrix}$, find:

    a $\mathbf{p} + \mathbf{q} - \mathbf{r}$ **b** $\mathbf{p} - \mathbf{q} - \mathbf{r}$ **c** the length of **q**.

8 A kayak is paddled in the direction 45° at a speed of 12 km/h. A wind blows from the direction 130° at a constant speed of 5 km/h.

    a Write the kayak's velocity vector in component form.

    b Write the wind's velocity vector in component form.

    c Find the resulting velocity vector of the kayak.

    d Hence find the actual speed and direction of the kayak.

Chapter 19

Exponential functions

Contents:

We often deal with numbers that are repeatedly multiplied together. Mathematicians use **indices** or **exponents** to represent such expressions. For example $5 \times 5 \times 5 = 5^3$.

Indices have many applications in areas such as finance, engineering, physics, biology, electronics and computer science.

Problems encountered in these areas may involve quantities that increase or decrease over time. These may be examples of **exponential growth** or **decay**.

OPENING PROBLEM

In 1995, scientists started testing the rabbit calicivirus on Wardang Island in an attempt to eradicate rabbits. The island was relatively isolated and overrun by rabbits and it thus provided an excellent test site. The disease was found to be highly contagious and the introduction of the virus had a dramatic impact on the island's rabbit population.

Scientists monitored rabbit numbers over a series of weeks and found that the number of rabbits R, could be predicted by the formula

$R = 8000 \times (0.837)^t$ where t is the number of weeks after the calicivirus was released.

Consider the following questions:

1 If we let $t = 0$ weeks, how many rabbits were on the island?

2 If we let $t = 3\frac{1}{2}$ weeks, we get $R = 8000 \times (0.837)^{3.5}$.
   Discuss 'to the power of 3.5'.

3 How long would it take to reduce the rabbit numbers to 80?

4 Will all rabbits ever be eradicated?

5 What would the graph of rabbit numbers plotted against the time after the release of the virus look like?

A   REVISION OF INDEX LAWS

Recall the following **index laws** where the bases a and b are both positive and the indices m and n are integers.

- $a^m \times a^n = a^{m+n}$ To **multiply** numbers with the **same base**, keep the base and **add** the indices.

- $\dfrac{a^m}{a^n} = a^{m-n}$ To **divide** numbers with the same base, keep the base and **subtract** the indices.

- $(a^m)^n = a^{m \times n}$ When **raising** a **power** to a **power**, keep the base and **multiply** the indices.

- $(ab)^n = a^n b^n$ The power of a product is the product of the powers.

- $\left(\dfrac{a}{b}\right)^n = \dfrac{a^n}{b^n}$ The power of a quotient is the quotient of the powers.

- $a^o = 1$, $a \neq 0$ Any non-zero number raised to the power of zero is 1.

- $a^{-n} = \dfrac{1}{a^n}$ and $\dfrac{1}{a^{-n}} = a^n$ and in particular $a^{-1} = \dfrac{1}{a}$.

EXERCISE 19A

1 Simplify using $a^m \times a^n = a^{m+n}$:

a $3^2 \times 3^5$	b $4^3 \times 4^2$	c $x^6 \times x^3$	d $x^9 \times x$
e $y^5 \times y^4$	f $x^5 \times x^n$	g $y^m \times y^2$	h $t^3 \times t^4 \times t^5$

2 Simplify using $\dfrac{a^m}{a^n} = a^{m-n}$:

a $\dfrac{3^6}{3^2}$	b $\dfrac{7^9}{7^5}$	c $8^4 \div 8^3$	d $\dfrac{x^7}{x^3}$
e $\dfrac{y^9}{y^4}$	f $\dfrac{t^6}{t^x}$	g $\dfrac{p^n}{p^2}$	h $t^{3m} \div t$

3 Simplify using $(a^m)^n = a^{mn}$:

a $(5^3)^2$	b $(3^4)^5$	c $(2^3)^6$	d $(t^4)^3$
e $(x^2)^7$	f $(y^3)^m$	g $(m^a)^5$	h $(a^{3m})^4$

Example 1   ◀)) **Self Tutor**

Express in simplest form with a prime number base:

a 9^4 b 4×2^p c $\dfrac{3^x}{9^y}$ d 25^{x-1}

a 9^4
$= (3^2)^4$
$= 3^{2\times4}$
$= 3^8$

b 4×2^p
$= 2^2 \times 2^p$
$= 2^{2+p}$

c $\dfrac{3^x}{9^y}$
$= \dfrac{3^x}{(3^2)^y}$
$= \dfrac{3^x}{3^{2y}}$
$= 3^{x-2y}$

d 25^{x-1}
$= (5^2)^{x-1}$
$= 5^{2(x-1)}$
$= 5^{2x-2}$

---

4 Express in simplest form with a prime number base:

a 4	b 16	c 27	d 4^2
e 25^2	f $2^t \times 8$	g $3^a \div 3$	h $2^n \times 4^n$
i $\dfrac{9}{3^x}$	j $\dfrac{5^{n+2}}{5^{n-2}}$	k $(3^4)^{a+1}$	l $3^x \times 3^{4-x}$
m $\dfrac{4^a}{2^b}$	n $\dfrac{8^x}{16^y}$	o $\dfrac{5^{1+x}}{5^{x-1}}$	p $\dfrac{3^a \times 9^a}{27^{a+2}}$

Example 2

🔊 **Self Tutor**

Remember that each factor within the brackets has to be raised to the power outside them.

Remove the brackets of: **a** $(2x)^3$ **b** $\left(\dfrac{3c}{b}\right)^4$

a $(2x)^3$
$= 2^3 \times x^3$
$= 8x^3$

b $\left(\dfrac{3c}{b}\right)^4$

$= \dfrac{3^4 \times c^4}{b^4}$

$= \dfrac{81c^4}{b^4}$

5 Remove the brackets of:

a $(xy)^2$ **b** $(ab)^3$ **c** $(rs)^4$ **d** $(xyz)^2$

e $(2a)^3$ **f** $(3b)^3$ **g** $(5a)^4$ **h** $(3xy)^3$

i $(10xy)^5$ **j** $\left(\dfrac{p}{q}\right)^2$ **k** $\left(\dfrac{m}{n}\right)^3$ **l** $\left(\dfrac{2a}{b}\right)^4$

6 Simplify the following expressions using one or more of the index laws:

a $\dfrac{x^4}{x}$ **b** $4b^2 \times 2b^3$ **c** $\dfrac{a^6 b^3}{a^4 b}$

d $\dfrac{18x^6}{3x^3}$ **e** $\dfrac{5x^3 y^2}{15xy}$ **f** $\dfrac{24t^6 r^4}{15t^6 r^2}$

g $3pq^3 \times 5p^5$ **h** $\dfrac{x^{12}}{(x^3)^2}$ **i** $\dfrac{t^6 \times t^4}{(t^2)^3}$

Notice that
$$\left(\frac{a}{b}\right)^{-2} = \left(\frac{b}{a}\right)^2$$

Example 3

🔊 **Self Tutor**

Simplify, giving answers in simplest rational form:

a 7^0 **b** 3^{-2} **c** $3^0 - 3^{-1}$ **d** $\left(\dfrac{5}{3}\right)^{-2}$

a 7^0
$= 1$

b 3^{-2}
$= \dfrac{1}{3^2}$
$= \dfrac{1}{9}$

c $3^0 - 3^{-1}$
$= 1 - \dfrac{1}{3}$
$= \dfrac{2}{3}$

d $\left(\dfrac{5}{3}\right)^{-2}$
$= \left(\dfrac{3}{5}\right)^2$
$= \dfrac{9}{25}$

7 Simplify, giving answers in simplest rational form:

a 3^0 **b** 6^{-1} **c** 4^{-1} **d** 5^0

e 3^2 **f** 3^{-2} **g** 5^3 **h** 5^{-3}

i 7^2 **j** 7^{-2} **k** 10^3 **l** 10^{-3}

8 Simplify, giving answers in simplest rational form:

a $\left(\frac{1}{2}\right)^0$

b $\dfrac{5^4}{5^4}$

c $2t^0$

d $(2t)^0$

e 7^0

f 3×4^0

g $\dfrac{5^3}{5^5}$

h $\dfrac{2^6}{2^{10}}$

i $\left(\frac{1}{4}\right)^{-1}$

j $\left(\frac{3}{8}\right)^{-1}$

k $\left(\frac{2}{3}\right)^{-1}$

l $\left(\frac{1}{5}\right)^{-1}$

m $2^0 + 2^1$

n $5^0 - 5^{-1}$

o $3^0 + 3^1 - 3^{-1}$

p $\left(\frac{1}{3}\right)^{-2}$

q $\left(\frac{2}{3}\right)^{-3}$

r $\left(1\frac{1}{2}\right)^{-3}$

s $\left(\frac{5}{3}\right)^{-2}$

t $\left(2\frac{1}{2}\right)^{-2}$

Example 4   ◄)) **Self Tutor**

Write the following without brackets or negative indices:

a $(5x)^{-1}$ b $5x^{-1}$ c $(3b^2)^{-2}$

a $(5x)^{-1}$

$= \dfrac{1}{5x}$

b $5x^{-1}$

$= \dfrac{5}{x}$

c $(3b^2)^{-2}$

$= \dfrac{1}{(3b^2)^2}$

$= \dfrac{1}{3^2 b^4}$

$= \dfrac{1}{9b^4}$

In $5x^{-1}$ the index -1 refers to the x only.

---

9 Write the following without brackets or negative indices:

a $(3b)^{-1}$

b $3b^{-1}$

c $7a^{-1}$

d $(7a)^{-1}$

e $\left(\frac{1}{t}\right)^{-2}$

f $(4t)^{-2}$

g $(5t)^{-2}$

h $(5t^{-2})^{-1}$

i xy^{-1}

j $(xy)^{-1}$

k xy^{-3}

l $(xy)^{-3}$

m $(3pq)^{-1}$

n $3(pq)^{-1}$

o $3pq^{-1}$

p $\dfrac{(xy)^3}{y^{-2}}$

10 Find the smaller of 2^{175} and 5^{75} without a calculator.

(**Hint:** $2^{175} = (2^7)^{25}$)

INVESTIGATION 1   RATIONAL (FRACTIONAL) INDICES

This investigation will help you discover the meaning of numbers raised to fractional (rational) indices, for example, $5^{\frac{1}{2}}, 7^{\frac{1}{3}}$ etc.

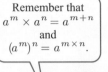

Remember that
$a^m \times a^n = a^{m+n}$
and
$(a^m)^n = a^{m \times n}$.

What to do:

1 Copy and complete the following:

a $5^{\frac{1}{2}} \times 5^{\frac{1}{2}} = 5^{\frac{1}{2}+\frac{1}{2}} = 5^1 = 5$

b $\sqrt{5} \times \sqrt{5} = 5$

c $3^{\frac{1}{2}} \times 3^{\frac{1}{2}} = \text{......} = \text{......} = \text{......}$

d $\sqrt{3} \times \sqrt{3} = \text{......}$

e $13^{\frac{1}{2}} \times 13^{\frac{1}{2}} = \text{......} = \text{......} = \text{.......}$

f $\sqrt{13} \times \sqrt{13} = \text{......}$

2 Copy and complete the following:

a $(7^{\frac{1}{3}})^3 = 7^{\frac{1}{3} \times 3} = 7^1 = 7$

b $(\sqrt[3]{7})^3 = 7$

c $(8^{\frac{1}{3}})^3 = \text{.......} = \text{.......} = \text{......}$

d $(\sqrt[3]{8})^3 = \text{......}$

e $(27^{\frac{1}{3}})^3 = \text{......} = \text{......} = \text{.......}$

f $(\sqrt[3]{27})^3 = \text{.......}$

$\sqrt[3]{7}$ is read as "the cube root of 7".

3 Suggest a rule for **a** $a^{\frac{1}{2}} = \text{.....}$ **b** $a^{\frac{1}{3}} = \text{.....}$ **c** the general case: $a^{\frac{1}{n}} = \text{.....}$

B   RATIONAL (FRACTIONAL) INDICES

Notice that $(a^{\frac{1}{2}})^2 = a^{\frac{1}{2} \times 2} = a^1 = a$ {using the law $(a^m)^n = a^{m \times n}$}

But, $(\sqrt{a})^2 = a$,   and so we conclude that $a^{\frac{1}{2}} = \sqrt{a}$.

Likewise, since $(a^{\frac{1}{3}})^3 = a$ and $(\sqrt[3]{a})^3 = a$ we conclude that $a^{\frac{1}{3}} = \sqrt[3]{a}$.

In general, we define $a^{\frac{1}{n}} = \sqrt[n]{a}$. { $\sqrt[n]{a}$ is the nth root of a}

Example 5			◀) Self Tutor

Simplify: **a** $49^{\frac{1}{2}}$ **b** $27^{\frac{1}{3}}$ **c** $49^{-\frac{1}{2}}$ **d** $27^{-\frac{1}{3}}$

a $49^{\frac{1}{2}}$

$= \sqrt{49}$

$= 7$

b $27^{\frac{1}{3}}$

$= \sqrt[3]{27}$

$= 3$

c $49^{-\frac{1}{2}}$

$= \dfrac{1}{49^{\frac{1}{2}}}$

$= \dfrac{1}{\sqrt{49}}$

$= \dfrac{1}{7}$

d $27^{-\frac{1}{3}}$

$= \dfrac{1}{27^{\frac{1}{3}}}$

$= \dfrac{1}{\sqrt[3]{27}}$

$= \dfrac{1}{3}$

EXERCISE 19B

1 Evaluate the following without using a calculator:

a $4^{\frac{1}{2}}$	b $4^{-\frac{1}{2}}$	c $16^{\frac{1}{2}}$	d $16^{-\frac{1}{2}}$
e $25^{\frac{1}{2}}$	f $25^{-\frac{1}{2}}$	g $8^{\frac{1}{3}}$	h $8^{-\frac{1}{3}}$
i $64^{\frac{1}{3}}$	j $64^{-\frac{1}{3}}$	k $32^{\frac{1}{5}}$	l $32^{-\frac{1}{5}}$
m $125^{\frac{1}{3}}$	n $(-125)^{\frac{1}{3}}$	o $(-1)^{\frac{1}{2}}$	p $(-1)^{\frac{1}{3}}$

Example 6   ◀)) **Self Tutor**

Write each of the following in index form:

a $\sqrt{5}$ b $\sqrt[3]{11}$ c $\dfrac{1}{\sqrt[4]{13}}$

a $\sqrt{5}$
$= 5^{\frac{1}{2}}$

b $\sqrt[3]{11}$
$= 11^{\frac{1}{3}}$

c $\dfrac{1}{\sqrt[4]{13}}$
$= \dfrac{1}{13^{\frac{1}{4}}}$
$= 13^{-\frac{1}{4}}$

---

2 Write each of the following in index form:

a $\sqrt{10}$	b $\dfrac{1}{\sqrt{10}}$	c $\sqrt[3]{15}$	d $\dfrac{1}{\sqrt[3]{15}}$
e $\sqrt[4]{19}$	f $\dfrac{1}{\sqrt[4]{19}}$	g $\sqrt[5]{13}$	h $\dfrac{1}{\sqrt[5]{13}}$

Example 7   ◀)) **Self Tutor**

Use your calculator to find: a $\sqrt[5]{32}$ b $\sqrt[4]{3.25}$

a Press: 32 $\boxed{\wedge}$ $\boxed{(}$ 1 $\boxed{\div}$ 5 $\boxed{)}$ $\boxed{\text{ENTER}}$ *Answer:* 2

b Press: 3.25 $\boxed{\wedge}$ $\boxed{(}$ 1 $\boxed{\div}$ 4 $\boxed{)}$ $\boxed{\text{ENTER}}$ *Answer:* ≑ 1.343

---

3 Use your calculator to evaluate, correct to 4 significant figures, where necessary:

a $\sqrt[3]{64}$	b $\sqrt[4]{81}$	c $\sqrt[5]{1024}$	d $\sqrt[3]{200}$
e $\sqrt[4]{400}$	f $\sqrt[5]{1000}$	g $\sqrt[7]{128}$	h $\sqrt[3]{10.83}$

Example 8

Evaluate to 3 significant figures where appropriate: **a** $8^{\frac{2}{3}}$ **b** $18^{-\frac{4}{3}}$

Answer

a Press: 8 ^ (2 ÷ 3) ENTER   4

b Press   18 ^ ((−) 4 ÷ 3) ENTER   0.0212

or press   18 x^y (4 +/− ÷ 3) =

4 Use your calculator to evaluate, correct to 3 significant figures, where necessary:

a $4^{\frac{3}{2}}$ **b** $27^{\frac{2}{3}}$ **c** $8^{\frac{4}{3}}$ **d** $9^{\frac{2}{5}}$ **e** $10^{\frac{3}{7}}$

f $4^{-\frac{5}{2}}$ **g** $27^{-\frac{5}{3}}$ **h** $15^{-\frac{2}{5}}$ **i** $53^{-\frac{3}{7}}$ **j** $3^{-\frac{7}{5}}$

C   EXPONENTIAL FUNCTIONS

Consider a population of 100 mice which is growing under plague conditions.

If the population doubles each week we can construct a **table** to show the population number (P) after t weeks.

t (weeks)	0	1	2	3	4	......
P	100	200	400	800	1600	......

We can also represent this information graphically as shown below:

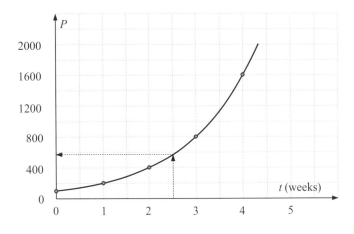

If we use a smooth curve to join the points, we can predict the mouse population when $t = 2.5$ weeks!

Can we find a relationship between P and t?   Examine the following:

t	P values
0	$100 = 100 \times 2^0$
1	$200 = 100 \times 2^1$
2	$400 = 100 \times 2^2$
3	$800 = 100 \times 2^3$
4	$1600 = 100 \times 2^4$

So, the relationship which connects P and t is

$$P = 100 \times 2^t.$$

This is an **exponential relationship** and the graph is an **exponential graph**.

t is an **index** or **exponent**.

Notice that P is a **function** of t, so we can write $P(t) = 100 \times 2^t$.

In the table above we have evaluated $P(t)$ for various values of t.

EVALUATING EXPONENTIAL FUNCTIONS

Recall that if we are asked to find $f(a)$, we find the value of the function $f(x)$ when $x = a$.

Example 9   ◀)) **Self Tutor**

For the function $f(x) = 2^x + 3$, find: a $f(0)$ b $f(2)$ c $f(-2)$

a $f(0) = 2^0 + 3$ b $f(2) = 2^2 + 3$ c $f(-2) = 2^{-2} + 3$
$\qquad = 1 + 3$ $\qquad\qquad = 4 + 3$ $\qquad\qquad\quad = \frac{1}{4} + 3$
$\qquad = 4$ $\qquad\qquad\qquad = 7$ $\qquad\qquad\qquad = 3\frac{1}{4}$

EXERCISE 19C.1

1 If $f(x) = 2^x - 3$ find the value of:
   a $f(0)$ b $f(1)$ c $f(2)$ d $f(-1)$ e $f(-2)$

2 If $f(x) = 2 \times 3^x$ find the value of:
   a $f(0)$ b $f(1)$ c $f(2)$ d $f(-1)$ e $f(-2)$

3 If $g(x) = 2^{x-1}$ find the value of:
   a $g(0)$ b $g(1)$ c $g(3)$ d $g(-1)$ e $g(-3)$

4 If $h(x) = 2^{-x}$ find the value of:
   a $h(0)$ b $h(2)$ c $h(4)$ d $h(-2)$ e $h(-4)$

5 If $P(x) = 3 \times 2^{-x}$ find the value of:
   a $P(0)$ b $P(1)$ c $P(-1)$ d $P(2)$ e $P(-2)$

GRAPHING SIMPLE EXPONENTIAL FUNCTIONS

We will consider the simplest exponential function $y = 2^x$.

A **table of values** can be constructed for $y = 2^x$.

x	-3	-2	-1	0	1	2	3
y	$\frac{1}{8}$	$\frac{1}{4}$	$\frac{1}{2}$	1	2	4	8

If $x = -3$,   If $x = 0$,   If $x = 3$,

$y = 2^{-3}$ $y = 2^0$ $y = 2^3$

$= \frac{1}{8}$ $= 1$ $= 8$

Graph of $y = 2^x$:

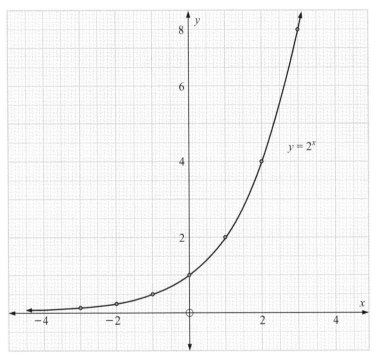

Graph to the left of the y-axis gets closer to the x-axis but always lies above it.

Graph to the right of the y-axis becomes very steep as x values increase.

HORIZONTAL ASYMPTOTE

We say that the graph of $y = 2^x$ is **asymptotic** to the x-axis, or the x-axis is a **horizontal asymptote** for the graph of $y = 2^x$.

All exponential graphs have a horizontal asymptote, but not necessarily the x-axis.

EXERCISE 19C.2

1 Alongside is the graph of $y = 2^x$.
Use the graph to estimate, to one
decimal place, the value of:

    a $2^{0.5}$ (find the y-value
              when $x = 0.5$)

    b $2^{1.5}$

    c $2^{2.5}$

    d Check your estimations using the

        $\boxed{\wedge}$ key of your calculator.

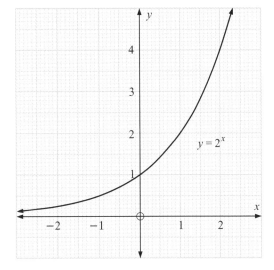

2 Alongside is the graph of $y = 3^x$.

    a Use the graph to estimate, to one
        decimal place, the value of:

        i 3^0 **ii** 3^1
        iii $3^{0.5}$ **iv** $3^{1.5}$

    b Check your estimations using the
        $\boxed{\wedge}$ key of your calculator.

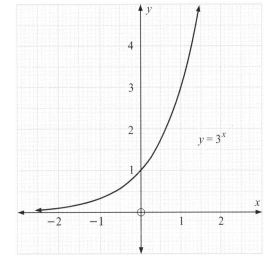

We have used the graphs of $y = 2^x$ and $y = 3^x$ to find the value of numbers raised to
decimal powers.

Exponential graphs can also be used to solve **exponential equations**.

3 **a** Use the graph of $y = 2^x$ in question **1** to estimate x to one decimal place if:

        i $2^x = 4$ **ii** $2^x = 5$ **iii** $2^x = 1$ **iv** $2^x = 2.5$

        (Hint: In **i** find the x value of a point on the graph with a y-value of 4.)

  b Check your estimations using the $\boxed{\wedge}$ key on your calculator.

4 **a** Use the graph of $y = 3^x$ in question **2** to estimate x to one decimal place if:
        i $3^x = 3$ **ii** $3^x = 5$ **iii** $3^x = 1$ **iv** $3^x = 0.8$

  b Check your estimations using your calculator.

Example 10   ◀) **Self Tutor**

a   *Without using technology*, sketch the graph of $y = 2^x$ and $y = 2^x + 1$ on the same set of axes.

b   State the equation of the horizontal asymptote of $y = 2^x + 1$.

c   To graph $y = 2^x + 1$ from $y = 2^x$ what transformation is used?

a

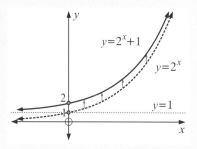

b $y = 1$

c   A vertical translation of $\begin{bmatrix} 0 \\ 1 \end{bmatrix}$.

---

5   Consider the following exponential functions:

    a $y = 2^x + 3$ **b** $y = 2^x - 1$ **c** $y = 2^x - 2$

    i   On separate axes, *without using technology*, sketch the graphs.

    ii   State the y-intercept and the equation of the horizontal asymptote.

    iii   Describe the transformation required to draw the graph of each function from the graph of $y = 2^x$.

    iv   Use a **graphing package** or **graphics calculator** to check each of your results.

6   Consider the following exponential functions:

    a $y = 2 \times 2^x$ **b** $y = \frac{1}{2} \times 2^x$ **c** $y = 5 \times 2^x$

    i   On separate axes, *without using technology*, sketch the graphs.

    ii   State the y-intercept and the equation of the horizontal asymptote.

    iii   Describe the transformation required to draw the graph of the function from the graph of $y = 2^x$.

    iv   Use a **graphing package** or **graphics calculator** to check each of your results.

7   **a**   On the same set of axes graph $y = 2^{-x}$ and $y = (0.5)^x$

    b   Explain your result in **a**.

INVESTIGATION 2   **SOLVING EXPONENTIAL EQUATIONS**

Consider the exponential equation $2^x = 10$.

Since $2^3 = 8$ and $2^4 = 16$,

the solution for x must lie between 3 and 4.

A **graphics calculator** can be used to solve this equation by drawing the graphs of $y = 2^x$ and $y = 10$ and finding the **point of intersection**. You can also use a graphing package.

What to do:

1 Draw the **graph** of $Y_1 = 2\char`^X$ using your graphics calculator.

2 Use **trace** to estimate x when $y = 10$.

3 Draw the **graph** of $Y_2 = 10$ on the same set of axes as $Y_1 = 2\char`^X$.

4 Check the estimation in **2** by finding the coordinates of the **point of intersection** of the graphs.

5 Use your graphics calculator and the method described above to solve for x, correct to 3 decimal places:

    a $2^x = 5$ **b** $2^x = 12$ **c** $2^x = 36$

    d $2^x = 100$ **e** $3^x = 20$ **f** $3^x = 42$

GRAPHING PACKAGE

(You may have to change the *viewing window scales*.)

D   GROWTH AND DECAY

We saw in the previous section that a population P, of 100 mice which doubles in size each week **grows exponentially** according to the relationship $P = 100 \times 2^t$ after t weeks.

We can use this relationship to answer questions about the mouse population.

Question: What is the size of the population after $6\frac{1}{2}$ weeks?

Answer: When $t = 6.5$, $P = 100 \times 2^{6.5}$

                      $\doteqdot 9051$ mice. $\{ 100 \; \boxed{\times} \; 2 \; \boxed{\char`^} \; 6.5 \; \boxed{\text{ENTER}} \}$

Populations of people, animals and bacteria are examples of quantities which may show **exponential growth**. Many other quantities also grow exponentially.

Example 11   ◄)) **Self Tutor**

An entomologist, monitoring a grasshopper plague, notices that the area affected by the grasshoppers is given by $A_n = 1000 \times 2^{0.2n}$ hectares, where n is the number of weeks after the initial observation.

  a   Find the original affected area.

  b   Find the affected area after   **i**   5 weeks   **ii**   10 weeks   **iii**   12 weeks.

  c   Draw the graph of A_n against n.

  d   How long would it take for the affected area to reach 3000 hectares?

---

  a $A_0 = 1000 \times 2^0 = 1000 \times 1 = 1000$

         $\therefore$ original area was 1000 ha.

  b   **i** $A_5 = 1000 \times 2^1 = 2000$ **ii** $A_{10} = 1000 \times 2^2 = 4000$

          i.e.,   area is 2000 ha.   i.e.,   area is 4000 ha.

      iii $A_{12} = 1000 \times 2^{0.2 \times 12}$

               $= 1000 \times 2^{2.4}$ {*Press:*   1000 $\boxed{\times}$ 2 $\boxed{\char`^}$ 2.4 $\boxed{\text{ENTER}}$ }

               $\doteqdot 5278$

        i.e.,   area is 5300 ha.

c

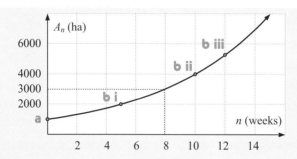

d From the graph, it takes approximately 8 weeks for the area to reach 3000 hectares.

The solution can be found by finding the **point of intersection** of $Y_1 = 1000 \times 2\hat{\ }(0.2X)$ and $Y_2 = 3000$ on a graphics calculator.

The solution $\doteq 7.92$ weeks.

EXERCISE 19D

1 The weight W_t grams, of bacteria in a culture t hours after establishment is given by $W_t = 30 \times 2^{0.2t}$ grams.   Find:
  a the initial weight
  b the weight after
   i   8 hours   **ii**   20 hours   **iii**   2 days.
  c Sketch the graph of W_t against t using only **a** and **b** results.
  d Use technology to graph $Y_1 = 30 \times 2^{0.2X}$ to find how many hours it takes for the weight of bacteria to reach 50 g.

2 A breeding program to ensure the survival of mongooses was established with an initial population of 40 (20 pairs). From a previous program the expected population P_n in n years time is given by $P_n = P_0 \times 2^{0.2n}$.
  a What is the value of P_0?
  b What is the expected population after:
   i   3 years   **ii**   10 years   **iii**   30 years?
  c Sketch the graph of P_n against n using only **a** and **b**.
  d Use technology to graph $Y_1 = 40 \times 2^{0.2X}$ to find how many years it takes for the population to reach 400.

3 The speed V_t of a chemical reaction is given by $V_t = V_0 \times 2^{0.04t}$ where t is the temperature in $^{\circ}C$.   Find:
  a   **i**   the speed at $0^{\circ}C$ **ii**   the speed at $40^{\circ}C$
  b Sketch the graph of V against t using the above.
  c Find the temperature when the speed of the reaction is eight times the original speed.

Decay problems occur when the size of a variable *decreases* over time.

Many quantities which decay over time are examples of **exponential decay**.

Example 12

Self Tutor

The weight of radioactive material remaining after t years is given by
$W_t = 11.7 \times 2^{-0.0067t}$ grams.

a   Find the original weight.

b   Find the weight after   **i**   10 years   **ii**   100 years   **iii**   1000 years.

c   Graph W_t against t using **a** and **b** only.

d   Use your graph and/or technology to find how long it takes for the weight to reach 1 gram.

$W_t = 11.7 \times 2^{-0.0067t}$

a   When $t = 0$, $W_0 = 11.7 \times 2^0 = 11.7$ grams

b   **i** W_{10}
$= 11.7 \times 2^{-0.067}$
$\doteqdot 11.17$ g

ii W_{100}
$= 11.7 \times 2^{-0.67}$
$\doteqdot 7.35$ g

iii W_{1000}
$= 11.7 \times 2^{-6.7}$
$\doteqdot 0.11$ g

c

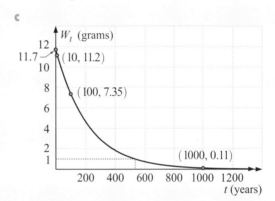

d   From the graph, it takes approximately 530 years for the weight to reach 1 gram.

The solution can be found by finding the **point of intersection** of
$Y_1 = 11.7 \times 2\char`^(-0.0067X)$ and $Y_2 = 1$ on a graphics calculator.
The solution $\doteqdot 529.6$ years.

---

4   The temperature $T_t(^oC)$ of a liquid which has been placed in a refrigerator is given by
$T_t = 100 \times 2^{-0.04t}$ where t is the time in minutes. Find:

  a   the initial temperature

  b   the temperature after

   i   10 minutes   **ii**   25 minutes   **iii**   60 minutes.

  c   Sketch the graph of T_t against t using **a** and **b** only.

  d   Find how long it takes for the temperature to reach 20°C.

5   The weight W_t of a radioactive substance remaining after t years is given by the formula
$W_t = W_0 \times 2^{-0.0005t}$ grams, $t \geqslant 0$.   Find:

  a   the original weight   **b**   the weight loss after 1200 years.

  c   Using technology, find the time taken for the weight to fall to half its original value.

6 The current I_t amps, flowing in a transistor radio, t seconds after it is switched off is given by $I_t = I_0 \times 2^{-0.04t}$ amps. Find:

    a   **i**   the initial current   **ii**   the current after 2 seconds

    b I_{20} and I_{50} and hence sketch the graph of I_t against t.

    c   Find the time after switching off when the current is one tenth its original value.

E   APPRECIATION

When the value of an item such as a house or investment increases, we say it **appreciates** in value. You may have noticed that the prices of everyday goods and services also increase over time due to **inflation**.

Example 13   ◀) **Self Tutor**

The inflation rate over the next three years is predicted to be 2% then 3% then 3.5%. What will be the cost in three years' time of an item which currently costs $140 if the cost rises in line with inflation?

cost in 3 years $= \$140 \times 1.02 \times 1.03 \times 1.035 = \$152.23$

EXERCISE 19E

1 What would you expect a bicycle costing $500 today to cost in four years' time, if the inflation rate is predicted to be 3%, 3.5%, 4% and then 5% over the four years?

2 If the rate of inflation is expected to remain constant at 4% per year for the next 5 years, what would you expect a $20 000 car to cost in 5 years' time?

3 An investment of $18 250 is left to accumulate interest over a 4-year period. During the first year the interest paid was 9.2%, and in successive years the rates paid were 8.6%, 7.5% and 5.6%. Find the value of the investment after 4 years.

Example 14   ◀) **Self Tutor**

Over 4 consecutive years, the value of a house increases by 15%, increases by 9%, decreases by 4%, and increases by 18%. What is the overall percentage increase in value over this period?

Let $\$x$ be the original value

$\therefore$ value after 1 year $= \$x \times 1.15$ {15% increase}

       value after 2 years $= \$x \times 1.15 \times 1.09$ {9% increase}

       value after 3 years $= \$x \times 1.15 \times 1.09 \times 0.96$ {4% decrease}

       value after 4 years $= \$x \times 1.15 \times 1.09 \times 0.96 \times 1.18$ {18% increase}

                        $\doteqdot \$x \times 1.4200$ {1.42 is 142%}

$\therefore$ a 42% increase in the value has occurred.

4 An amount of money is invested at 8% for the first year, 11% for the second year and 7% for the third year. What is the percentage increase in the value of the investment over this period?

5 A politician's wage increases by 3%, 8%, 5% and then 10% over a four year period. What is the percentage increase in the wage over this period of time?

6 A share fund reported a 9% increase in value for year 1, a 13% decrease in value for year 2 and a 4% increase in value for year 3. What was the overall percentage increase or decrease of the share fund over the 3 years?

F   COMPOUND INTEREST

If you bank $1000, you are, in effect, lending the money to the bank. The bank in turn uses your money to lend to other people. While banks pay you interest to encourage your custom, they charge interest to borrowers at a higher rate.

If you leave the money in the bank for a period of time, the interest is automatically added to your account. When this happens, the next lot of interest is calculated on a higher balance (or **principal**). This creates a **compounding** effect on the interest as the investor is getting **interest on interest**.

Consider an investment of $1000 with interest of 6% p.a. paid each year and compounded.

After year	Interest paid	Account balance
0		$1000.00
1	6% of $1000.00 = $60.00	$1000.00 + $60.00 = $1060.00
2	6% of $1060.00 = $63.60	$1060.00 + $63.60 = $1123.60
3	6% of $1123.60 = $67.42	$1123.60 + $67.42 = $1191.02

> Notice the increasing amount of interest each year.

Each year, the account balance becomes $(100\% + 6\%)$, or 106% of its previous value.

$$\therefore \quad \text{value after 3 years} = \$1000 \times 1.06 \times 1.06 \times 1.06$$
$$= \$1000 \times (1.06)^3$$
$$= \$1191.02$$

This seems to suggest that if the money is left in your account for n years it will amount to $\$1000 \times (1.06)^n$.

The **annual multiplier** is $(1 + i)$ where i is the annual interest rate expressed as a decimal.

These observations lead to the **compound growth formula**:

$$F_v = P_v(1+i)^n \quad \text{where} \quad \$F_v \quad \text{is the \textbf{future value}}$$

$\$P_v$ is the **present value** (amount initially invested)

i is the **annual interest rate** (as a decimal)

n is the **number of years of investment**.

EXERCISE 19F

1 Copy and complete the following table to find the future value when $8000 is invested at 5% p.a. compound interest:

After year	Interest paid	Future value
0		$8000
1	5% of $8000 = $400	
2		
3		

> Compounding money is an example of exponential growth!

> Interest earned is $F_v - P_v$!

Example 15 ◀) Self Tutor

a What will $5000 invested at 8% p.a. compound interest amount to after 2 years?

b How much interest is earned?

a $F_v = P_v(1+i)^n$

∴ $F_v = 5000 \times (1+0.08)^2$

$= 5000 \times (1.08)^2$

$= \$5832$

b   Interest earned

$= \$5832 - \$5000$

$= \$832$

---

2 **a** What will an investment of £40 000 at 10% p.a. compounded yearly amount to after 3 years?

b What part of this is interest?

3 How much compound interest is earned by investing ¥50 000 at 8% p.a. compounded yearly, if the investment is over a 2 year period?

FINDING THE PRINCIPAL

Example 16 ◀) Self Tutor

How much should I invest now if I want the maturing value to be $10 000 in 4 years' time, if I am able to invest at 8.5% p.a. compounding annually?

$$F_v = P_v(1+i)^n$$

∴ $10\,000 = P_v \times (1+0.085)^4$ {as 8.5% = 0.085}

∴ $10\,000 = P_v \times (1.085)^4$

∴ $\dfrac{10\,000}{(1.085)^4} = P_v$ {dividing by $(1.085)^4$}

∴ $7215.74 = P_v$ {*Calculator:* 10 000 ÷ 1.085 ^ 4 **ENTER** }

i.e., invest $7215.74 now

4 How much money must be invested now if you require $20 000 for a holiday in 4 years' time and the money can be invested at a fixed rate of 7.5% p.a. compounded annually?

5 What initial investment is required to produce a maturing amount of 15 000 euros in 60 months' time given that a fixed rate of 5.5% p.a. compounded annually is guaranteed?

FINDING THE RATE OF INTEREST

The compound interest formula can also be used to find the annual rate of increase for investments.

Example 17   ◀)) Self Tutor

If I bought a bottle of wine for $550 and 5 years later it was valued at $1550, at what annual rate has my investment increased? Give your answer correct to two decimal places.

$$P_v(1+i)^n = F_v$$
$$\therefore \quad 550 \times (1+i)^5 = 1550$$

$$\therefore \quad (1+i)^5 = \frac{1550}{550} \qquad \{\text{dividing by 550}\}$$

$$\therefore \quad 1+i = \sqrt[5]{\frac{1550}{550}} \qquad \{\text{finding the fifth root of both sides}\}$$

$$\therefore \quad i = \sqrt[5]{\frac{1550}{550}} - 1 \quad \{\text{subtracting 1 from both sides}\}$$

$$\therefore \quad i \doteqdot 0.2303$$

{*Calculator*: $\boxed{(}$ 1550 $\boxed{\div}$ 550 $\boxed{)}$ $\boxed{\wedge}$ $\boxed{(}$ 1 $\boxed{\div}$ 5 $\boxed{)}$ $\boxed{-}$ 1 $\boxed{\textbf{ENTER}}$ }

i.e.,   the investment increase $\doteqdot$ 23.03% p.a.

6 Ken bought a valuable coin for $2000 and three years later sold it for $3500. Find the yearly rate of increase for this investment.

7 A block of land was purchased for $150 000 and 4 years later was sold for $270 000. Find the annual rate of increase for this investment.

8 The local council valued your house at $146 000 and 5 years later they valued it at $213 000. Find the annual rate of increase for the valuation of your house.

G   DEPRECIATION

Depreciation describes how goods diminish in value over time.

Motor cars, office furniture, computers, etc. all generally decrease in value as they age.

The following table shows how a computer bought for $3500 reduces in value (depreciates) by 20% each year. The depreciated value is also called the **book value**. Notice that items are depreciated on their **reduced balance** each year.

Age (years)	Depreciation	Book value
0		$3500.00
1	20% of $3500.00 = $700.00	$3500.00 − $700.00 = $2800.00
2	20% of $2800.00 = $560.00	$2800.00 − $560.00 = $2240.00
3	20% of $2240.00 = $448.00	$2240.00 − $448.00 = $1792.00

The computer is only worth 80% of its original value at the end of 1 year. Thus, we multiply by 0.8, and

its value after 1 year is $\quad V_1 = \$3500 \times 0.8$

after 2 years, $\quad V_2 = V_1 \times 0.8 = \$3500 \times (0.8)^2$

after 3 years, $\quad V_3 = V_2 \times 0.8 = \$3500 \times (0.8)^3$

If we list the value of the computer in successive years we get:

$3500, \quad \$3500 \times 0.8, \quad \$3500 \times (0.8)^2, \quad \$3500 \times (0.8)^3.$

After n years, $\quad V_n = \$3500 \times (0.8)^n.$

Depreciation is an example of exponential decay!

The **depreciation formula** is:

$$F_v = P_v(1-i)^n \quad \text{where} \quad F_v \text{ is the \textbf{future value} after } n \text{ time periods}$$

P_v is the **original purchase price** or **present value**

i is the **depreciation rate per period** as a decimal

n is the **number** of periods.

Example 18   ◀) **Self Tutor**

A photocopier was purchased for $18 500.

a   Given that photocopiers generally depreciate at 15% per year, find its value after 5 years.

b   By how much did it depreciate?

Depreciation equals $P_v - F_v$.

a $P_v = 18\,500$

$i = 0.15$

$n = 5$

Now $\quad F_v = P_v(1-i)^n$

$\therefore \quad F_v = 18\,500\,(1 - 0.15)^5$

$= 18\,500(0.85)^5$

$\doteqdot \$8208.55$

b   Depreciation $= \$18\,500 - \$8208.55 = \$10\,291.45$

EXERCISE 19G

1   A car was purchased for $32 500 and depreciated annually by 16%. Find its value after 10 years.

2 A motorbike was purchased for $8495 in July 2001 and depreciates at 12% each year. Copy and complete the following table:

Number of years owned	Depreciation or annual loss in value	Value after n years
0	-	$8495
1	$1019.40	$7475.60
2		
3		
4		

a For taxation purposes, the motorbike is essential for making an income (as it is used exclusively in a delivery service). Annual loss in value (called depreciation) can be used as a tax deduction. How much can be 'claimed' during the 4th year of use?

b Find the value of the motorbike at the end of the 8th year.

c What is the significance of $F_{10} - F_9$?

3 **a** If I buy a car for $38\,500 and keep it for 3 years, what will its value be at the end of that period given that its annual depreciation rate is 20%?

b By how much did it depreciate?

4 A cabin cruiser was bought for $120\,000 in April 1998 and was sold for $45\,000 in April 2006. At what average annual rate of depreciation did the boat lose its value?

5 A small jet aeroplane was purchased for 3.4 million dollars in January 1998 and was sold for 2.35 million dollars in July 2005. What was its average annual rate of depreciation over this period?

H   **EXPONENTIAL EQUATIONS**

An **exponential equation** is an equation in which the unknown occurs as part of the index or exponent. For example: $2^x = 8$ and $30 \times 3^x = 7$ are both exponential equations.

If $2^x = 8$, then $2^x = 2^3$. Thus $x = 3$, and this is the only solution.

Hence: If $a^x = a^k$, then $x = k$,

i.e., if the base numbers are the same, we can **equate indices**.

Example 19   🔊 **Self Tutor**

Solve for x: **a** $2^x = 16$ **b** $3^{x+2} = \frac{1}{27}$

a $\qquad 2^x = 16$

$\therefore \quad 2^x = 2^4$

$\therefore \quad x = 4$

b $\qquad 3^{x+2} = \frac{1}{27}$

$\therefore \quad 3^{x+2} = 3^{-3}$

$\therefore \quad x + 2 = -3$

$\therefore \quad x = -5$

Once we have the same base we then equate the indices.

EXERCISE 19H

1 Solve for x:

a $3^x = 3$ b $3^x = 9$ c $2^x = 8$ d $5^x = 1$

e $3^x = \frac{1}{3}$ f $5^x = \frac{1}{5}$ g $2^x = \frac{1}{16}$ h $5^{x+1} = 25$

i $2^{x+2} = \frac{1}{4}$ j $3^{x-1} = \frac{1}{27}$ k $2^{x-1} = 32$ l $3^{1-2x} = \frac{1}{27}$

m $4^{2x+1} = \frac{1}{2}$ n $9^{x-3} = 3$ o $(\frac{1}{2})^{x-1} = 2$ p $(\frac{1}{3})^{2-x} = 9$

USING LOGARITHMS (EXTENSION)

In many exponential equations it is not possible to easily make the base numbers the same on both sides of the equation.

For example, if $2^x = 5$ we cannot easily write 5 with a base number of 2.

To overcome this problem, we write both sides with a base of 10, and to do this we use the $\boxed{\log}$ key on our calculator.

> The **logarithm** (or simply, **log**) of a positive number is its power of 10.
> This means that any positive number a can be written in base 10 as $a = 10^{\log a}$.

INVESTIGATION 3   LOGARITHMS

What to do:

1 Copy and complete:

Number	Number as a power of 10	log of number (**from calculator**)
10		
100		
1000		
Example → 100 000	10^5	$\log(100\,000) = 5$
0.1		
0.001		

and also this:

Number	Number as a power of 10	log of number (**from calculator**)
$\sqrt{10}$		
$\sqrt[3]{10}$		
$\sqrt{1000}$		
$\frac{1}{\sqrt{10}}$		

2 Can you draw any conclusion from your table? For example, you may wish to comment on when a logarithm is positive or negative.

3 From your table estimate the values of the logarithms for   **a** 2 **b** 20 **c** 200.
Check your estimations using your calculator.

4 Explain your calculator values in **3**.

Example 20   ◀) **Self Tutor**

Write the following numbers as powers of 10:
  a 2   **b** 20

  a $2 = 10^{\log 2}$ **b** $20 = 10^{\log 20}$
  $\doteqdot 10^{0.301\,029\,995}$ $\doteqdot 10^{1.301\,029\,995}$

Note: $20 = 2 \times 10 = 10^{\log 2} \times 10^1 = 10^{1+\log 2}$ gives an explanation for the answers in
a and **b** above.

EXERCISE 19I

1 Write the following as powers of 10 using $a = 10^{\log a}$:

a 8	**b** 80	**c** 800	**d** 80 000
e 0.03	**f** 0.003	**g** 0.3	**h** 0.000 003
i 25	**j** 2500	**k** 2.5	**l** 2 500 000
m 37	**n** 0.0614	**o** 26 700	**p** 0.006 372 1

2 Solve for x using logarithms (answer to 4 significant figures):

  a $10^x = 80$ **b** $10^x = 8000$ **c** $10^x = 0.025$

  d $10^x = 456.3$ **e** $10^x = 0.8764$ **f** $10^x = 0.000\,179\,2$

Example 21   ◀) **Self Tutor**

Solve for x using logarithms (answer to 4 significant figures):
  a $2^x = 100$ **b** $(1.12)^x = 3$

  a $2^x = 100$ **b** $(1.12)^x = 3$

  $\therefore (10^{\log 2})^x = 10^2$ $\therefore (10^{\log 1.12})^x = 10^{\log 3}$

  $\therefore x \times \log 2 = 2$ $\therefore x \times \log 1.12 = \log 3$

  $\therefore x = \dfrac{2}{\log 2}$ $\therefore x = \dfrac{\log 3}{\log 1.12}$

  $\therefore x \doteqdot 6.644$ $\therefore x \doteqdot 9.694$

  One calculator sequence   *One calculator sequence*

  2 ÷ log 2) ENTER   log 3) ÷ log 1.12) ENTER

3 Solve for x using logarithms (answer to 4 significant figures):

a $2^x = 3$ b $2^x = 10$ c $2^x = 400$

d $2^x = 0.0075$ e $5^x = 1000$ f $6^x = 0.836$

g $(1.1)^x = 1.86$ h $(1.25)^x = 3$ i $(0.87)^x = 0.001$

j $(0.7)^x = 0.21$ k $(1.085)^x = 2$ l $(0.997)^x = 0.5$

4 The weight of bacteria in a culture t hours after it has been established is given by $W_t = 2.5 \times 2^{0.04t}$ grams. After what time will the weight reach

a   4 grams   b   15 grams?

5 The population of bees in a hive, t hours after it has been discovered, is given by $P_n = 5000 \times 2^{0.09t}$. After what time will the population reach

a   15 000   b   50 000?

J   THE LAWS OF LOGARITHMS (EXTENSION)

Since the logarithm of any positive number is its power of 10, then $\log 10^x = x$.

For example, $\log 10^2 = 2$ and $\log \sqrt{10} = \log 10^{\frac{1}{2}} = \frac{1}{2}$,   etc.

Example 22	◀⟩ Self Tutor
Without using a calculator, find: a $\log(0.01)$ b $\log(\sqrt[6]{10})$	a $\log(0.01)$ b $\log(\sqrt[6]{10})$ $= \log\left(\frac{1}{100}\right)$ $= \log\left(10^{\frac{1}{6}}\right)$ $= \log 10^{-2}$ $= \frac{1}{6}$ $= -2$

EXERCISE 19J

1 Without using a calculator, find:

a $\log 1000$ b $\log(0.001)$ c $\log 1$ d $\log 10$

e $\log(\sqrt{10})$ f $\log(\sqrt[4]{10})$ g $\log(\frac{1}{10})$ h $\log\left(\frac{1}{\sqrt{10}}\right)$

2 Find:

a $\log 10^n$ b $\log 10^{-m}$ c $\log\left(\frac{10^m}{10^n}\right)$ d $\log\left(10^m 10^n\right)$

e $\log(10^m)^2$ f $\log(10^m)^n$ g $\log(10 \times 10^n)$ h $\log\left(\frac{10^m}{100}\right)$

3 a   Use your calculator to find: i $\log 2$ ii $\log 20$

   b   What is the connection between $\log 2$ and $\log 20$?

   c   Give a reason for your answer to **b**.

4 If $\log x = 4$ then $x = 10^{\log x} = 10^4 = 10\,000$. Use this argument to find x if:

   a $\log x = 2$ **b** $\log x = 1$ **c** $\log x = -1$

   d $\log x = 0$ **e** $\log x = \frac{1}{2}$ **f** $\log x = -\frac{1}{3}$

   g $\log x = 0.1684$ **h** $\log x = 2.38$ **i** $\log x = -3.675$

Notice that $x = 10^{\log x}$ and $y = 10^{\log y}$ and so

$$xy = 10^{\log x} \times 10^{\log y} = 10^{\log x + \log y} \quad ...... \ (1)$$

But $xy = 10^{\log(xy)}$ ...... (2)

and so as $10^{\log(xy)} = 10^{\log x + \log y}$

then $\log(xy) = \log x + \log y$ {equating indices}

Similarly, it can be shown that: $\log\left(\dfrac{x}{y}\right) = \log x - \log y$ and $\log(x^n) = n\log x$

Consequently the three important laws of logarithms are:

$$\log(xy) = \log x + \log y$$

$$\log\left(\frac{x}{y}\right) = \log x - \log y$$

$$\log(x^n) = n\log x$$

Example 23   ◀⑴ **Self Tutor**

Write as a single logarithm: **a** $\log 2 + \log 7$ **b** $\log 6 - \log 3$

  a $\log 2 + \log 7$ **b** $\log 6 - \log 3$

      $= \log(2 \times 7)$ $= \log\left(\frac{6}{3}\right)$

      $= \log 14$ $= \log 2$

Use your calculator to check the answers to **Example 23**.

5 Write as a single logarithm in the form $\log k$:

   a $\log 6 + \log 5$ **b** $\log 10 - \log 2$ **c** $2\log 2 + \log 3$

   d $\log 5 - 2\log 2$ **e** $\frac{1}{2}\log 4 - \log 2$ **f** $\log 2 + \log 3 + \log 5$

   g $\log 20 + \log(0.2)$ **h** $-\log 2 - \log 3$ **i** $3\log\left(\frac{1}{8}\right)$

   j $4\log 2 + 3\log 5$ **k** $6\log 2 - 3\log 5$ **l** $1 + \log 2$

   m $1 - \log 2$ **n** $2 - \log 5$ **o** $3 + \log 2 + \log 7$

Example 24   ◀⑴ **Self Tutor**

Simplify, without using a calculator: $\dfrac{\log 49}{\log\left(\frac{1}{7}\right)} = \dfrac{\log 7^2}{\log 7^{-1}}$

$$\frac{\log 49}{\log\left(\frac{1}{7}\right)}$$

$$= \frac{2\log 7}{-1\log 7}$$

$$= -2$$

6 Without using a calculator, simplify:

a $\dfrac{\log 8}{\log 2}$ **b** $\dfrac{\log 9}{\log 3}$ **c** $\dfrac{\log 4}{\log 8}$ **d** $\dfrac{\log 5}{\log \left(\frac{1}{5}\right)}$

e $\dfrac{\log(0.5)}{\log 2}$ **f** $\dfrac{\log 8}{\log(0.25)}$ **g** $\dfrac{\log 2^b}{\log 8}$ **h** $\dfrac{\log 4}{\log 2^a}$

7 Without using a calculator, show that:

a $\log 8 = 3 \log 2$ **b** $\log \left(\frac{1}{7}\right) = -\log 7$

c $\log \left(\frac{1}{4}\right) = -2 \log 2$ **d** $\log 50 = 2 - \log 2$

8 By finding the logarithm of both sides of the equation, show that:

a if $y = a^2 b$ then $\log y = 2 \log a + \log b$

b if $y = \dfrac{a}{b^3}$ then $\log y = \log a - 3 \log b$

c if $y = \dfrac{a}{bc}$ then $\log y = \log a - \log b - \log c$

9 Write the following logarithmic equations without using logarithms.

For example, if $\log a = \log b + \log c$, then $\log a = \log(bc)$ and so $a = bc$.

a $\log p = 3 \log q$ **b** $\log p = \frac{1}{2} \log q$

c $\log p = -2 \log r$ **d** $\log p = \log q - \log r$

e $2 \log a = 3 \log b$ **f** $3 \log c = -4 \log d$

g $\log y = 2 \log x - \log t$ **h** $\log M = -\log a - 2 \log b$

i $\log D = x + 2$ **j** $\log G = -2x + 1$

10 **a** If $2^{x-1} = 3^{1-2x}$, show that $x = \dfrac{\log 6}{\log 18}$.

b If $4^{1-x} = 3^{2x+1}$, show that $x = \dfrac{\log \left(\frac{4}{3}\right)}{\log 36}$.

(**Hint:** In **a**, $\dfrac{2^x}{2} = \dfrac{3}{3^{2x}}$ and so $2^x \times 9^x = 6$, etc.)

11 **a** Graph $y = 10^x$ and $y = \log x$ on the same set of axes.

b What transformation maps $y = 10^x$ onto $y = \log x$?

HOME RESEARCH

Who invented logarithms?

Research logarithms in bases other than 10, especially in base e.

Write a one page report on your findings.

REVIEW SET 19A

1 Simplify:

    a $\ 2a^4 \times a^5$ **b** $\ \dfrac{a^b}{a^x}$ **c** $\ (3a^2)^3$

2 Express $\ \dfrac{4^{n+1}}{2^{2n}}\ $ in simplest form with a prime number base.

3 Simplify, giving answers in simplest rational form:

    a $\ 3^0 + 3^{-1}$ **b** $\ \left(\frac{2}{5}\right)^{-2}$ **c** $\ 64^{-\frac{1}{3}}$

4 If $\ f(x) = 3^x - 1,\ $ find the value of:

    a $\ f(0)$ **b** $\ f(3)$ **c** $\ f(-1)$ **d** $\ f(-2)$

5 On the same set of axes, without using technology, draw the graphs of $\ y = 2^x$ and $\ y = 2^x + 2$.

    a State the y-intercepts and the equations of the horizontal asymptotes.

    b Describe the transformation required to draw the graph of $\ y = 2^x + 2\ $ from the graph of $\ y = 2^x$.

6 The weight W_t grams of radioactive substance remaining after t years is given by $W_t = 1000 \times 2^{-0.03t}\ $ grams. Find:

    a the initial weight

    b the weight after **i** 10 years **ii** 100 years **iii** 1000 years.

    c Graph W_t against t using **a** and **b** only.

    d Use your graph or technology to find how long it takes for the weight to reach 50 grams.

7 A bank offers 7.4% compound interest on amounts greater than £100 000 invested for a 5 year period. How much interest would be earned if £120 000 was invested?

8 A new caravan costing $15 000 depreciates at a rate of 16% p.a. What will be its value in 5 years?

9 Solve for x without using a calculator: $\ 27^x = 3$

10 **a** Write 50 as a power of 10 using $\ a = 10^{\log a}$.

    b Solve $\ 7^x = 2.32\ $ for x using logarithms (answer to 4 significant figures).

11 Without using a calculator, simplify the following showing all working:

    a $\ \log 4 + \log 2$ **b** $\ \log a^2 - \log a$ **c** $\ \dfrac{\log 8}{\log 2}$

REVIEW SET 19B

1 Simplify:

  a $3xy^2 \times 5x^2y^3$

  b $\dfrac{4x^2y}{8xy^3}$

  c $\dfrac{(2a)^3}{ab^2}$

2 Write in simplest form without negative indices:

  a $(5x)^{-2}$

  b $\dfrac{3x^2y}{y^{-4}}$

  c $125^{-\frac{1}{3}}$

3 If $P(x) = 2 \times 3^{-x}$, find the value of:

  a $P(0)$ **b** $P(1)$ **c** $P(2)$ **d** $P(-1)$ **e** $P(-2)$

4 On the same set of axes, without using technology, draw the graphs of $y = 2^x$ and $y = 3 \times 2^x$.

  a State the y-intercepts and the equations of the horizontal asymptotes.

  b Describe the transformation required to draw the graph of the function $y = 3 \times 2^x$ from the graph of $y = 2^x$.

5 The weight of radioactive substance after t years is given by the formula $W_t = W_0 \times 3^{-0.003t}$ grams.   Find:

  a the initial weight of radioactive substance

  b the percentage remaining after **i**   100 years   **ii**   500 years   **iii**   1000 years.

  c Graph W_t against t using **a** and **b** only.

6 What would you expect a car costing \$28 000 today to cost in 3 years' time if the rate of inflation:

  a is expected to remain constant at 2.5% during that time

  b is 2%, 3.5% and 3% over the next three years?

7 Henri and Michaela wish to have 800 000 euros saved in a superannuation fund in 20 years' time.

  a How much do they need to invest now if the fund earns 9.5% p.a.?

  b How much interest will be generated in this time?

8 Find the value of a motor vehicle purchased for \$25 000 after a period of 6 years if it depreciates at a rate of $12\frac{1}{2}\%$ p.a.

9 Find x, without using your calculator: $2^{1-x} = 8$

10 Solve for x using logarithms (answer to 4 significant figures): $(0.2)^x = 1.8$

11 Without using a calculator, simplify the following showing all working:

  a $\log 8 - \log 2$

  b $\frac{1}{3} \log 27$

  c $\dfrac{\log 4}{\log \sqrt{2}}$

12 If $2^a = 3^{a+1}$, show that $a = \dfrac{\log 3}{\log(\frac{2}{3})}$.

Chapter 20

Quadratic functions

Contents:

In this chapter, we will concentrate on relationships between variables which are **quadratic** in nature. Such relationships, when described algebraically by an equation, give rise to the study of **quadratic functions**.

OPENING PROBLEM

A cannonball fired vertically upwards from ground level has a height H metres, t seconds after firing, according to the relationship $H = 36t - 3t^2$.

Consider the following:

1 If we sketch a graph of the height H against the time t after firing, on a set of axes, what shape would result?

2 How long would it take for the cannonball to reach its maximum height?

3 What is the maximum height reached?

4 How long does the person who fired the cannonball have to clear the area?

A   QUADRATIC FUNCTIONS

A **quadratic function** is a relationship between two variables which can be written in the form $y = ax^2 + bx + c$ where x and y are the variables and a, b, and c represent constants with $a \neq 0$.

Using function notation, $y = ax^2 + bx + c$ can be written as $f(x) = ax^2 + bx + c$.

As with linear functions, for any value of x a corresponding value of y can be found by substituting into the function equation.

Example 1   ◀》 Self Tutor

If $y = -2x^2 + 3x - 4$ find the value of y when: **a** $x = 0$ **b** $x = 3$

a When $x = 0$
$$y = -2(0)^2 + 3(0) - 4$$
$$= 0 + 0 - 4$$
$$= -4$$

b When $x = 3$
$$y = -2(3)^2 + 3(3) - 4$$
$$= -2(9) + 9 - 4$$
$$= -18 + 9 - 4$$
$$= -13$$

EXERCISE 20A

1 Which of the following are quadratic functions?

a $y = 3x^2 - 4x + 1$ **b** $y = 5x - 7$ **c** $y = -x^2$

d $y = \frac{2}{3}x^2 + 4$ **e** $2y + 3x^2 - 5 = 0$ **f** $y = 5x^3 + x - 6$

2 For each of the following functions, find the value of y for the given value of x:

   a $y = x^2 + 5x - 4$ $\{x = 3\}$ **b** $y = 2x^2 + 9$ $\{x = -3\}$

   c $y = -2x^2 + 3x - 5$ $\{x = 1\}$ **d** $y = 4x^2 - 7x + 1$ $\{x = 4\}$

Example 2   ◀) **Self Tutor**

State whether the following quadratic functions are satisfied by the given ordered pairs:

  a $y = 3x^2 + 2x$ $(2, 16)$ **b** $f(x) = -x^2 - 2x + 1$ $(-3, 1)$

a $y = 3(2)^2 + 2(2)$
      $= 12 + 4$
      $= 16$
   i.e.,   when $x = 2$, $y = 16$
   $\therefore$ $(2, 16)$ does satisfy
       $y = 3x^2 + 2x$

b $f(-3) = -(-3)^2 - 2(-3) + 1$
         $= -9 + 6 + 1$
         $= -2$
   i.e., $f(-3) \neq 1$
   $\therefore$ $(-3, 1)$ does not satisfy
       $f(x) = -x^2 - 2x + 1$

---

3 State whether the following quadratic functions are satisfied by the given ordered pairs:

  a $f(x) = 5x^2 - 10$ $(0, 5)$ **b** $y = 2x^2 + 5x - 3$ $(4, 9)$

  c $y = -2x^2 + 3x$ $(-\frac{1}{2}, 1)$ **d** $y = -7x^2 + 8x + 15$ $(-1, 16)$

  e $f(x) = 3x^2 - 13x + 4$ $(2, -10)$ **f** $f(x) = -3x^2 + x + 2$ $(\frac{1}{3}, 2)$

FINDING x GIVEN y

It is also possible to substitute a value for y to find a corresponding value for x. However, unlike linear functions, with quadratic functions there may be 0, 1 or 2 possible values for x for any one value of y.

Example 3   ◀) **Self Tutor**

If $y = x^2 - 6x + 8$ find the value(s) of x when: **a** $y = 15$ **b** $y = -1$

a   If $y = 15$
     $x^2 - 6x + 8 = 15$
   $\therefore$ $x^2 - 6x - 7 = 0$
   $\therefore$ $(x + 1)(x - 7) = 0$
   $\therefore$ $x = -1$ or $x = 7$
   i.e.,   2 solutions.

b   If $y = -1$
     $x^2 - 6x + 8 = -1$
   $\therefore$ $x^2 - 6x + 9 = 0$
   $\therefore$ $(x - 3)^2 = 0$
   $\therefore$ $x = 3$
   i.e.,   only one solution

---

4 Find the value(s) of x for the given value of y for each of the following quadratic functions:

  a $y = x^2 + 6x + 10$ $\{y = 1\}$ **b** $y = x^2 + 5x + 8$ $\{y = 2\}$

  c $y = x^2 - 5x + 1$ $\{y = -3\}$ **d** $y = 3x^2$ $\{y = -3\}$

Example 4   ◀⅏ **Self Tutor**

If $f(x) = x^2 + 4x + 11$ find x when   **a** $f(x) = 23$ **b** $f(x) = 7$

a   If $f(x) = 23$

$\therefore$ $x^2 + 4x + 11 = 23$

$\therefore$ $x^2 + 4x - 12 = 0$

$\therefore$ $(x+6)(x-2) = 0$ {factorising}

$\therefore$ $x = -6$ or 2

i.e.,   2 solutions.

b   If $f(x) = 7$

$\therefore$ $x^2 + 4x + 11 = 7$

$\therefore$ $x^2 + 4x + 4 = 0$

$\therefore$ $(x+2)^2 = 0$ {factorising}

$\therefore$ $x = -2$

i.e.,   one solution only.

5 Find the value(s) of x given that:

a $f(x) = 3x^2 - 2x + 5$ and $f(x) = 5$

b $f(x) = x^2 - x - 5$ and $f(x) = 1$

c $f(x) = -2x^2 - 13x + 3$ and $f(x) = -4$

d $f(x) = 2x^2 - 12x + 1$ and $f(x) = -17$

Example 5   ◀⅏ **Self Tutor**

A stone is thrown into the air and its height in metres above the ground is given by the function $h(t) = -5t^2 + 30t + 2$ where t is the time (in seconds) from when the stone is thrown.

a   How high above the ground is the stone at time $t = 3$ seconds?

b   How high above the ground was the stone released?

c   At what time was the stone's height above the ground 27 m?

a $h(3) = -5(3)^2 + 30(3) + 2$

$= -45 + 90 + 2$

$= 47$

i.e.,   47 m above ground.

b   The stone is released when $t = 0$ sec

$\therefore$ $h(0) = -5(0)^2 + 30(0) + 2 = 2$

$\therefore$ released 2 m above ground level.

c   When $h(t) = 27$

$-5t^2 + 30t + 2 = 27$

$\therefore$ $-5t^2 + 30t - 25 = 0$

$\therefore$ $t^2 - 6t + 5 = 0$ {dividing each term by -5}

$\therefore$ $(t-1)(t-5) = 0$ {factorising}

$\therefore$ $t = 1$ or 5

i.e.,   after 1 sec and after 5 sec.   Can you explain the two answers?

6 An object is projected into the air with a velocity of 30 m/s. Its height in metres, after t seconds is given by the function $h(t) = 30t - 5t^2$.

a Calculate the height after: **i**   1 second   **ii**   5 seconds   **iii**   3 seconds.

b Calculate the time(s) at which the height is: **i**   40 m   **ii**   0 m.

c Explain your answers in part **b**.

7   A cake manufacturer finds that the profit in dollars, of making x
cakes per day is given by the function $P(x) = -\frac{1}{4}x^2 + 16x - 30$.

   a   Calculate the profit if: **i**   0 cakes   **ii**   10 cakes   are made per day.

   b   How many cakes per day are made if the profit is $57?

B   GRAPHS OF QUADRATIC FUNCTIONS

The graphs of all quadratic functions are **parabolas**. The parabola is one of the conic sections.
Conic sections are curves which can be obtained by cutting a cone with a plane. The Ancient
Greek mathematicians were fascinated by conic sections.

You may like to find the conic sections for yourself by
cutting an icecream cone.

Cutting parallel to the side produces a parabola,   i.e.,

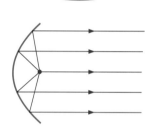

There are many examples of parabolas in every day
life. The name parabola comes from the Greek word
for **thrown** because when an object is thrown its path
makes a parabolic shape.

Parabolic mirrors are used in car headlights, heaters,
radar discs and radio telescopes because of their special
geometric properties.

Alongside is a single span parabolic
bridge. Other suspension bridges,
such as the Golden Gate bridge in
San Francisco, also form parabolic
curves.

THE SIMPLEST QUADRATIC FUNCTION

The simplest quadratic function is $y = x^2$ and its graph
can be drawn from a table of values.

x	-3	-2	-1	0	1	2	3
y	9	4	1	0	1	4	9

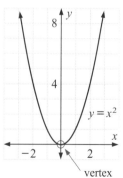

Note:

- The curve is a **parabola** and it opens upwards.
- There are no negative y values,   i.e., the curve
  does not go below the x-axis.
- The curve is **symmetrical** about the y-axis because,
  for example, when $x = -3$, $y = (-3)^2$ and when
  $x = 3$, $y = 3^2$ have the same value.
- The curve has a **turning point** or **vertex** at (0, 0).

The vertex is the point
where the graph is at its
maximum or minimum.

Draw the graph of $y = x^2 + 2x - 3$ from a table of values from $x = -3$ to $x = 3$.

Consider $f(x) = x^2 + 2x - 3$

Now, $f(-3) = (-3)^2 + 2(-3) - 3$
$$= 9 - 6 - 3$$
$$= 0 \quad \text{etc}$$

Tabled values are:

x	-3	-2	-1	0	1	2	3
y	0	-3	-4	-3	0	5	12

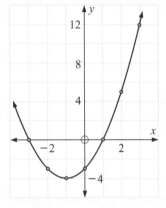

EXERCISE 20B.1

1 From a table of values for $x = -3, -2, -1, 0, 1, 2, 3$ draw the graph of:

    a $y = x^2 - 2x + 8$ **b** $y = -x^2 + 2x + 1$ **c** $y = 2x^2 + 3x$

    d $y = -2x^2 + 4$ **e** $y = x^2 + x + 4$ **f** $y = -x^2 + 4x - 9$

2 Use your **graphing package** or **graphics calculator** to check your graphs in question **1**.

INVESTIGATION 1   **GRAPHS OF QUADRATIC FUNCTIONS**

    Part 1:   Graphs of the form $y = x^2 + k$ **where** k **is a constant**

    What to do:

                        GRAPHING [TI]
                        PACKAGE

1 Using your **graphing package** or **graphics calculator**:

    i graph the two functions on the same set of axes

    ii state the coordinates of the vertex of each function.

    a $y = x^2$ and $y = x^2 + 2$ **b** $y = x^2$ and $y = x^2 - 2$

    c $y = x^2$ and $y = x^2 + 4$ **d** $y = x^2$ and $y = x^2 - 4$

2 What effect does the value of k have on:

    a the position of the graph   **b** the shape of the graph?

3 To graph $y = x^2 + k$ from $y = x^2$, what transformation is used?

Part 2:   Graphs of the form $y = (x - h)^2$

What to do:

    1 Using your **graphing package** or **graphics calculator**:

        i graph the two functions on the same set of axes

        ii state the coordinates of the vertex of each function.

a $y = x^2$ and $y = (x-2)^2$ **b** $y = x^2$ and $y = (x+2)^2$

c $y = x^2$ and $y = (x-4)^2$ **d** $y = x^2$ and $y = (x+4)^2$

2 What effect does the value of h have on:

   a the position of the graph   **b** the shape of the graph?

3 To graph $y = (x-h)^2$ from $y = x^2$ what transformation is used?

Part 3:   Graphs of the form $y = (x-h)^2 + k$
What to do:

1 *Without using the assistance of technology* sketch the graph of $y = (x-2)^2 + 3$, stating the coordinates of the vertex and commenting on the shape of the graph. (Use your findings from parts **1** and **2**.)

2 Use your **graphing package** or **graphics calculator** to draw, on the same set of axes, the graphs of $y = x^2$ and $y = (x-2)^2 + 3$.

3 Compare the two graphs you have drawn commenting on their shape and position.

4 Repeat steps **1**, **2** and **3** for $y = (x+4)^2 - 1$.

5 Copy and complete:

- The graph of $y = (x-h)^2 + k$ is the same shape as the graph of ......
- The graph of $y = (x-h)^2 + k$ is a .... of the graph of $y = x^2$ through a translation of ....

Part 4:   Graphs of the form $y = ax^2$, $a \neq 0$
What to do:

1 Using your **graphing package** or **graphics calculator**:

   i   graph the two functions on the same set of axes

   ii state the coordinates of the vertex of each function.

   a $y = x^2$ and $y = 2x^2$ **b** $y = x^2$ and $y = 4x^2$

   c $y = x^2$ and $y = \frac{1}{2}x^2$ **d** $y = x^2$ and $y = -x^2$

   e $y = x^2$ and $y = -2x^2$ **f** $y = x^2$ and $y = -\frac{1}{2}x^2$

2 What effect does a have on:

   a the position of the graph   **b** the shape of the graph

   c the direction in which the graph opens?

Part 5:   Graphs of the form $y = a(x-h)^2 + k$, $a \neq 0$
What to do:

1 *Without the assistance of technology*, on the same set of axes, sketch the graph of $y = 2x^2$ and hence the graph of $y = 2(x-1)^2 + 3$, stating the coordinates of the vertex and commenting on the shape of the two graphs. (Use your findings from previous parts.)

2 Use your **graphing package** or **graphics calculator** to check your graphs in step **1**.

3 Compare the two graphs you have drawn commenting on their shape and position.

4 Repeat steps **1**, **2** and **3** for

   a $y = -x^2$ and $y = -(x+2)^2 + 3$ **b** $y = \frac{1}{2}x^2$ and $y = \frac{1}{2}(x-2)^2 - 4$

5 Copy and complete:

- The graph of $y = a(x - h)^2 + k$ is the same shape and opens in the same direction as the graph of ......

- The graph of $y = a(x - h)^2 + k$ is a .... of the graph of $y = ax^2$ through a translation of ......

From the investigation the following important facts should have been discovered.

Summary of findings:

- Graphs of the form $y = x^2 + k$ have exactly the same shape as the graph of $y = x^2$. In fact k is the **vertical translation** factor.

  Every point on the graph of $y = x^2$ is translated $\begin{bmatrix} 0 \\ k \end{bmatrix}$ to give the graph of $y = x^2 + k$.

- Graphs of the form $y = (x - h)^2$ have exactly the same shape as the graph of $y = x^2$. In fact, h is the **horizontal translation** factor.

  Every point on the graph of $y = x^2$ is translated $\begin{bmatrix} h \\ 0 \end{bmatrix}$ to give the graph of $y = (x - h)^2$.

- Graphs of the form $y = (x - h)^2 + k$ have the same shape as the graph of $y = x^2$ and can be obtained from $y = x^2$ by using a **horizontal shift** of h units and a **vertical shift** of k units. This is a **translation** of $\begin{bmatrix} h \\ k \end{bmatrix}$. The **vertex** is at (h, k).

- If $a > 0$, $y = ax^2$ opens upwards i.e.,

  If $a < 0$, $y = ax^2$ opens downwards i.e.,

  Graphs of the form $y = ax^2$ are 'wider' or 'thinner' than $y = x^2$.
  If $a < -1$ or $a > 1$, $y = ax^2$ is 'thinner' than $y = x^2$.
  If $-1 < a < 1$ $(a \neq 0)$, $y = ax^2$ is 'wider' than $y = x^2$.

-

$a > 0$

$a < 0$

vertical shift of k units:
if $k > 0$ it goes up
if $k < 0$ it goes down

$$y = a(x - h)^2 + k$$

affects the width

$a < -1$ or $a > 1$, thinner than $y = x^2$

$a \neq 0$, $-1 < a < 1$, wider than $y = x^2$

horizontal shift of h units:
$h > 0$ right, $h < 0$ left

Example 7   ◀) **Self Tutor**

Sketch $y = x^2$ on a set of axes and hence sketch $y = x^2 + 3$. Mark the vertex of $y = x^2 + 3$.

Draw $y = x^2$ and translate

it 3 units upwards, i.e., $\begin{bmatrix} 0 \\ 3 \end{bmatrix}$.

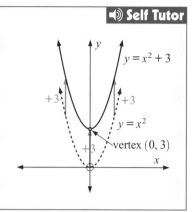

EXERCISE 20B.2

1 Without using your graphics calculator or graphing package, sketch the graph of $y = x^2$ on a set of axes and hence sketch each of the following functions, stating the coordinates of the vertex: (Use separate sets of axes for each part.)

    a $y = x^2 - 3$ **b** $y = x^2 - 1$ **c** $y = x^2 + 1$

    d $y = x^2 - 5$ **e** $y = x^2 + 5$ **f** $y = x^2 - \frac{1}{2}$

2 Use your **graphics calculator** or **graphing package** to check your graphs in question **1**.

Example 8   ◀) **Self Tutor**

Sketch $y = x^2$ on a set of axes and hence sketch $y = (x + 3)^2$. Mark the vertex of $y = (x + 3)^2$.

Draw $y = x^2$ and translate it

3 units left, i.e., $\begin{bmatrix} -3 \\ 0 \end{bmatrix}$.

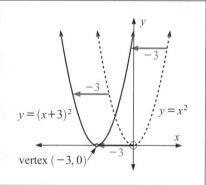

3 Without using your graphics calculator or graphing package, sketch the graph of $y = x^2$ on a set of axes and hence sketch each of the following functions, stating the coordinates of the vertex: (Use separate axes for each part.)

    a $y = (x - 3)^2$ **b** $y = (x + 1)^2$ **c** $y = (x - 1)^2$

    d $y = (x - 5)^2$ **e** $y = (x + 5)^2$ **f** $y = (x - \frac{3}{2})^2$

4 Use your **graphics calculator** or **graphing package** to check your graphs in question **3**.

Example 9   ◀》 **Self Tutor**

Sketch $y = x^2$ on a set of axes, then sketch the following, stating the coordinates of the vertex:

a $y = (x - 2)^2 + 3$ b $y = (x + 2)^2 - 5$

a   Draw $y = x^2$ and translate it $\begin{bmatrix} 2 \\ 3 \end{bmatrix}$.   b   Draw $y = x^2$ and translate it $\begin{bmatrix} -2 \\ -5 \end{bmatrix}$.

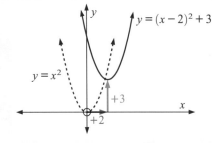   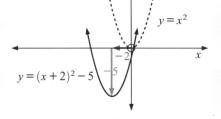

The vertex is at (2, 3).   The vertex is at (−2, −5).

5   On separate sets of axes sketch $y = x^2$ and each of the following, stating the coordinates of the vertex:

a $y = (x - 1)^2 + 3$ b $y = (x - 2)^2 - 1$ c $y = (x + 1)^2 + 4$
d $y = (x + 2)^2 - 3$ e $y = (x + 3)^2 - 2$ f $y = (x - 3)^2 + 3$

6   Use your **graphics calculator** or **graphing package** to check your graphs in question **5**.

COMPLETING THE SQUARE

Recall that in **Chapter 11** we used the process of completing the square to assist us in solving quadratic equations which did not factorise.

This same process can be used here to convert quadratics into the form $y = (x - h)^2 + k$.

Consider $y = x^2 - 4x + 1$

$\qquad \therefore \quad y = x^2 - 4x + 2^2 + 1 - 2^2$ {keeping the equation balanced}

$\qquad \therefore \quad y = x^2 - 4x + 2^2 \; - \; 3$

$\qquad \therefore \quad y = (x - 2)^2 - 3$

So, $y = x^2 - 4x + 1$ is really $y = (x - 2)^2 - 3$

and therefore the graph of $y = x^2 - 4x + 1$ can be considered as the graph of $y = x^2$ after it has been translated 2 units to the right and 3 units down,

i.e., $\begin{bmatrix} 2 \\ -3 \end{bmatrix}$.

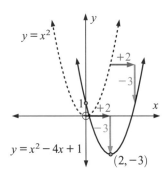

Example 10

Write $y = x^2 + 4x + 3$ in the form $y = (x - h)^2 + k$ using completing the square and hence sketch $y = x^2 + 4x + 3$, stating the coordinates of the vertex.

$$y = x^2 + 4x + 3$$
$$\therefore \quad y = x^2 + 4x + 2^2 + 3 - 2^2$$
$$\therefore \quad y = (x + 2)^2 - 1$$

$$\downarrow \qquad \downarrow$$

shift 2   shift 1
units left   unit down

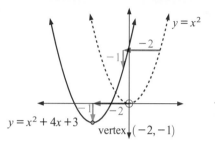

7 Write the following quadratics in the form $y = (x - h)^2 + k$ using 'completing the square' and hence sketch each function, stating the vertex:

   a $y = x^2 - 2x + 3$ **b** $y = x^2 - 6x + 4$ **c** $y = x^2 + 4x - 2$

   d $y = x^2 - 2x + 5$ **e** $y = x^2 - 4x$ **f** $y = x^2 + 3x$

   g $y = x^2 + 5x - 2$ **h** $y = x^2 - 3x + 2$ **i** $y = x^2 - 5x + 1$

8 Use your **graphing package** or **graphics calculator** to check your graphs in question **7**.

9 By using your **graphing package** or **graphics calculator**, graph each of the following functions, and hence write each function in the form $y = (x - h)^2 + k$:

   a $y = x^2 - 4x + 7$ **b** $y = x^2 + 6x + 3$ **c** $y = x^2 + 4x + 5$

   d $y = x^2 + 2x - 4$ **e** $y = x^2 - 3x + 1$ **f** $y = x^2 - 9x - 5$

Example 11

Sketch $y = x^2$ on a set of axes and hence sketch:

   a $y = 3x^2$ **b** $y = -3x^2$

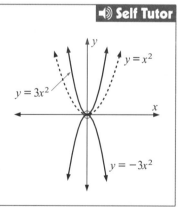

   a $y = 3x^2$ is 'thinner' than $y = x^2$.

   b $y = -3x^2$ is the same shape as $y = 3x^2$ but opens downwards.

10 On separate sets of axes sketch $y = x^2$ and then sketch the following, commenting on: **i** the shape of the graph   **ii** the direction in which the graph opens.

   a $y = 5x^2$ **b** $y = -5x^2$ **c** $y = \frac{1}{3}x^2$

   d $y = -\frac{1}{3}x^2$ **e** $y = -4x^2$ **f** $y = \frac{1}{4}x^2$

11 Use your **graphics calculator** or **graphing package** to check your graphs in **10**.

Example 12   ◄ϑ **Self Tutor**

Sketch the graph of $y = -(x-2)^2 - 3$
from the graph of $y = -x^2$ and hence
state the coordinates of the vertex.

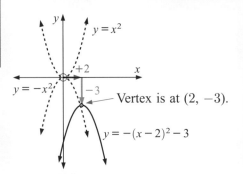

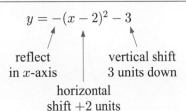

12 Sketch the graphs of the following functions without using tables of values and state the
coordinates of the vertex:

  a $y = -(x-1)^2 + 3$ **b** $y = 2x^2 + 4$ **c** $y = -(x-2)^2 + 4$

  d $y = 3(x+1)^2 - 4$ **e** $y = \frac{1}{2}(x+3)^2$ **f** $y = -\frac{1}{2}(x+3)^2 + 1$

  g $y = -2(x+4)^2 + 3$ **h** $y = 2(x-3)^2 + 5$ **i** $y = \frac{1}{2}(x-2)^2 - 1$

13 Use your **graphics calculator** or **graphing package** to check your graphs in question **12**.

14 Match each quadratic function with its corresponding graph:

  a $y = -1(x+1)^2 + 3$ **b** $y = -2(x-3)^2 + 2$ **c** $y = x^2 + 2$

  d $y = -1(x-1)^2 + 1$ **e** $y = (x-2)^2 - 2$ **f** $y = \frac{1}{3}(x+3)^2 - 3$

  g $y = -x^2$ **h** $y = -\frac{1}{2}(x-1)^2 + 1$ **i** $y = 2(x+2)^2 - 1$

A 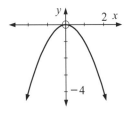   **B** 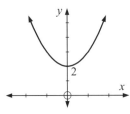   **C**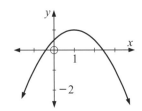

D 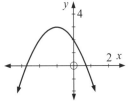   **E** 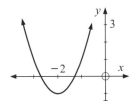   **F**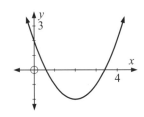

G 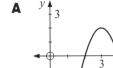   **H** 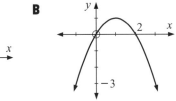   **I**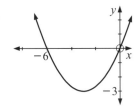

C AXIS INTERCEPTS

Given the equation of any curve:

An x-**intercept** is a value of x where the graph meets the x-axis,

A y-**intercept** is a value of y where the graph meets the y-axis.

x-intercepts are found by letting y be 0 in the equation of the curve.

y-intercepts are found by letting x be 0 in the equation of the curve.

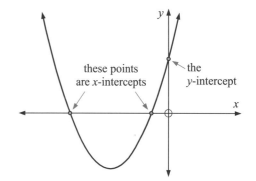

INVESTIGATION 2   AXIS INTERCEPTS

What to do:

GRAPHING PACKAGE

1   For the following quadratic functions, use your graphing package or graphics calculator to:

   i draw the graph   **ii** find the y-intercept   **iii** find the x-intercepts (if any exist)

   a $y = x^2 - 3x - 4$ **b** $y = -x^2 + 2x + 8$ **c** $y = 2x^2 - 3x$

   d $y = -2x^2 + 2x - 3$ **e** $y = (x-1)(x-3)$ **f** $y = -(x+2)(x-3)$

   g $y = 3(x+1)(x+4)$ **h** $y = 2(x-2)^2$ **i** $y = -3(x+1)^2$

2   From your observations in question **1**:

   a   State the y-intercept of a quadratic function in the form $y = ax^2 + bx + c$.

   b   State the x-intercepts of quadratic function in the form $y = a(x-\alpha)(x-\beta)$.

   c   What do you notice about the x-intercepts of quadratic functions in the form $y = a(x-\alpha)^2$?

THE y-INTERCEPT

You will have noticed that for a quadratic function of the form $y = ax^2 + bx + c$, the y-intercept is the constant term c. This is because any curve cuts the y-axis when $x = 0$.

So, if we substitute $x = 0$ into a function we can find the y-intercept.

For example,   if $y = x^2 - 2x - 3$ and we let $x = 0$

                  then $y = 0^2 - 2(0) - 3$

                  $\therefore$ $y = -3$ (the constant term)

EXERCISE 20C.1

1   For the following functions state the y-intercept:

   a $y = x^2 + 3x + 3$ **b** $y = x^2 - 5x + 2$ **c** $y = 2x^2 + 7x - 8$

   d $y = 3x^2 - x + 1$ **e** $y = -x^2 + 3x + 6$ **f** $y = -2x^2 + 5 - x$

   g $y = 6 - x - x^2$ **h** $y = 8 + 2x - 3x^2$ **i** $y = 5x - x^2 - 2$

THE x-INTERCEPTS

You will have noticed that for a quadratic function of the form $y = a(x - \alpha)(x - \beta)$, the x-intercepts are α and β. This is because any curve cuts the x-axis when $y = 0$.

So, if we substitute $y = 0$ into the function we get $a(x - \alpha)(x - \beta) = 0$

$$\therefore \quad x = \alpha \text{ or } \beta \qquad \{\text{by the Null Factor law}\}$$

This suggests that x-intercepts are easy to find when the quadratic is in **factorised** form.

Example 13   ◀)) **Self Tutor**

Find the x-intercepts of:

  a $y = 2(x - 3)(x + 2)$ **b** $y = -(x - 4)^2$

a We let $y = 0$	**b** We let $y = 0$
$\therefore \quad 2(x - 3)(x + 2) = 0$	$\therefore \quad -(x - 4)^2 = 0$
$\therefore \quad x = 3 \quad \text{or} \quad x = -2$	$\therefore \quad x = 4$
$\therefore$ the x-intercepts are 3 and -2.	$\therefore$ the x-intercept is 4.

EXERCISE 20C.2

> If a quadratic function has only one x-intercept then its graph must touch the x-axis.

1 For the following functions, find the x-intercepts:

  a $y = (x - 3)(x + 1)$ **b** $y = -(x - 2)(x - 4)$

  c $y = 2(x + 3)(x + 2)$ **d** $y = -3(x - 4)(x - 5)$

  e $y = 2(x + 3)^2$ **f** $y = -5(x - 1)^2$

FACTORISING TO FIND x-INTERCEPTS

If the quadratic function is given in the form $y = ax^2 + bx + c$ and we wish to find the x-intercepts, we let $y = 0$ and solve for x by **factorising**.

In general: for any quadratic function of the form $y = ax^2 + bx + c$, the x-intercepts can be found by solving the equation $ax^2 + bx + c = 0$.

You will recall from **Chapter 11** that quadratic equations may have *two solutions, one solution* or *no solutions.*

Consequently, parabolas drawn from quadratic functions can have   • two x-intercepts,
  • one x-intercept, or
  • no x-intercepts.

Example 14   ◀)) **Self Tutor**

Find the x-intercept(s) of the quadratic functions:

  a $y = x^2 - 6x + 9$ **b** $y = -x^2 - x + 6$

a	When $y = 0$,	b	When $y = 0$,

a When $y = 0$,
$$x^2 - 6x + 9 = 0$$
$$\therefore \quad (x-3)^2 = 0$$
$$\therefore \quad x = 3$$

$$\therefore \quad x\text{-intercept is 3.}$$

b When $y = 0$,
$$-x^2 - x + 6 = 0$$
$$\therefore \quad x^2 + x - 6 = 0$$
$$\therefore \quad (x+3)(x-2) = 0$$
$$\therefore \quad x = -3 \text{ or } 2$$

$$\therefore \quad x\text{-intercepts are } -3 \text{ and } 2.$$

EXERCISE 20C.3

1 For the following functions find the x-intercepts:

a $y = x^2 - 9$
b $y = 2x^2 - 6$
c $y = x^2 + 7x + 10$
d $y = x^2 + x - 12$
e $y = 4x - x^2$
f $y = -x^2 - 6x - 8$
g $y = -2x^2 - 4x - 2$
h $y = 4x^2 - 24x + 36$
i $y = x^2 - 4x + 1$
j $y = x^2 + 4x - 3$
k $y = x^2 - 6x - 2$
l $y = x^2 + 8x + 11$

D   GRAPHS FROM AXIS INTERCEPTS

Consider the quadratic function $y = 3(x-1)^2 + 2$.

$$y = 3(x-1)^2 + 2$$
$$a = 3 \qquad h = 1 \qquad k = 2$$

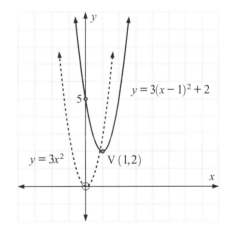

$y = 3(x-1)^2 + 2$

$y = 3x^2$

V (1,2)

This graph has the same shape as the graph of $y = 3x^2$ and has vertex $(1, 2)$.

On expanding:
$$y = 3(x-1)^2 + 2$$
$$\therefore \quad y = 3(x^2 - 2x + 1) + 2$$
$$\therefore \quad y = 3x^2 - 6x + 3 + 2$$
$$\therefore \quad y = 3x^2 - 6x + 5$$

From this we can see that:

the graph of a quadratic of the form $y = ax^2 + bx + c$ has the same shape as the graph of $y = ax^2$.

EXERCISE 20D

1 **i** Use your **graphing package** or **graphics calculator** to graph, on the same set of axes, the following quadratic functions.

 ii Compare the shapes of the two graphs.

a $y = 2x^2$ and $y = 2x^2 - 3x + 1$
b $y = -x^2$ and $y = -x^2 - 6x + 4$
c $y = 3x^2$ and $y = 3x^2 - 5x$
d $y = -2x^2$ and $y = -2x^2 + 5$

Example 15   ◀ Self Tutor

Sketch the graph of the following by considering:
  i the value of a **ii** the y-intercept   **iii** the x-intercepts.
  a $y = x^2 - 2x - 3$ **b** $y = -2(x+1)(x-2)$

a $y = x^2 - 2x - 3$ **b** $y = -2(x+1)(x-2)$

   i since $a = 1$ the parabola
     opens upwards   i.e.,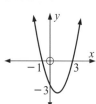

    ii y-intercept occurs when
       $x = 0$, i.e., $y = -3$
       i.e., y-intercept is -3

   iii x-intercepts occur when
      $y = 0$
       $\therefore \quad x^2 - 2x - 3 = 0$
       $\therefore \quad (x-3)(x+1) = 0$
       $\therefore \quad x = 3$ or $x = -1$
      i.e.,   the x-intercepts are
        3 and -1

Sketch:

b **i** Since $a = -2$ the parabola opens
    downwards   i.e.,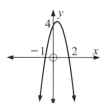

   ii y-intercept occurs when $x = 0$
      $\therefore \quad y = -2(0+1)(0-2)$
         $y = -2 \times 1 \times -2$
         $y = 4$
    i.e., y-intercept is 4

   iii x-intercepts occur when $y = 0$
      $\therefore \quad -2(x+1)(x-2) = 0$
      $\therefore \quad x = -1$ or $x = 2$
    i.e., x-intercepts are -1 and 2

Sketch:

Example 16   ◀ Self Tutor

Sketch the graph of $y = 2(x-3)^2$ by considering:
  a the value of a **b** the y-intercept   **c** the x-intercepts.

$y = 2(x-3)^2$

a Since $a = 2$ the parabola opens upwards   i.e.,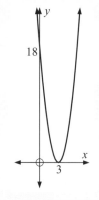

b y-intercept occurs when $x = 0$
   $\therefore \quad y = 2(0-3)^2 = 18$
  i.e., y-intercept is 18

c x-intercepts occur when $y = 0$
   $\therefore \quad 2(x-3)^2 = 0$
     $\therefore \quad x = 3$
  i.e., x-intercept is 3   {only one x-intercept $\therefore$ *touches*}

2 Sketch the graphs of the following by considering:

    i the value of a **ii** the y-intercept   **iii** the x-intercepts.

  a $y = x^2 - 4x + 4$ **b** $y = (x-1)(x+3)$ **c** $y = 2(x+2)^2$

  d $y = -(x-2)(x+1)$ **e** $y = -3(x+1)^2$ **f** $y = -3(x-4)(x-1)$

  g $y = 2(x+3)(x+1)$ **h** $y = 2x^2 + 3x + 2$ **i** $y = -2x^2 - 3x + 5$

Recall from **Exercise 20B**:

- the graph of a quadratic function is a **parabola**
- the curve is symmetrical about an **axis of symmetry**
- the curve has a **turning point** or **vertex**.

Example 17   ◀) Self Tutor

  a Sketch the graph of $y = 2(x-2)(x+4)$ using axis intercepts.

  b Find the equation of the axis of symmetry and the coordinates of the vertex.

---

  a $y = 2(x-2)(x+4)$

    Since $a = 2$ the parabola opens upwards i.e.,

    When $x = 0$

        $y = 2 \times -2 \times 4 = -16$

    i.e., y-intercept is -16.

    When $y = 0$

        $\therefore \quad 2(x-2)(x+4) = 0$

        $\therefore \quad x = 2 \quad \text{or} \quad x = -4$

    i.e., x-intercepts are 2 and -4.

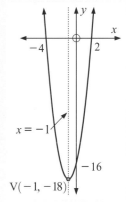

  b Axis of symmetry is halfway between x-intercepts

    $\therefore$ axis of symmetry is $x = -1$ {-1 is the average of -4 and 2}

    when $x = -1$, $y = 2(-1-2)(-1+4)$

                    $= 2 \times -3 \times 3$

                    $= -18$

    i.e., coordinates of vertex are $(-1, -18)$.

---

3 For each of the following find the equation of the axis of symmetry:

  a   **b**   **c**

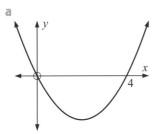 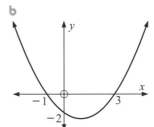 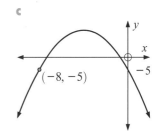

4 For each of the following quadratic functions:

    i   sketch the graph using axis intercepts and hence find

    ii the equation of the axis of symmetry

    iii the coordinates of the vertex.

a $y = x^2 + 4x + 4$ **b** $y = x(x - 4)$ **c** $y = 3(x - 2)^2$

d $y = -(x - 1)(x + 3)$ **e** $y = -2(x - 1)^2$ **f** $y = -3(x + 2)(x - 2)$

g $y = 2(x + 1)(x + 4)$ **h** $y = 2x^2 - 3x - 2$ **i** $y = -2x^2 - x + 3$

Example 18   **◀)) Self Tutor**

Sketch the parabola which has x-intercepts -3 and 1, and y-intercept -2.
Find the equation of the axis of symmetry.

The axis of symmetry lies halfway
between the x-intercepts   ∴   axis of
symmetry is $x = -1$.

$\{\dfrac{-3 + 1}{2} = -1\}$

Note: The graph must open upwards.
Can you see why?

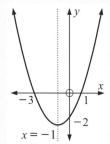

---

5 For each of the following:

    i sketch the parabola

    ii find the equation of the axis of symmetry.

a x-intercepts 3 and -1, y-intercept -4

b x-intercepts 2 and -2, y-intercept 4

c x-intercept -3 (touching), y-intercept 6

d x-intercept 1 (touching), y-intercept -4

6 Find all x-intercepts of the following graphs of quadratic functions:

a cuts the x-axis at 2, axis of symmetry $x = 4$

b cuts the x-axis at -1, axis of symmetry $x = -3$

c touches the x-axis at 3.

7 Consider the quadratic function
$y = ax^2 + bx + c$ whose graph cuts the x-axis at
A and B. Let the equation of the axis of symmetry be $x = h$.   The x-intercepts are an equal
distance (d) from the axis of symmetry.

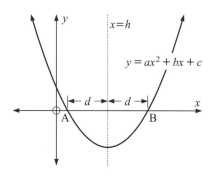

    a Find in terms of h and d the coordinates of
        A and B.

    b Substitute the coordinates of A into
        $y = ax^2 + bx + c$ to create equation (1).

c Substitute the coordinates of B into $y = ax^2 + bx + c$ to create equation (2).

d Use equations (1) and (2) to show that $h = \dfrac{-b}{2a}$.

E | AXIS OF SYMMETRY AND VERTEX

AXIS OF SYMMETRY

As we have seen from the previous exercise:

the equation of the **axis of symmetry** of $y = ax^2 + bx + c$ is $x = \dfrac{-b}{2a}$.

The problem with the method used to demonstrate this is that not all quadratic functions have a graph which cuts the x-axis.

To prove this formula we can use an expansion method and compare coefficients.

Proof: Suppose $y = ax^2 + bx + c$ is converted to $y = a(x - h)^2 + k$

i.e., $y = a(x^2 - 2hx + h^2) + k$

i.e., $y = ax^2 - 2ahx + [ah^2 + k]$.

Comparing the coefficients of x we obtain $-2ah = b$ $\therefore$ $h = \dfrac{-b}{2a}$.

Example 19 ◀)) **Self Tutor**

Find the equation of the axis of symmetry of $y = 2x^2 + 3x + 1$.

$y = 2x^2 + 3x + 1$ has $a = 2$, $b = 3$, $c = 1$

$\therefore$ axis of symmetry has equation $x = \dfrac{-b}{2a} = \dfrac{-3}{2 \times 2}$ i.e., $x = -\frac{3}{4}$

EXERCISE 20E

1 Determine the equation of the axis of symmetry of:

a $y = x^2 + 4x + 1$ b $y = 2x^2 - 6x + 3$ c $y = 3x^2 + 4x - 1$

d $y = -x^2 - 4x + 5$ e $y = -2x^2 + 5x + 1$ f $y = \frac{1}{2}x^2 - 10x + 2$

g $y = \frac{1}{3}x^2 + 4x$ h $y = 100x - 4x^2$ i $y = -\frac{1}{10}x^2 + 30x$

TURNING POINT (OR VERTEX)

The **turning point** (or **vertex**) of any parabola is the point at which the function has a

maximum value (for $a < 0$)   or, a **minimum value** (for $a > 0$) .

As the turning point lies on the axis of symmetry, its x-coordinate will be $x = \dfrac{-b}{2a}$.

The y-coordinate can be found by substituting for x into the function.

Example 20   ◀)) **Self Tutor**

Determine the coordinates of the vertex of $y = 2x^2 - 8x + 1$.

The vertex is sometimes called the maximum turning point or the minimum turning point depending on whether the graph is opening downwards or upwards.

$y = 2x^2 - 8x + 1$ has $a = 2$, $b = -8$, $c = 1$

and so $\dfrac{-b}{2a} = \dfrac{-(-8)}{2 \times 2} = 2$

$\therefore$ equation of axis of symmetry is $x = 2$

and when $x = 2$, $y = 2(2)^2 - 8(2) + 1 = 8 - 16 + 1 = -7$

$\therefore$ the vertex has coordinates $(2, -7)$.

---

2   Find the turning point (vertex) for the following quadratic functions:

    a $y = x^2 - 4x + 2$ **b** $y = x^2 + 2x - 3$ **c** $y = 2x^2 + 4$

    d $y = -3x^2 + 1$ **e** $y = 2x^2 + 8x - 7$ **f** $y = -x^2 - 4x - 9$

    g $y = 2x^2 + 6x - 1$ **h** $y = 2x^2 - 10x + 3$ **i** $y = -\frac{1}{2}x^2 + x - 5$

Example 21   ◀)) **Self Tutor**

For the quadratic function $y = -x^2 + 2x + 3$:
a   find its axis intercepts
b   find the equation of the axis of symmetry
c   find the coordinates of the vertex
d   sketch the function showing all important features.

a   When $x = 0$, $y = 3$
    $\therefore$ y-intercept is 3.

    When $y = 0$, $-x^2 + 2x + 3 = 0$
        $\therefore$ $x^2 - 2x - 3 = 0$
        $\therefore$ $(x - 3)(x + 1) = 0$
          $\therefore$ $x = 3$ or -1

   so, x-intercepts are 3 and -1.

c   From **b** when $x = 1$
      $y = -(1)^2 + 2(1) + 3$
        $= -1 + 2 + 3$
        $= 4$

   $\therefore$ vertex is $(1, 4)$.

b $a = -1$, $b = 2$, $c = 3$

   $\therefore$ $\dfrac{-b}{2a} = \dfrac{-2}{-2} = 1$

   $\therefore$ axis of symmetry is $x = 1$.

d

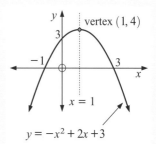

3 For each of the following quadratic functions find :

    i   the axis intercepts   **ii**   the equation of the axis of symmetry

    iii   the coordinates of the vertex   **iv**   and hence sketch the graph.

   a $y = x^2 - 2x - 8$ **b** $y = x^2 + 3x$ **c** $y = 4x - x^2$

   d $y = x^2 + 4x + 4$ **e** $y = x^2 + 3x - 4$ **f** $y = -x^2 + 2x - 1$

   g $y = -x^2 - 6x - 8$ **h** $y = -x^2 + 3x - 2$ **i** $y = 2x^2 + 5x - 3$

   j $y = 2x^2 - 5x - 12$ **k** $y = -3x^2 - 4x + 4$ **l** $y = -\frac{1}{4}x^2 + 5x$

F   QUADRATIC MODELLING

If the relationship between two variables is a quadratic function, then its graph will be either

$\bigcup$ or $\bigcap$ and the function will have a minimum or maximum value.

For $y = ax^2 + bx + c$:

- if $a > 0$, the **minimum** value of y occurs at $x = -\dfrac{b}{2a}$

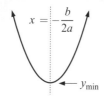

- if $a < 0$, the **maximum** value of y occurs at $x = -\dfrac{b}{2a}$.

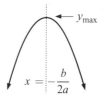

The process of finding the maximum or minimum value of a function is called **optimisation**.

Optimisation is a very useful tool when looking at such issues as:

- maximising profits   •   minimising costs   •   maximising heights reached etc.

Example 22   ◄⑴ Self Tutor

The height H metres, of a rocket t seconds after it is fired vertically upwards is given by $H(t) = 80t - 5t^2$, $t \geqslant 0$.

a How long does it take for the rocket to reach its maximum height?

b What is the maximum height reached by the rocket?

c How long does it take for the rocket to fall back to earth?

a
$$H(t) = 80t - 5t^2$$
$$\therefore \quad H(t) = -5t^2 + 80t \quad \text{where} \quad a = -5 \quad \therefore$$

The maximum height reached occurs when $t = \dfrac{-b}{2a} = \dfrac{-80}{2(-5)} = 8$

i.e.,   the maximum height is reached after 8 seconds.

b $H(8) = 80 \times 8 - 5 \times 8^2$
$\qquad\quad = 640 - 320$
$\qquad\quad = 320$

i.e.,   the maximum height reached is 320 m.

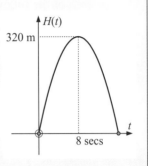

c The rocket falls back to earth when $H(t) = 0$

$\therefore \quad 0 = 80t - 5t^2$

$\therefore \quad 5t^2 - 80t = 0$

$\therefore \quad 5t(t - 16) = 0 \qquad \{\text{factorising}\}$

$\therefore \quad t = 0 \text{ or } t = 16$

i.e.,   the rocket falls back to earth after 16 seconds.

EXERCISE 20F

1 The height H metres, of a ball hit vertically upwards t seconds after it is hit is given by $H(t) = 36t - 2t^2$.

    a How long does it take for the ball to reach its maximum height?

    b What is the maximum height of the ball?

    c How long does it take for the ball to hit the ground?

2 A skateboard manufacturer finds that the cost $\$C$ of making x skateboards per day is given by $C(x) = x^2 - 24x + 244$.

    a How many skateboards should be made per day to minimise the cost of production?

    b What is the minimum cost?

    c What is the cost if no skateboards are made in a day?

3 The driver of a car travelling downhill on a road applied the brakes. The speed (s) of the car in kmph, t seconds after the brakes were applied is given by $s(t) = -4t^2 + 12t + 80$.

    a How fast was the car travelling when the driver applied the brakes?

    b After how many seconds was the speed of the car 88 kmph? Can you explain your answer?

    c After how many seconds did the car reach its maximum speed?

    d What was the maximum speed reached?

4 The hourly profit ($\$P$) obtained from operating a fleet of n taxis is given by $P(n) = 84n - 45 - 2n^2$.

    a What number of taxis gives the maximum hourly profit?

    b What is the maximum hourly profit?

    c How much money is lost per hour if no taxis are on the road?

5 The temperature T^o Celsius in a greenhouse t hours after dusk (7.00 pm) is given by $T(t) = \frac{1}{4}t^2 - 5t + 30, (t \leqslant 20)$.

    a What was the temperature in the greenhouse at dusk?

    b At what time was the temperature at a minimum?

    c What was the minimum temperature?

6 A vegetable gardener has 40 m of fencing to enclose a rectangular garden plot where one side is an existing brick wall. If the width is x m as shown:

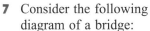

 a Show that the area (A) enclosed is given by
   $A = -2x^2 + 40x$ m^2.

 b Find x such that the vegetable garden has maximum area.

 c What is the maximum area?

7 Consider the following diagram of a bridge:

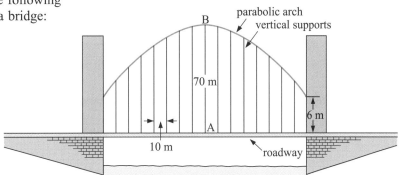

AB is the longest vertical support of a bridge which contains a parabolic arch. The vertical supports are 10 m apart. The arch meets the vertical end supports 6 m above the road.

 a If axes are drawn on the diagram of the bridge above, with x-axis the road and y-axis on AB, find the equation of the parabolic arch in the form $y = ax^2 + c$.

 b Hence, determine the lengths of all other vertical supports.

8 Two towers OP and RQ of a suspension bridge are 50 m high and 60 m apart. A cable is suspended between P and Q and approximates the shape of a parabola under its own weight.

The maximum sag in the middle of the cable is 20 m.

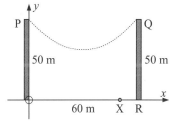

 a Find the coordinates of the vertex of the parabola.

 b Hence, find the equation of the parabola.

 c How high is the cable directly above X, given that XR $= 10$ m?

9 Revisit the **Opening Problem** on page **476**. Answer the questions posed.

REVIEW SET 20A

1 For $f(x) = 5x - 2$ and $g(x) = x^2 - 3x - 15$ find:
  a $f(-2)$ **b** $g(1)$ **c** x if $g(x) = 3$

2 On separate axes sketch $y = x^2$ and hence sketch:
  a $y = 3x^2$ **b** $y = (x-2)^2 + 1$ **c** $y = -(x+3)^2 - 2$

3 For $y = -2(x-1)(x+3)$ find the:

  a   **i**   direction the parabola opens   **ii** y-intercept

      iii x-intercepts   **iv**   equation of the axis of symmetry

  b Hence, sketch the graph showing all of the above features.

4 For $y = x^2 - 2x - 15$ find the:

  a   **i** y-intercept   **ii** x-intercepts

      iii   equation of the axis of symmetry **iv**   coordinates of the vertex

  b Hence sketch the graph showing all of the above features.

5 A stone was thrown from the top of a cliff 60 metres above sea level. The height H metres, of the stone above sea level t seconds after it was released is given by $H(t) = -5t^2 + 20t + 60$.

  a Find the time taken for the stone to reach its maximum height.

  b What is the maximum height above sea level reached by the stone?

  c How long is it before the stone strikes the water?

REVIEW SET 20B

1 For $f(x) = 2x^2 + x - 2$ and $g(x) = 3 - 2x$ find:

  a $f(-1)$ **b** $g(4)$ **c** x if $f(x) = 4$

2 On separate axes sketch $y = x^2$ and hence sketch:

  a $y = -\frac{1}{2}x^2$ **b** $y = (x+2)^2 + 5$ **c** $y = -(x-1)^2 - 3$

3 For $y = 3(x-2)^2$ find the:

  a   **i**   direction the parabola opens   **ii** y-intercept

      iii x-intercepts   **iv**   equation of the axis of symmetry

  b Hence sketch the graph showing all of the above features.

4 For $y = -x^2 + 7x - 10$ find the:

  a   **i** y-intercept   **ii** x-intercepts

      iii   equation of the axis of symmetry **iv**   coordinates of the vertex

  b Hence sketch the graph showing all of the above features.

5 The height H metres of a cannonball t seconds after it is fired into the air is given by $H(t) = -4t^2 + 16t + 9$.

  a Find the time taken for the cannonball to reach its maximum height.

  b What is the maximum height reached by the cannonball?

  c How long does it take for the cannonball to fall back to earth?

Chapter 21

 **Click on the icon to access this printable chapter**

Logic

Contents:

Chapter 22

 Click on the icon to access this printable chapter

Networks and trees

Contents:

Chapter 23

Click on the icon to access this printable chapter

Bivariate statistics

Contents:

Chapter 24

Click on the icon to access this printable chapter

Matrices

Contents:

Chapter **25**

Click on the icon to access this printable chapter

Linear programming

ANSWERS

EXERCISE 1A

1 a true **b** true **c** true **d** true **e** false **f** false
  g true **h** true

2 **a, b, c, d, f, g, h** are rational; **e** is irrational

3 a $\{1, 2, 3, 6\}$ **b** $\{6, 12, 18, 24, ...\}$ **c** $\{1, 17\}$
  d $\{17, 34, 51, 68, ...\}$ **e** $\{2, 3, 5, 7, 11, 13, 17, 19\}$
  f $\{12, 14, 15, 16, 18, 20, 21, 22, 24, 25, 26, 27, 28\}$

4 a $0.\overline{7} = \frac{7}{9}$ **b** $0.\overline{41} = \frac{41}{99}$ **c** $0.\overline{324} = \frac{12}{37}$

5 a 0.527 can be written as $\frac{527}{1000}$, and 527, 1000 are integers

  b Let $x = 0.\overline{9} = 0.999\,99......$
    $\therefore$ $10x = 9.999\,99...... = 9 + x$
    i.e., $9x = 9$ so $x = 1$ which is an integer that can
    be written as $\frac{1}{1}$ which is rational.

6 a e.g., $\sqrt{2} + (-\sqrt{2}) = 0$ which is rational
  b e.g., $\sqrt{2} \times \sqrt{50} = \sqrt{100} = 10$ which is rational

EXERCISE 1B

1 a The set of all values of real x such that x is greater
    than 4.
  b The set of all values of real x such that x is less than
    or equal to 5.
  c The set of all values of real y such that y lies between
    0 and 8.
  d The set of all values of real x such that x lies between
    1 and 4 or is equal to 1 or 4.
  e The set of all values of real t such that t lies between
    2 and 7.
  f The set of all values of real n such that n is less than
    or equal to 3 or n is greater than 6.

2 a $\{x \mid x > 3\}$ **b** $\{x \mid 2 < x \leqslant 5\}$
  c $\{x \mid x \leqslant -1 \text{ or } x \geqslant 2\}$ **d** $\{x \mid x \in \mathbb{Z}, \ -1 \leqslant x < 5\}$
  e $\{x \mid x \in \mathbb{N}, \ 0 \leqslant x \leqslant 6\}$ **f** $\{x \mid x < 0\}$

3 a   **b**
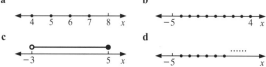

c   **d**

e   **f**

EXERCISE 1C

1 a

  $A = \{2, 3, 5, 7\}$
  b $A' = \{1, 4, 6, 8\}$

2 a
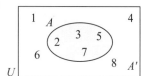

  b $V' = \{b, c, d, f, g, h, j, k, l, m, n, p, q, r, s, t, v, w,$
    $x, y, z\}$

3 a/b
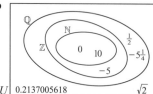

  c i true
    ii true
    iii true

  d (shaded section
    of diagram
    alongside)

4 a
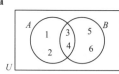

  b
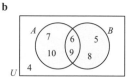

  c
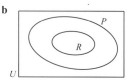

5 a   **b**
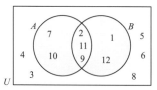

EXERCISE 1D

1 a i $C = \{1, 3, 7, 9\}$ **ii** $D = \{1, 2, 5\}$
    iii $U = \{1, 2, 3, 4, 5, 6, 7, 8, 9\}$ **iv** $C \cap D = \{1\}$
    v $C \cup D = \{1, 2, 3, 5, 7, 9\}$
  b i $n(C) = 4$ **ii** $n(D) = 3$ **iii** $n(U) = 9$
    iv $n(C \cap D) = 1$ **v** $n(C \cup D) = 6$

2 a i $A = \{2, 7\}$ **ii** $B = \{1, 2, 4, 6, 7\}$
    iii $U = \{1, 2, 3, 4, 5, 6, 7, 8\}$ **iv** $A \cap B = \{2, 7\}$
    v $A \cup B = \{1, 2, 4, 6, 7\}$
  b i $n(A) = 2$ **ii** $n(B) = 5$ **iii** $n(U) = 8$
    iv $n(A \cap B) = 2$ **v** $n(A \cup B) = 5$

3 a

  b i $A \cap B = \{2, 9, 11\}$
    ii $A \cup B = \{1, 2, 7, 9, 10, 11, 12\}$
    iii $B' = \{3, 4, 5, 6, 7, 8, 10\}$
  c i $n(A) = 5$ **ii** $n(B') = 7$ **iii** $n(A \cap B) = 3$
    iv $n(A \cup B) = 7$

4 a $A \cap B = \{1, 3, 9\}$
  b $A \cup B = \{1, 2, 3, 4, 6, 7, 9, 12, 18, 21, 36, 63\}$

5 a $X \cap Y = \{B, M, T, Z\}$
  b $X \cup Y = \{A, B, C, D, M, N, P, R, T, W, Z\}$

6 a i $n(A) = 8$ **ii** $n(B) = 10$ **iii** $n(A \cap B) = 3$
    iv $n(A \cup B) = 15$
  b $n(A) + n(B) - n(A \cap B) = 8 + 10 - 3 = 15 = n(A \cup B)$

7 $n(A) + n(B) - n(A \cap B)$ $= (a+b) + (b+c) - b$
$= a + b + c$
$= n(A \cup B)$

8 **a** not in A – shaded pink   **b** in both A and B

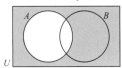

c $A \cap B'$ **d** in either A or B

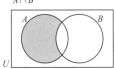

e $A \cup B'$ **f** $(A \cup B)'$

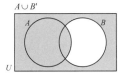

g $(A \cap B)'$ **h** in exactly one of A or B

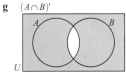

9 **a** in X but not in Y
   b the complement of 'in exactly one of X and Y'
   c in exactly two or three of X, Y and Z

10 **a** $X \cap Y = \{\ \ \}$ (an empty set)
   b **i** $A \cup A' = U$ **ii** $A \cap A' = \{\ \ \}$ (an empty set)

11 **a** A' **b** $A' \cap B$

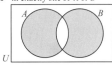

c $A \cup B'$ **d** $A' \cap B'$

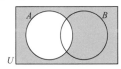

12 **a** A **b** B'

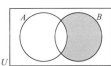

c $B \cap C$ **d** $A \cup C$

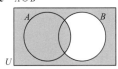

e $A \cap B \cap C$ **f** $(A \cup B) \cap C$

13 **a**

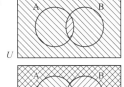

/////// represents $A \cap B$
\\\\\\\ represents $(A \cap B)'$

/////// represents A'
\\\\\\\ represents B'
XXXXXX represents $A' \cup B'$

b

||||||| represents $B \cap C$
——— represents A
whole shaded region represents
$A \cup (B \cap C)$

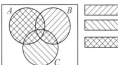

/////// represents $A \cup B$
\\\\\\\ represents $A \cup C$
XXXXXX represents
$(A \cup B) \cap (A \cup C)$

c

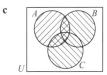

/////// represents A
\\\\\\\ represents $B \cup C$
XXXXXX represents $A \cap (B \cup C)$

/////// represents $A \cap B$
\\\\\\\ represents $A \cap C$
whole shaded region represents
$(A \cap B) \cup (A \cap C)$

EXERCISE 1E

1 **a** 18 **b** 2 **c** 17 **d** 12
2 **a** 75 **b** 9 **c** 24 **d** 42
3

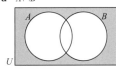

   a 15 **b** 21
   c 4 **d** 6
   e 9

4 **a** 19 **b** 20 **c** 32 **d** 25 **e** 13
5 10 play both **6** **a** 18 **b** 38 **7** **a** 22 **b** 18
8 **a** 15 **b** 14 **c** 8 **9** 200 families had both
10 **a** 65% **b** 35% **c** 22% **d** 28% **e** 9%

EXERCISE 1F

1 11 violin players
2 19 places
3 43%
4 14 members

5

   a 15 students
   b 55 students

6 The number who participate in all three sports must be less than or equal to 30.

EXERCISE 1G

1

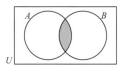 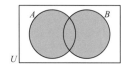

$A \cap B = B \cap A$

The common area is the same.

$A \cup B = B \cup A$

The combined area is the same.

2

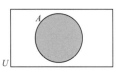

$A \cap A = A$
$A \cup A = A$

The intersection is the area common to both $= A$
The union is the total area in both $= A$

3

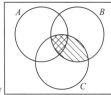 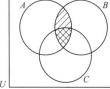

 represents $B \cap C$
represents $A \cap (B \cap C)$

represents $A \cap B$
represents $(A \cap B) \cap C$

Area shaded is the same in each case.

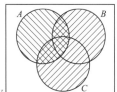 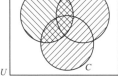

represents A
represents $B \cup C$
whole shaded region represents $A \cup (B \cup C)$

represents C
represents $A \cup B$
whole shaded region represents $(A \cup B) \cup C$

Total shaded area is the same in each case.

4

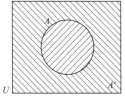

represents A
represents A'

A and A' are the complement of each other. When combined, they make up the universal set U, i.e., $(A')' = A$.

5 a $A \cap A' = \{\ \}$, the empty set
  b $A \cup A' = U$, the universal set

REVIEW SET 1A

1 a 1.3 can be written as $\frac{13}{10}$, and 13, 10 are integers
  b false **c** $\{23, 29, 31, 37\}$
  d The set of all values of real t such that t lies between -1 and 3 but could be equal to -1.

e $\{x \mid 0 < x \leqslant 5\}$ **f**

2 a

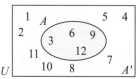

  b $A' = \{1, 2, 4, 5, 7, 8, 10, 11\}$ **c** $n(A') = 8$ **d** false

3 a false **b** false

4 a i $A = \{1, 2, 3, 4, 5\}$ **ii** $B = \{1, 2, 7\}$
    iii $U = \{1, 2, 3, 4, 5, 6, 7\}$
    iv $A \cup B = \{1, 2, 3, 4, 5, 7\}$ **v** $A \cap B = \{1, 2\}$
  b i $n(A) = 5$ **ii** $n(B) = 3$ **iii** $n(A \cup B) = 6$

5 a

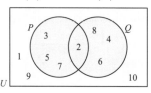

  b i $P \cap Q = \{2\}$ **ii** $P \cup Q = \{2, 3, 4, 5, 6, 7, 8\}$
    iii $Q' = \{1, 3, 5, 7, 9, 10\}$
  c i $n(P') = 6$ **ii** $n(P \cap Q) = 1$ **iii** $n(P \cup Q) = 7$
  d true

6 a shaded region is the complement of X, i.e., everything not in X
  b shaded region represents 'in exactly one of X or Y but not both'
  c shaded region represents everything in X or not in Y

REVIEW SET 1B

1 a false **b** false **c** $0.\overline{41} = \frac{41}{99}$, and 41, 99 are integers
  d $\{t \mid t \leqslant -3 \text{ or } t > 4\}$ **e**

2

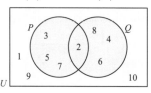

3 a 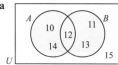 **b**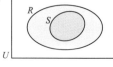

4 a $A \cap B = \{1, 2, 3, 6\}$
  b $A \cup B = \{1, 2, 3, 4, 6, 8, 9, 12, 18, 24\}$

5 a 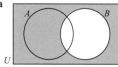 **b**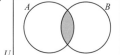

  c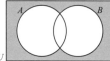

6

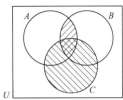 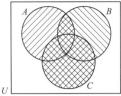

represents $A \cap B$
represents C
whole shaded region
represents $(A \cap B) \cup C$

represents $A \cup C$
represents $B \cup C$
represents $(A \cup C) \cap (B \cup C)$

Area shaded is the same in each case.

EXERCISE 2A

1 a $\sqrt{65}$ cm **b** $\sqrt{50}$ cm **c** $\sqrt{233}$ km
2 a $\sqrt{85}$ cm **b** $\sqrt{4.23}$ km **c** $\sqrt{45.125}$ cm
3 a $x = \sqrt{11}$ **b** $x = \sqrt{2}$ **c** $x = \sqrt{5}$
4 a $x = \sqrt{\frac{5}{4}}$ **b** $x = \sqrt{\frac{10}{4}}$ **c** $x = \frac{1}{2}$
5 a $x = \sqrt{27}$ **b** $x = \sqrt{52}$ **c** $x = 2$
6 a $x = \sqrt{17},\ y = \sqrt{8}$ **b** $x = \sqrt{29},\ y = \sqrt{45}$
c $x = \sqrt{5},\ y = \sqrt{6}$
7 a $x = \sqrt{2}$ **b** $x = 14$ **8** AC $= \sqrt{39}$ m
9 a AB $= \sqrt{17}$ cm **b** AB $= \sqrt{29}$ m **c** AB $= \sqrt{41}$ m

EXERCISE 2B

1 b, e, f are right angled **2 a** $\angle$BAC **b** $\angle$ABC **c** $\angle$ACB
3 a, b, d, f are Pythagorean triples.
4 a $k = 17$ **b** $k = 10$ **c** $k = 48$ **d** $k = 25$
e $k = 24$ **f** $k = 60$
5 $n = 3$ **6** $(n+3)^2 \neq n^2 + (n+1)^2$ for $n \in \mathbb{Z}^+$

EXERCISE 2C.1

1 8.54 cm **2** 3.16 cm $\times$ 9.49 cm
3 a 53.67 cm **b** 160 cm^2 **4** 6.63 cm **5** 7.07 cm
6 25.61 cm **7** 9.43 km
8 By car, $1.\overline{4}$ h; by train, $1.41\overline{6}$ h $\therefore$ quicker to go by train.
9 11.18 km/h and 22.36 km/h
10 a $x = \sqrt{2},\ y = 45$ **b** $x = 6,\ h = \sqrt{13}$
c $x = \frac{1}{2},\ y = \frac{\sqrt{3}}{2}$
11 10.4 cm **12** 22.25 cm^2 **13** 6.025 m
14 8 cm **15 1** 240 m **2** 40 m **3** 202.48 m

EXERCISE 2C.2

1 19.21 km **2** 6.088 km **3** 189.74 km/h

EXERCISE 2D.1

1 3.71 cm **2** 4.24 cm **3** 12.49 cm

EXERCISE 2D.2

1 8.49 cm **2** 10.58 cm **3** 716.66 km **4** 0.41 m
5 10.05 m **6** 5.29 cm **7** 5 cm

EXERCISE 2E

1 15 cm **2** 10 cm **3** 3.16 cm **4** 5.20 cm **5** 7.81 m
6 4.12 cm **7** 8.06 m **8** 70.71 m **9** 15.81 cm **10** 2.45 m

EXERCISE 2F

1 17 km from B **2** 80.30 m
3 Hint: Find area of trapezium ABED. **4** 10.83 cm
5 Use Area A + Area B = total area $-$ area of semi-circle
6 5.11 m **7** 5.66 cm

REVIEW SET 2A

1 a $\sqrt{29}$ cm **b** $\sqrt{33}$ cm **c** $\sqrt{27}$ cm, $2\sqrt{27}$ cm
2 Yes, $1^2 + 4^2 = (\sqrt{17})^2$ **3** $5^2 + 11^2 \neq 13^2$
4 41.38 cm **5** 10.63 cm **6** 7.07 cm
7 14.14 km, 315°T **8** 9.89 cm **9** 180.6 km

REVIEW SET 2B

1 a $x = \sqrt{18}$ **b** $x = \sqrt{61}$ **c** $x = \sqrt{2}$
2 $2^2 + 5^2 = (\sqrt{29})^2$, $\angle$ABC is a right angle. **3** 6 cm
4 1.431 m (to nearest mm) **5** 42.43 m **6** 34.21 km
7 13.42 m **8** Yes, diagonal of shed is 11.05 m. **9** 9.95 cm

EXERCISE 3A.1

1 a 7 **b** 13 **c** 15 **d** 24 **e** $\frac{1}{3}$ **f** $\frac{1}{11}$ **g** $\frac{1}{17}$ **h** $\frac{1}{23}$
2 a 24 **b** -30 **c** -30 **d** 12 **e** 18 **f** $54\sqrt{2}$
g 12 **h** $24\sqrt{3}$ **i** 64

EXERCISE 3A.2

1 a $2\sqrt{2}$ **b** 0 **c** $\sqrt{2}$ **d** $\sqrt{3}$ **e** $7\sqrt{7}$ **f** $-3\sqrt{5}$
g $6\sqrt{2}$ **h** $-3\sqrt{2}$ **i** $8\sqrt{5}$ **j** $-3\sqrt{2}$ **k** $4\sqrt{3}$
l $10\sqrt{5} - 10$
2 a $2\sqrt{2} + 7\sqrt{3}$ **b** $5\sqrt{2} - \sqrt{3}$ **c** $-7\sqrt{2} + 4\sqrt{3}$
d $11\sqrt{5} - 5\sqrt{2}$ **e** $2\sqrt{2} - 10\sqrt{7}$ **f** $2\sqrt{2} + 3\sqrt{11} + 3$
g $\sqrt{6} - 3\sqrt{2} + 4$ **h** $9\sqrt{3} - 5\sqrt{7} - 13$

EXERCISE 3A.3

1 a $\sqrt{10}$ **b** $\sqrt{21}$ **c** $\sqrt{33}$ **d** 7 **e** 6 **f** $2\sqrt{10}$
g $6\sqrt{6}$ **h** $6\sqrt{15}$ **i** $\sqrt{30}$ **j** $4\sqrt{3}$ **k** -12 **l** $162\sqrt{6}$
2 a 2 **b** $\frac{1}{2}$ **c** 3 **d** $\frac{1}{3}$ **e** 2 **f** $\frac{1}{2}$ **g** 3 **h** $\sqrt{6}$
i $\frac{1}{\sqrt{10}}$ **j** 5 **k** 1 **l** 25
3 a $2\sqrt{2}$ **b** $3\sqrt{2}$ **c** $5\sqrt{2}$ **d** $7\sqrt{2}$ **e** $10\sqrt{2}$
f $12\sqrt{2}$ **g** $100\sqrt{2}$ **h** $\frac{1}{2}\sqrt{2}$
4 a $2\sqrt{3}$ **b** $3\sqrt{3}$ **c** $5\sqrt{3}$ **d** $\frac{1}{3}\sqrt{3}$
5 a $2\sqrt{5}$ **b** $3\sqrt{5}$ **c** $5\sqrt{5}$ **d** $\frac{1}{5}\sqrt{5}$
6 a $2\sqrt{6}$ **b** $5\sqrt{2}$ **c** $3\sqrt{6}$ **d** $2\sqrt{10}$ **e** $2\sqrt{14}$
f $3\sqrt{7}$ **g** $2\sqrt{13}$ **h** $2\sqrt{11}$ **i** $2\sqrt{15}$ **j** $3\sqrt{10}$
k $4\sqrt{6}$ **l** $2\sqrt{17}$ **m** $5\sqrt{7}$ **n** $9\sqrt{2}$ **o** $8\sqrt{2}$ **p** $10\sqrt{7}$
7 a i 7 **ii** 5 **iii** 2 **iv** 4 **b i** no **ii** no
c $\sqrt{a+b} \neq \sqrt{a} + \sqrt{b}$ and $\sqrt{a-b} \neq \sqrt{a} - \sqrt{b}$

EXERCISE 3B

1 a $\sqrt{10} + 2$ **b** $3\sqrt{2} - 2$ **c** $3 + \sqrt{3}$ **d** $\sqrt{3} - 3$
e $7\sqrt{7} - 7$ **f** $2\sqrt{5} - 5$ **g** $22 - \sqrt{11}$ **h** $\sqrt{6} - 12$
i $3 + \sqrt{6} - \sqrt{3}$ **j** $6 - 2\sqrt{15}$ **k** $6\sqrt{5} - 10$ **l** $30 + 3\sqrt{10}$
2 a $2 - 3\sqrt{2}$ **b** $-2 - \sqrt{6}$ **c** $2 - 4\sqrt{2}$ **d** $-3 - \sqrt{3}$
e $-3 - 2\sqrt{3}$ **f** $-5 - 2\sqrt{5}$ **g** $-3 - \sqrt{2}$ **h** $-5 + 4\sqrt{5}$
i $\sqrt{7} - 3$ **j** $11 - 2\sqrt{11}$ **k** $\sqrt{7} - \sqrt{3}$ **l** $4 - 2\sqrt{2}$
m $9 - 15\sqrt{3}$ **n** $-14 - 7\sqrt{12}$ **o** $4 - 6\sqrt{2}$

3 a $4+3\sqrt{2}$ **b** $7+4\sqrt{3}$ **c** $1+\sqrt{3}$ **d** $10+\sqrt{2}$
e -2 **f** $3-3\sqrt{7}$ **g** $-1-\sqrt{5}$ **h** 4 **i** 5 **j** $14-7\sqrt{2}$

4 a $3+2\sqrt{2}$ **b** $7-4\sqrt{3}$ **c** $7+4\sqrt{3}$ **d** $6+2\sqrt{5}$
e $5-2\sqrt{6}$ **f** $27-10\sqrt{2}$ **g** $9+2\sqrt{14}$ **h** $22-8\sqrt{6}$
i $8-4\sqrt{3}$ **j** $13+4\sqrt{10}$ **k** $13-4\sqrt{10}$ **l** $44+24\sqrt{2}$
m $51-10\sqrt{2}$ **n** $17-12\sqrt{2}$ **o** $19+6\sqrt{2}$

5 a 13 **b** 23 **c** 1 **d** -9 **e** 14 **f** 19 **g** -2
h -28 **i** -174

EXERCISE 3C

1 a $\frac{\sqrt{2}}{2}$ **b** $\sqrt{2}$ **c** $2\sqrt{2}$ **d** $5\sqrt{2}$ **e** $\frac{\sqrt{14}}{2}$ **f** $\frac{\sqrt{3}}{3}$ **g** $\sqrt{3}$
h $\frac{4\sqrt{3}}{3}$ **i** $6\sqrt{3}$ **j** $\frac{\sqrt{33}}{3}$ **k** $\frac{\sqrt{5}}{5}$ **l** $\frac{3\sqrt{5}}{5}$ **m** $\frac{\sqrt{15}}{5}$ **n** $3\sqrt{5}$
o $25\sqrt{5}$ **p** $\sqrt{5}$ **q** $\frac{\sqrt{3}}{6}$ **r** $\frac{2\sqrt{6}}{3}$ **s** $\frac{3\sqrt{5}}{2}$ **t** $\frac{\sqrt{2}}{4}$

2 a $\dfrac{3+\sqrt{5}}{4}$ **b** $2-\sqrt{3}$ **c** $\dfrac{4+\sqrt{11}}{5}$ **d** $\dfrac{5\sqrt{2}-2}{23}$
e $\dfrac{\sqrt{3}-1}{2}$ **f** $\dfrac{10+15\sqrt{2}}{-14}$ **g** $\dfrac{3\sqrt{5}-10}{11}$ **h** $\dfrac{5\sqrt{7}-13}{3}$

REVIEW SET 3A

1 a 18 **b** -30 **c** $\sqrt{2}$ **d** $4\sqrt{3}$
2 a $8\sqrt{3}-6$ **b** $16-6\sqrt{7}$ **c** 1 **d** $\sqrt{5}-4$ **e** $8+5\sqrt{2}$
3 a $4\sqrt{2}$ **b** $5\sqrt{3}$ **c** $\frac{\sqrt{6}}{2}$ **d** $\dfrac{30+5\sqrt{3}}{33}$ **4** $\frac{1}{7}\sqrt{7}$

REVIEW SET 3B

1 a $6\sqrt{15}$ **b** 20 **c** $-2\sqrt{2}$ **d** $2-2\sqrt{2}$ **e** 9 **f** 15
2 $5\sqrt{3}$ **3 a** 22 **b** $4\sqrt{5}-9$ **c** $6-4\sqrt{3}$ **d** $7\sqrt{2}-9$
4 a $7\sqrt{2}$ **b** $\frac{\sqrt{6}}{3}$ **c** $\dfrac{3\sqrt{2}-2}{7}$ **d** $\dfrac{-20-5\sqrt{3}}{13}$

EXERCISE 4A

1 a twice a **b** the product of p and q
c the square root of m **d** the square of a **e** 3 less than a
f the sum of b and c **g** the sum of twice x and c
h the square of twice a **i** twice the square of a
j c squared less than a **k** the sum of a and the square of b
l the square of the sum of a and b

2 a $a+c$ **b** $p+q+r$ **c** ab **d** $r+s^2$ **e** $(r+s)^2$
f r^2+s^2 **g** $2a+b$ **h** $p-q$ **i** b^2-a **j** $\dfrac{a+b}{2}$
k $a+\frac{1}{4}b$ **l** $\sqrt{m+n}$ **m** $x+\dfrac{1}{x}$ **n** $\dfrac{a+b}{4}$ **o** $\sqrt{x^2+y^2}$

3 a L is equal to the sum of a and b.
b K is equal to half the sum of a and b.
c M is equal to three times d.
d N is equal to the product of b and c.
e T is equal to the product of b and the square of c.
f F is equal to the product of m and a.
g K is equal to the square root of the quotient of n and t.
h c is equal to the square root of the sum of the squares of a and b.
i A is equal to the average of a, b and c.

4 a $S=p+r$ **b** $D=b-a$ **c** $A=\dfrac{k+l}{2}$ **d** $M=a+\dfrac{1}{a}$
e $K=t+s^2$ **f** $N=gh$ **g** $y=x+x^2$ **h** $P=\sqrt{d+e}$

EXERCISE 4B

1 a 25 **b** 12 **c** 45 **d** -60 **e** 9 **f** -32 **g** 20 **h** -25

2 a $-\frac{2}{3}$ **b** 1 **c** $\frac{5}{3}$ **d** $-\frac{13}{3}$ **e** 0 **f** $-\frac{1}{3}$ **g** -7 **h** -5
3 a 1 **b** -64 **c** 25 **d** 49 **e** -65 **f** -125
g 36 **h** 18
4 a 1 **b** $\doteqdot 1.73$ **c** $\doteqdot 1.73$ **d** $\doteqdot 2.83$ **e** 3
f $\doteqdot 4.12$ **g** 2 **h** undefined

EXERCISE 4C

1 a $x=-5$ **b** $x=9$ **c** $x=4$ **d** $x=-9$
e $x=6$ **f** $x=-4$ **g** $x=5$ **h** $x=\frac{1}{2}$
2 a $x=48$ **b** $x=12$ **c** $x=-10$ **d** $x=-18$
e $x=-13$ **f** $x=7$ **g** $x=11$ **h** $x=9$
3 a $x=7$ **b** $x=-1$ **c** $x=-7$ **d** $x=4$
e $x=-3$ **f** $x=-2$
4 a $x=-9$ **b** $x=\frac{9}{4}$ **c** $x=\frac{3}{2}$ **d** $x=-\frac{4}{3}$ **e** $x=\frac{1}{2}$
f $x=\frac{5}{4}$ **g** no solution **h** $x=0$ **i** $x=\frac{5}{2}$ **j** $x=-\frac{13}{10}$
5 a $x=\frac{3}{5}$ **b** $x=2$ **c** $x=\frac{18}{7}$ **d** $x=-\frac{5}{3}$
e $x=\frac{2}{11}$ **f** $x=-\frac{19}{10}$
6 a True for all values of x. **b** no solution

EXERCISE 4D

1 a $x=\frac{8}{7}$ **b** $x=\frac{15}{4}$ **c** $x=-4$ **d** $x=\frac{7}{2}$
e $x=\frac{15}{7}$ **f** $x=\frac{9}{4}$ **g** $x=\frac{6}{5}$ **h** $x=\frac{7}{5}$ **i** $x=\frac{2}{15}$
2 a $x=\frac{15}{2}$ **b** $x=10$ **c** $x=\frac{15}{4}$ **d** $x=\frac{9}{7}$
e $x=\frac{9}{14}$ **f** $x=-14$ **g** $x=-15$
h No solution, $8x=21x$ gives $x=0$ but you cannot divide by 0.
3 a $x=-4$ **b** $x=-\frac{1}{3}$ **c** $x=8$ **d** $x=-10$
e $x=3$ **f** $x=-\frac{5}{3}$ **g** $x=1$ **h** $x=15$ **i** $x=0$
4 a $x=12$ **b** $x=-\frac{36}{5}$ **c** $x=-\frac{16}{5}$ **d** $x=\frac{13}{7}$
e $x=16$ **f** $x=\frac{40}{7}$ **g** $x=\frac{16}{3}$ **h** $x=\frac{11}{5}$
i $x=\frac{55}{28}$ **j** $x=\frac{4}{5}$ **k** $x=-\frac{6}{5}$ **l** $x=\frac{17}{24}$

EXERCISE 4E

1 a $x<-\frac{2}{3}$
b $x>\frac{9}{5}$
c $x\leqslant\frac{1}{3}$
d $x\geqslant-3$
e $x<1$
f $x\leqslant-\frac{1}{5}$

2 a $x\leqslant4$
b $x>-5$
c $x>-4$
d $x\geqslant\frac{7}{3}$

e $x < 1$

f $x \leqslant \frac{3}{5}$

3 a $x > -\frac{7}{2}$

b $x > \frac{4}{3}$

c $x \leqslant \frac{1}{3}$

d $x \geqslant 1$

e $x < 0$

f $x \leqslant -\frac{5}{3}$

4 a no solution **b** true for all values of x
c true for all values of x

EXERCISE 4F

1 7 **2** 6 **3** $\frac{5}{2}$ **4** 24 **5** 6 and 9 **6** 19 **7** $\frac{5}{2}$
8 10 years **9** 6 years **10** 7 years

EXERCISE 4G

1 35 5-cent stamps and 40 10-cent stamps
2 35 of 600 mL cartons
3 8 five-cent, 60 ten-cent and 20 25-cent coins
4 8500 $8 tickets, 17 000 $15 tickets, 23 000 $20 tickets
5 20 kg of A, 30 kg of B **6** 7 kg **7** $6550
8 $5000 in mining shares, $10 000 in technology shares
9 $5000 in A shares, $10 000 in B shares, $35 000 in C shares
10 $9000

EXERCISE 4H

1 16 km/h **2** 84 km/h **3** 10 km **4** 50 km/h
5 48 km **6** $\frac{24}{7}$ km/h

REVIEW SET 4A

1 a $x^2 + 3$ **b** $(3 + x)^2$
2 a three more than the square root of a
b the square root of the sum of a and 3
3 3 **4 a** $x = \frac{1}{5}$ **b** $x = \frac{47}{39}$
5 $x \leqslant -\frac{13}{5}$

6 $-3\frac{6}{7}$ **7** 114 small, 342 medium, 202 large **8** 200 km

REVIEW SET 4B

1 a half the sum of a and b **b** the sum of a and a half b
2 a $a + \sqrt{b}$ **b** $\sqrt{a + b}$ **3** 5
4 $x < \frac{1}{2}$

5 a $x = 3\frac{1}{2}$ **b** $x = -15$ **6** $-\frac{5}{2}$ **7** $17 000 **8** 24 km/h

EXERCISE 5A.1

1 a 2 units **b** $\sqrt{37}$ units **c** $\sqrt{13}$ units **d** 3 units
e $2\sqrt{2}$ units **f** $\sqrt{29}$ units **g** 5 units **h** 7 units
2 a $\sqrt{2}$ units **b** $\sqrt{29}$ units **c** $3\sqrt{5}$ units

EXERCISE 5A.2

1 a $2\sqrt{2}$ units **b** 7 units **c** $2\sqrt{5}$ units **d** 6 units
e 7 units **f** $\sqrt{5}$ units **g** $\sqrt{10}$ units **h** $3\sqrt{5}$ units
2 a isosceles (AB = AC) **b** scalene
c isosceles (AB = BC) **d** isosceles (BC = AC)
e equilateral **f** isosceles (AC = BC)
3 a $\angle$ABC **b** $\angle$ABC **c** $\angle$BAC **d** $\angle$BAC
4 a $a = 2$ **b** $a = 3$ or -5 **c** $a = \pm 2$ **d** $a = -1$

EXERCISE 5B

1 a $(-1\frac{1}{2}, 3\frac{1}{2})$ **b** $(-1, -2)$ **c** $(1, 1\frac{1}{2})$ **d** $(2, 1)$
e $(1, -1\frac{1}{2})$ **f** $(-4, 1\frac{1}{2})$ **g** $(-4\frac{1}{2}, \frac{1}{2})$ **h** $(-1\frac{1}{2}, \frac{1}{2})$
2 a $(5, 3)$ **b** $(1, -1)$ **c** $(1\frac{1}{2}, 3)$ **d** $(0, 4)$
e $(2, -1\frac{1}{2})$ **f** $(1, 1)$ **g** $(1, 2\frac{1}{2})$ **h** $(2, -3\frac{1}{2})$
3 a B$(0, -6)$ **b** B$(5, -2)$ **c** B$(0, 6)$ **d** B$(0, 7)$
e B$(-7, 3)$ **f** B$(-3, 0)$
5 a P$(-9, 10)$ **b** P$(6, 3)$ **6** C$(1, -3)$ **7** P$(7, -3)$
8 S$(-2, 0)$ **9** $\frac{\sqrt{89}}{2}$ units

EXERCISE 5C.1

1 a $\frac{1}{3}$ **b** 0 **c** -3 **d** $\frac{2}{3}$ **e** $-\frac{3}{4}$ **f** undefined
g -4 **h** $-\frac{2}{5}$

2 a **b**

c **d**

e **f**

EXERCISE 5C.2

1 a $\frac{1}{5}$ **b** $\frac{1}{4}$ **c** 4 **d** 0 **e** undefined **f** $\frac{2}{7}$ **g** $-\frac{2}{7}$ **h** 1
2

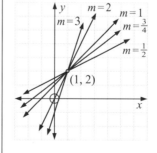

3

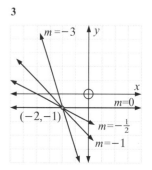

EXERCISE 5C.3

1 **a** -2 **b** $-\frac{5}{2}$ **c** $-\frac{1}{3}$ **d** $-\frac{1}{7}$ **e** $\frac{5}{2}$ **f** $\frac{3}{7}$ **g** $\frac{1}{5}$ **h** 1

2 **c**, **d**, **f** and **h** are perpendicular.

3 **a** $a = 9$ **b** $a = 1$ **c** $a = 6\frac{1}{3}$

4 **a** $t = \frac{1}{5}$ **b** $t = 5$ **c** $t = 3\frac{3}{5}$

5 **a** $t = 4$ **b** $t = 4$ **c** $t = 14$ **d** $t = 3\frac{1}{7}$

6 **a** not collinear **b** collinear **c** not collinear **d** collinear

7 **a** $c = 3$ **b** $c = -5$

EXERCISE 5D

1 **a** $6\frac{2}{3}$ **b** $6\frac{2}{3}$ m/s **c** Speed is constant as gradient is constant.

2 **a** 72 km/h **b i** 85 km/h **ii** 85 km/h
   c O to A (0 - 2 hours) and B to C (5 - 7 hours)

3 **a** Retainer of \$50 is paid.
   b gradient is 15, paid \$15 per hour **c i** \$140 **ii** \$320
   d \$21.25 per hour

4 **a** A has gradient $\frac{35}{3} = 11\frac{2}{3}$, B has gradient $\frac{75}{8} = 9\frac{3}{8}$
   b Gradient is number of km travelled per litre of petrol.
   c \$25.98

5 **a** \$3 initial charge
   b AB has gradient $\frac{3}{2}$, BC has gradient $\frac{3}{5}$, these values give the charge per km.
   c gradient is $\frac{6}{5}$, average charge is \$1.20 per km.

EXERCISE 5E

1 **a** PQ = PR = $\sqrt{20}$ **b** $(4, 4)$
   c slope of PM = $-\frac{1}{3}$,
      slope of QR = 3
   d

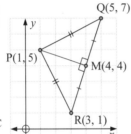

2 **a i** slope of AB = $-\frac{1}{4}$
         = slope of DC
      ii slope of BC = $\frac{3}{5}$
         = slope of AD
   b a parallelogram
   c AB = $\sqrt{68}$ units = DC, BC = $\sqrt{306}$ units = AD
   d i $(\frac{5}{2}, \frac{5}{2})$ **ii** $(\frac{5}{2}, \frac{5}{2})$ **e** diagonals bisect each other

3 **a** slope of MN = 0 = slope of AC
   b MN = 3 units, AC = 6 units

4 **a** AB = BC = CD = DA = 5 units **b** (2, 1) and (2, 1)
   c slope of AC = -2, slope of BD = $\frac{1}{2}$

5 **a i** P(0, 5) **ii** Q($4\frac{1}{2}$, 2) **iii** R($\frac{1}{2}$, $-2\frac{1}{2}$) **iv** S(-4, $\frac{1}{2}$)
   b i $-\frac{2}{3}$ **ii** $\frac{9}{8}$ **iii** $-\frac{2}{3}$ **iv** $\frac{9}{8}$ **c** PQRS is a parallelogram

6 **a** $s = 6$ **b i** $\frac{1}{2}$ **ii** -2
   c slope of PS $\times$ slope of SQ = $\frac{1}{2} \times -2 = -1$

EXERCISE 5F

1 **a i** 0 **ii** $y = 2$ **b i** undefined **ii** $x = 5$
   c i 0 **ii** $y = -2$ **d i** undefined **ii** $x = -4$
   e i undefined **ii** $x = 5$ **f i** 0 **ii** $y = -4$

2 **a** 0 **b** undefined **c** undefined **d** 0 **e** undefined
   f 0 **g** undefined **h** 0

3 **a**

   b

   c

   d

EXERCISE 5G

1 **a** $y = 5x - 15$ **b** $y = -2x - 4$ **c** $y = -4x + 25$
   d $y = \frac{1}{2}x + \frac{5}{2}$ **e** $y = -\frac{1}{3}x + \frac{7}{3}$ **f** $y = -1$

2 **a** $3x - 4y = -14$ **b** $2x - 5y = -22$ **c** $x + 2y = 5$
   d $3x + 4y = 10$ **e** $5x - y = -14$ **f** $3x + y = 12$

3 **a** $x - y = -4$ **b** $x + y = 4$ **c** $y = -2$
   d $x + 9y = 6$ **e** $x - 3y = 5$ **f** $x + y = -5$

4 **a** $y = \frac{1}{2}x + 3$ **b** $y = 2x + 6$ **c** $2x - 5y = 10$
   d $y = -2x - 2$ **e** $4x + 3y = 20$ **f** $x - 2y = -8$

5 **a** 3 **b** -2 **c** 0 **d** undefined **e** $\frac{2}{3}$ **f** -3
   g $\frac{2}{7}$ **h** $-\frac{2}{7}$ **i** $\frac{3}{4}$ **j** $-\frac{3}{4}$ **k** $\frac{A}{B}$ **l** $-\frac{A}{B}$

6 **a** $y = 3x + 5$ **b** $y = 2x - 5$ **c** $y = -3x - 2$
   d $y = -\frac{1}{2} - 1$ **e** $y = 4$ **f** $x = -1$

7 **a** $y = \frac{2}{3}x + 2$ **b** $y = \frac{5}{4}x - 2$ **c** $y = -\frac{3}{5}x + 3$
   d $x - y = -5$ **e** $5x + 3y = -10$ **f** $5x + 7y = -15$

8 **a** $M = \frac{1}{3}t + 4$ **b** $N = \frac{2}{3}x - 2$ **c** $G = -\frac{3}{4}s + 3$
   d $H = -g + 2$ **e** $F = \frac{3}{10}x + 5$ **f** $P = -\frac{1}{3}t - 2$

EXERCISE 5H

1 **a** $y = \frac{1}{2}x + 1$

   b $y = 3x + 4$

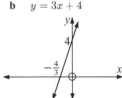

   c $y = -x - 1$

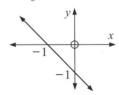

   d $y = -3x - 3$

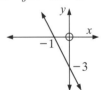

   e $y = -\frac{1}{2}x$

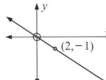

   f $y = -2x + 2$

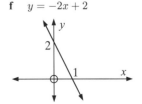

g $y = \frac{3}{2}x$

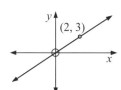

h $y = \frac{2}{3}x - 1$

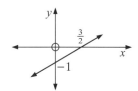

i $y = -\frac{3}{4}x + 4$

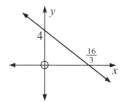

2 a $y = 4x - 3$ **b** $y = \frac{1}{2}x + 3$

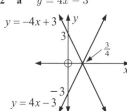 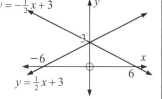

3 a $x + 2y = 4$ **b** $3x - y = 9$

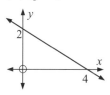 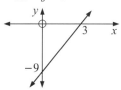

c $2x + 3y = 6$ **d** $4x + 3y = 18$

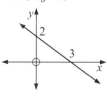 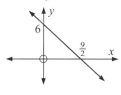

e $x + y = 4$ **f** $x - y = -2$

 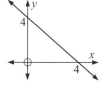

g $2x - y = -6$ **h** $9x + 2y = 9$

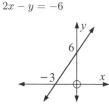 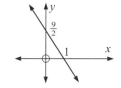

i $3x + 4y = -12$

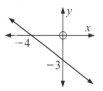

4 a i

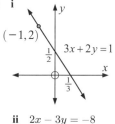

ii $2x - 3y = -8$

b $3x - 5y = 15$

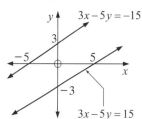

EXERCISE 5I

1 a yes **b** no **c** yes **2 a** $k = -4$ **b** $k = 1$
3 a $a = 7$ **b** $a = 9$ **c** $a = 5$ **d** $a = 7$
4 a $b = -3$ **b** $b = -\frac{9}{4}$ **c** $b = -\frac{7}{5}$ **d** $b = \frac{5}{4}$

EXERCISE 5J

1 a $(-1, 2)$ **b** $(2, 4)$ **c** $(3, 1)$ **d** $(-2, 3)$ **e** $(0, 6)$
 f $(1, \frac{10}{3})$ **g** $(2, 1)$ **h** no point of intersection
 i infinitely many points of intersection
2 a none, as the lines are parallel
 b infinitely many, as the lines are coincident
 c if $k = 5$, infinitely many, as the lines are coincident;
  if $k \neq 5$, none, as the lines are parallel

REVIEW SET 5A

1 a $x = -1$ **b** $\sqrt{73}$ units **c** $(0, \frac{1}{2})$ **d** 2 **e** 3
 f $-\frac{4}{5}$ **g** x-intercept is 3, y-intercept is 2, gradient is $-\frac{2}{3}$
2 $a = -2 \pm 2\sqrt{5}$ **3** $y = -\frac{1}{2}x + 4$ **4** $3x - y = 5$
5 slope of AB = slope of BC = 2 and B is common
6 $b = -3$
7 $y = -3x + 5$ **8** $k = \frac{5}{2}$

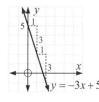

9 $2x - 5y = 10$

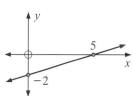

10 $(1, 3)$
11 a $\frac{1000}{3}$
 b The gradient represents the number of litres of water run from the tank per hour.
 c rate is constant as gradient is contant
12 a AB = BC = 5 units **b** X$(\frac{1}{2}, \frac{1}{2})$
 c gradient BX × gradient AC = $7 \times -\frac{1}{7} = -1$

REVIEW SET 5B

1 a $(-3, 3)$ **b** $\sqrt{58}$ units **c** $y = 0$ **d** $-\frac{3}{2}$
 e gradient is -2, y-intercept is 5

2 $y = 2x + 2$ **3** $m = 2 \pm 3\sqrt{5}$ **4** $a = -8$

5 a $y = -2x + 5$ **b** $2x + 3y = 7$ **c** $3x - 2y = 15$

6 $k = -1$ **7**

8 $2t + 3P = 10$

9 $(3, -2)$

10 a A has gradient 14, B has gradient 10
   b Gradient is the number of km travelled per litre of petrol.
   c \$33.43

11 a gradient AB = gradient DC $= \frac{1}{5}$
   b gradient AD = gradient BC $= -2$
   c AB ∥ DC and AD ∥ BC ∴ ABCD is a parallelogram.
   d $(\frac{1}{2}, \frac{1}{2})$;   diagonals bisect each other

EXERCISE 6A

1 a $12x$ **b** $18x$ **c** $-18x$ **d** $-12x$ **e** $6x^2$ **f** $3x^2$
   g $-4x^2$ **h** $-30x$ **i** $8x^2$ **j** $-6x^3$ **k** $14x^3$
   l $-12n^2$ **m** b^2 **n** $4b^2$ **o** $12a^4$ **p** $-12a^3$

2 a $2x + 6$ **b** $3 - 6x$ **c** $-x - 5$ **d** $3x - 2$
   e $-5x - 10$ **f** $-6x + 4$ **g** $2x^2 + x$ **h** $3x^2 - 6x$
   i $ab + bc$ **j** $-x^2 + xy$ **k** $2t^2 - t$ **l** $2x^3 - 6x^2 - 14x$

3 a $5x + 10$ **b** $5a - 3b$ **c** $a + 3b$ **d** $-3y + 19$
   e $-5y - 10$ **f** $13x - 6$ **g** $5b - a$ **h** $x^2 + 5x - 3$
   i $x^2 - x + 6$ **j** $3x^2 - 5x$ **k** $-3x^2 + 4x$ **l** $x^2 - z^2$
   m $-x + 4$ **n** $14x - 15$ **o** $7x^2 - 45x$

EXERCISE 6B

1 a $A_1 = ac$ **b** $A_2 = ad$ **c** $A_3 = bc$ **d** $A_4 = bd$
   e $A = ac + ad + bc + bd$
   $ac + ad + bc + bd = (a + b)(c + d)$

2 a $x^2 + 8x + 12$ **b** $x^2 + 4x - 21$ **c** $x^2 + 6x - 16$
   d $x^2 - 9$ **e** $x^2 - 5x - 36$ **f** $6x^2 + 5x + 1$
   g $-15x^2 + 7x + 2$ **h** $-3x^2 + 7x + 6$ **i** $6x^2 - 7x - 3$
   j $-x^2 - 2x + 24$ **k** $-3x^2 + 23x + 36$ **l** $16x^2 + 40x + 25$

3 a $x^2 - 25$ **b** $a^2 - 64$ **c** $9 - x^2$ **d** $9x^2 - 1$
   e $49a^2 - 16$ **f** $25 - 4a^2$

4 a $x^2 + 8x + 16$ **b** $x^2 - 6x + 9$ **c** $4x^2 - 12x + 9$
   d $4x^2 - 4x + 1$ **e** $25x^2 - 20x + 4$ **f** $9x^2 - 6xy + y^2$
   g $4x^2 - 4xy + y^2$ **h** $a^2b^2 - 2abc + c^2$ **i** $9x^2 - 24xy + 16y^2$

EXERCISE 6C

1 a $x^2 - 9$ **b** $x^2 - 81$ **c** $9 - x^2$ **d** $25 - x^2$ **e** $x^2 - 49$
   f $4 - x^2$ **g** $x^2 - 100$ **h** $c^2 - 144$ **i** $d^2 - 169$
   j $x^2 - a^2$ **k** $36 - d^2$ **l** $121 - e^2$

2 a $9x^2 - 1$ **b** $4x^2 - 9$ **c** $16y^2 - 25$ **d** $49y^2 - 25$
   e $25x^2 - 9$ **f** $9 - 49x^2$ **g** $16 - y^2$ **h** $36 - 25a^2$
   i $49 - 36a^2$

3 a $9a^2 - b^2$ **b** $a^2 - 9b^2$ **c** $36x^2 - y^2$ **d** $64x^2 - 25y^2$
   e $49x^2 - 9y^2$ **f** $81x^2 - 4y^2$

EXERCISE 6D

1 a $A_1 = a^2$ **b** $A_2 = ab$ **c** $A_3 = ab$ **d** $A_4 = b^2$
   e $A = a^2 + 2ab + b^2$, $(a + b)^2 = a^2 + 2ab + b^2$

2 a $x^2 + 6x + 9$ **b** $x^2 + 14x + 49$ **c** $x^2 + 16x + 64$
   d $a^2 + 2a + 1$ **e** $25 + 10c + c^2$ **f** $100 + 20x + x^2$

3 a $x^2 - 18x + 81$ **b** $x^2 - 10x + 25$ **c** $y^2 - 22y + 121$
   d $a^2 - 16a + 64$ **e** $36 - 12x + x^2$ **f** $25 - 10y + y^2$

4 a $4x^2 + 20x + 25$ **b** $9a^2 - 24a + 16$ **c** $4y^2 + 4y + 1$
   d $9x^2 - 30x + 25$ **e** $16y^2 - 40y + 25$ **f** $49 + 70a + 25a^2$
   g $1 + 12x + 36x^2$ **h** $64 - 48y + 9y^2$ **i** $25 + 40a + 16a^2$

5 a $x^4 + 6x^2 + 9$ **b** $y^4 - 8y^2 + 16$ **c** $4a^4 + 12a^2 + 9$
   d $1 - 10x^2 + 25x^4$ **e** $x^4 + 2x^2a^2 + a^4$ **f** $x^4 - 2x^2y^2 + y^4$

6 a $-x^2 - 6x - 13$ **b** $x^2 + 2x - 2$ **c** $2x^2 + 8x - 9$
   d $-12x - 45$ **e** $8x^2 - 7x + 7$ **f** $10x^2 - 13x - 8$
   g $x^2 + x - 16$ **h** $2x^2 + 3x - 5$ **i** $2x^2 - 2x + 5$ **j** $-12x$

EXERCISE 6E

1 a $x^3 + 3x^2 + 6x + 8$ **b** $x^3 + 5x^2 + 3x - 9$
   c $x^3 + 5x^2 + 7x + 3$ **d** $2x^3 + x^2 - 6x - 5$
   e $2x^3 + 7x^2 + 8x + 3$ **f** $2x^3 - 9x^2 + 4x + 15$
   g $3x^3 + 14x^2 - x + 20$ **h** $8x^3 - 14x^2 + 7x - 1$

2 a $x^3 + 3x^2 + 3x + 1$ **b** $x^3 + 12x^2 + 48x + 64$
   c $x^3 - 6x^2 + 12x - 8$ **d** $x^3 - 15x^2 + 75x - 125$
   e $8x^3 + 12x^2 + 6x + 1$ **f** $27x^3 - 54x^2 + 36x - 8$

3 a $x^3 + 6x^2 + 8x$ **b** $x^3 - x^2 - 6x$ **c** $x^3 - 9x^2 + 20x$
   d $2x^3 + 14x^2 + 20x$ **e** $-3x^3 + 15x^2 - 18x$
   f $x^3 - 4x^2 - 12x$ **g** $-9x^3 - 33x^2 + 12x$
   h $-10x^3 - 13x^2 + 3x$ **i** $x^3 - 3x^2 - 4x + 12$

4 a $x^3 + 9x^2 + 26x + 24$ **b** $x^3 - x^2 - 14x + 24$
   c $x^3 - 10x^2 + 31x - 30$ **d** $2x^3 + x^2 - 12x + 9$
   e $3x^3 + 14x^2 + 21x + 10$ **f** $12x^3 + 11x^2 - 2x - 1$
   g $-3x^3 + 26x^2 - 33x - 14$ **h** $-3x^3 + 16x^2 - 12x - 16$

5 a 4 **b** 6 **c** 6 **d** 9 **e** 8 **f** 12 **g** 8 **h** 12

EXERCISE 6F

1 a $x^3 + 3x^2 + 3x + 1$ **b** $x^3 + 9x^2 + 27x + 27$
   c $x^3 + 12x^2 + 48x + 64$ **d** $x^3 + 3x^2y + 3xy^2 + y^3$
   e $x^3 - 3x^2 + 3x - 1$ **f** $x^3 - 15x^2 + 75x - 125$
   g $x^3 - 12x^2 + 48x - 64$ **h** $x^3 - 3x^2y + 3xy^2 - y^3$
   i $8 + 12y + 6y^2 + y^3$ **j** $8x^3 + 12x^2 + 6x + 1$
   k $27x^3 + 27x^2 + 9x + 1$ **l** $8y^3 + 36xy^2 + 54x^2y + 27x^3$
   m $8 - 12y + 6y^2 - y^3$ **n** $8x^3 - 12x^2 + 6x - 1$
   o $27x^3 - 27x^2 + 9x - 1$ **p** $8y^3 - 36xy^2 + 54x^2y - 27x^3$

2 $(a + b)^4 = a^4 + 4a^3b + 6a^2b^2 + 4ab^3 + b^4$

3 a $x^4 + 4x^3y + 6x^2y^2 + 4xy^3 + y^4$
   b $x^4 + 4x^3 + 6x^2 + 4x + 1$ **c** $x^4 + 8x^3 + 24x^2 + 32x + 16$
   d $x^4 + 12x^3 + 54x^2 + 108x + 81$
   e $x^4 - 4x^3y + 6x^2y^2 - 4xy^3 + y^4$
   f $x^4 - 4x^3 + 6x^2 - 4x + 1$ **g** $x^4 - 8x^3 + 24x^2 - 32x + 16$
   h $16x^4 - 32x^3 + 24x^2 - 8x + 1$

4 a   1   5   10   10   5   1
         1   6   15   20   15   6   1
   b i $a^5 + 5a^4b + 10a^3b^2 + 10a^2b^3 + 5ab^4 + b^5$
      ii $a^5 - 5a^4b + 10a^3b^2 - 10a^2b^3 + 5ab^4 - b^5$
      iii $a^6 + 6a^5b + 15a^4b^2 + 20a^3b^3 + 15a^2b^4 + 6ab^5 + b^6$
      iv $a^6 - 6a^5b + 15a^4b^2 - 20a^3b^3 + 15a^2b^4 - 6ab^5 + b^6$

REVIEW SET 6A

1 a $-32x$ **b** $10x^3$ **c** $24x^2$

2 a $-3x - 18$ **b** $2x^3 - 8x$ **c** $-x - 4$ **d** $-7x + 7$

3 a $3x^2 - 4x - 4$ **b** $4x^2 - 4x + 1$ **c** $16x^2 - 1$
   d $x^2 - 10x + 25$ **e** $6x^2 - 29x + 35$ **f** $x^3 - 4x$

4 a $-x^2 - 4x - 4$ **b** $x^3 + 6x^2 + 12x + 8$
   c $3x^3 + 4x^2 + 17x - 14$ **d** $x^3 - 6x^2 + 11x - 6$

5 a   1   1
         1   2   1
       1   3   3   1
   b $a^3 + 3a^2b + 3ab^2 + b^3$
   c $8x^3 + 60x^2 + 150x + 125$

REVIEW SET 6B

1   **a** $-6x^3$ **b** $-6x^3$ **c** $40x^2$

2   **a** $-14x + 35$ **b** $-x$ **c** $2x^2 - 5x$

3   **a** $2x^2 - x - 15$ **b** $9x^2 - 12x + 4$ **c** $4x^2 - 9$
    d $5x^2 - 11x + 2$ **e** $4x^2 - 12x + 9$ **f** $1 - 25x^2$

4   **a** $5x^2 - x + 7$ **b** $2x^3 - 9x^2 + 10x - 3$
    c $x^3 + 9x^2 + 27x + 27$ **d** $x^3 + 4x^2 - 7x - 10$

5   **a** $16x^4 + 32x^3 + 24x^2 + 8x + 1$
    b $x^4 - 12x^3 + 54x^2 - 108x + 81$

EXERCISE 7A

1   **a** $\begin{bmatrix} 5 \\ 0 \end{bmatrix}$ **b** $\begin{bmatrix} 0 \\ 3 \end{bmatrix}$ **c** $\begin{bmatrix} 2 \\ -2 \end{bmatrix}$ **d** $\begin{bmatrix} -4 \\ 1 \end{bmatrix}$ **e** $\begin{bmatrix} 3 \\ -3 \end{bmatrix}$ **f** $\begin{bmatrix} -3 \\ -3 \end{bmatrix}$

2   **a** $\begin{bmatrix} -4 \\ 2 \end{bmatrix}$ **b** $\begin{bmatrix} 6 \\ 1 \end{bmatrix}$ **c** $\begin{bmatrix} 2 \\ 3 \end{bmatrix}$

3   **a** 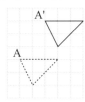   **b**

    c   **d**

    e    **f**

4   **a**   yes   **b**   no   **c**   no   **d**   no

5   **a**   A(2, 4), B(3, −2), C(−2, −3), D(−5, 1)
    b   A′(7, 6), B′(8, 0), C′(3, −1), D′(0, 3)

6   **a**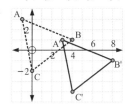

    b   A′(3, 1), B′(8, −1), C′(4, −4)   **c** $-\frac{1}{2}, -\frac{1}{2}, -\frac{1}{2}$
    d $\sqrt{20}$ units

EXERCISE 7B

1   **a** 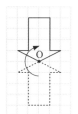   **b**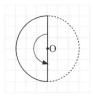

    c    **d**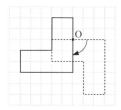

    e 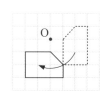   **f**

2   H, I, M, N, O, S, W, X, Z

3   **a**   yes   **b**   yes   **c**   no   **d**   yes   **4 a** 180° **b**   X

5   Rotate 75° anticlockwise about O.

6   **a**   (−1, 4)   **b**   (2, 5)   **c**   (5, 0)   **d**   (5, −1)   **e**   (−4, −3)

7   **a**   (3, −5)   **b**   (−3, 0)   **c**   (−1, −4)   **d**   (3, 2)   **e**   (−4, 2)

8   **a**   (−2, 0)   **b**   (2, −4)   **c**   (−5, 1)   **d**   (−2, −4)   **e**   (2, 3)

9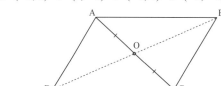

    a   ABCB′ is a parallelogram.
    b   opposite sides equal and parallel, diagonals bisect each other, opposite angles equal

10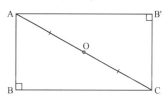

    a   ABCB′ is a rectangle.
    b   opposite sides equal and parallel, all angles are right angles, diagonals equal and bisect each other

EXERCISE 7C

1   **a**   **b**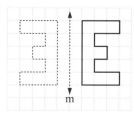

    c 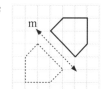   **d**

e   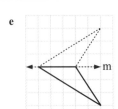   **f**

2   a yes **b** no **c** yes **d** no

3   a   i   no on   **ii**   think think

4   a

	P	P'
i	(5, 2)	(5, −2)
ii	(−3, 4)	(−3, −4)
iii	(−2, −5)	(−2, 5)
iv	(3, −7)	(3, 7)
v	(4, 0)	(4, 0)
vi	(0, 3)	(0, −3)

b $(a, -b)$

5   a

	P	P'
i	(5, 2)	(−5, 2)
ii	(−3, 4)	(3, 4)
iii	(−2, −5)	(2, −5)
iv	(3, −7)	(−3, −7)
v	(4, 0)	(−4, 0)
vi	(0, 3)	(0, 3)

b $(-a, b)$

6   a

	P	P'
i	(5, 2)	(2, 5)
ii	(−3, 4)	(4, −3)
iii	(−2, −5)	(−5, −2)
iv	(3, −7)	(−7, 3)
v	(4, 0)	(0, 4)
vi	(0, 3)	(3, 0)

b (b, a)

7   a $\triangle BXB'$ is isosceles since the pipeline perpendicularly bisects BB′.

   b The shortest distance between A and B′ is through X, and since BX = B′X, AX + XB must also be the shortest distance from A to B via the pipeline.

8   a   **b**   **c**

   d   **e**   **f**

9   a 4 **b** 3 **c** 0

   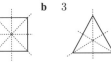

   d 2 **e** 2 **f** 5

g infinite **h** 1 **i** 1

   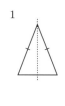

EXERCISE 7D

1   a 2 **b** 3 **c** 1.5 **2   a** $\frac{1}{2}$ **b** $\frac{1}{6}$ **c** $\frac{3}{4}$

3   a   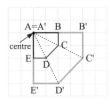   **b**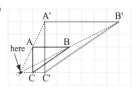

   c

4   a      **b**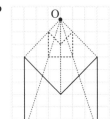

   c   **d**

   e   **f**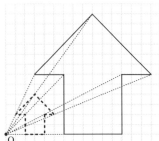

5   a   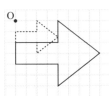   **b**

c

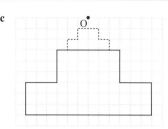

6

	Area of Object	Area of Image	k	$\dfrac{Area\ of\ Image}{Area\ of\ Object}$	k^2
a	5	20	2	4	4
b	20	5	$\frac{1}{2}$	$\frac{1}{4}$	$\frac{1}{4}$
c	6	54	3	9	9

$\dfrac{\text{area of image}}{\text{area of object}} = k^2$

7 56 m²   **8 a** 2.5   **b** 20 cm   **c** \$18.75

9 $5\sqrt{2}$ m × $8\sqrt{2}$ m ≑ 7.07 m × 11.31 m

EXERCISE 7E

1 a

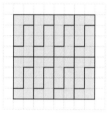

b

c

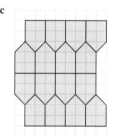

2 a yes   **b** yes   **c** no

3 a

b

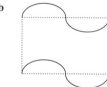

c

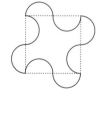

4 b

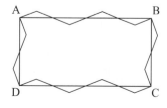

c

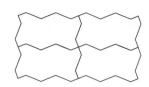

d They do not slide past one another so lock in tightly.

REVIEW SET 7A

1 a

b

c

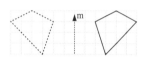

d

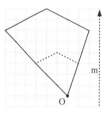

2 $\begin{bmatrix} 3 \\ -2 \end{bmatrix}$

3 a

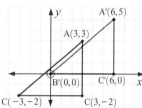

b A′(6, 5), B′(0, 0), C′(6, 0)

4

	P	P'
a	(1, 4)	(1, −4)
b	(−2, 3)	(−2, −3)
c	(−3, −1)	(−3, 1)
d	(4, 2)	(4, −2)

5 a

b

c no lines of symmetry

6 a

b

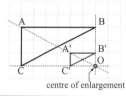

centre of enlargement

REVIEW SET 7B

1 a

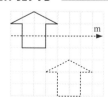

b

c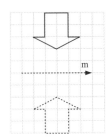

d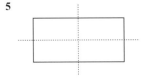

2 **a** $\begin{bmatrix} -4 \\ -2 \end{bmatrix}$ **b** $\begin{bmatrix} 6 \\ -2 \end{bmatrix}$ **c** $\begin{bmatrix} 2 \\ -4 \end{bmatrix}$

3 **a** $(-2, 0)$ **b** $(0, -5)$ **c** $(3, 1)$ **d** $(4, -2)$ **e** $(-2, -3)$

4

	P	P'
a	$(1, 5)$	$(-1, 5)$
b	$(-2, 4)$	$(2, 4)$
c	$(-4, -3)$	$(4, -3)$
d	$(3, 2)$	$(-3, 2)$

5

6 Area is enlarged with a scale factor of 4.

7 **a** yes   **b** yes   **c** no

EXERCISE 8A

1 **a** 9 **b** 5 **c** 12 **d** 30 **e** 7 **f** 36
2 **a** $2a$ **b** $2b$ **c** $2xy$ **d** $3x$ **e** x **f** $-2x$ **g** $-b$
  h $2a$ **i** $-2xy$
3 **a** 2 **b** c **c** 1 **d** k **e** $4a$ **f** $3n$ **g** $5x$ **h** $8y$ **i** $9d$
4 **a** st **b** abc **c** $12c$ **d** a **e** r **f** q **g** $3d$ **h** dp
  i $4r$ **j** $3pq$ **k** $2ab$ **l** $6xy$ **m** 5 **n** $12wz$ **o** $6pqr$
5 **a** $x + 2$ **b** $2(x + 5)$ **c** x **d** $3(x + 1)$ **e** $2(x + 3)$
  f $2x(x - 2)$

EXERCISE 8B

1 **a** $3(x + 2)$ **b** $4(a - 3)$ **c** $5(4 - p)$ **d** $4(4x + 3)$
  e $3x(x - 3)$ **f** $2m(1 + 4m)$
2 **a** $4(x + 3)$ **b** $3(3 + d)$ **c** $3(c - 1)$ **d** $d(c + e)$
  e $2a(3 + 4b)$ **f** $2x(2 - x)$ **g** $4a(b - 1)$ **h** $2b(2a - 3c)$
3 **a** $5(a + b)$ **b** $2(x - 2)$ **c** $7(d + 2)$ **d** $7(3 - 2x)$
  e $6(x - 2)$ **f** $3(4 + x)$ **g** $c(a + b)$ **h** $6(2y - a)$
  i $a(2 + b)$ **j** $c(b - 3d)$ **k** $x(2 - y)$ **l** $y(x + 1)$
  m $a(1 + b)$ **n** $b(a - c)$ **o** $a(2n + b)$ **p** $a(b - 1)$
4 **a** $x(x + 5)$ **b** $x(7 - 2x)$ **c** $3x(x + 2)$ **d** $3x(3 - x)$
  e $4x(x + 3)$ **f** $x^2(x + 2)$ **g** $xy(x + y)$ **h** $2x^2(x - 2)$
  i $2x(x^2 - 4y)$ **j** $a(a^2 + a + 1)$ **k** $3(a^2 + 2a + 3)$
  l $3a(a^2 - 2a + 3)$
5 **a** $2(b - a)$ **b** $3(2b - 1)$ **c** $4(2b - a)$ **d** $c(d - 3)$
  e $a(b - 1)$ **f** $7x(2 - x)$ **g** $6x(2x - 1)$ **h** $2b(a - 2b)$
  i $a(a - 1)$
6 **a** $-3(a + b)$ **b** $-4(1 + 2x)$ **c** $-3(y + 2b)$
  d $-c(5 + d)$ **e** $-x(1 + y)$ **f** $-5x(x + 2)$
  g $-4y(1 + 3y)$ **h** $-3a(2a + b)$ **i** $-8x(x + 3)$
7 **a** $(4 + x)(x + 7)$ **b** $(5 + a)(x - 3)$ **c** $(3 - x)(x + 2)$
  d $(x + 1)(x + 7)$ **e** $(a - 1)(b + 3)$ **f** $(a + d)(b + c)$
  g $(a - b)(m + n)$ **h** $(x - 1)(x + 2)$
8 **a** $(x + 3)(x + 7)$ **b** $(x + 7)^2$ **c** $(x + 6)(x - 11)$
  d $(x - 2)(x - 5)$ **e** $(x + 2)(2x + 3)$

f $(a + b)(4 - a)$ **g** $3a(a + 2)$ **h** $(x + 4)(6 - x)$
i $(x + 1)(10 - x)$ **j** $-2(x + 3)(2x + 5)$

EXERCISE 8C

1 **a** $(c + d)(c - d)$ **b** $(m + n)(m - n)$ **c** $(n + m)(n - m)$
  d $(m + x)(m - x)$ **e** $(x + 4)(x - 4)$ **f** $(x + 9)(x - 9)$
  g $(a + 3)(a - 3)$ **h** $(2x + 1)(2x - 1)$ **i** $(2x + 3)(2x - 3)$
  j $(3y + 5)(3y - 5)$ **k** $(8 + x)(8 - x)$ **l** $(4 + 3a)(4 - 3a)$
2 **a** $3(x + 2)(x - 2)$ **b** $8(x + 3)(x - 3)$ **c** $2(a + 5)(a - 5)$
  d $(2x + 5)(2x - 5)$ **e** $9(b + 10)(b - 10)$ **f** $3(b + 4)(b - 4)$
  g $\pi(R + r)(R - r)$ **h** $10(1 + x)(1 - x)$
  i $p(p + 2)(p - 2)$ **j** $x(x + 1)(x - 1)$
  k $x^2(x + 1)(x - 1)$ **l** $xy(x + y)(x - y)$
3 **a** $(7a + b)(7a - b)$ **b** $(y + 6x)(y - 6x)$
  c $(3x + 5y)(3x - 5y)$ **d** $(3a + 4b)(3a - 4b)$
  e $(a + 9b)(a - 9b)$ **f** $(ab + 2)(ab - 2)$
  g $(6x + pq)(6x - pq)$ **h** $(4a + 5bc)(4a - 5bc)$
4 **a** $(x + 5)(x + 1)$ **b** $(x + 3)(x - 7)$ **c** $(3 - x)(5 + x)$
  d $(9 - x)(3 + x)$ **e** $(x + 5)(x + 3)$ **f** $(5 - x)(x - 3)$
  g $(2x + 5)(2x - 1)$ **h** $(4x + 13)(5 - 4x)$
  i $(4x - 1)(5 - 2x)$ **j** $(3x - 11)(x - 9)$
  k $4(2x + 1)(x - 1)$ **l** $3x(x + 4)$

EXERCISE 8D

1 **a** $x^2 + 2x + 1$, $x^2 - 2x + 1$ **b** $x^2 + 4x + 4$, $x^2 - 4x + 4$
  c $x^2 + 8x + 16$, $x^2 - 8x + 16$
  d $4x^2 + 4x + 1$, $4x^2 - 4x + 1$
  e $9x^2 + 12x + 4$, $9x^2 - 12x + 4$
  f $16x^2 + 72x + 81$, $16x^2 - 72x + 81$
  g $4x^2 + 4cx + c^2$, $4x^2 - 4cx + c^2$
  h $x^2 + 4dx + 4d^2$, $x^2 - 4dx + 4d^2$
  i $a^2c^2 + 4ac + 4$, $a^2c^2 - 4ac + 4$
2 **a** $(x + 1)^2$ **b** $(x - 2)^2$ **c** $(x - 3)^2$ **d** $(x + 5)^2$ **e** $(x - 8)^2$
  f $(x + 10)^2$ **g** $(x - 6)^2$ **h** $(x + 7)^2$ **i** $(x - 9)^2$
3 **a** $(2x + 1)^2$ **b** $(4x - 5)^2$ **c** $(2x + 7)^2$ **d** $(2x - 3)^2$
  e $(3x + 1)^2$ **f** $(3x - 5)^2$
4 **a** $2(x + 1)^2$ **b** $2(x - 3)^2$ **c** $3(x + 5)^2$ **d** $-(x - 3)^2$
  e $-(x + 4)^2$ **f** $-(x - 8)^2$ **g** $-2(x - 10)^2$
  h $-(2b - 7)^2$ **i** $a(x - 5)^2$

EXERCISE 8E

1 **a** $(b + 2)(a + 1)$ **b** $(a + 4)(c + d)$ **c** $(a + 2)(b + 3)$
  d $(m + p)(n + 3)$ **e** $(x + 3)(x + 7)$ **f** $(x + 4)(x + 5)$
  g $(2x + 1)(x + 3)$ **h** $(3x + 2)(x + 4)$ **i** $(5x + 3)(4x + 1)$
2 **a** $(x + 5)(x - 4)$ **b** $(x + 2)(x - 7)$ **c** $(x - 3)(x - 2)$
  d $(x - 5)(x - 3)$ **e** $(x + 7)(x - 8)$ **f** $(2x + 1)(x - 3)$
  g $(3x + 2)(x - 4)$ **h** $(4x - 3)(x - 2)$ **i** $(9x + 2)(x - 1)$

EXERCISE 8F

1 **a** 3, 4 **b** 3, 5 **c** 2, 8 **d** 2, 9 **e** $-3, 7$ **f** $3, -7$
  g $-6, 2$ **h** $-2, 15$
2 **a** $(x + 1)(x + 3)$ **b** $(x + 3)(x + 8)$ **c** $(x + 3)(x + 7)$
  d $(x + 6)(x + 9)$ **e** $(x + 4)(x + 5)$ **f** $(x + 3)(x + 5)$
  g $(x + 4)(x + 6)$ **h** $(x + 2)(x + 7)$ **i** $(x + 2)(x + 4)$
3 **a** $(x - 1)(x - 2)$ **b** $(x - 1)(x - 3)$ **c** $(x - 2)(x - 3)$
  d $(x - 3)(x - 11)$ **e** $(x - 3)(x - 13)$ **f** $(x - 3)(x - 16)$
  g $(x - 4)(x - 7)$ **h** $(x - 2)(x - 12)$ **i** $(x - 2)(x - 18)$
4 **a** $(x - 8)(x + 1)$ **b** $(x + 7)(x - 3)$ **c** $(x - 2)(x + 1)$
  d $(x - 4)(x + 2)$ **e** $(x + 8)(x - 3)$ **f** $(x - 5)(x + 2)$

g $(x+9)(x-6)$ **h** $(x+9)(x-8)$ **i** $(x-7)(x+3)$
j $(x-3)(x+2)$ **k** $(x-12)(x+5)$ **l** $(x+12)(x-5)$
5 a $2(x+1)(x+4)$ **b** $3(x-1)(x-6)$ **c** $2(x+3)(x+4)$
d $2(x-10)(x-12)$ **e** $4(x-3)(x+1)$ **f** $3(x-3)(x-11)$
g $2(x-10)(x+9)$ **h** $3(x-4)(x+2)$ **i** $2(x+4)(x+5)$
j $x(x-8)(x+1)$ **k** $x(x-7)(x+4)$ **l** $x^2(x+1)^2$
6 a $-(x+9)(x-6)$ **b** $-(x+2)(x+5)$ **c** $-(x+3)(x+7)$
d $-(x-3)(x-1)$ **e** $-(x-2)^2$ **f** $-(x+3)(x-1)$
g $-2(x-9)(x+7)$ **h** $-2(x-5)^2$ **i** $-x(x-2)(x+1)$

EXERCISE 8G.1

1 a $x(3x+2)$ **b** $(x+9)(x-9)$ **c** $2(p^2+4)$
d $3(b+5)(b-5)$ **e** $2(x+4)(x-4)$ **f** $n^2(n+2)(n-2)$
g $(x-9)(x+1)$ **h** $(d+7)(d-1)$ **i** $(x+9)(x-1)$
j $4t(1+2t)$ **k** $3(x+6)(x-6)$ **l** $2(g-11)(g+5)$
m $(2a+3d)(2a-3d)$ **n** $5(a-2)(a+1)$ **o** $2(c-3)(c-1)$
p $x^2(x+1)(x-1)$ **q** $d^2(d+3)(d-1)$ **r** $x(x+2)^2$
2 a $(x-3)^2$ **b** $(x+11)(x-11)$ **c** $(x-1)^2$ **d** $(y+5)^2$
e $(x+11)^2$ **f** $(x-y)^2$ **g** $(1+x)(1-x)$
h $(5y+1)(5y-1)$ **i** $(7y+6z)(7y-6z)$ **j** $(2d+7)^2$
k $a(2b+c)(2b-c)$ **l** $2\pi(R+r)(R-r)$
3 a $a(b+c-2)$ **b** $ab(ab-2)$ **c** $2x(3+x)(3-x)$
d $(x+7)^2$ **e** $4a(a+b)(a-b)$ **f** $xy(x+2)(x-2)$
g $4x^2(x+1)(x-1)$ **h** $(x-2)(y-z)$ **i** $(a+b)(x+1)$
j $(x-y)(a+1)$ **k** $(x+2)(x+3)$ **l** $(x^2+1)(x+1)$
4 a $7(x-5y)$ **b** $2(g+2)(g-2)$ **c** $-5x(x+2)$
d $m(m+3p)$ **e** $(a+3)(a+5)$ **f** $(m-3)^2$
g $5x(x+y-xy)$ **h** $(x+2)(y+2)$ **i** $(y+5)(y-9)$
j $(2x+1)(x+5)$ **k** $3(y+7)(y-7)$ **l** $3(p+q)(p-q)$
m $(2c+1)(2c-1)$ **n** $3(x+4)(x-3)$ **o** $2(b+5)(x-3)$
5 a $-(x-1)(x+12)$ **b** $-2(x-1)(x-3)$ **c** $-(x+7)(x-2)$
d $-2x(x-1)^2$ **e** $(a+b+3)(a+b-3)$ **f** $x(x+4)$

EXERCISE 8G.2

1 a $(2x+3)(x+1)$ **b** $(2x+5)(x+1)$ **c** $(7x+2)(x+1)$
d $(3x+4)(x+1)$ **e** $(3x+1)(x+4)$ **f** $(3x+2)(x+2)$
g $(4x+1)(2x+3)$ **h** $(7x+1)(3x+2)$ **i** $(3x+1)(2x+1)$
j $(6x+1)(x+3)$ **k** $(5x+1)(2x+3)$ **l** $(7x+1)(2x+5)$
2 a $(2x+1)(x-5)$ **b** $(3x-1)(x+2)$ **c** $(3x+1)(x-2)$
d $(2x-1)(x+2)$ **e** $(2x+5)(x-1)$ **f** $(5x+1)(x-3)$
g $(5x-3)(x-1)$ **h** $(11x+2)(x-1)$ **i** $(3x+2)(x-3)$
j $(2x+3)(x-3)$ **k** $(3x-2)(x-5)$ **l** $(5x+2)(x-3)$
m $(3x-2)(x+4)$ **n** $(2x-1)(x+9)$ **o** $(2x-3)(x+6)$
p $(2x-3)(x+7)$ **q** $(5x+2)(3x-1)$ **r** $(21x+1)(x-3)$
3 a $(3x+2)(5x+3)$ **b** $(3x+2)(5x-3)$ **c** $(3x-2)(5x+3)$
d $2(3x-2)(5x-3)$ **e** $2(3x-1)^2$ **f** $3(4x+3)^2$
g $2(4x+1)(2x+1)$ **h** $2(4x-1)(2x+1)$ **i** $5(8x^2-x-1)$
j $4(4x-1)(2x-1)$ **k** $(5x+3)(5x+2)$ **l** $(5x-3)(5x-2)$
m $(5x-4)(5x+2)$ **n** $(25x+1)(x-6)$ **o** $(6x+5)(6x-1)$
p $(9x+5)(4x-1)$ **q** $(12x-5)(3x+2)$ **r** $(18x-1)(2x+3)$

REVIEW SET 8A

1 a $3ab$ **b** $3(x+1)$ **2 a** $x(x-3)$ **b** $3n(m+2n)$
3 a $(d-4)(t+2)$ **b** $(3x+7)(1+2b)$
4 a $(3+4x)(3-4x)$ **b** $(x-6)^2$ **5** $(x-1)(5+y)$
6 a $(x+3)(x+7)$ **b** $(x-3)(x+7)$ **c** $(x-7)(x+3)$
d $(x-2)(x-3)$ **e** $4(x-3)(x+1)$ **f** $-(x+4)(x+9)$
7 a $(4x+5)(2x+3)$ **b** $(6x-1)(2x-3)$ **c** $(4x-5)(3x+2)$

REVIEW SET 8B

1 a $2y$ **b** $2(x-2)$ **2 a** $2x(x+3)$ **b** $-2x(y+2)$
3 a $(p-q)(a+2)$ **b** $(x+1)(y+2)$
4 a $2(x+5)(x-5)$ **b** $(2x+5)^2$ **5** $(y-z)(2x+1)$
6 a $(x+5)(x+7)$ **b** $(x+7)(x-5)$ **c** $(x-5)(x-7)$
d $2(x-7)(x+5)$ **e** $(x-5)(x-6)$ **f** $-(x-2)(x-10)$
7 a $(3x+2)(4x-1)$ **b** $(3x-2)(4x+3)$ **c** $4(3x-1)(2x+3)$

EXERCISE 9A

1 a and **d**, **b** and **e** **2 A**, **D** and **M**, **C** and **O**, **I** and **L**
3 a i QR **ii** $\angle$QRS **b i** NO **ii** $\angle$MON
c i QR **ii** $\angle$QRP **d i** HE **ii** $\angle$HEF
e i DE **ii** $\angle$DEF **f i** ON **ii** $\angle$ONM

EXERCISE 9B

1 a   **b**

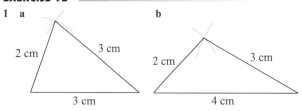

c cannot form a triangle

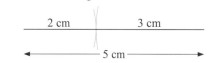

d cannot form a triangle

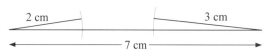

2 The sum of the lengths of any two sides of a triangle must be greater than the length of the third side.

EXERCISE 9C

1 a A and C, SAS **b** B and C, AAcorS **c** A and B, RHS
d A and C, SSS **e** B and C, AAcorS **f** A and C, SAS
g A and C, SSS **h** B and C, RHS
2 a $\triangle$ABC $\cong$ $\triangle$FED (AAcorS) **b** $\triangle$PQR $\cong$ $\triangle$ZYX (SAS)
c $\triangle$ABC $\cong$ $\triangle$EDF (AAcorS) **d** $\triangle$ABC $\cong$ $\triangle$LKM (SSS)
e $\triangle$XYZ $\cong$ $\triangle$FED (RHS) **f** no **g** no **h** no
i $\triangle$ABC $\cong$ $\triangle$PQR (SSS) **j** $\triangle$ABC $\cong$ $\triangle$FED (AAcorS)
3 a BC = DC {given}, $\angle$ACB = $\angle$ECD {vert. opposite},
$\angle$ABC = $\angle$EDC {alternate} $\therefore$ $\triangle$'s congruent {AAcorS}
b i 5 cm **ii** 37°
4 a SSS
b $\angle$PQS = $\angle$RQS, $\angle$QPS = $\angle$QRS, $\angle$PSQ = $\angle$RSQ
5 a AAcorS **b** DC = BC, AC = EC
6 a AC = BC = CD = CE, $\angle$ACB = $\angle$DCE, i.e., SAS
b AB = DE, $\angle$ABC = $\angle$BAC = $\angle$CDE = $\angle$CED, AB $\parallel$ DE
7 a SSS **b** $\angle$WZX = $\angle$YXZ so WZ $\parallel$ XY
and $\angle$WXZ = $\angle$YZX so WX $\parallel$ ZY
10 c ACBD is a parallelogram **11 c** a parallelogram

EXERCISE 9D

2 a $x=1.2$ **b** $x=10.8$ **c** $x=3\frac{1}{3}$ **d** $x=10.5$
e $x=12$ **f** $x=2\frac{6}{7}$ **g** $x=7.5$ **h** $x=5$ **i** $x=6$

REVIEW SET 9A

1 **A**, **B** and **E** and **C** and **D**

2

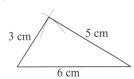

3 cm   5 cm
6 cm

3 **a** **B** and **C** (AAcorS)
b **A** and **C** (RHS)

5 **a** $\angle UYV = \angle WXV$ {given}, $\angle UVY = \angle WVX$ {vert. opp.}
∴ Δ's UYV and WXV are equiangular, i.e., similar.

b $\angle JLK = \angle NLM$ {vertically opposite},
$\angle JKL = \angle NML$ {alternate angles, JK ∥ MN}
∴ Δ's JLK, NLM are equiangular, i.e., similar.

c $\angle CBD = \angle CEA$ {given}, $\angle C$ is common to both
∴ Δ's CBD and CEA are equiangular, i.e., similar.

6 $116\frac{2}{3}$ m

REVIEW SET 9B

1 **a** DF **b** $\angle DFE$
2 **b** PB = QB, $\angle PAB = \angle QAB$, $\angle PBA = \angle QBA$
3

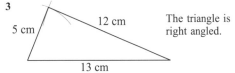

5 cm   12 cm
13 cm

The triangle is right angled.

5 **a** $x = 1\frac{5}{8}$ **b** $x = 7\frac{2}{3}$ **c** $x = 13\frac{1}{3}$ **6** **c** $V = \frac{2}{3}\pi x^3$

EXERCISE 10A.1

1 **a** numerical **b** numerical **c** categorical **d** numerical
e numerical **f** categorical **g** categorical **h** numerical

2 **a** male, female
b Australian Rules, Soccer, Gridiron, Rugby
c black, blonde, brown, grey, brunette
d unleaded, premium unleaded, diesel, LPG, super

3 **a** quantitative discrete **b** quantitative continuous
c categorical **d** quantitative discrete
e quantitative discrete **f** categorical
g quantitative discrete **h** quantitative continuous
i quantitative discrete **j** quantitative continuous
k categorical **l** categorical **m** quantitative continuous
n quantitative discrete **o** quantitative discrete

4 **a** sample **b** census **c** sample **d** census **e** census
f sample

EXERCISE 10A.2

1 **a** type of fruit, frequency **b** type of fruit
c no, sample is from students at one place **d** **i** no **ii** 80
e banana
f

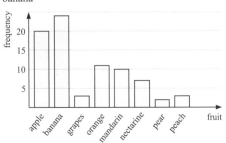

2 **a** favourite subject, frequency
b dependent: subject; independent: frequency
c Science **d** randomly selected **e** yes
f

Art
Science
Mathematics
English
Language
Geography
Music   History

3 **a** **i** ⩾ 1690 **ii** ⩾ 3759 **iii** ⩾ 2019
b

Number of persons	% of households of corresponding size		
	Year		
	1935	1960	1985
1	2.1%	0.8%	9.8%
2	15.6%	17.6%	26.2%
3	16.7%	16.1%	35.4%
4	24.9%	37.3%	23.1%
5+	40.7%	28.2%	5.4%
Totals	1	1	1

EXERCISE 10B

1 **a** continuous **b** continuous **c** continuous
d continuous **e** discrete **f** discrete **g** continuous

2 **a** number of TV sets
b Discrete since you can't have part of a TV set.
c

Household televisions

frequency

0   1   2   3   4   number of TV sets

d positively skewed, no outliers **e** 30% **f** 15%

3 **a** 45 shoppers **b** 18 shoppers **c** 15.6%
d positively skewed, no outliers

4 **a** the number of business appointments out of the office each day
b You can only have whole appointments.
c 22.2% **d** 4.44% **e** 11 appointments
f positively skewed with an outlier
g Data value 10 is an outlier.

5 **a** number of tooth picks in a box **b** discrete
c

No. of tooth picks	Tally	Freq.
47	|	1
48	卌	5
49	卌 卌	10
50	卌 卌 卌 卌 |||	23
51	卌 卌	10
52	卌 ||||	9
53	||	2

d

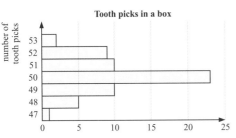

Tooth picks in a box

e approximately symmetrical   **f** 38.3%

6 a

No. of pumpkins	Tally	Frequency
3	|	1
4	||||	4
5	|||	3
6							5
7										8
8	||||| |	6
9	||||| |	6
10							5
11	|	1
12		0
13		0
14		0
15	|	1
	Total	40

b

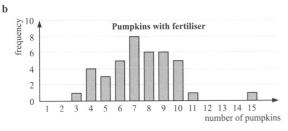

Pumpkins with fertiliser

c Yes, data value 15 is an outlier
d approximately symmetrical
e On average the number of pumpkins is higher in the "with fertiliser" group.
f Yes, assuming the fertiliser is not too expensive and the pumpkins are as big as they were previously.

EXERCISE 10C

1 a

Test Score	Tally	Freq.
0 - 9		0
10 - 19		0
20 - 29	|	1
30 - 39	||	2
40 - 49	|||	3
50 - 59	||||| ||||	9
60 - 69	||||| ||||| |||	13
70 - 79	||||| |||	8
80 - 89	||||| |||||	10
90 - 100	||||	4
	Total	50

b 28%
c 12%

d More students had a test score in the interval 60 - 69 than in any other interval.

2 a

Stem	Leaf
2	9 7 4 1 7 5
3	3 0 5 4 6 4
4	6 0 2 8
5	8 7 1 0

b

Stem	Leaf
2	1 4 5 7 7 9
3	0 3 4 4 5 6
4	0 2 6 8
5	0 1 7 8

5 | 8 represents 58

3 a 1 **b** 43 **c** 10 **d** 1 **e** 21.4%

4 a

Stem	Leaf
0	
1	8
2	9 9 7
3	4 7 9 3 7 5 9 1 4 7 4
4	4 0 2 3 3 7 1 3 8 4 4 4 5 9 1 2 2 3 3 5
5	1 3 8 0 5 2 4 9 7 1

b

Stem	Leaf
0	
1	8
2	7 9 9
3	1 3 4 4 4 5 7 7 7 9 9
4	0 1 1 2 2 2 3 3 3 3 3 4 4 4 4 5 5 7 8 9
5	0 1 1 2 3 4 5 7 8 9

c The stem-and-leaf plot shows all the actual data values.
d i 59 **ii** 18 **e** 22.2% **f** 8.9%
g negatively skewed with no outliers

EXERCISE 10D

1 a Weights can take any value from 75 kg to 105 kg.
b

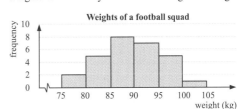

Weights of a football squad

c The modal class is (85 - < 90) kg as this occurred the most frequently.
d approximately symmetrical with no outliers
2 a continuous numerical
b

Stem	Leaf
0	3 6 8 8 8
1	0 0 0 0 2 2 4 4 4 5 5 5 6 6 6 6 6 7 8 8 8 8 9
2	0 0 0 1 4 5 5 5 6 7 7
3	2 2 3 4 7
4	0 2 5 5 6

c positively skewed
d The modal travelling time was between 10 and 20 minutes.
3 a column graph

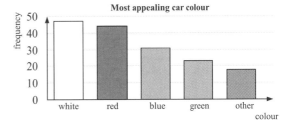

Most appealing car colour

b   column graph

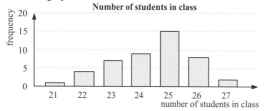

c   histogram

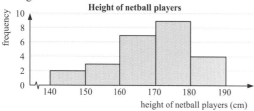

d   histogram

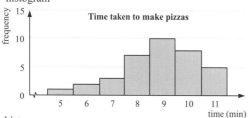

e   histogram

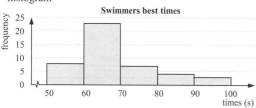

4   **a**

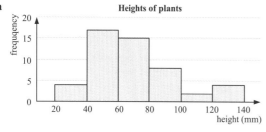

b   46   **c**   30%   **d**   **i**   754   **ii**   686

EXERCISE 10E.1

1   **a**   **i**   24   **ii**   24   **iii**   no mode
   b   **i**   13.3   **ii**   11.5   **iii**   8
   c   **i**   10.3   **ii**   10.0   **iii**   11.2
   d   **i**   428.6   **ii**   428   **iii**   415 and 427

2   **a** A: 7.73 B: 8.45   **b** A: 7 B: 7
   c   The data sets are the same except for the last value, and the last value of A is less than the last value of B, so the mean of A is less than the mean of B.
   d   The middle value of the data sets is the same, so the median is the same.

3   **a**   mean: $582\,000$, median: $420\,000$, mode: $290\,000$
   b   The mode is the second lowest value, so does not take the higher values into account.

c   No, since the data is unevenly distributed, the median is not in the centre.

4   **a**   mean: 3.1, median: 0, mode: 0
   b   The data is very positively skewed so the median is not in the centre.
   c   The mode is the lowest value so does not take the higher values into account.
   d   yes, 15 and 27   **e**   no

5   **a**   44   **b**   44   **c**   40.57   **d**   increase mean to 40.75   **6**   105.6

7   2275 km   **8** $2\,592\,000$ **9** $x = 12$ **10** $a = 8$ **11**   27

12   **a**   1696 km   **b**   1632 km   **c**   475.4 km   **13**   7.875   **14**   15

EXERCISE 10E.2

1   **a**   1   **b**   1   **c**   1.4

2   **a**   **i**   5.74   **b**
     ii   7
     iii   8

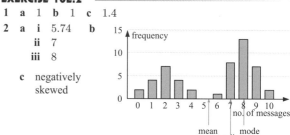

   c   negatively skewed

   d   The mean takes into account the full range of numbers of text messages and is affected by extreme values.
   e   median

3   **a**

Donation ($)	Frequency
1	7
2	9
3	2
4	4
5	8

   b   30
   c   **i** $2.90   **ii** $2
      iii $2
   d   mode

4   **a**   **i**   2.61   **ii**   2   **iii**   2
   b   This school has more children per family than the average Canadian family.
   c   positive
   d   The mean is larger than the median and the mode.

EXERCISE 10F

1   **a**   **i**

Score	Frequency	Cum. Freq.
0	1	1
1	3	4
2	3	7
3	6	13
4	12	25
5	15	40
6	8	48
7	5	53
8	2	55

     ii

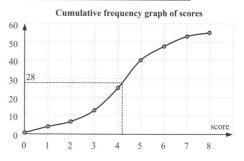

iii from graph, median $\doteqdot 4.2$

b i

No. of goals	Frequency	Cum. Freq.
0	7	7
1	11	18
2	20	38
3	22	60
4	12	72
5	9	81
6	5	86

ii

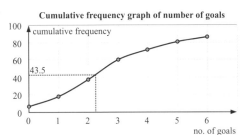

Cumulative frequency graph of number of goals

iii from graph, median $\doteqdot 2.3$

c i

Height	Frequency	Cum. Freq.
$0 \leqslant h < 5$	4	4
$5 \leqslant h < 10$	8	12
$10 \leqslant h < 15$	14	26
$15 \leqslant h < 20$	16	42
$20 \leqslant h < 25$	10	52
$25 \leqslant h < 30$	6	58
$30 \leqslant h < 35$	2	60

ii

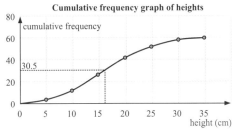

Cumulative frequency graph of heights

iii from graph, median $\doteqdot 16.5$

2 a

Salmon lengths (cm)	Freq.	Cum. Freq.
$24 \leqslant x < 27$	2	2
$27 \leqslant x < 30$	5	7
$30 \leqslant x < 33$	7	14
$33 \leqslant x < 36$	11	25
$36 \leqslant x < 39$	12	37
$39 \leqslant x < 42$	2	39
$42 \leqslant x < 45$	1	40

b

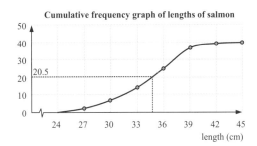

Cumulative frequency graph of lengths of salmon

c median $\doteqdot 34.7$

d Median is 34. The graph is assuming a constant change over the interval whereas original data is not uniform over the interval.

3 a 65 **b** 93 **c** 58 **d** 32 **e** 78

4 a $7\frac{1}{2}$ **b i** 41 **ii** 43 **5 a** 30 **b** 97 **c** 27 mins

6 a 52 m **b** 23 **c** 28 **d** 32

EXERCISE 10G

1 a i 9 **ii** $Q_1 = 7, Q_3 = 10$ **iii** 7 **iv** 3
  b i 18.5 **ii** $Q_1 = 16, Q_3 = 20$ **iii** 14 **iv** 4
  c i 26.9 **ii** $Q_1 = 25.5, Q_3 = 28.1$ **iii** 7.7 **iv** 2.6

2 a median $= 2.35$, $Q_1 = 1.4$, $Q_3 = 3.7$
  b range $= 5.1$, IQR $= 2.3$
  c i ...... greater than 2.35 minutes
    ii ...... less than 3.7 minutes
    iii The minimum waiting time was 0.1 minutes and the maximum waiting time was 5.2 minutes. The waiting times were spread over 5.1 minutes.

3 a 20 **b** 58 **c** 40 **d** 30 **e** 49 **f** 38 **g** 19

EXERCISE 10H

1 a i 31 **ii** 54 **iii** 16 **iv** 40 **v** 26 **b i** 38 **ii** 14

2 a ...... 89 points **b** ...... 25 points **c** ...... 62 points
  d ...... at least 73 points
  e ...... between 45 and 73 points **f** 64 **g** 28

3 a i min $= 2$, $Q_1 = 5$, median $= 6$, $Q_3 = 9$, max $= 11$
    ii

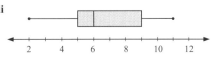

    iii range $= 9$ **iv** IQR $= 4$
  b i min $= 0$, $Q_1 = 4$, median $= 7$, $Q_3 = 8$, max $= 9$
    ii

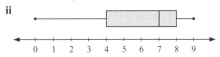

    iii range $= 9$ **iv** IQR $= 4$

4 a median $= 20.2$ kg, $Q_1 = 19.8$ kg, $Q_3 = 21.1$ kg
    max. weight $= 22.3$ kg, min. weight $= 18.8$ kg
  b

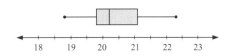

  c i IQR $= 1.3$ kg **ii** range $= 3.5$ kg
  d i ...... 20.2 kg **ii** 31.8% of the bags ......
    iii ...... 1.3 kg **iv** ...... 19.8 kg or less
  e approximately symmetrical

5 a

Statistic	A	C
min value	2	8
Q_1	7	10
median	10	14
Q_3	12	16
max value	16	17

  b i A: 14, C: 9
    ii A: 5, C: 6

6 a i class B **ii** class B **iii** class B
  b i 49 **ii** 13 **c** 75%
  d i almost symmetrical **ii** almost symmetrical
  e The students in class A generally scored higher marks. The marks in class B were more varied.

7 a

Statistic	Boys	Girls
min value	160	152
Q_1	167	163
median	171	166
Q_3	175	170
max value	188	177

   b The distributions show that in general, the boys are taller than the girls and are more varied in their heights.

EXERCISE 10I.1

1 $\overline{x} \doteqdot 4.87$, min $= 1$, $Q_1 = 3$, median $= 5$, $Q_3 = 7$, max $= 9$

2

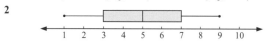

3

4 $\overline{x} \doteqdot 5.24$, min $= 2$, $Q_1 = 4$, median $= 5$, $Q_3 = 6.5$, max $= 9$

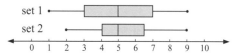

EXERCISE 10I.2

1 **Set 1**
mean $= 6.625$, mode $= 7$, min $= 3$, $Q_1 = 6$, median $= 7$, $Q_3 = 8$, max $= 9$, range $= 6$, IQR $= 2$

   Set 2
mean $= 7.45$, mode $= 7$, min $= 3$, $Q_1 = 6$, median $= 7$, $Q_3 = 9$, max $= 15$, range $= 12$, IQR $= 3$

2 **Set 1**
mean $= 11.936$, mode $= 11.9$, min $= 11.6$, $Q_1 = 11.8$, median $= 11.9$, $Q_3 = 12$, max $= 12.2$, range $= 0.6$, IQR $= 0.2$

   Set 2
mean $= 11.84$, mode $= 11.8$, min $= 11.5$, $Q_1 = 11.7$, median $= 11.8$, $Q_3 = 11.9$, max $= 12.2$, range $= 0.7$, IQR $= 0.2$

EXERCISE 10J

1 a Sample A **b** A: 7, B: 5
   c i A: 8, B: 4 **ii** A: 2, B: 1 **d** A: 1.90, B: 0.894
   e When s is smaller as in Sample B, it indicates most values are closer to the mean, and hence shows less spread.
2 a 5.74 **b** 1.41
   c much less, indicating the outlier had a marked effect on the standard deviation
3 a Andrew: mean $= 25$, SD $= 4.97$
     Brad: mean $= 30.5$, SD $= 12.56$
   b standard deviation
4 a Mickey: mean $= 3$, range $= 5$
     Julio: mean $= 3$, range $= 5$
   b Mickey's **c** Mickey: SD $= 1.95$, Julio: SD $= 1.26$

d standard deviation
5 1.5 **6** mean $= 28.8$, SD $= 1.64$
7 mean length $= 38.3$ cm, SD $= 2.66$
8 mean wage $= \$392.11$, SD $= \$16.35$

EXERCISE 10K

1 a

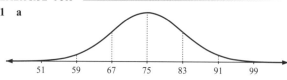

   b i 99 **ii** 51 **c i** 80 **ii** 13 **iii** 408
2 a

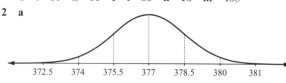

   b i 285 **ii** 252 **c** 16%
3 a 2.5% **b** 84% **c** 97.35% **d** 84% **4** once

REVIEW SET 10A

1 a categorical **b** numerical **c** numerical
2 a 49 **b** 15 **c** 26.5% **d** positively skewed
3 a the number of children in the household
   b Discrete, since you cannot have part of a child.
   c

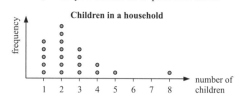

   d positively skewed, one outlier at 8
4 a
Stem	Leaf
0	9
1	8 8
2	5 8 4 9 2 6 5 0 3 8 7
3	5 2 4 9 3 4 9 1 6 5 6 3 5 2
4	0 0 4	0 represents 40

   b
Stem	Leaf
0	9
1	8 8
2	0 2 3 4 5 5 6 7 8 8 9
3	1 2 2 3 3 4 4 5 5 5 6 6 9 9
4	0 0 4	0 represents 40

   c The stem-and-leaf plot displays all the actual data values.
   d i 40 **ii** 9 **e** 20%
5 $x = 7$ **6 a** 32 kg **b** 91 kg **c** 20 **d** 5 **e** 20%
7 a Mass can be any decimal of a gram.
   b

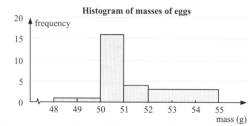

   c Modal class is 50 - . This class has the most eggs.

d   slightly positively skewed

8 **a** 29 **b** $Q_1 = 22$, $Q_3 = 41.5$ **c** 45 **d** 19.5

9 **a i** 48 **ii** 98 **iii** 15 **iv** 66 **v** 42 **b i** 83 **ii** 24

10 **a**   mean $= 0.88$, SD $= 0.0980$
   b   mean $= 1.76$, SD $= 0.196$
   c   Both mean and standard deviation doubled when the individual scores were doubled.

REVIEW SET 10B

1 **a** survey
   b It may depend on the time of day the survey was carried out.

2 **a**

Stem	Leaf
3	1
4	9 5
5	8 8 7 8 3 5
6	9 0 8 5 9 6 4 1 6 4 1 6 3
7	0 1 2 5 6 7 8 4 0
8	0 2 3 9 2 2
9	1 4 0 2 4 1 1 7

9 | 1 represents 91

   b

Stem	Leaf
3	1
4	5 9
5	3 5 7 8 8 8
6	0 1 1 3 4 4 5 6 6 6 8 9 9
7	0 0 1 2 4 5 6 7 8
8	0 2 2 2 3 9
9	0 1 1 1 2 4 4 7

9 | 1 represents 91

   c The stem-and-leaf plot displays all the actual data values.
   d i 97 **ii** 31 **e** 20%
   f iii   neither symmetric nor skewed

3 **a** 14.55 **b** 14.5 **c** 14 and 15 **4** 13.56

5 mean $= 6$, $x = 2$

6 **a i** 8.47 **ii** 9 **iii** 9 **iv** 4 **b** well above average
   c negative

7 **a**

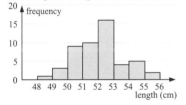

Histogram of lengths of newborn babies

   b 27
   c 70%

   d

Length (cm)	Frequency	Cum. Freq.
$48 \leqslant l < 49$	1	1
$49 \leqslant l < 50$	3	4
$50 \leqslant l < 51$	9	13
$51 \leqslant l < 52$	10	23
$52 \leqslant l < 53$	16	39
$53 \leqslant l < 54$	4	43
$54 \leqslant l < 55$	5	48
$55 \leqslant l < 56$	2	50

   e

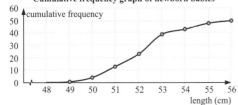

Cumulative frequency graph of newborn babies

   f i 52.1 cm **ii** 18 babies

8 **a** min $= 8.6$, $Q_1 = 9.6$, median $= 10.15$, $Q_3 = 11.45$, max $= 12.0$

   b

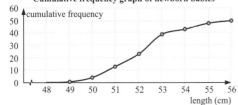

   c range $= \$3.40$ **d** IQR $= \$1.85$

9 **a** Comparing the median swim times for girls and boys shows that, in general, boys swim 2.5 seconds faster than the girls.
   b The range of the girls' swim times is 10 seconds compared to the range of 7 seconds for the boys.
   c The fastest 25% of the boys swim faster than 100% of the girls.
   d 100% of the boys swim faster than 60 seconds whereas 75% of the girls swim faster than 60 seconds.

10 **a** 420 **b** 13 **c** 238

EXERCISE 11A

1 **a** $x = \pm 10$ **b** $x = \pm 5$ **c** $x = \pm 2$ **d** $x = \pm 3$
   e no solution **f** $x = 0$ **g** $x = \pm 3$ **h** no solution
   i $x = \pm \sqrt{2}$

2 **a** $x = 4$ or -2 **b** $x = 0$ or -8 **c** no solution
   d $x = 4 \pm \sqrt{5}$ **e** no solution **f** $x = -2$ **g** $x = 2\frac{1}{2}$
   h $x = 0$ or $-\frac{4}{3}$ **i** $x = \dfrac{\pm\sqrt{6} - 3}{2}$

EXERCISE 11B

1 **a** $x = 0$ **b** $y = 0$ **c** $a = 0$ **d** $b = 0$ **e** $y = 0$
   f $a = 0$ or $b = 0$ **g** $x = 0$ or $y = 0$
   h $a = 0$ or $b = 0$ or $c = 0$ **i** $x = 0$ **j** $a = 0$
   k $p = 0$ or $q = 0$ or $r = 0$ or $s = 0$ **l** $a = 0$ or $b = 0$

2 **a** $x = 0$ or 5 **b** $x = 0$ or -3 **c** $x = -1$ or 3
   d $x = 0$ or 7 **e** $x = 0$ or -1 **f** $x = -6$ or $\frac{3}{2}$
   g $x = 0$ **h** $x = 5$ **i** $x = \frac{1}{3}$

3 **a** $x = 0$ or 7 **b** $x = 0$ or 5 **c** $x = 0$ or 8
   d $x = 0$ or 4 **e** $x = 0$ or -2 **f** $x = 0$ or $-\frac{5}{2}$
   g $x = 0$ or $\frac{3}{4}$ **h** $x = 0$ or $\frac{5}{4}$ **i** $x = 0$ or 3

4 **a** $x = 1$ or -1 **b** $x = 3$ or -3 **c** $x = 5$
   d $x = -2$ **e** $x = -1$ or -2 **f** $x = 1$ or 2
   g $x = -2$ or -3 **h** $x = 2$ or 3 **i** $x = -1$ or -6
   j $x = -2$ or -7 **k** $x = -5$ or -6 **l** $x = -5$ or 3
   m $x = -6$ or 2 **n** $x = 3$ or 8 **o** $x = 7$

5 **a** $x = -7$ or -2 **b** $x = -5$ or -6 **c** $x = -5$ or 3
   d $x = -4$ or 3 **e** $x = 3$ or 2 **f** $x = 2$
   g $x = 3$ or -2 **h** $x = 12$ or -5 **i** $x = 10$ or -7
   j $x = -5$ or 2 **k** $x = 3$ or 4 **l** $x = 12$ or -3

6 **a** $x = \frac{1}{2}$ or 2 **b** $x = -3$ or $\frac{1}{3}$ **c** $x = -4$ or $-\frac{5}{3}$
   d $x = \frac{1}{2}$ or -3 **e** $x = \frac{1}{2}$ or 5 **f** $x = -1$ or $-\frac{5}{2}$
   g $x = -\frac{1}{3}$ or -4 **h** $x = -\frac{2}{3}$ or 3 **i** $x = \frac{1}{2}$ or -9
   j $x = 1$ or $-\frac{5}{2}$ **k** $x = \frac{4}{3}$ or -2 **l** $x = \frac{3}{2}$ or -6

7 **a** $x = \frac{1}{3}$ or $-\frac{5}{2}$ **b** $x = \frac{2}{3}$ or $-\frac{1}{2}$ **c** $x = -\frac{1}{2}$ or $-\frac{1}{3}$
   d $x = -\frac{1}{21}$ or 3 **e** $x = \frac{2}{5}$ or $-\frac{1}{2}$ **f** $x = -\frac{3}{10}$ or 1

8 **a** $x = -4$ or -3 **b** $x = -3$ or 1 **c** $x = \pm 3$
   d $x = -1$ or $\frac{2}{3}$ **e** $x = -\frac{1}{2}$ **f** $x = \frac{5}{2}$ or 4

EXERCISE 11C

1 **a i** 1 **ii** $(x + 1)^2 = 6$ **b i** 1 **ii** $(x - 1)^2 = -6$

c **i** 9 **ii** $(x+3)^2 = 11$ **d** **i** 9 **ii** $(x-3)^2 = 6$
e **i** 25 **ii** $(x+5)^2 = 26$ **f** **i** 16 **ii** $(x-4)^2 = 21$
g **i** 36 **ii** $(x+6)^2 = 49$ **h** **i** $\frac{25}{4}$ **ii** $(x+\frac{5}{2})^2 = 4\frac{1}{4}$
i **i** $\frac{49}{4}$ **ii** $(x-\frac{7}{2})^2 = 16\frac{1}{4}$

2 **a** $x = 2 \pm \sqrt{3}$ **b** $x = 1 \pm \sqrt{3}$ **c** $x = 2 \pm \sqrt{7}$
d $x = -1 \pm \sqrt{2}$ **e** no solution **f** $x = -2 \pm \sqrt{3}$
g $x = -3 \pm \sqrt{6}$ **h** no solution **i** $x = -4 \pm \sqrt{2}$

3 **a** $x = -1$ or -2 **b** $x = 2 \pm \sqrt{12}$ **c** $x = 2$ or 3
d $x = \dfrac{-1 \pm \sqrt{5}}{2}$ **e** $x = \dfrac{-3 \pm \sqrt{13}}{2}$ **f** $x = \dfrac{-5 \pm \sqrt{33}}{2}$

4 **b** **i** $x = \dfrac{-2 \pm \sqrt{6}}{2}$ **ii** $x = \dfrac{6 \pm \sqrt{15}}{3}$ **iii** $x = \dfrac{5 \pm \sqrt{10}}{5}$

EXERCISE 11D

1 9 or -10 **2** -9 or 12 **3** 8 or -4 **4** 12 and -3
5 1 and -4, or 4 and -1 **6** width is 10 cm
7 altitude is 5 cm **8** 9 m $\times$ 16 m
9 9 m $\times$ 8 m, or 16 m $\times$ $4\frac{1}{2}$ m **10** **a** $x = 4$ **b** $x = 8$
11 7 cm, 24 cm, 25 cm **12** 30 rows
13 BC is 5 cm or 16 cm **14** 5 metres **16** $\frac{3}{4}$ or $\frac{4}{3}$
17 $\frac{2}{3}$ or 3 **18** 5 cm $\times$ 5 cm **19** **c** $1\frac{1}{2}$ metres wide **20** $x = 5$

EXERCISE 11E.1

1 **a** $2 \pm \sqrt{7}$ **b** $-3 \pm \sqrt{2}$ **c** $2 \pm \sqrt{3}$ **d** $-2 \pm \sqrt{5}$
e $2 \pm \sqrt{2}$ **f** $\dfrac{1 \pm \sqrt{7}}{2}$ **g** $\sqrt{2}$ **h** $\dfrac{-4 \pm \sqrt{7}}{9}$ **i** $\dfrac{-7 \pm \sqrt{97}}{4}$

2 **a** $-2 \pm 2\sqrt{2}$ **b** $\dfrac{-5 \pm \sqrt{57}}{8}$ **c** $\dfrac{5 \pm \sqrt{13}}{2}$

EXERCISE 11E.2

1 **a** $x \doteq -3.4142$ or -0.5858 **b** $x \doteq -6.3166$ or 0.3166
c $x \doteq -1.2656$ or 2.7656 **d** $x \doteq -1.0756$ or 3.4089
e $x \doteq -0.8923$ or 3.6423 **f** $x \doteq -2.5391$ or 1.3391
2 **a** $x \doteq -4.8284$ or 0.8284 **b** $x \doteq -1.5687$ or 0.3187
c $x \doteq 0.6972$ or 4.3028
3 **a** $x = \pm 5$ **b** no real solutions **c** $x = \pm \sqrt{7}$
d no real solutions **e** $x = \pm \frac{3}{2}$ **f** no real solutions
g no real solutions **h** $x = 5$ or -1 **i** no real solutions
j no real solutions **k** no real solutions **l** no real solutions
4 **a** 32 **b** -39 **c** 44 **d** 68 **e** 61 **f** -127
5 **a** 2 distinct real roots **b** a repeated root
c 2 distinct real roots **d** 2 distinct real roots
e no real roots **f** a repeated root
6 a, b, c, d, f

EXERCISE 11F

1 **a** $x = \pm \sqrt{6}$ **b** $x = \pm \sqrt{8}$ **c** $x = \pm \sqrt{10}$
d $x = 4$ or -3 **e** $x = -1$ or -5 **f** $x = 2$ or -1
g $x = \frac{1}{2}$ or -1 **h** $x = 1$ or $-\frac{1}{3}$ **i** $x = -1$ or 4
j $x = \dfrac{1 \pm \sqrt{7}}{2}$ **k** $x = \dfrac{1 \pm \sqrt{5}}{2}$ **l** $x = \dfrac{3 \pm \sqrt{17}}{4}$

REVIEW SET 11A

1 **a** $x = \pm \sqrt{2}$ **b** no real solutions **c** $x = 0$ or 3
d $x = 3$ or 8 **e** $x = -\frac{2}{5}$ or $\frac{3}{2}$ **f** $x = -\frac{7}{3}$ or 3
2 **a** $x = 0$ or 1 **b** no real solutions **c** $x = 2 \pm \sqrt{5}$

3 **a** $x = -4 \pm \sqrt{11}$ **b** $x = 7 \pm \sqrt{42}$
4 $3\sqrt{3}$ cm $\times \sqrt{3}$ cm
5 $\frac{2}{3}$ or $1\frac{1}{2}$ **6** The number is $2 + \sqrt{3}$ or $2 - \sqrt{3}$. **7** $\dfrac{5 \pm \sqrt{17}}{2}$
8 **a** 2 real distinct roots **b** no real roots

REVIEW SET 11B

1 **a** $x = 3$ **b** $x = -5$ or 4 **c** no real solutions
d $x = 8$ or -3 **e** $x = \pm 2$ **f** $x = -\frac{1}{2}$ or $\frac{2}{3}$
2 **a** $x = 2 \pm \sqrt{14}$ **b** $x = \dfrac{-1 \pm \sqrt{37}}{2}$ **3** 12 cm $\times$ 7 cm
4 -1 or $\frac{4}{5}$ **5** 5 cm, 12 cm, 13 cm **6** $b = -6$, $c = -7$
7 **a** no real solutions **b** no real solutions
8 **a** no real roots **b** 2 distinct real roots

EXERCISE 12A

1 **a** 4.0 m **b** 7.2 m **2** 51.3 m
3 $\angle ZXY = 57^o$, $\angle XYZ = 43^o$, $\angle XZY = 80^o$ **4** 1072 m

EXERCISE 12B.1

1 **a** 0 **b** 0.26 **c** 0.42 **d** 0.5 **e** 0.71 **f** 0.87
g 0.97 **h** 1
3 **a** 1 **b** 0.97 **c** 0.91 **d** 0.87 **e** 0.71 **f** 0.5
g 0.26 **h** 0
5 $(0.57, 0.82)$ **6**

EXERCISE 12B.2

1 **a** 0 **b** 0.18 **c** 0.36 **d** 0.70 **e** 0.84 **f** 1
g 1.19 **h** 1.43
3 triangle TON is
isosceles, ON = TN

4 $\tan 80^o$ is too large; $\tan 80^o \doteq 5.671$
5 **a** $(\cos \theta, \sin \theta)$ **b** **i** $\cos \theta$ **ii** $\sin \theta$ **iii** $\tan \theta$

EXERCISE 12C

1 **a** **i** AC **ii** BC **iii** AB **b** **i** RS **ii** TR **iii** ST
c **i** AB **ii** BC **iii** AC
2 **a** b **b** c **c** c **d** b

EXERCISE 12D.1

1 **a** **i** $\frac{p}{r}$ **ii** $\frac{q}{r}$ **iii** $\frac{p}{q}$ **iv** $\frac{q}{r}$ **v** $\frac{p}{r}$ **vi** $\frac{q}{p}$
b **i** $\frac{y}{x}$ **ii** $\frac{z}{x}$ **iii** $\frac{y}{z}$ **iv** $\frac{z}{x}$ **v** $\frac{y}{x}$ **vi** $\frac{z}{y}$
c **i** $\frac{4}{5}$ **ii** $\frac{3}{5}$ **iii** $\frac{4}{3}$ **iv** $\frac{3}{5}$ **v** $\frac{4}{5}$ **vi** $\frac{3}{4}$
d **i** $\frac{4}{7}$ **ii** $\frac{\sqrt{33}}{7}$ **iii** $\frac{4}{\sqrt{33}}$ **iv** $\frac{\sqrt{33}}{7}$ **v** $\frac{4}{7}$ **vi** $\frac{\sqrt{33}}{4}$
e **i** $\frac{5}{\sqrt{34}}$ **ii** $\frac{3}{\sqrt{34}}$ **iii** $\frac{5}{3}$ **iv** $\frac{3}{\sqrt{34}}$ **v** $\frac{5}{\sqrt{34}}$ **vi** $\frac{3}{5}$
f **i** $\frac{7}{\sqrt{65}}$ **ii** $\frac{4}{\sqrt{65}}$ **iii** $\frac{7}{4}$ **iv** $\frac{4}{\sqrt{65}}$ **v** $\frac{7}{\sqrt{65}}$ **vi** $\frac{4}{7}$

EXERCISE 12D.2

1 **a** $\sin 70^o = \dfrac{x}{a}$ **b** $\sin 35^o = \dfrac{x}{b}$ **c** $\tan 64^o = \dfrac{x}{c}$

d $\cos 40^o = \dfrac{d}{x}$ **e** $\cos 49^o = \dfrac{x}{e}$ **f** $\tan 73^o = \dfrac{f}{x}$

g $\cos 54^o = \dfrac{g}{x}$ **h** $\tan 30^o = \dfrac{h}{x}$ **i** $\sin 68^o = \dfrac{i}{x}$

2 a 15.52 **b** 12.99 **c** 9.84 **d** 6.73 **e** 11.86 **f** 22.94
g 24.41 **h** 16.86 **i** 5.60 **j** 16.37 **k** 22.66 **l** 10.43

3 a $\theta = 62$, $a = 10.60$, $b = 5.63$
b $\theta = 27$, $a = 16.83$, $b = 7.64$
c $\theta = 65$, $a = 49.65$, $b = 20.98$

EXERCISE 12D.3

1 a 56.3^o **b** 34.8^o **c** 48.2^o **d** 34.8^o **e** 41.1^o
f 48.6^o **g** 25.3^o **h** 37.1^o **i** 35.5^o

2 a $x = 6.2$, $\theta = 38.7^o$, $\phi = 51.3^o$
b $x = 5.9$, $\alpha = 53.9^o$, $\beta = 36.1^o$
c $x = 7.5$, $a = 38.4^o$, $b = 51.6^o$

4 The 3 triangles do not exist.

EXERCISE 12E.1

1 109.6 m **2** 57.14^o **3** 237.9 m **4** 34.87 m **5** 2.65 m
6 761.1 m **7** 279.7 m **8** 6.89^o **9** 1.92 m **10** 23.55 m
11 a 10.77 cm **b** 21.80^o **12** 106.3^o **13** 15.76 cm
14 6.10 m **15** 5-cuts (including the cut to fell the tree)
16 252.2 m **17** 588.8 km/h **18** 41.41^o **19** 53.18^o
20 a 247.5 m **b** 128.3 m **21** 7.485 m **22** 162.9 m
23 729.0 m **24** 1.664 units

EXERCISE 12E.2

1 a

N

O 136°

b

N

O 240°

c

N

51°

O

d

N

O 327°

2 a 234° **b** 293° **c** 083° **d** 124°
3 a i 041° **ii** 142° **iii** 322° **iv** 099° **v** 221° **vi** 279°
b i 027° **ii** 151° **iii** 331° **iv** 066° **v** 207° **vi** 246°
4 122.7^o **5** 7.810 km, 129.8^o **6** 22.45 km **7** 38.57 km
8 220.7 km **9 a** 36.06 km, 057.69^o **b** 237.7^o

EXERCISE 12F.1

1 a 21.2 cm **b** 35.3^o
2 a 9.43 cm **b** 32.5^o **c** 10.8 cm **d** 29.1^o
3 a 8.94 cm **b** 18.5^o **4** 69.2 cm **5** 45°

EXERCISE 12F.2

1 a i GF **ii** HG **iii** HF **iv** GM
b i CD **ii** DE **iii** DF **iv** DX **c i** MA **ii** MN

EXERCISE 12F.3

1 a i $\angle$DEH **ii** $\angle$CEG **iii** $\angle$AGE **iv** $\angle$BXF
b i $\angle$PYS **ii** $\angle$QWR **iii** $\angle$QXR **iv** $\angle$QYR
c i $\angle$AQX **ii** $\angle$AYX
2 a i 45° **ii** 35.3^o **iii** 63.4^o **iv** 41.8^o
b i 21.8^o **ii** 18.9^o **iii** 21.0^o

c i 36.9^o **ii** 33.9^o **iii** 33.9^o **d i** 58.6^o **ii** 64.9^o

EXERCISE 12G

1 a 0.94 **b** 0.77 **c** 0.87 **d** 0.87 **e** 0.34 **f** 0.5
g 0 **h** 0
3 a $\sin(180 - \theta)^o = \sin \theta^o$
4 a -0.17 **b** 0.5 **c** -0.5 **d** 0.17 **e** -0.64
f 0.94 **g** -1 **h** 1
6 a $\cos(180 - \theta)^o = -\cos \theta^o$
7 a 154° **b** 135° **c** 111° **d** 94°
8 a 82° **b** 53° **c** 24° **d** 12°
9 a 0.9272 **b** 0.4384 **c** -0.9781 **d** 0.6561
e 0.5736 **f** -0.1392
10 a -5.671 **b** 5.671 **c** -2.747 **d** 2.747
e -1.732 **f** 1.732 **g** -1.192 **h** 1.192
i -0.8391 **j** 0.8391 **k** -0.5774 **l** 0.5774
11 a $\tan(180 - \theta)^o = -\tan \theta^o$
12 a -0.7813 **b** 1.3764 **c** -0.2679 **d** 0.5095

EXERCISE 12H

1 a 55.2 cm^2 **b** 346.6 km^2 **c** 23.1 cm^2 **d** 429.6 m^2
e 53.0 cm^2 **f** 1.15 m^2
2 50.0 cm^2 **3** $x = 22.2$

EXERCISE 12I.1

1 a 1 **b** 0 **c** 0 **d** 1 **e** 0 **f** -1 **g** -1 **h** 0
i 1 **j** 0 **k** 0 **l** 1
2 a 0.64 **b** 0.77 **c** -0.34 **d** 0.94 **e** 0.17 **f** -0.98
g -0.77 **h** -0.64 **i** 0.77 **j** -0.64 **k** 0.87 **l** -0.5
4 a y-coordinate is the same **b** x-coordinate is opposite
c x-coordinate is the same **d** y-coordinate is opposite
5 a $-\sin \theta$ **b** $-\cos \theta$

EXERCISE 12I.2

1 a 0 **b** 1 **c** very large number
2 a i $\cos \theta$ **ii** $\sin \theta$ **iii** $\tan \theta$ **3** $\tan(180 - \theta) = -\tan \theta$

EXERCISE 12J

1 a

θ	0°	10°	20°	30°	40°	50°	60°	70°	80°	90°
$\sin \theta$	0	0.17	0.34	0.5	0.64	0.77	0.87	0.94	0.98	1

θ	100°	110°	120°	130°	140°	150°	160°	170°	180°
$\sin \theta$	0.98	0.94	0.87	0.77	0.64	0.5	0.34	0.17	0

b

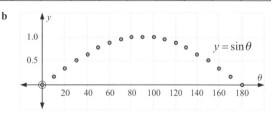

c

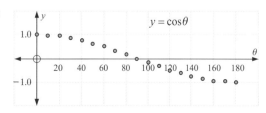

2 a $\theta = 0^o, 180^o, 360^o, 540^o, 720^o$
  b $\theta = 17.5^o, 162.5^o, 377.5^o, 522.5^o$
  c $\theta = 53.1^o, 126.9^o, 413.1^o, 486.9^o$
  d $\theta = 203.6^o, 336.4^o, 563.6^o, 696.4^o$

3 a $\theta = 0^o, 360^o, 720^o$ **b** $\theta = 45.6^o, 314.4^o, 405.6^o, 674.4^o$
  c $\theta = 78.5^o, 281.5^o, 438.5^o, 641.5^o$
  d $\theta = 120^o, 240^o, 480^o, 600^o$

EXERCISE 12K

1 a $2\sin\theta$ **b** $3\cos\theta$ **c** $2\sin\theta$ **d** $\sin\theta$ **e** $-2\cos\theta$
  f $-3\cos\theta$

2 a 3 **b** -2 **c** -1 **d** $3\cos^2\theta$ **e** $4\sin^2\theta$ **f** $\sin\theta$
  g $-\sin^2\theta$ **h** $-\cos^2\theta$ **i** $-2\sin^2\theta$ **j** 1 **k** $\sin\theta$ **l** $\sin\theta$

3 a $1 + 2\sin\theta + \sin^2\theta$ **b** $\sin^2\alpha - 4\sin\alpha + 4$
  c $\cos^2\alpha - 2\cos\alpha + 1$ **d** $1 + 2\sin\alpha\cos\alpha$
  e $1 - 2\sin\beta\cos\beta$ **f** $-4 + 4\cos\alpha - \cos^2\alpha$

4 a $(1 + \sin\theta)(1 - \sin\theta)$ **b** $(\sin\alpha + \cos\alpha)(\sin\alpha - \cos\alpha)$
  c $(\cos\alpha + 1)(\cos\alpha - 1)$ **d** $\sin\beta(2\sin\beta - 1)$
  e $\cos\phi(2 + 3\cos\phi)$ **f** $3\sin\theta(\sin\theta - 2)$
  g $(\sin\theta + 2)(\sin\theta + 3)$ **h** $(2\cos\theta + 1)(\cos\theta + 3)$
  i $(3\cos\alpha + 1)(2\cos\alpha - 1)$

5 a $1 + \sin\alpha$ **b** $\cos\beta - 1$ **c** $\cos\phi - \sin\phi$
  d $\cos\phi + \sin\phi$ **e** $\dfrac{1}{\sin\alpha - \cos\alpha}$ **f** $\dfrac{\cos\theta}{2}$

EXERCISE 12L.1

1 a $x = 11.05$ **b** $x = 11.52$ **c** $x = 5.19$

2 a $a = 27.96$ cm **b** $b = 54.31$ cm **c** $c = 5.23$ cm

EXERCISE 12L.2

1 a $\theta = 31.4$ **b** $\theta = 77.5$ or 102.5 **c** $\theta = 43.6$ or 136.4

2 a $\angle A = 49.1^o$ **b** $\angle B = 71.6^o$ or 108.4^o **c** $\angle C = 44.8^o$

EXERCISE 12M

1 a 27.45 cm **b** 4.15 km **c** 15.20 m **2 a** 45.57^o **b** 95.74^o

EXERCISE 12N

1 $AC = 11.68$ km, $BC = 8.49$ km **2** 74.94 cm^2 **3** 10.10 km
4 a 8.08 km **b** 098.57^o **5** 39.15 km **6** 23.90^o **7** 213.8^o

REVIEW SET 12A

1 $\sin\theta = \frac{5}{13}$, $\cos\theta = \frac{12}{13}$, $\tan\theta = \frac{5}{12}$

2 a $x = 14.03$ **b** $x = 35.20$

3 $\theta = 36$, $x = 12.35$, $y = 21.01$ **4** 80.94 m **5** 62.26 m
6 22.37 km **7 a** 56.3^o **b** 33.9^o **8** 3.88 km^2

9 a a **b** b **c** $\dfrac{b}{a}$ **d** b **e** $-a$

10 a 120° **b** 30° **c** -1.732

11 a $\theta = 30^o, 150^o, 390^o, 510^o$
   b $224.4^o, 315.6^o, 584.4^o, 675.6^o$

12 a $(\sin\theta + \cos\theta)(\sin\theta - \cos\theta)$ **b** $4(\cos\theta + 1)(\cos\theta - 1)$

13 a $\tan\theta - 1$ **b** $2\sin\theta$

REVIEW SET 12B

1 a 0.2756 **b** 0.7431 **c** -8.1443

2 a $x = 38.68$ **b** $x = 37.07$

3 $x = 25.75$, $\alpha = 36.42$, $\theta = 53.58$ **4** 64.03 km, 128.7^o

5 638.3 m **6** 32.20^o **7 a** 78.10 km **b** 311.2^o

8 a 45° **b** 60° **9** $\cos\theta = \frac{4}{5}$, $\tan\theta = \frac{3}{4}$

10 a 60 **b** 17.3 cm^2 **11 a** 23° **b** 240° **c** 128°

12 a $\theta = 60^o, 300^o, 420^o, 660^o$
   b $\theta = 134.4^o, 225.6^o, 494.4^o, 585.6^o$

EXERCISE 13A

1 a 498 people **b**

Brand	Count	Rel. Freq.
Silktouch	115	0.23
Super	87	0.17
Just Soap	108	0.22
Indulgence	188	0.38
Total	498	1

  c i 0.22
    ii 0.38
    iii 0.23

2 a

Outcome	Freq.	Rel. Freq.
0 heads	89	0.25
1 head	172	0.48
2 heads	95	0.27
Total	356	1

  b i 0.25
    ii 0.48
    iii 0.27

3 a 750 people **b i** $\frac{1}{4}$ **ii** $\frac{3}{4}$

EXERCISE 13C

1 a $\{1, 2, 3, 4, 5, 6\}$
  b $\{BBB, BBG, BGB, GBB, BGG, GBG, GGB, GGG\}$
  c $\{ABC, ACB, BAC, BCA, CAB, CBA\}$
  d $\{ABCD, ABDC, ACBD, ACDB, ADBC, ADCB,$
    $BACD, BADC, BCAD, BCDA, BDAC, BDCA,$
    $CABD, CADB, CBAD, CBDA, CDAB, CDBA,$
    $DABC, DACB, DBAC, DBCA, DCAB, DCBA\}$

2 a

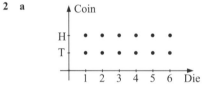

b

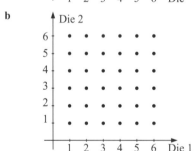

c

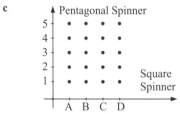

d

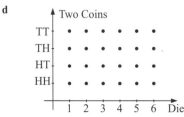

3 a

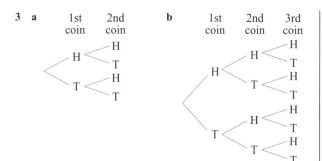

1st coin   2nd coin

H — H
H — T
T — H
T — T

b

1st coin   2nd coin   3rd coin

H — H — H
H — T
T — H
T — T
T — H — H
T — T

c

1st child   2nd child   3rd child   4th child

G
 G
  G — G
  B — G
       B
  B
   G — G
        B
   B — G
        B
B
 G
  G — G
       B
  B — G
       B
 B
  G — G
       B
  B — G
       B

d

1st goal   2nd goal   3rd goal   4th goal   5th goal

X
 X — X — X
       Y — X
            Y
 Y — X — X
            Y
       Y — X
            Y
Y
 X — X — X
            Y
       Y — X
            Y
 Y — X — X
            Y
       Y — X
            Y

EXERCISE 13D

1 a $\frac{1}{3}$ **b** 1 **c** 0 **d** $\frac{1}{3}$ **e** $\frac{5}{6}$

2 a $\frac{1}{8}$ **b** $\frac{3}{8}$ **c** 0 **d** $\frac{3}{4}$ **3 a** $\frac{2}{5}$ **b** $\frac{3}{5}$ **c** $\frac{3}{5}$

4 a $\frac{3}{10}$ **b** $\frac{7}{10}$ **c** 1 **d** 0 **5 a** $\frac{9}{10}$ **b** $\frac{2}{25}$ **c** $\frac{11}{50}$

6 $\frac{1}{12}$ or $\frac{30}{365}$ (more accurate) or $\frac{120}{1461}$ (more accurate again)

7 {ABC, ACB, BAC, BCA, CAB, CBA}

a $\frac{1}{3}$ **b** $\frac{1}{6}$ **c** $\frac{1}{3}$ **d** $\frac{1}{3}$

8 a {GGG, GGB, GBG, BGG, GBB, BGB, BBG, BBB}

b i $\frac{1}{8}$ **ii** $\frac{1}{8}$ **iii** $\frac{1}{8}$ **iv** $\frac{3}{8}$ **v** $\frac{1}{2}$ **vi** $\frac{7}{8}$

9 a

W	W	W	W	W	W	X	X	X	X	X	X
X	Y	Z	X	Y	Z	Y	Y	Z	Z	W	W
Y	Z	X	Z	X	Y	Z	W	W	Y	Y	Z
Z	X	Y	Y	Z	X	W	Z	Y	W	Z	Y
Y	Y	Y	Y	Y	Y	Z	Z	Z	Z	Z	Z
Z	Z	W	W	X	X	W	W	X	X	Y	Y
W	X	X	Z	W	Z	X	Y	W	X	X	W
X	W	Z	X	Z	X	Y	X	W	Y	W	X

b i $\frac{1}{4}$ **ii** $\frac{1}{2}$ **iii** $\frac{1}{2}$ **iv** $\frac{1}{2}$

EXERCISE 13E

1 a $\frac{1}{4}$ **b** $\frac{1}{2}$ **c** $\frac{3}{4}$

2

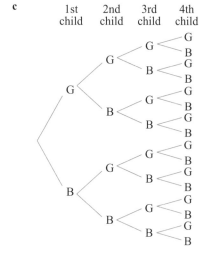

square spinner

D • • • • • •
C • • • • • •
B • • • • • •
A • • • • • •
  1 2 3 4 5 6 → die

a $\frac{1}{24}$
b $\frac{1}{8}$
c $\frac{1}{4}$

3 a $\frac{1}{36}$ **b** $\frac{1}{18}$ **c** $\frac{5}{9}$ **d** $\frac{11}{36}$ **e** $\frac{5}{18}$ **f** $\frac{25}{36}$ **g** $\frac{1}{4}$

h $\frac{5}{36}$ **i** $\frac{7}{12}$ **j** $\frac{5}{12}$

EXERCISE 13F

1 a $\frac{8}{21}$ **b** $\frac{1}{7}$ **c** $\frac{2}{7}$ **2 a** 0.0973 **b** 0.4733

3 a $\frac{2}{15}$ **b** $\frac{2}{5}$ **c** $\frac{1}{5}$ **d** $\frac{4}{15}$

4 a i $\frac{3}{8}$ **ii** $\frac{5}{8}$ **b** $\frac{9}{64}$ **c** $\frac{25}{64}$

EXERCISE 13G

1 a

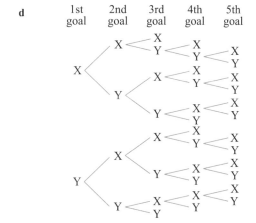

jar   marble

$\frac{1}{2}$ A $\frac{3}{5}$ R
         $\frac{2}{5}$ W
$\frac{1}{2}$ B $\frac{4}{5}$ R
         $\frac{1}{5}$ W

b $\frac{7}{10}$

2 a i $\frac{5}{9}$ **ii** $\frac{4}{9}$ **b**

dart 1   dart 2

$\frac{5}{9}$ R $\frac{5}{9}$ R
         $\frac{4}{9}$ B
$\frac{4}{9}$ B $\frac{5}{9}$ R
         $\frac{4}{9}$ B

c i $\frac{16}{81}$

ii $\frac{25}{81}$

iii $\frac{20}{81}$

iv $\frac{40}{81}$

3

$\frac{1}{5}$ rain $\frac{4}{5}$ win
            $\frac{1}{5}$ lose
$\frac{4}{5}$ no rain $\frac{1}{2}$ win
              $\frac{1}{2}$ lose

P(win) = $\frac{14}{25}$

4 0.008 **5 a** $\frac{5}{12}$ **b** $\frac{7}{12}$

EXERCISE 13H

1 a $\frac{25}{49}$ **b** $\frac{4}{49}$ **c** $\frac{10}{49}$ **d** $\frac{20}{49}$ **2 a** $\frac{1}{7}$ **b** $\frac{2}{7}$ **c** $\frac{2}{7}$ **d** $\frac{4}{7}$

3 a $\frac{2}{15}$ **b** $\frac{1}{3}$ **c** $\frac{4}{15}$ **d** $\frac{4}{15}$

These cases cover all possibilities, so their probabilities must sum to 1.

4 a

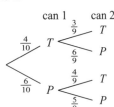

b $\frac{2}{15}$

c $\frac{8}{15}$

5 a $\frac{11}{42}$ **b** $\frac{101}{168}$ **6 a** $\frac{2}{7}$ **b** $\frac{4}{7}$ **c** $\frac{6}{7}$ **7** $\frac{19}{45}$

8 a $\frac{2}{100} \times \frac{1}{99} \doteqdot 0.0002$ **b** $\frac{98}{100} \times \frac{97}{99} \doteqdot 0.9602$

c $1 - \frac{98}{100} \times \frac{97}{99} \doteqdot 0.0398$

EXERCISE 13I

1 a 29 **b** 17 **c** 26 **d** 4 **2 a** 65 **b** 46 **c** 4 **d** 15

3 a $\frac{2}{5}$ **b** $\frac{17}{35}$ **c** $\frac{27}{35}$ **d** $\frac{22}{35}$ **e** $\frac{13}{35}$

4 a $\frac{8}{25}$ **b** $\frac{7}{50}$ **c** $\frac{12}{25}$

5 a i $\dfrac{b+c}{a+b+c+d}$ **ii** $\dfrac{b}{a+b+c+d}$

iii $\dfrac{a+b+c}{a+b+c+d}$ **iv** $\dfrac{a+b+c}{a+b+c+d}$

b P(A or B) = P(A) + P(B) − P(A and B)

EXERCISE 13J

1 a 11 **b i** $\frac{29}{50}$ **ii** $\frac{11}{40}$ **2 a** $\frac{12}{25}$ **b** $\frac{3}{25}$ **c** $\frac{7}{25}$ **d** $\frac{12}{19}$

3 a $\frac{5}{7}$ **b** $\frac{13}{14}$ **c** $\frac{1}{14}$ **d** $\frac{5}{23}$ **e** $\frac{9}{10}$ **4 a** $\frac{24}{25}$ **b** $\frac{1}{25}$

5 a $\frac{1}{20}$ **b** $\frac{19}{20}$ **c** $\frac{31}{50}$ **d** $\frac{39}{50}$ **e** $\frac{12}{19}$ **f** $\frac{17}{78}$

6 a $\frac{3}{4}$ **b** $\frac{5}{9}$ **7 a** $\frac{13}{15}$ **b** $\frac{7}{52}$ **8** $\frac{35}{47}$

REVIEW SET 13A

1 a 39 days **b i** $\frac{1}{39}$ **ii** $\frac{11}{39}$ **iii** $\frac{19}{39}$

2

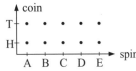

3 The occurrence of one event does not affect the occurrence of the other event.

4 a $\frac{1}{16}$ **b** $\frac{3}{8}$ **c** $\frac{5}{16}$

5 a 0.72 **b** 0.02 **c** 0.98 **d** 0.18

6 $\frac{1}{6}$ **7 a** $\frac{16}{49}$ **b** $\frac{24}{49}$

8 a

b i $\frac{1}{10}$

ii $\frac{3}{5}$

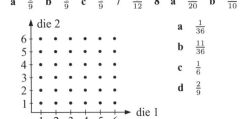

9

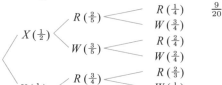

10

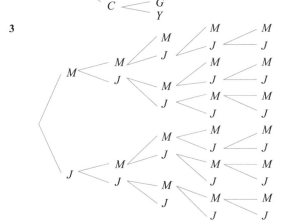

a $\frac{13}{20}$ **b** $\frac{1}{5}$

c $\frac{4}{5}$ **d** $\frac{7}{20}$

e $\frac{9}{13}$

REVIEW SET 13B

1 a 0.364 **b** 0.551 **c** 0.814

2 a {AH, BH, CH, DH, AT, BT, CT, DT}

b

3

4 a 0.60 **b** 0.40

5 a $\frac{3}{14}$ **b**

c i $\frac{33}{91}$

ii $\frac{36}{91}$

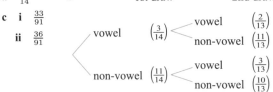

6 a $\frac{1}{9}$ **b** $\frac{4}{9}$ **c** $\frac{4}{9}$ **7** $\frac{5}{12}$ **8 a** $\frac{1}{20}$ **b** $\frac{3}{10}$

9

a $\frac{1}{36}$

b $\frac{11}{36}$

c $\frac{1}{6}$

d $\frac{2}{9}$

10

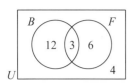

a $\frac{4}{25}$ **b** $\frac{12}{25}$
c $\frac{1}{5}$ **d** $\frac{2}{5}$

EXERCISE 14A

1 **a** 3 **b** 2 **c** $\frac{1}{2}$ **d** -6 **e** $4\frac{1}{2}$ **f** 1 **g** $4\frac{1}{2}$
h 12 **i** 2 **j** 6

2 **a** -2 **b** $-\frac{1}{2}$ **c** $\frac{1}{3}$ **d** 8 **e** 4 **f** -1 **g** $\frac{1}{2}$
h -3 **i** $-\frac{2}{3}$ **j** -4

EXERCISE 14B

1 **a** $5 \neq 14$, $\therefore$ false
b $3 = 3$, $5 = 5$, $7 = 7$ $\therefore$ likely to be correct
c $7\frac{1}{2} \neq 9$, $\therefore$ false **d** $3 \neq 7$, $\therefore$ false

2 **a** $\frac{a}{2}$ **b** $2m$ **c** 6 **d** 3 **e** $2a$ **f** x^2 **g** $2x$ **h** 2
i $\frac{1}{2a}$ **j** $2m$ **k** 4 **l** $\frac{2}{t}$ **m** $2d$ **n** $\frac{b}{2}$ **o** $\frac{2b}{3a}$

3 **a** 4 **b** $2n$ **c** a **d** 1 **e** a^2 **f** $\frac{3n}{2}$ **g** $x+y$ **h** $\frac{2}{x+2}$

4 **a** $a+3$ **b** $2(x+2)$ **c** $2(c+3)$ **d** $\frac{d-3}{3}$ **e** $\frac{2}{x+1}$
f $\frac{3}{2-x}$ **g** $\frac{1}{3}$ **h** 2 **i** $\frac{x+y}{3}$ **j** $\frac{y}{3}$ **k** $\frac{y-3}{3}$ **l** $\frac{x+1}{3}$

5 **a** $\frac{x+2}{2}$ **b** $2(x+2)$ **c** cannot be simplified
d cannot be simplified **e** $\frac{x-1}{2(x+1)}$
f cannot be simplified **g** $\frac{x+3}{5}$ **h** $\frac{1}{a+3}$

EXERCISE 14C

1 **a** $\frac{5a}{6}$ **b** $\frac{b}{10}$ **c** $\frac{7c}{4}$ **d** $\frac{-5x}{14}$ **e** $\frac{4a+3b}{12}$ **f** $\frac{-2t}{9}$
g $\frac{5m}{21}$ **h** $\frac{d}{2}$ **i** $\frac{11p}{35}$ **j** m **k** $\frac{5a}{12}$ **l** $\frac{x}{12}$

2 **a** $\frac{7b+3a}{ab}$ **b** $\frac{3c+2a}{ac}$ **c** $\frac{4d+5a}{ad}$ **d** $\frac{a}{m}$ **e** $\frac{2a+b}{2x}$
f $\frac{5}{2a}$ **g** $\frac{4y-1}{xy}$ **h** $\frac{ad+bc}{bd}$ **i** $\frac{ay-bx}{by}$ **j** $\frac{4+3a}{6}$
k $\frac{4x+9}{12}$ **l** $\frac{3x+2y}{3y}$

3 **a** $\frac{x+2}{2}$ **b** $\frac{y-3}{3}$ **c** $\frac{3a}{2}$ **d** $\frac{b-12}{4}$ **e** $\frac{x-8}{2}$
f $\frac{6+a}{3}$ **g** $\frac{15-x}{5}$ **h** $\frac{2x+1}{x}$ **i** $\frac{5x-2}{x}$
j $\frac{a^2+2}{a}$ **k** $\frac{3+b^2}{b}$ **l** $\frac{-5x}{3}$

4 **a** $\frac{9x}{10}$ **b** $\frac{-7x}{10}$ **c** $\frac{11}{3a}$ **d** $\frac{5}{2y}$ **e** $\frac{5b+3a}{ab}$
f $\frac{4b-15a}{3ab}$ **g** $\frac{x+14}{7}$ **h** $\frac{12-x}{4}$

EXERCISE 14D

1 **a** $\frac{xy}{10}$ **b** $\frac{3}{2}$ **c** $\frac{a^2}{2}$ **d** $\frac{1}{6}$ **e** $\frac{1}{5}$ **f** $\frac{c^2}{10}$ **g** $\frac{ac}{bd}$ **h** 1

i $\frac{1}{2m}$ **j** 2 **k** $\frac{a}{b}$ **l** 4 **m** $\frac{3}{m}$ **n** $\frac{a^2}{b^2}$ **o** $\frac{4}{x^2}$ **p** $\frac{1}{c}$

2 **a** $\frac{3}{2}$ **b** $\frac{3}{a}$ **c** $\frac{3x}{16}$ **d** $\frac{3}{4}$ **e** 2 **f** $\frac{c}{25}$ **g** $\frac{1}{5}$
h $\frac{m^2}{2}$ **i** 2 **j** $\frac{n}{m}$ **k** $\frac{3}{4g}$ **l** $\frac{g}{3}$

3 **a** 1 **b** $\frac{2}{3b}$ **c** $\frac{23c}{20}$ **d** $\frac{2a-bc}{2c}$ **e** $\frac{21a}{2b^2}$ **f** $\frac{2}{3a}$
g 1 **h** $\frac{2a+15}{6b}$

EXERCISE 14E

1 **a** $\frac{2}{x+1}$ **b** $\frac{3}{2-x}$ **c** $x+2$ **d** $x+2$ **e** $\frac{x+2}{2}$
f $\frac{x+5}{2}$ **g** $\frac{y+3}{3}$ **h** $a+b$ **i** $\frac{a+b}{c+d}$ **j** $\frac{a+2}{2}$
k $\frac{1}{2(b-4)}$ **l** $\frac{2(p+q)}{3}$

2 **a** $\frac{3}{4}$ **b** $\frac{a+b}{2}$ **c** x **d** x **e** $\frac{1}{a+b}$ **f** $\frac{1}{y}$ **g** $\frac{x}{y}$
h x^2 **i** $4x$ **j** $3x$ **k** $4x$ **l** x

3 **a** -2 **b** $-\frac{3}{2}$ **c** not possible **d** -1 **e** $-\frac{1}{2}$ **f** -3
g $-\frac{2}{x}$ **h** $-\frac{ab}{2}$ **i** $-2x$ **j** $2x+3$ **k** not possible
l $\frac{2x+3}{2}$ **m** not possible **n** $\frac{2x+3}{3}$ **o** not possible
p not possible **q** $\frac{3a+1}{2}$ **r** not possible **s** $\frac{b+3}{2}$
t not possible

4 **a** $x+1$ **b** $x-1$ **c** $-(x+1)$ **d** $\frac{1}{x-2}$ **e** $a-b$
f $-(a+b)$ **g** $\frac{2}{x-1}$ **h** $\frac{3+x}{x}$ **i** $\frac{3(x+y)}{2y}$
j $-\frac{2(b+a)}{a}$ **k** $\frac{y}{4x+y}$ **l** $-\frac{4x}{4+x}$

5 **a** $x+1$ **b** $\frac{1}{x-5}$ **c** $\frac{2x}{x-5}$ **d** $\frac{x-2}{x+2}$ **e** $\frac{x+3}{x-1}$
f $\frac{x+1}{1-x}$ **g** $\frac{x-5}{x+3}$ **h** $\frac{x+2}{x+3}$ **i** $\frac{x+2}{2x-1}$ **j** $\frac{2x+1}{x-1}$
k $\frac{4x-3}{2x+1}$ **l** $\frac{3x+4}{x+2}$

EXERCISE 14F

1 **a** $\frac{9x-4}{20}$ **b** $\frac{5x+10}{6}$ **c** $\frac{20x-7}{42}$ **d** $\frac{a+5b}{6}$
e $\frac{13x-9}{20}$ **f** $\frac{5x+11}{14}$ **g** $\frac{x+15}{30}$ **h** $\frac{x-7}{42}$
i $\frac{2-3x}{10}$ **j** $\frac{3x-1}{12}$ **k** $\frac{2x+1}{15}$ **l** $\frac{25x+5}{24}$

2 **a** $\frac{5x-1}{(x+1)(x-2)}$ **b** $\frac{12x+17}{(x+1)(x+2)}$ **c** $\frac{x+14}{(x-1)(x+2)}$
d $\frac{-6}{(x+2)(2x+1)}$ **e** $\frac{7x+8}{(x-1)(x+4)}$ **f** $\frac{15x+6}{(1-x)(x+2)}$
g $\frac{4x+3}{x(x+1)}$ **h** $\frac{3x+15}{x(x+3)}$ **i** $\frac{x^2-x+6}{(x+2)(x-4)}$ **j** $\frac{2x-2}{x-3}$
k $\frac{2x-2}{x+2}$ **l** $\frac{2x^2+4x-3}{(x+3)(x+2)}$ **m** $\frac{x+2}{x(x+1)}$

n $\dfrac{x^2+1}{x(x-1)(x+1)}$ **o** $\dfrac{4x^2-x-9}{(x+1)(x-1)(x+2)}$

p $\dfrac{2x^3-x^2+1}{x(x+1)(x-1)}$

3 a $\dfrac{2+x}{x(x+1)}$ **b** $\dfrac{2+x^2}{x(x+1)}$ **c** $\dfrac{2x^2+4x+4}{(x+2)(x-3)}$ **d** $\dfrac{2(x+5)}{x+2}$

e $\dfrac{x^2-2x+3}{(x-2)(x+3)}$ **f** $\dfrac{x-5}{x-2}$ **g** $\dfrac{2(x-5)}{x-1}$ **h** $\dfrac{x+14}{x+7}$

4 a $\dfrac{2(x+1)^2}{(x+2)(x-3)}$ **b i** $x=-2$ or 3 **ii** $x=-1$

EXERCISE 14G

1 a x^3+3x^2+x **b** $x^5+3x^3-2x^2$ **c** $x-1$ **d** $1-\dfrac{2}{x}$

e $2x^2-x$ **f** $2^{2x}+2^x$ **g** 3^x-1 **h** $1+\dfrac{3}{2^x}$ **i** 5^x+1

2 a $9^x+3^{x+1}+2$ **b** $4^x+6(2^x)+5$ **c** $25^x-9(5^x)+14$

d $4^x+2^{x+1}+1$ **e** $9^x+4(3^x)+4$ **f** $16^x-14(4^x)+49$

g $9^x+2(3^x)+1$ **h** $9^x-16(3^x)+64$ **i** $25^x-6(5^x)+9$

j $x-9$ **k** 4^x-25 **l** $x-\dfrac{1}{x}$ **m** $x^2+6+\dfrac{9}{x^2}$

n $e^{2x}-2+e^{-2x}$ **o** $9-6(2^{-x})+4^{-x}$ or $9-\dfrac{6}{2^x}+\dfrac{1}{4^x}$

EXERCISE 14H

1 a $3^x(3^x+1)$ **b** $5(2^n)$ **c** $4^n(1+4^{2n})$ **d** $6(6^n-1)$

e $7(7^{n+1}-1)$ **f** $9(3^n-1)$ **g** $9(2^n)$ **h** $13(3^n)$ **i** $11(2^{n-1})$

2 a $(2^x+3)(2^x-3)$ **b** $(3^x+5)(3^x-5)$

c $(8+3^x)(8-3^x)$ **d** $(4+5^x)(4-5^x)$

e $(2^x+3^x)(2^x-3^x)$ **f** $(2^x+3)^2$ **g** $(3^x+5)^2$

h $(2^x-7)^2$ **i** $(5^x-2)^2$

3 a $(2^x+2)(2^x+9)$ **b** $(2^x-5)(2^x+4)$

c $(3^x+2)(3^x+7)$ **d** $(3^x+5)(3^x-1)$

e $(5^x+2)(5^x-1)$ **f** $(7^x-3)(7^x-4)$

4 a 3^n **b** 4^a **c** 2^b **d** $\dfrac{1}{6^n}$ **e** 6^x **f** $(\tfrac{3}{5})^a$ **g** 3 **h** 4^n

5 a 3^m+1 **b** $1+6^n$ **c** $1+3^a$ **d** 4^n+2^n **e** 6^n

f 2^m **g** 5^n **h** 6^n **i** 4 **j** 5 **k** $\tfrac{1}{2}$ **l** $1\tfrac{1}{2}$ **m** $\tfrac{1}{2}$

n $\tfrac{3}{2}$ **o** 5^y+1

6 a $x=1$ or 2 **b** $x=1$ **c** $x=1$ or 2 **d** $x=1$

e $x=2$ **f** no solutions

REVIEW SET 14A

1 a $3x$ **b** $3n$ **c** $\dfrac{x}{6}$ **d** $\dfrac{2}{x}$ **2 a** 2 **b** 0 **c** -3 **d** -3

3 a $\dfrac{2}{c+3}$ **b** cannot be simplified   **c** $x+2$ **d** $\dfrac{x}{3(x+2)}$

4 a $\dfrac{19x}{15}$ **b** $\dfrac{2x^2}{5}$ **c** $\dfrac{10}{9}$ **d** $\dfrac{x}{15}$ **5 a** 4 **b** -5 **c** $2x$

6 a $\dfrac{11x+1}{12}$ **b** $\dfrac{16x-9}{14}$ **c** $\dfrac{3x+2}{x(x+2)}$

7 a $\dfrac{-2}{x+4}$ **b** $\dfrac{x+3}{x}$ **c** $\dfrac{2x+1}{3x+2}$

8 a $\dfrac{3(x+5)}{x+1}$ **b i** $x=-1$ or 4 **ii** $x=-5$

9 a 4^x-1 **b** 9^x+3^x-2 **c** $25^x-4(5^x)+4$

10 a $24(5^n)$ **b** $(5+4^x)(5-4^x)$ **c** $(2^x-2)(2^x-4)$

11 $x=1$

REVIEW SET 14B

1 a $\tfrac{2}{3}$ **b** $2x$ **c** $3n$ **d** $2x$ **2 a** 7 **b** 2 **c** 3 **d** -5

3 a cannot be simplified   **b** $x+5$ **c** $\dfrac{2}{a+4}$ **d** $\dfrac{b}{2(b-a)}$

4 a $\dfrac{11x}{4}$ **b** $\dfrac{-5x}{4}$ **c** $\dfrac{3x^2}{2}$ **d** $\tfrac{3}{8}$

5 a -1 **b** $\tfrac{5}{2}$ **c** $\dfrac{3x}{a}$

6 a $\dfrac{13x-5}{15}$ **b** $\dfrac{16x-7}{14}$ **c** $\dfrac{x+6}{2x(x+2)}$

7 a $2(x-2)$ **b** $\dfrac{x-7}{x-2}$ **c** $\dfrac{3x+1}{4x+1}$

8 a $\dfrac{2(x-7)}{x-2}$ **b i** $x=7$ **ii** $x=-5$ or 2

9 a $6x^2-8$ **b** $25-10(2^x)+4^x$ **c** $x+4\sqrt{x}+4$

10 a 2 **b** 3^n **c** 2 **11** $x=0$ or 3

EXERCISE 15A

1 a 26.4 cm   **b** 17.8 cm   **c** 127.3 m   **2 a** 19.6 m   **b** 112.9 m

3 a 71.4 km/h   **b** 220 km   **c** 8 h 19 min

4 a 128.7 cm^2 **b** 7.1 m

5 a 4262.5 cm^3 **b** 1.1 cm   **c** 5.0 mm

6 a 706.9 cm^2 **b** 39.9 cm   **7 a** 15.9 km   **b** 49.3 m

8 a 1.3 sec   **b** 81 cm

EXERCISE 15B

1 a $y=2-\tfrac{2}{5}x$ **b** $y=5-\tfrac{3}{4}x$ **c** $y=2x-8$

d $y=2-\tfrac{2}{7}x$ **e** $y=10-\tfrac{5}{2}x$ **f** $y=\tfrac{2}{3}x+4$

2 a $x=r-p$ **b** $x=\dfrac{z}{y}$ **c** $x=\dfrac{d-a}{3}$

d $x=\dfrac{d-2y}{5}$ **e** $x=\dfrac{p-by}{a}$ **f** $x=\dfrac{y-c}{m}$

g $x=\dfrac{s-2}{t}$ **h** $x=\dfrac{m-p}{q}$ **i** $x=\dfrac{6-a}{b}$

3 a $y=mx-c$ **b** $y=\dfrac{c-p}{2}$ **c** $y=\dfrac{a-t}{3}$

d $y=\dfrac{n-5}{k}$ **e** $y=\dfrac{a-n}{b}$ **f** $y=\dfrac{a-p}{n}$

4 a $z=\dfrac{b}{ac}$ **b** $z=\dfrac{a}{d}$ **c** $z=\dfrac{2d}{3}$ **d** $z=\pm\sqrt{2a}$

e $z=\pm\sqrt{bn}$ **f** $z=\pm\sqrt{m(a-b)}$

5 a $a=\dfrac{F}{m}$ **b** $r=\dfrac{C}{2\pi}$ **c** $d=\dfrac{V}{lh}$ **d** $K=\dfrac{b}{A}$

e $h=\dfrac{2A}{b}$ **f** $T=\dfrac{100I}{PR}$

EXERCISE 15C

1 $y=-\tfrac{5}{3}x+6$ **a** $-\tfrac{5}{3}$ **b** 6

2 a $a=\dfrac{d^2}{2bK}$ **b i** 1.29   **ii** 16.2

3 a $d=st$ **i** 180 km   **ii** 120 km   **iii** 126.7 km

b $t=\dfrac{d}{s}$ **i** 3 hours   **ii** 4 hours   **iii** 2 hours 12 mins

4 a $T=\dfrac{100I}{PR}$ **b i** 2.05 years   **ii** 10 years

EXERCISE 15D

1 **a** $A = 200 \times 17$ **b** $A = 200m$ **c** $A = Dm$

2 **a** $A = 2000 + 150 \times 8$ **b** $A = 2000 + 150w$
 c $A = 2000 + dw$ **d** $A = P + dw$

3 **a** $C = 40 + 60 \times 5$ **b** $C = 40 + 60t$
 c $C = 40 + xt$ **d** $C = F + xt$

4 **a** $A = 200 - 8 \times 5$ **b** $A = 200 - 5x$
 c $A = 200 - bx$ **d** $A = P - bx$

5 **a** $C = 5000 - 10 \times 200$ **b** $C = 5000 - 200r$
 c $C = 5000 - mr$ **d** $C = L - mr$

EXERCISE 15E

1 **a** $3, 5, 7$ **b** $9, 11$ **c** 21 **d** $M = 2n + 1$

2 **a** $22, 27$ **b** 102 **c** $M = 5n + 2$ **3 a** 46 **b** $M = 6n - 2$

4 **a** $S_1 = \frac{1}{2}$, $S_2 = \frac{2}{3}$, $S_3 = \frac{3}{4}$, $S_4 = \frac{4}{5}$

 b **i** $S_{10} = \frac{10}{11}$ **ii** $S_n = \dfrac{n}{n+1}$

5 **b** $338\,350$

EXERCISE 15F

1 **a** $x = \dfrac{c - a}{3 - b}$ **b** $x = \dfrac{c}{a + b}$ **c** $x = \dfrac{a + 2}{n - m}$

 d $x = \dfrac{-a}{b + 8}$ **e** $x = \dfrac{b - a}{c - 1}$ **f** $x = \dfrac{e - d}{r + s}$

2 **a** $r = \sqrt{\dfrac{A}{\pi}}$ **b** $x = \sqrt[5]{aN}$ **c** $r = \sqrt[3]{\dfrac{3V}{4\pi}}$ **d** $x = \sqrt[3]{\dfrac{n}{D}}$

 e $x = \pm\sqrt{\dfrac{y + 7}{4}} = \pm\dfrac{\sqrt{y + 7}}{2}$ **f** $Q = \pm\sqrt{P^2 - R^2}$

3 **a** $a = d^2 n^2$ **b** $l = 25T^2$ **c** $a = \pm\sqrt{b^2 + c^2}$

 d $d = \dfrac{25a^2}{k^2}$ **e** $l = \dfrac{gT^2}{4\pi^2}$ **f** $b = \dfrac{16a}{A^2}$

4 **a** $r = \sqrt[3]{\dfrac{3V}{4\pi}}$ **b** **i** 2.12 cm **ii** 62.04 cm

5 **a** $t = \sqrt{\dfrac{2S}{a}}$ **b** **i** 3.16 sec **ii** 15.81 sec

6 **a** $v = \sqrt{c^2\left(1 - \dfrac{m_0^2}{m^2}\right)} = \dfrac{c}{m}\sqrt{m^2 - m_0^2}$ **b** $v = \dfrac{\sqrt{8}}{3}c$

 c 2.998×10^8 m/s

REVIEW SET 15A

1 **a** 11.4 g/cm^3 **b** 37.94 g **c** 9230.8 cm^3

2 **a** 1.72 sec **b** 156.3 cm **3 a** $x = \dfrac{y - c}{m}$ **b** $x = \pm\sqrt{\dfrac{2}{a}}$

4 **a** **i** $V = 6 \times 8$ **ii** $V = 8n$ **iii** $V = nl$ **b** $V = 25 + nl$

5 **a** 20 **b** $M = 2n$ **6 a** $p = 3r - q$ **b** $p = \sqrt[3]{y^2 - 3}$

REVIEW SET 15B

1 **a** 7226 cm^3 **b** 0.943 m **2 a** $x = \dfrac{3q - y}{2}$ **b** $x = \dfrac{4}{3y}$

3 **a** $C = 2 + 1 \times 1.20$ **b** $C = 2 + 5 \times 1.20$
 c $C = p + 1.2b$ **d** $C = p + bx$

4 $y = \frac{2}{3}x - \frac{4}{3}$ **a** $m = \frac{2}{3}$ **b** $c = -\frac{4}{3}$ **5 a** 25 **b** $M = 3n + 1$

6 $y = \dfrac{64}{x^2}$ **7** **a** $r = \sqrt{\dfrac{A}{4\pi}}$ **b** 34.5 cm

EXERCISE 16A

1 **a** $x = 100$ **b** $x = 40$ **c** $x = 70$ **d** $x = 35$
 e $x = 36$ **f** $x = 90$, $y = 110$
 g $a = 35, b = 70, c = 70$ **h** $x = 33\frac{1}{3}$ **i** $x = 107\frac{1}{2}$

2 **a** $a = 85$ **b** $a = 61$

3 **a** $\angle PSQ = a^o$, $\angle QSR = b^o$ {base angles of isosceles $\triangle$}
 b 180°

4 **a** 360° {sum of interior angles of a quadrilateral} **b** 180°
 c co-interior angles are supplementary
 d The quadrilateral is a parallelogram.

5 **a** $\angle TPQ = \alpha^o$, $\angle TQP = \beta^o$
 b 180° {co-interior angles between parallel lines}
 c $\angle PTQ = 180 - (\alpha + \beta) = 180 - 90 = 90$ {$\angle$ sum of $\triangle$}

EXERCISE 16B

1 **a** $x = 37$ **b** $x = 30$ **c** $x = 18$ **d** $x = 2.5$
 e $x = 2\sqrt{2}$ **f** $x = 2\sqrt{5}$

2 **a** $x = 3$ **b** $x = 2\sqrt{7}$ **c** $x = \sqrt{29}$

3 **a** $2\sqrt{5}$ cm **b** $2\sqrt{21}$ cm

4 **a** CY $= 5$ cm **b** $x = 30$ **c** $a = 40, b = 50$
 d $a = 55, b = 55$ **e** XY $= 12$ cm **f** $a = 60, b = 40$

5 8 cm

6 **a** $x = 2\sqrt{3}$ {radius tangent theorem, Pythagoras}
 b $x = 3.9$ {radius tangent theorem, Pythagoras}

8 1 cm

EXERCISE 16C

1 **a** $x = 64$ **b** $x = 70$ **c** $x = 45$ **d** $x = 66$
 e $x = 94$ **f** $x = 25$

2 **a** $x = 46$ **b** $x = 30, y = 30$ **c** $a = 50, b = 40$
 d $a = 55, c = 70$ **e** $a = 80, b = 200$
 f $x = 75, y = 118$ **g** $x = 42$ **h** $x = 25$ **i** $x = 25$

3 **a** $x = 70$ **b** $x = 40$ **c** $x = 35$

EXERCISE 16D

1 **a** isosceles triangle
 b The line from the centre of a circle perpendicular to a chord • bisects the chord • bisects the angle at the centre subtended by the chord.

2 **c** The two tangents to a circle from an external point are equal in length.

3 **a** equal radii
 b **i** a^o **ii** b^o **iii** $2a^o$ **iv** $2b^o$ **v** $(a + b)^o$ **vi** $(2a + 2b)^o$
 c The angle at the centre of a circle is twice the angle at the circle subtended by the same arc.

4 **a** $2\alpha^o$ **b** α^o **c** $\angle ADB = \angle ACB$

5 **a** **i** 90° **ii** 90°
 b **i** $(90 - \alpha)^o$ {radius tangent theorem}
  ii α^o {angle sum of triangle}
  iii α^o {angle between tangent and chord}

6 **a** **i** α^o **ii** $2\alpha^o$ **iii** $2\alpha^o$ **iv** $4\alpha^o$ **v** $3\alpha^o$
 b $\angle BOY = 3\angle YOX$

7 **a** $\angle BXA = \angle BXC = 90^o$ **b** collinear **c** yes
 d Yes, 4 semi-circles overlap such that whole area is covered.

EXERCISE 16E

1 **a** $\theta = 60$, $x = 10$ {midpoint theorem}
 b $x = 8$ {converse midpoint theorem}

6 **(1)** given **(2)** {alternate angles} **(3)** $\angle AQP = \angle CQR$
 (4) AAcorS **(5)** BP **(6)** parallelogram **(7)** BC

EXERCISE 16F.1

1 a 6 vertices **b** 7 edges **c** 4 regions

2 a   **b**   **c**

3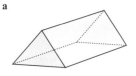

EXERCISE 16F.2

1 a 6 vertices **b** 18 edges

2 a 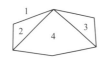 **b**

3 a A triangular pyramid is the polyhedron with the least number of faces ($F = 4$).

b Using $E = F + V - 2$, $F = 3$ which is a contradiction.

REVIEW SET 16A

1 a $x = 35$ {vertically opposite angles}
  b $x = 30$ {angles on a line} **c** $x = 6$ {midpoint theorem}

2 a $a = 54$ **b** $a = 62$ **c** $a = 61$ **d** $a = 140$
  e $a = 104$ **f** $a = 2\sqrt{5}$

3 $\alpha + \beta + \gamma = 180$ **4 a** $\angle DBO = \alpha^o$

6 a 6 vertices **b**

REVIEW SET 16B

1 a $a = 3$ {midpoint theorem} **b** $a = 55$ {$\angle$ at centre}
  c $a = 55$ {radius tangent, sum of $\angle$s in $\triangle$, isosceles $\triangle$}

3 a **i** $2\alpha^o$ **ii** $2\alpha^o$ **iii** $2\alpha^o$ **iv** $2\alpha^o$ **c** 90° **d** RS is a diameter

4 a $\angle ACB = \alpha^o$

5 a the angle subtended by the chord in the alternate segment
  b i $\angle PQB = \alpha^o$, $\angle PQA = \beta^o$, $\angle AQB = (\alpha + \beta)^o$

EXERCISE 17A

1 a, b, e no two different ordered pairs have the same x-coordinate.

2 a, b, d, e, g, h, i

3 No, a vertical line is not a function as it does not satisfy the vertical line test.

EXERCISE 17B

1 a Domain is $\{x: x > -4\}$. Range is $\{y: y > -2\}$.
  b Domain is $\{x: x = 2\}$. Range is $\{y: y$ is in $\mathbb{R}\}$.
  c Domain is $\{x: -3 \leqslant x \leqslant 3\}$. Range is $\{y: -3 \leqslant y \leqslant 3\}$.
  d Domain is $\{x: x$ is in $\mathbb{R}\}$. Range is $\{y: y \leqslant 0\}$.
  e Domain is $\{x: x$ is in $\mathbb{R}\}$. Range is $\{y: y = -5\}$.
  f Domain is $\{x: x$ is in $\mathbb{R}\}$. Range is $\{y: y \geqslant 1\}$.
  g Domain is $\{x: x$ is in $\mathbb{R}\}$. Range is $\{y: y \leqslant 4\}$.

h Domain is $\{x: x \geqslant -5\}$. Range is $\{y: y$ is in $\mathbb{R}\}$.
i Domain is $\{x: x$ is in $\mathbb{R}, x \neq 1\}$.
  Range is $\{y: y$ is in $\mathbb{R}, y \neq 0\}$.

EXERCISE 17C

1 a 3 **b** 7 **c** 1 **d** -7 **e** 2

2 a 3 **b** $4\frac{1}{2}$ **c** -3 **d** $-4\frac{1}{2}$ **e** $-4\frac{1}{2}$

3 a 2 **b** 11 **c** 29 **d** 121 **e** 1

4 a $5 - 2a$ **b** $5 + 2a$ **c** $3 - 2a$ **d** $11 - 2x$ **e** $5 - 4x$

5 a $x^2 + 8x + 9$ **b** $x^2 - 6x + 2$ **c** $x^2 - 4x - 3$
  d $x^4 + 4x^2 - 3$ **e** $x^4 + 6x^2 + 2$

6 a i $-\frac{3}{2}$ **ii** $-\frac{1}{3}$ **iii** $-\frac{8}{3}$ **b** $x = -2$ **c** $2 - \frac{7}{x}$ **d** $x = -1$

7 a $V(4) = \$12\,000$, the value of the car after 4 years.
  b $t = 5$; the car is worth \$8000 after 5 years **c** \$28\,000

EXERCISE 17D

1 a Independent variable is the number of pavers, A.
  Dependent variable is the price, P.

b

$A(\times 1000)$	0	1	2	3	4	5
$P(\$)$	50	850	1650	2450	3250	4050

c There is a constant increase in price for each 1000 pavers.

d

Price of pavers

e $P = 800A + 50$ **f** \$4450 **g** 3937 pavers

2 a Each increase of $10^\circ C$ corresponds to an increase of $18^\circ F$.
  b $1.8^\circ F$ **c** $T_F = \frac{9}{5}T_c + 32$ **d** $37.8^\circ C$ **e** $0^\circ C$

3 a

Days elapsed (t)	0	1	2	3	4
Pellets in bin (F, kg)	1000	987	974	961	948

b Independent variable is days elapsed, t.
  Dependent variable is number of pellets in bin, F.

c The y-axis as it is the dependent variable.

d

Amount of pellets

e slope $= -13$, $F = -13t + 1000$

f Slope is the amount of pellets removed each day.
  Vertical intercept is the original amount of pellets.

g 818 kg **h** after 77 days, i.e., 11 weeks

EXERCISE 17E.1

1 a $x = 8, y = -6$ **b** $x = 5, y = 1$ **c** $x = -2, y = 1$
  d $x = -2, y = 5$ **e** $x = 0, y = -4$ **f** $x = -2, y = 1$

2 a obtain $-5 = 1$ **b** no solution

3 a obtain $-6 = -6$ **b** an infinite number of solutions

EXERCISE 17E.2

1 a $9x = 9$ **b** $-y = -1$ **c** $5x = 5$ **d** $-2x = -10$
   e $8y = 8$ **f** $-y = -9$

2 a $x = 3, y = 0$ **b** $x = 1, y = 3$ **c** $x = -1, y = 1$
   d $x = -\frac{4}{3}, y = 2$ **e** $x = 2, y = -\frac{13}{2}$ **f** $x = 4, y = -3$

EXERCISE 17E.3

1 a $6x + 15y = 3$ **b** $-6x + 2y = -8$ **c** $35x - 5y = 45$
   d $-6x - 9y = 3$ **e** $-8x + 12y = -24$ **f** $-4x + 7y = 8$

2 a $x = -10, y = -15$ **b** $x = -3, y = 4$ **c** $x = 2, y = -2$
   d $x = -1, y = 5$ **e** $x = 5, y = 6$ **f** $x = 3, y = -4$
   g $x = 5, y = -1$ **h** $x = -1, y = 5$ **i** $x = -4, y = -4$

3 a infinite number of solutions **b** no solution

EXERCISE 17F

1 36 and 17 **2** 18 and 10 **3** 14 and 42

4 pencil, 65 cents; biro, \$1.05

5 orange, 15 cents; apple, 25 cents

6 19 \$1 coins, 38 \$2 coins **7** Anya, \$13.80; Michelle, \$20.70

8 24, 200 g blocks; 36, 350 g blocks **9** $a = 5, b = 3$

10 length 14 cm, width 4 cm **11** current 3 km/h, boat 15 km/h

12 wind 100 km/h, plane 900 km/h

13 a 15 km **b** 1 h 15 min **14** 72

EXERCISE 17G

1 a 0.01, 0.1, 1, 2, 5,
   10, 20, 100, 1000

   b $-0.01, -0.1, -1,$
   $-2, -5, -10, -20,$
   $-100, -1000$

   c, d see diagram

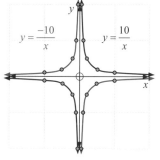

2 a

Words per min (n)	10	20	30	40	50
Time taken (t)	40	20	13.3	10	8

b

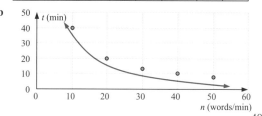

c Yes, it is reasonable; curve is a hyperbola. **d** $t = \dfrac{400}{n}$

3 a $y = \dfrac{8}{x}$ **b** $y = \dfrac{3}{x}$ **c** $y = -\dfrac{12}{x}$ **4 a** $y = -x$ **b** $y = x$

EXERCISE 17H.1

1 a consecutive terms differ by 7 **b** $u_n = 7n - 3$
   c 347 **d** no **e** no

2 a consecutive terms differ by -4 **b** $u_n = 71 - 4n$
   c -89 **d** no **e** no

3 a $u_1 = 4, \quad d = 11$ **b** 620 **c** $u_{42} = 455$

4 a consecutive terms differ by -2 **b** $u_1 = 8\frac{1}{2}, \quad d = -2$
   c $-139\frac{1}{2}$ **d** $n \geqslant 106$

5 a $k = 17$ **b** $k = 2\frac{1}{2}$ **c** $k = 4\frac{1}{3}$

6 a $u_n = 17 + 5n$ **b** $u_n = 10 - 4n$ **c** $u_n = 3n - 16$
   d $u_n = -\frac{17}{2} - \frac{3}{4}n$

7 a $u_1 = 3, \quad d = -\frac{1}{2}$ **b** 19 terms **8** $u_{5713} = 40\,001$

EXERCISE 17H.2

1 a $b = 12, c = 24$ **b** $b = \frac{1}{2}, c = \frac{1}{8}$ **c** $b = \frac{5}{3}, c = -\frac{5}{9}$

2 a consecutive terms have a common ratio of 3
   b $u_n = 3^{n-1}, \quad u_{10} = 3^9 = 19\,683$

3 a consecutive terms have a common ratio of $-\frac{1}{2}$
   b $u_n = 40 \times \left(-\frac{1}{2}\right)^{n-1}, \quad u_{12} = -\frac{5}{256}$

4 consecutive terms have a common ratio of $-\frac{1}{4}$,
   $u_8 = -0.000\,976\,562\,5$

5 a $k = \pm 9$ **b** $k = -7$ **c** $k = -\frac{8}{7}$ or 2

6 a $u_n = 4 \times 2^{n-1} \, (= 2^{n+1})$ **b** $u_n = 128 \times \left(-\frac{1}{2}\right)^{n-1}$
   c $u_n = 3 \times \left(\sqrt{2}\right)^{n-1}$ **d** $u_n = 6 \times \left(\frac{1}{\sqrt{2}}\right)^{n-1}$

EXERCISE 17I

1 a 5, 8, 11 **b** 9.6, 7.5, 5.4 **c** 1291.9, 1315.8, 1339.7
   d 12, 36, 108 **e** 100, 10, 1 **f** $-64, 32, -16$

2 a $u_n = 5n + 36$ **b** $u_n = -1.7n + 13.5$
   c $u_n = 12 \times \left(\frac{1}{3}\right)^{n-1}$ **d** $u_n = 36 \times \left(-\frac{1}{2}\right)^{n-1}$

3 a 1, 1, 1 **b** 1, 2, 1 **c** $0, -1, -\frac{4}{3}$ **d** 0, -1, 0

4 a $-1, -1, 0, 1$ **b** 5, 13, 41, 121

5 a $u_2 = 2.7, \quad u_3 = 1.72\overline{037}, u_4 = 1.441\,455\,368,$
   $u_5 = 1.414\,470\,981, u_6 = 1.414\,213\,586$

   b $\sqrt{2} = 1.414\,213\,562$; the terms of the sequence are
   getting closer to $\sqrt{2}$.

   c $u_2 = 5.1, u_3 = 2.746\,078\,431, u_4 = 1.737\,194\,874,$
   $u_5 = 1.444\,238\,095, u_6 = 1.414\,525\,655$

   d $u_2 = 1.5, u_3 = 1.41\overline{6}, u_4 = 1.414\,215\,686,$
   $u_5 = 1.414\,213\,562, u_6 = 1.414\,213\,562$

   e Both sequences approach $\sqrt{2}$ but with $u_1 = 2$, the
   terms approach $\sqrt{2}$ sooner.

6 $x = \frac{1}{2}\left(x + \dfrac{2}{x}\right)$ then $\therefore \quad 2x^2 = x^2 + 2$
   $\therefore \quad x^2 = 2$
   $\therefore \quad x = \sqrt{2}$

EXERCISE 17J

1 a $(1, 7)$ and $(2, 8)$ **b** $(2, 1)$ and $(-1, -2)$
   c $(-3, -9)$ and $(4, 5)$ **d** $(-\frac{1}{5}, -5)$ and $(1, 1)$
   e $(3, 0)$ (touching)

2 a $(0.59, 5.59)$ and $(3.41, 8.41)$ **b** $(4.71, 0.64)$
   c graphs do not meet **d** $(1, 1)$ and $(-2.73, -20.39)$

REVIEW SET 17A

1 a i Range is $\{y: y \geqslant -2\}$. Domain is $\{x: x \text{ is in } \mathbb{R}\}$.
   ii function

   b i Range is $\{y: y \text{ is in } \mathbb{R}\}$. Domain is $\{x: x \geqslant 0\}$.
   ii not a function

   c i Range is $\{y: y \text{ is in } \mathbb{R}\}$. Domain is $\{x: x \text{ is in } \mathbb{R}\}$.
   ii function

   d i Range is $\{y: y = 2, 4, 6\}$. Domain is $\{x: x \geqslant 0\}$.
   ii not a function

2 a 2 **b** -4 **c** $1\frac{1}{4}$ **3 a** $x^2 + 3x$ **b** $x^2 + x - 2$

4 a

hours (h)	0	1	2	3	4
Cost \$C	60	108	156	204	252

   b Dependent variable is the cost, C.
   Independent variable is the hours, h.

c

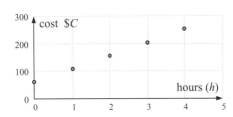

d $C = 60 + 48h$ **e** $360

5 31 and 26   **6** $y = -\dfrac{3}{x}$

7 a consecutive terms differ by 4   **b** $u_n = 4n - 10$
   c 390   **d** $u_{127} = 498$

8 $u_n = -3(-2)^{n-1}$ **9** 8, 20, 44   **10** $(-3, -5)$ and $(1, 3)$

REVIEW SET 17B

1 a i Range is $\{y: y > -2\}$. Domain is $\{x: x > -6\}$.
      ii function
   b i Range is $\{y: y \neq 3\}$. Domain is $\{x: x \neq -2\}$.
      ii function
   c i Range is $\{y: y$ is in $\mathbb{R}\}$. Domain is $\{x: x = -3\}$.
      ii not a function
   d i Range is $\{y: y$ is in $\mathbb{R}\}$. Domain is $\{x: x \leqslant 1\}$.
      ii not a function

2 a 7 **b** 3 **c** 13   **3 a** $-5x - x^2$ **b** $-x^2 + 3x + 4$

4 a

no. of logos (n)	0	1	2	3	4
Cost $C	40	45	50	55	60

   b Dependent variable is cost, $C.
      Independent variable is number of logos, n.

   c

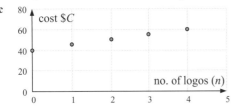

   d $C = 40 + 5n$ **e** 78 shirts

5 sausage, 60 cents; chop $2.20   **6** $u_n = 39 - \frac{15}{2}(n-1)$

7 consecutive terms have a common ratio of $-\frac{1}{2}$; $u_{16} = -\frac{1}{512}$

8 $k = -5$ or 10;   if $k = -5$, terms are $-3, 6, -12$;
   if $k = 10$, terms are $27, -9, 3$

9 a $u_n = 10 - 3n$ **b** $u_n = 24 \times (-\frac{2}{3})^{n-1}$

10 $(\frac{3}{2}, 2)$ and $(-1, -3)$

EXERCISE 18A.1

1 a *Scale:*
      $1 \text{ cm} \equiv 10 \text{ km/h}$
   b *Scale:*
      $1 \text{ cm} \equiv 10 \text{ m/s}$

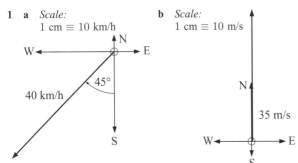

c

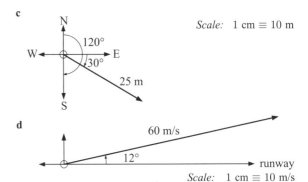

Scale: $1 \text{ cm} \equiv 10 \text{ m}$

d

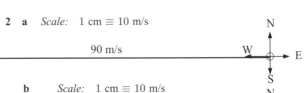

Scale: $1 \text{ cm} \equiv 10 \text{ m/s}$

2 a *Scale:* $1 \text{ cm} \equiv 10 \text{ m/s}$

   b *Scale:* $1 \text{ cm} \equiv 10 \text{ m/s}$

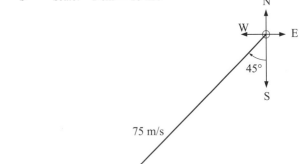

3 a *Scale:* $1 \text{ cm} \equiv 10 \text{ km/h}$

   b *Scale:* $1 \text{ cm} \equiv 10 \text{ m/s}$

c
   d *Scale:* $1 \text{ cm} \equiv 40 \text{ km/h}$

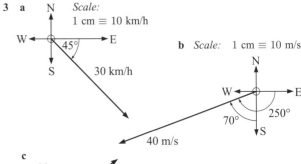

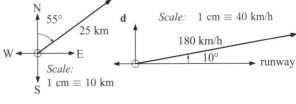

EXERCISE 18A.2

1 a **a, c** and **e**; **b** and **d**   **b** **a, b, c** and **d**
   c **a** and **b**; **c** and **d**   **d** none are equal   **e** **a** and **c**; **b** and **d**

2 a false **b** true **c** false **d** true **e** true

EXERCISE 18B.1

1 **a**

b
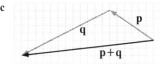

c
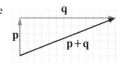

d

e
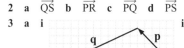

f
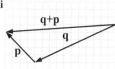

2 **a** $\overrightarrow{QS}$ **b** $\overrightarrow{PR}$ **c** $\overrightarrow{PQ}$ **d** $\overrightarrow{PS}$

3 **a i**
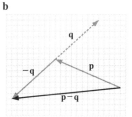
ii

b $\mathbf{p} + \mathbf{q} = \mathbf{q} + \mathbf{p}$ for any two vectors $\mathbf{p}$ and $\mathbf{q}$

4 Paola is 25 km from his starting point at a bearing of $347°$.

5 Gina is 67.6 km from her starting point at a bearing of $006.60°$.

6 **a** 600 km/h due north   **b** 400 km/h due north
   c 510 km/h at a bearing of $011.3°$

7 **a** 0 km/h   **b** 20 km/h east   **c** 14.1 km/h north east

8 The aircraft is travelling at a speed of 404 km/h at a bearing of $098.5°$.

9 The ship is travelling at a speed of 23.3 knots at a bearing of $134°$.

EXERCISE 18B.2

1 **a**
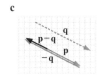

b
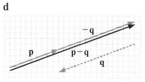

c
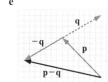

d
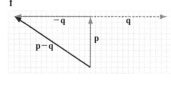

e

f

2 The plane must fly $4.57°$ west of north at 501.6 kmph.

3 The boat must head $26.6°$ west of north at 31.6 kmph.

4 **a** $\overrightarrow{QS}$ **b** $\overrightarrow{PR}$ **c** $\mathbf{0}$ (zero vector) **d** $\overrightarrow{RQ}$ **e** $\overrightarrow{QS}$ **f** $\overrightarrow{RQ}$

EXERCISE 18C.1

1 **a**   **b**   **c**   **d**
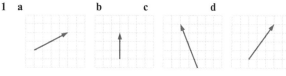

2 **a** $\begin{bmatrix} 7 \\ 4 \end{bmatrix}$ **b** $\begin{bmatrix} 0 \\ -6 \end{bmatrix}$ **c** $\begin{bmatrix} 3 \\ -5 \end{bmatrix}$ **d** $\begin{bmatrix} -6 \\ 0 \end{bmatrix}$ **e** $\begin{bmatrix} -6 \\ 4 \end{bmatrix}$ **f** $\begin{bmatrix} -4 \\ -5 \end{bmatrix}$

3 **a**
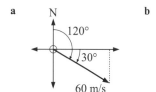

b
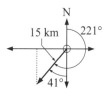

The vector is $\begin{bmatrix} 52.0 \\ -30 \end{bmatrix}$

The vector is $\begin{bmatrix} -9.84 \\ -11.3 \end{bmatrix}$

c

The vector is $\begin{bmatrix} 158 \\ 25.0 \end{bmatrix}$

EXERCISE 18C.2

1 **a** $\begin{bmatrix} 5 \\ -4 \end{bmatrix}$ **b** $\begin{bmatrix} 5 \\ -4 \end{bmatrix}$ **c** $\begin{bmatrix} 1 \\ -4 \end{bmatrix}$ **d** $\begin{bmatrix} 1 \\ -4 \end{bmatrix}$ **e** $\begin{bmatrix} 0 \\ -6 \end{bmatrix}$
   f $\begin{bmatrix} 0 \\ -6 \end{bmatrix}$ **g** $\begin{bmatrix} 4 \\ -6 \end{bmatrix}$ **h** $\begin{bmatrix} 3 \\ -7 \end{bmatrix}$

2 **a** $\begin{bmatrix} 1 \\ 6 \end{bmatrix}$ **b** $\begin{bmatrix} -5 \\ 1 \end{bmatrix}$ **c** $\begin{bmatrix} -6 \\ 4 \end{bmatrix}$ **d** $\begin{bmatrix} -2 \\ 10 \end{bmatrix}$ **e** $\begin{bmatrix} -4 \\ -2 \end{bmatrix}$ **f** $\begin{bmatrix} 2 \\ -10 \end{bmatrix}$

3 **a** $\sqrt{17}$ units **b** 6 units **c** $\sqrt{13}$ units **d** $\sqrt{26}$ units
   e $\sqrt{20}$ units **f** $\sqrt{37}$ units

EXERCISE 18D

1 **a** $\begin{bmatrix} 222.9 \\ 200.7 \end{bmatrix}$ **b** $\begin{bmatrix} -10.1 \\ 43.8 \end{bmatrix}$ **c** $\begin{bmatrix} 213 \\ 245 \end{bmatrix}$

   d Actual speed is 324 km/h at a bearing of $041°$.

REVIEW SET 18

1 **a**
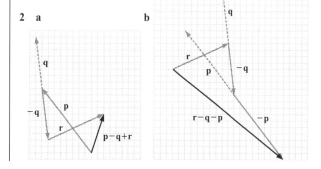

Scale: 1 cm ≡ 10 m/s

60 m/s

$8°$

runway

b

N

45 m

$60°$

Scale: 1 cm ≡ 10 m

E

2 **a**   **b**

3   **a** $\overrightarrow{CA} = -\mathbf{c}$ **b** $\overrightarrow{AB} = -\mathbf{a} + \mathbf{b}$ **c** $\overrightarrow{OC} = \mathbf{a} + \mathbf{c}$
    d $\overrightarrow{BC} = -\mathbf{b} + \mathbf{a} + \mathbf{c}$
4   **a** $\overrightarrow{AD}$ **b** $\overrightarrow{BD}$ **c** $\mathbf{0}$ (the zero vector)
5   Speed is 12.3 km/h at a bearing of $145°$.
6   He must fly $7.06°$ north of east at 230 km/h.
7   **a** $\begin{bmatrix} 7 \\ 2 \end{bmatrix}$ **b** $\begin{bmatrix} 1 \\ 12 \end{bmatrix}$ **c** $\sqrt{34}$ units
8   **a** $\begin{bmatrix} 8.49 \\ 8.49 \end{bmatrix}$ **b** $\begin{bmatrix} -3.83 \\ 3.21 \end{bmatrix}$ **c** $\begin{bmatrix} 4.66 \\ 11.7 \end{bmatrix}$
    d Speed of kayak is 12.6 km/h at a bearing of $021.7°$.

EXERCISE 19A

1   **a** 3^7 **b** 4^5 **c** x^9 **d** x^{10} **e** y^9 **f** x^{n+5} **g** y^{m+2} **h** t^{12}
2   **a** 3^4 **b** 7^4 **c** 8 **d** x^4 **e** y^5 **f** t^{6-x} **g** p^{n-2} **h** t^{3m-1}
3   **a** 5^6 **b** 3^{20} **c** 2^{18} **d** t^{12} **e** x^{14} **f** y^{3m} **g** m^{5a} **h** a^{12m}
4   **a** 2^2 **b** 2^4 **c** 3^3 **d** 2^4 **e** 5^4 **f** 2^{t+3} **g** 3^{a-1}
    h 2^{3n} **i** 3^{2-x} **j** 5^4 **k** 3^{4a+4} **l** 3^4 **m** 2^{2a-b}
    n 2^{3x-4y} **o** 5^2 **p** 3^{-6}
5   **a** x^2y^2 **b** a^3b^3 **c** r^4s^4 **d** $x^2y^2z^2$ **e** $8a^3$ **f** $27b^3$
    g $625a^4$ **h** $27x^3y^3$ **i** $10^5x^5y^5$ **j** $\dfrac{p^2}{q^2}$ **k** $\dfrac{m^3}{n^3}$ **l** $\dfrac{16a^4}{b^4}$
6   **a** x^3 **b** $8b^5$ **c** a^2b^2 **d** $6x^3$ **e** $\dfrac{x^2y}{3}$ **f** $\dfrac{8r^2}{5}$
    g $15p^6q^3$ **h** x^6 **i** t^4
7   **a** 1 **b** $\frac{1}{6}$ **c** $\frac{1}{4}$ **d** 1 **e** 9 **f** $\frac{1}{9}$ **g** 125 **h** $\frac{1}{125}$
    i 49 **j** $\frac{1}{49}$ **k** 1000 **l** $\frac{1}{1000}$
8   **a** 1 **b** 1 **c** 2 **d** 1 **e** 1 **f** 3 **g** $\frac{1}{25}$ **h** $\frac{1}{16}$
    i 4 **j** $\frac{8}{3}$ **k** $\frac{3}{2}$ **l** 5 **m** 3 **n** $\frac{4}{5}$ **o** $\frac{11}{3}$ **p** 9
    q $\frac{27}{8}$ **r** $\frac{8}{27}$ **s** $\frac{9}{25}$ **t** $\frac{4}{25}$
9   **a** $\dfrac{1}{3b}$ **b** $\dfrac{3}{b}$ **c** $\dfrac{7}{a}$ **d** $\dfrac{1}{7a}$ **e** t^2 **f** $\dfrac{1}{16t^2}$ **g** $\dfrac{1}{25t^2}$
    h $\dfrac{t^2}{5}$ **i** $\dfrac{x}{y}$ **j** $\dfrac{1}{xy}$ **k** $\dfrac{x}{y^3}$ **l** $\dfrac{1}{x^3y^3}$ **m** $\dfrac{1}{3pq}$
    n $\dfrac{3}{pq}$ **o** $\dfrac{3p}{q}$ **p** x^3y^5
10 5^{75}

EXERCISE 19B

1   **a** 2 **b** $\frac{1}{2}$ **c** 4 **d** $\frac{1}{4}$ **e** 5 **f** $\frac{1}{5}$ **g** 2 **h** $\frac{1}{2}$ **i** 4
    j $\frac{1}{4}$ **k** 2 **l** $\frac{1}{2}$ **m** 5 **n** -5 **o** no real solution **p** -1
2   **a** $10^{\frac{1}{2}}$ **b** $10^{-\frac{1}{2}}$ **c** $15^{\frac{1}{3}}$ **d** $15^{-\frac{1}{3}}$ **e** $19^{\frac{1}{4}}$
    f $19^{-\frac{1}{4}}$ **g** $13^{\frac{1}{5}}$ **h** $13^{-\frac{1}{5}}$
3   **a** 4 **b** 3 **c** 4 **d** 5.848 **e** 4.472 **f** 3.981 **g** 2 **h** 2.212
4   **a** 8 **b** 9 **c** 16 **d** 2.41 **e** 2.68 **f** 0.0313
    g $0.004\,12$ **h** 0.339 **i** 0.182 **j** 0.215

EXERCISE 19C.1

1   **a** -2 **b** -1 **c** 1 **d** $-2\frac{1}{2}$ **e** $-2\frac{3}{4}$
2   **a** 2 **b** 6 **c** 18 **d** $\frac{2}{3}$ **e** $\frac{2}{9}$
3   **a** $\frac{1}{2}$ **b** 1 **c** 4 **d** $\frac{1}{4}$ **e** $\frac{1}{16}$
4   **a** 1 **b** $\frac{1}{4}$ **c** $\frac{1}{16}$ **d** 4 **e** 16
5   **a** 3 **b** $\frac{3}{2}$ **c** 6 **d** $\frac{3}{4}$ **e** 12

EXERCISE 19C.2

1   **a** 1.4 **b** 2.8 **c** 5.7 2 **a i** 1 **ii** 3 **iii** 1.7 **iv** 5.2
3   **a i** $x = 2$ **ii** $x \doteq 2.3$ **iii** $x = 0$ **iv** $x \doteq 1.3$
4   **a i** $x = 1$ **ii** $x \doteq 1.5$ **iii** $x = 0$ **iv** $x \doteq -0.2$

5   **a i**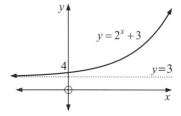
    ii y-int $(0, 4)$; horizontal asymptote $y = 3$
    iii a vertical translation of $\begin{bmatrix} 0 \\ 3 \end{bmatrix}$
    b i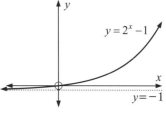
    ii y-int $(0, 0)$; horizontal asymptote $y = -1$
    iii a vertical translation of $\begin{bmatrix} 0 \\ -1 \end{bmatrix}$
    c i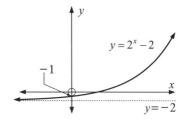
    ii y-int $(0, -1)$; horizontal asmptote $y = -2$
    iii a vertical translation of $\begin{bmatrix} 0 \\ -2 \end{bmatrix}$
6   **a i**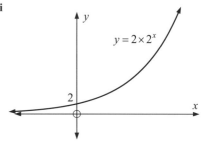
    ii y-int $(0, 2)$; horizontal asymptote $y = 0$
    iii vertical stretching by a factor of 2
    b i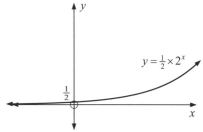
    ii y-int $(0, \frac{1}{2})$; horizontal asymptote $y = 0$
    iii vertical stretching by a factor of $\frac{1}{2}$

c i

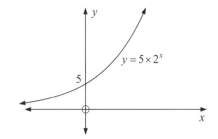

ii y-int $(0, 5)$; horizontal asymptote $y = 0$
iii vertical stretching by a factor of 5

7 a

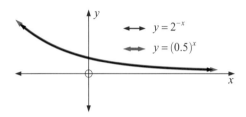

$$y = 2^{-x}$$
$$y = (0.5)^x$$

b $y = (0.5)^x = (\frac{1}{2})^x = 2^{-x}$ The two graphs are the same.

EXERCISE 19D

1 a 30 grams
b i 90.9 grams **ii** 480 grams **iii** 23 300 grams
c

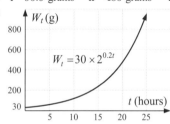

$$W_t = 30 \times 2^{0.2t}$$

d 3.68 hours

2 a $P_0 = 40$ **b i** 61 **ii** 160 **iii** 2560
c

$$P_n = 40 \times 2^{0.2n}$$

d 16.6 years

3 a i V_0 **ii** $3.03V_0$
b

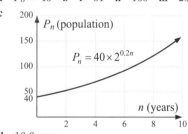

$$V_t = V_0 \times 2^{0.04t}$$

c $t = 75°C$

4 a 100°C **b i** 75.8°C **ii** 50°C **iii** 18.9°C

c

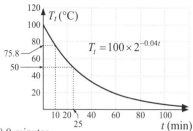

$$T_t = 100 \times 2^{-0.04t}$$

d 58.0 minutes

5 a W_0 grams **b** weight loss is $0.340W_0$ **c** 2000 years
6 a i I_0 amps **ii** $0.946I_0$ amps
  b $I_{20} = 0.574I_0$ amps, $I_{50} = 0.25I_0$ amps

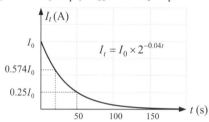

$$I_t = I_0 \times 2^{-0.04t}$$

c 83.0 seconds

EXERCISE 19E

1 $582 **2** $24 333 **3** $24 569 **4** 28.3% increase
5 28.5% increase **6** 1.38% decrease

EXERCISE 19F

1

After year	Interest paid	Future Value
0	–	$8000
1	5% of $8000 = $400	$8400
2	5% of $8400 = $420	$8820
3	5% of $8820 = $441	$9261

2 a £53 240 **b** £13 240 **3** ¥8320 **4** $14 976.01
5 11 477.02 euros **6** 20.5% **7** 15.8% **8** 7.85%

EXERCISE 19G

1 $5684.29

2

Number of owners	Depreciation or annual loss in value	Value after n years
0	–	$8495
1	$1019.40	$7475.60
2	$897.07	$6578.53
3	$789.42	$5789.11
4	$694.69	$5094.42

  a $3400.58 **b** $3055.10
  c $F_{10} - F_9$ is the depreciation in the tenth year.
3 a $19 712 **b** $18 788 **4** 11.5% **5** 4.81%

EXERCISE 19H

1 a $x = 1$ **b** $x = 2$ **c** $x = 3$ **d** $x = 0$ **e** $x = -1$
  f $x = -1$ **g** $x = -4$ **h** $x = 1$ **i** $x = -4$
  j $x = -2$ **k** $x = 6$ **l** $x = 2$ **m** $x = -\frac{3}{4}$
  n $x = \frac{7}{2}$ **o** $x = 0$ **p** $x = 4$

EXERCISE 19I

1 a $8 = 10^{0.9031}$ **b** $80 = 10^{1.903}$ **c** $800 = 10^{2.903}$
  d $80\,000 = 10^{4.903}$ **e** $0.03 = 10^{-1.523}$

f $0.003 = 10^{-2.523}$ **g** $0.3 = 10^{-0.5229}$
h $0.000\,003 = 10^{-5.523}$ **i** $25 = 10^{1.398}$ **j** $2500 = 10^{3.398}$
k $2.5 = 10^{0.3979}$ **l** $2\,500\,000 = 10^{6.398}$ **m** $37 = 10^{1.568}$
n $0.0614 = 10^{-1.212}$ **o** $26\,700 = 10^{4.427}$
p $0.006\,372\,1 = 10^{-2.196}$

2 a $x = 1.903$ **b** $x = 3.903$ **c** $x = -1.602$
d $x = 2.659$ **e** $x = -0.057\,30$ **f** $x = -3.747$

3 a $x = 1.585$ **b** $x = 3.322$ **c** $x = 8.644$
d $x = -7.059$ **e** $x = 4.292$ **f** $x = -0.099\,97$
g $x = 6.511$ **h** $x = 4.923$ **i** $x = 49.60$
j $x = 4.376$ **k** $x = 8.497$ **l** $x = 230.7$

4 a 17.0 hours **b** 64.6 hours **5 a** 17.6 hours **b** 36.9 hours

EXERCISE 19J

1 a 3 **b** -3 **c** 0 **d** 1 **e** $\frac{1}{2}$ **f** $\frac{1}{4}$ **g** -1 **h** $-\frac{1}{2}$

2 a n **b** $-m$ **c** $m - n$ **d** $m + n$ **e** $2m$ **f** mn
g $1 + n$ **h** $m - 2$

3 a i 0.301 03 (5 d.p.) **ii** 1.301 03 (5 d.p.)
b $\log 20 = 1 + \log 2$ **c** $\qquad 20 = 2 \times 10^1$
$$\therefore \quad 10^{\log 20} = 10^{\log 2} \times 10^1$$
$$= 10^{\log 2 + 1}$$
So, $\log 20 = 1 + \log 2$

4 a $x = 100$ **b** $x = 10$ **c** $x = \frac{1}{10}$ **d** $x = 1$ **e** $x = \sqrt{10}$
f $x = \frac{1}{\sqrt[3]{10}}$ **g** $x \doteq 1.474$ **h** $x \doteq 239.9$ **i** $x \doteq 0.000\,211\,3$

5 a $\log 30$ **b** $\log 5$ **c** $\log 12$ **d** $\log(\frac{5}{4})$ **e** 0 **f** $\log 30$
g $\log 4$ **h** $-\log 6$ or $\log(\frac{1}{6})$ **i** $\log(\frac{1}{512})$ **j** $\log 2000$
k $\log(\frac{64}{125})$ **l** $\log 20$ **m** $\log 5$ **n** $\log 20$ **o** $\log(14\,000)$

6 a 3 **b** 2 **c** $\frac{2}{3}$ **d** -1 **e** -1 **f** $-1\frac{1}{2}$ **g** $\frac{b}{3}$ **h** $\frac{2}{a}$

9 a $p = q^3$ **b** $p = \sqrt{q}$ **c** $p = \frac{1}{r^2}$ **d** $p = \frac{q}{r}$
e $a^2 = b^3$ **f** $c^3 = \frac{1}{d^4}$ **g** $y = \frac{x^2}{t}$ **h** $m = \frac{1}{ab^2}$
i $D = 10^{x+2}$ **j** $G = 10^{1-2x}$

11 a

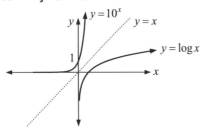

b a reflection in $y = x$

REVIEW SET 19A

1 a $2a^9$ **b** a^{b-x} **c** $27a^6$ **2** 2^2
3 a $\frac{4}{3}$ **b** $\frac{25}{4}$ **c** $\frac{1}{4}$ **4 a** 0 **b** 26 **c** $-\frac{2}{3}$ **d** $-\frac{8}{9}$
5

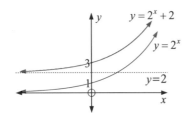

a For $y = 2^x$: y-int (0, 1); horizontal asymptote $y = 0$
For $y = 2^x + 2$: y-int (0, 3); horizontal asymptote $y = 2$

b a vertical translation of $\begin{bmatrix} 0 \\ 2 \end{bmatrix}$

6 a 1000 grams
b i 812 grams **ii** 125 grams **iii** 9.31×10^{-7} grams
c

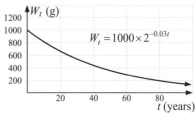

d 144 years

7 £51 475.73 **8** $6273.18 **9** $x = \frac{1}{3}$

10 a $50 = 10^{1.699}$ **b** $x = 0.4325$

11 a $\log 8$ **b** $\log a$ **c** 3

REVIEW SET 19B

1 a $15x^3 y^5$ **b** $\frac{x}{2y^2}$ **c** $\frac{8a^2}{b^2}$ **2 a** $\frac{1}{25x^2}$ **b** $3x^2 y^5$ **c** $\frac{1}{5}$

3 a 2 **b** $\frac{2}{3}$ **c** $\frac{2}{9}$ **d** 6 **e** 18

4

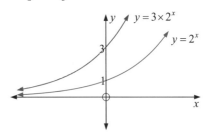

a For $y = 2^x$: y-int (0, 1); horizontal asymptote $y = 0$
For $y = 3 \times 2^x$: y-int (0, 3); horizontal asymptote $y = 0$
b vertical stretching by a factor of 3

5 a W_0 grams
b i 71.9% of W_0 **ii** 19.2% of W_0 **iii** 3.70% of W_0
c

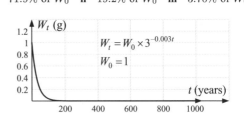

6 a $30 152.94 **b** $30 446.39
7 a 130 258.96 euros **b** 669 741.04 euros **8** $11 219.88
9 $x = -2$ **10** $x = -0.3652$ **11 a** $\log 4$ **b** $\log 3$ **c** 4

EXERCISE 20A

1 a, c, d, e
2 a $y = 20$ **b** $y = 27$ **c** $y = -4$ **d** $y = 37$
3 a no **b** no **c** no **d** no **e** yes **f** yes
4 a $x = -3$ **b** $x = -3$ or -2 **c** $x = 1$ or 4
d no solution
5 a $x = 0$ or $\frac{2}{3}$ **b** $x = 3$ or -2 **c** $x = \frac{1}{2}$ or -7 **d** $x = 3$

6 a i 25 m **ii** 25 m **iii** 45 m
   b i 2 secs and 4 secs **ii** 0 secs and 6 secs
   c once going up and once coming down

7 a i −$30 **ii** $105 **b** 6 or 58 cakes

EXERCISE 20B.1

1 a

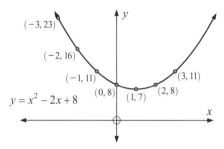

$y = x^2 - 2x + 8$

Points: $(-3, 23)$, $(-2, 16)$, $(-1, 11)$, $(0, 8)$, $(1, 7)$, $(2, 8)$, $(3, 11)$

b

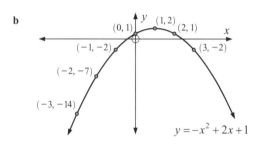

$y = -x^2 + 2x + 1$

Points: $(0, 1)$, $(1, 2)$, $(2, 1)$, $(-1, -2)$, $(3, -2)$, $(-2, -7)$, $(-3, -14)$

c

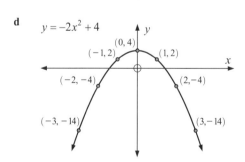

$y = 2x^2 + 3x$

Points: $(-3, 9)$, $(3, 27)$, $(-2, 2)$, $(2, 14)$, $(-1, -1)$, $(1, 5)$, $(0, 0)$

d

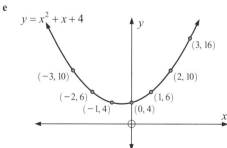

$y = -2x^2 + 4$

Points: $(0, 4)$, $(-1, 2)$, $(1, 2)$, $(-2, -4)$, $(2, -4)$, $(-3, -14)$, $(3, -14)$

e

$y = x^2 + x + 4$

Points: $(3, 16)$, $(-3, 10)$, $(2, 10)$, $(-2, 6)$, $(1, 6)$, $(-1, 4)$, $(0, 4)$

f

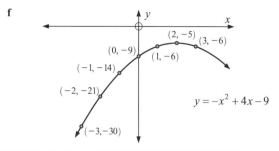

$y = -x^2 + 4x - 9$

Points: $(2, -5)$, $(3, -6)$, $(1, -6)$, $(0, -9)$, $(-1, -14)$, $(-2, -21)$, $(-3, -30)$

EXERCISE 20B.2

1 a

$y = x^2$, $y = x^2 - 3$, $(0, -3)$

b

$y = x^2$, $y = x^2 - 1$, $(0, -1)$

c

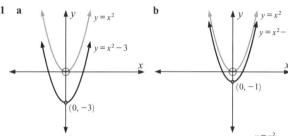

$y = x^2 + 1$, $y = x^2$, $(0, 1)$

d

$y = x^2$, $y = x^2 - 5$, $(0, -5)$

e

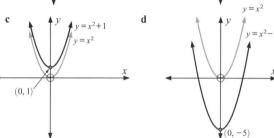

$y = x^2 + 5$, $y = x^2$, $(0, 5)$

f

$y = x^2$, $y = x^2 - \frac{1}{2}$, $(0, -\frac{1}{2})$

3 a

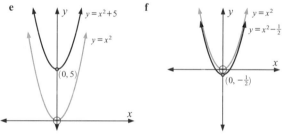

$y = x^2$, $y = (x - 3)^2$, $(3, 0)$

b

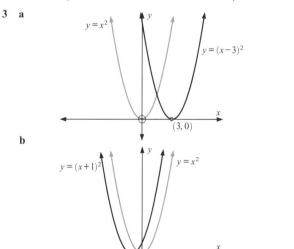

$y = (x + 1)^2$, $y = x^2$, $(-1, 0)$

c

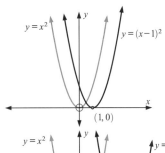

d

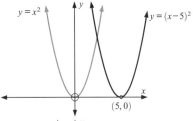

e

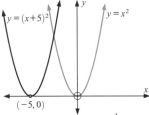

f

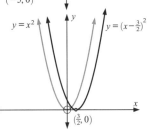

5   a $y = (x-1)^2 + 3$ **b** $y = (x-2)^2 - 1$

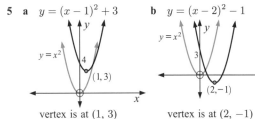

vertex is at $(1, 3)$ vertex is at $(2, -1)$

c $y = (x+1)^2 + 4$ **d** $y = (x+2)^2 - 3$

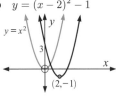

vertex is at $(-1, 4)$ vertex is at $(-2, -3)$

e $y = (x+3)^2 - 2$ **f** $y = (x-3)^2 + 3$

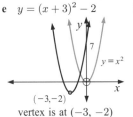

vertex is at $(-3, -2)$ vertex is at $(3, 3)$

7   a $y = (x-1)^2 + 2$ **b** $y = (x-3)^2 - 5$

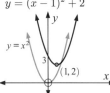
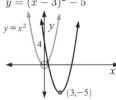

c $y = (x+2)^2 - 6$ **d** $y = (x-1)^2 + 4$

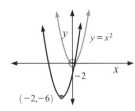

e $y = (x-2)^2 - 4$ **f** $y = (x+\frac{3}{2})^2 - \frac{9}{4}$

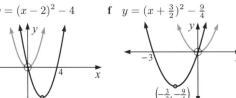
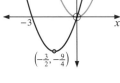

g $y = (x+\frac{5}{2})^2 - \frac{33}{4}$ **h** $y = (x-\frac{3}{2})^2 - \frac{1}{4}$

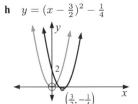

i $y = (x-\frac{5}{2})^2 - \frac{21}{4}$

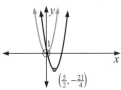

9   a $y = (x-2)^2 + 3$ **b** $y = (x+3)^2 - 6$
     c $y = (x+2)^2 + 1$ **d** $y = (x+1)^2 - 5$
     e $y = (x-\frac{3}{2})^2 - \frac{5}{4}$ **f** $y = (x-\frac{9}{2})^2 - \frac{101}{4}$

10   a

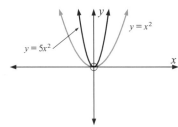

i $y = 5x^2$ is 'thinner' than $y = x^2$
ii graph opens upwards

b

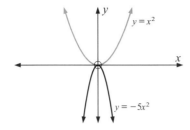

  i $y = -5x^2$ is 'thinner' than $y = x^2$
  ii graph opens downwards

c

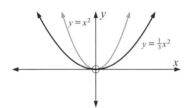

  i $y = \frac{1}{3}x^2$ is 'wider' than $y = x^2$
  ii graph opens upwards

d

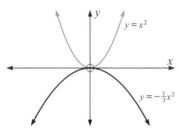

  i $y = -\frac{1}{3}x^2$ is 'wider' than $y = x^2$
  ii graph opens downwards

e

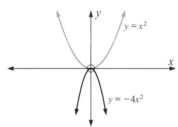

  i $y = -4x^2$ is 'thinner' than $y = x^2$
  ii graph opens downwards

f

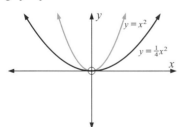

  i $y = \frac{1}{4}x^2$ is 'wider' than $y = x^2$
  ii graph opens upwards

12 a

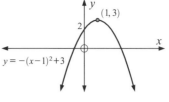

b

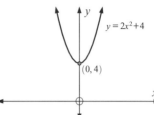

c

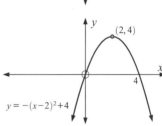

d

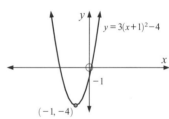

e

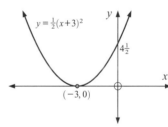

f

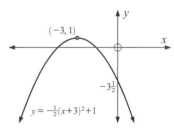

g

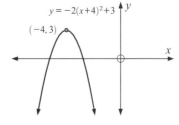

h

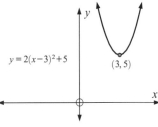

$y = 2(x-3)^2 + 5$

$(3, 5)$

i

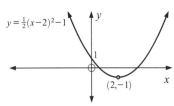

$y = \frac{1}{2}(x-2)^2 - 1$

1

$(2, -1)$

14 a G **b** A **c** E **d** B **e** I **f** C **g** D
h F **i** H

EXERCISE 20C.1

1 a 3 **b** 2 **c** -8 **d** 1 **e** 6 **f** 5 **g** 6
h 8 **i** -2

EXERCISE 20C.2

1 a 3 and -1 **b** 2 and 4 **c** -3 and -2
d 4 and 5 **e** -3 (touching) **f** 1 (touching)

EXERCISE 20C.3

1 a ± 3 **b** $\pm\sqrt{3}$ **c** -5 and -2 **d** 3 and -4
e 0 and 4 **f** -4 and -2 **g** -1 (touching)
h 3 (touching) **i** $2 \pm \sqrt{3}$ **j** $-2 \pm \sqrt{7}$
k $3 \pm \sqrt{11}$ **l** $-4 \pm \sqrt{5}$

EXERCISE 20D

1 a i

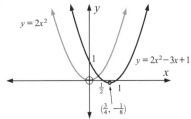

$y = 2x^2$

1

$y = 2x^2 - 3x + 1$

$\frac{1}{2}$ 1

$\left(\frac{3}{4}, -\frac{1}{8}\right)$

ii same shape

b i

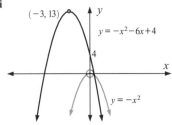

$(-3, 13)$

$y = -x^2 - 6x + 4$

4

$y = -x^2$

ii same shape

c i

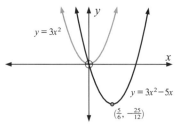

$y = 3x^2$

$y = 3x^2 - 5x$

$\left(\frac{5}{6}, -\frac{25}{12}\right)$

ii same shape

d i

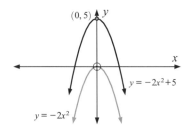

$(0, 5)$

$y = -2x^2 + 5$

$y = -2x^2$

ii same shape

2 a

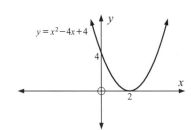

$y = x^2 - 4x + 4$

4

2

b

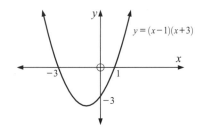

$y = (x-1)(x+3)$

-3 1

-3

c

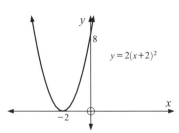

8

$y = 2(x+2)^2$

-2

d

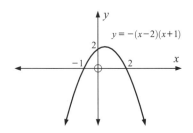

$y = -(x-2)(x+1)$

2

-1 2

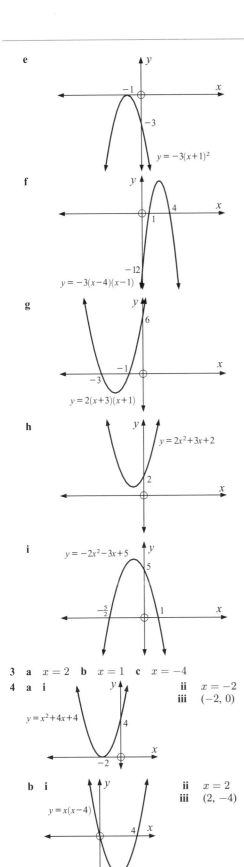

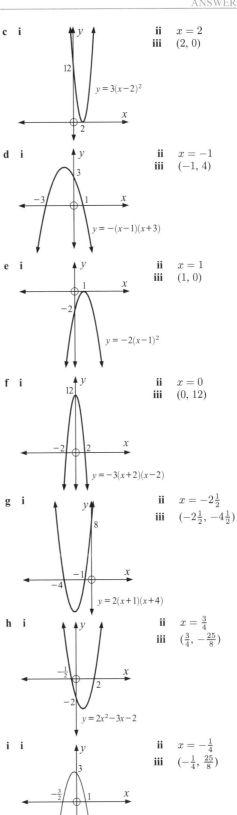

e

$y = -3(x+1)^2$

f

$y = -3(x-4)(x-1)$

g

$y = 2(x+3)(x+1)$

h

$y = 2x^2+3x+2$

i

$y = -2x^2-3x+5$

3 a $x = 2$ **b** $x = 1$ **c** $x = -4$

4 a i

$y = x^2+4x+4$

    ii $x = -2$
    iii $(-2, 0)$

b i

$y = x(x-4)$

    ii $x = 2$
    iii $(2, -4)$

c i

$y = 3(x-2)^2$

    ii $x = 2$
    iii $(2, 0)$

d i

$y = -(x-1)(x+3)$

    ii $x = -1$
    iii $(-1, 4)$

e i

$y = -2(x-1)^2$

    ii $x = 1$
    iii $(1, 0)$

f i

$y = -3(x+2)(x-2)$

    ii $x = 0$
    iii $(0, 12)$

g i

$y = 2(x+1)(x+4)$

    ii $x = -2\frac{1}{2}$
    iii $(-2\frac{1}{2}, -4\frac{1}{2})$

h i

$y = 2x^2-3x-2$

    ii $x = \frac{3}{4}$
    iii $(\frac{3}{4}, -\frac{25}{8})$

i i

$y = -2x^2-x+3$

    ii $x = -\frac{1}{4}$
    iii $(-\frac{1}{4}, \frac{25}{8})$

5 a i

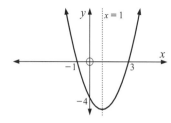

  ii axis of symmetry $x = 1$

b i

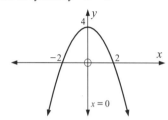

  ii axis of symmetry $x = 0$

c i

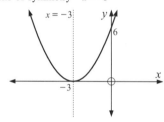

  ii axis of symmetry $x = -3$

d i

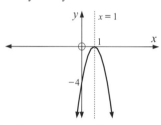

  ii axis of symmetry $x = 1$

6 a 2 and 6 **b** -1 and -5 **c** 3 (touching)

7 a A$(h - d,\ 0)$ B$(h + d,\ 0)$
   b $ah^2 - 2adh + ad^2 + bh - bd + c = 0$
   c $ah^2 + 2adh + ad^2 + bh + bd + c = 0$

EXERCISE 20E

1 a $x = -2$ **b** $x = \frac{3}{2}$ **c** $x = -\frac{2}{3}$
   d $x = -2$ **e** $x = \frac{5}{4}$ **f** $x = 10$
   g $x = -6$ **h** $x = \frac{25}{2}$ **i** $x = 150$

2 a $(2, -2)$ **b** $(-1, -4)$ **c** $(0, 4)$ **d** $(0, 1)$ **e** $(-2, -15)$
   f $(-2, -5)$ **g** $(-\frac{3}{2}, -\frac{11}{2})$ **h** $(\frac{5}{2}, -\frac{19}{2})$ **i** $(1, -\frac{9}{2})$

3 a **i** x-intercepts $4, -2$, y-intercept -8
      ii axis of symmetry $x = 1$
      iii vertex $(1, -9)$
      iv $y = x^2 - 2x - 8$

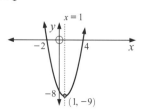

b i x-intercepts $0, -3$, y-intercept 0
   ii axis of symmetry $x = -\frac{3}{2}$
   iii vertex $(-\frac{3}{2}, -\frac{9}{4})$
   iv $y = x^2 + 3x$

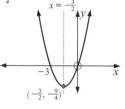

c i x-intercepts $0, 4$, y-intercept 0
   ii axis of symmetry $x = 2$
   iii vertex $(2, 4)$
   iv $y = 4x - x^2$

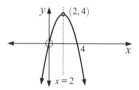

d i x-intercept -2, y-intercept 4
   ii axis of symmetry $x = -2$
   iii vertex $(-2, 0)$
   iv $y = x^2 + 4x + 4$

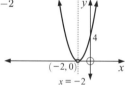

e i x-intercepts $-4, 1$, y-intercept -4
   ii axis of symmetry $x = -\frac{3}{2}$
   iii vertex $(-\frac{3}{2}, -\frac{25}{4})$
   iv $y = x^2 + 3x - 4$

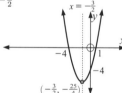

f i x-intercept 1, y-intercept -1
   ii axis of symmetry $x = 1$
   iii vertex $(1, 0)$
   iv $y = -x^2 + 2x - 1$

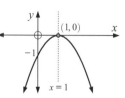

g i x-intercepts $-2, -4$, y-intercept -8
   ii axis of symmetry $x = -3$
   iii vertex $(-3, 1)$
   iv $y = -x^2 - 6x - 8$

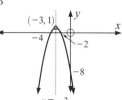

h **i** x-intercepts 1, 2, y-intercept -2
  ii axis of symmetry $x = \frac{3}{2}$
  iii vertex $(\frac{3}{2}, \frac{1}{4})$
  iv $y = -x^2 + 3x - 2$

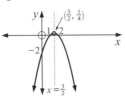

i **i** x-intercepts $\frac{1}{2}$, -3, y-intercept -3
  ii axis of symmetry $x = -\frac{5}{4}$
  iii vertex $(-\frac{5}{4}, -\frac{49}{8})$
  iv $y = 2x^2 + 5x - 3$

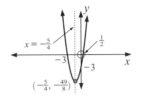

j **i** x-intercepts $-\frac{3}{2}$, 4, y-intercept -12
  ii axis of symmetry $x = \frac{5}{4}$
  iii vertex $(\frac{5}{4}, -\frac{121}{8})$
  iv $y = 2x^2 - 5x - 12$

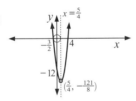

k **i** x-intercepts $\frac{2}{3}$, -2, y-intercept 4
  ii axis of symmetry $x = -\frac{2}{3}$
  iii vertex $(-\frac{2}{3}, \frac{16}{3})$
  iv $y = -3x^2 - 4x + 4$

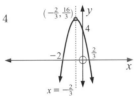

l **i** x-intercepts 0, 20, y-intercept 0
  ii axis of symmetry $x = 10$
  iii vertex $(10, 25)$
  iv $y = -\frac{1}{4}x^2 + 5x$

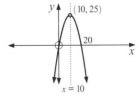

EXERCISE 20F

1 **a** 9 seconds   **b** 162 m   **c** 18 seconds
2 **a** 12   **b** $100   **c** $244
3 **a** 80 kmph
  b after 1 second and after 2 seconds;
    car continues to speed up before slowing down
  c $1\frac{1}{2}$ seconds   **d** 89 kmph
4 **a** 21   **b** $837   **c** $45

5 **a** $30°C$ **b** 5.00 am   **c** $5°C$
6 **b** $x = 10$ **c** 200 m^2
7 **a** $y = -\frac{1}{100}x^2 + 70$
  b supports are 21 m, 34 m, 45 m, 54 m, 61 m, 66 m, 69 m
8 **a** vertex $(30, 30)$ **b** $y = \frac{1}{45}(x - 30)^2 + 30$
  c 38.89 m
9 **1**

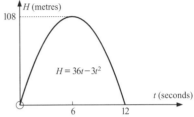

  2 maximum height after 6 seconds
  3 maximum height is 108 m
  4 12 seconds to leave the area

REVIEW SET 20A

1 **a** -12 **b** -17 **c** $x = 6$ or -3
2 **a**

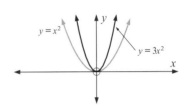

  b

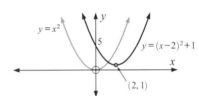

  c

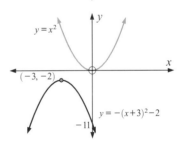

3 **a** **i** opens downwards   **ii** 6   **iii** 1 and -3
     iv $x = -1$
  b

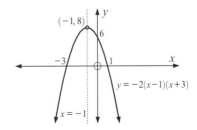

4 a i -15 **ii** 5 and -3 **iii** $x = 1$
  iv $(1, -16)$

b

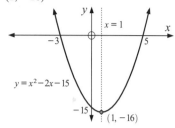

5 a 2 seconds **b** 80 m **c** 6 seconds

REVIEW SET 20B

1 a -1 **b** -5 **c** $x = -2$ or $\frac{3}{2}$
2 a

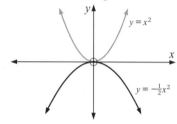

b

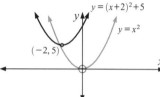

c

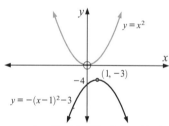

3 a i opens upwards **ii** 12 **iii** 2 (touching)
  iv $x = 2$

b

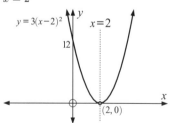

4 a i -10 **ii** 2 and 5 **iii** $x = \frac{7}{2}$
  iv $(\frac{7}{2}, \frac{9}{4})$

b

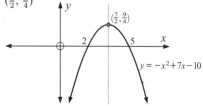

5 a 2 seconds **b** 25 m **c** 4.5 seconds

INDEX